USING MICROPROCESSORS AND MICROCOMPUTERS

THE MOTOROLA FAMILY

Third Edition

William C. Wray

Joseph D. Greenfield

Prentice-Hall International, Inc.

Acquisitions Editor: *Holly Hodder*
Editorial Assistant: *Melissa Steffens*
Managing Editor: *Mary Carnis*
Manufacturing Buyer: *Ilene Sanford*
Production Editor and Interior Designer: *Adele M. Kupchik*
Director of Production & Manufacturing: *David W. Riccardi*

©1994, 1988 by Prentice Hall Career & Technology
Prentice-Hall, Inc.
A Paramount Communications Company
Englewood Cliffs, New Jersey 07632

Printed in the United States of America

10 9 8 7 6 5 4 3 2 1

ISBN 0-13-300351-5

Prentice-Hall International (UK) Limited, *London*
Prentice-Hall of Australia Pty. Limited, *Sydney*
Prentice-Hall Canada Inc., *Toronto*
Prentice-Hall Hispanoamericana, S.A., *Mexico*
Prentice-Hall of India Private Limited, *New Delhi*
Prentice-Hall of Japan, Inc., *Tokyo*
Simon & Schuster Asia Pte. Ltd., *Singapore*
Editora Prentice-Hall do Brasil, Ltda., *Rio de Janeiro*
Prentice-Hall, *Englewood Cliffs, New Jersey*

CONTENTS

PREFACE

Like the second edition, the organization and goals of this third edition remain the same as for the first edition, with the possible exception of an increased emphasis on Microcontrollers and new development methods. However, again, the primary changes have been to update everything to include the many new Microprocessors as well as even more Microcontrollers. As in the first edition, the first nine chapters are devoted to the basic concepts of Microcomputers, to attempt to answer the question, What is a Microcomputer?

As explained in earlier editions, the Motorola **6800** Microprocessor is used because it is the model that has been used by Motorola for all of the later Microcomputers as well as Microcontrollers.

The first nine chapters are unchanged except to modernize some examples, references, or problems—the basics do not change. This edition does include quite a few descriptions of new 16- and 32-bit Microprocessors and Microcontrollers, however, because Motorola has expanded the Microcontroller families to include many new high-performance designs.

- In Chapter 1 we discuss today's trends in the Microcomputer and Micro-controller worlds.
- Chapters 2 through 9 are little changed because they cover computer basics.
- In Chapter 10 (formerly Chapter 11) we describe the new members of the 8-bit **68HC11** and **68HC05** families. These families are continuing to grow at an even faster rate, and include many new features.
- In Chapter 11 we explain System Debugging using Evaluation Boards.
- Chapter 12 now includes much more material on the System design process, including the use of Logic Analyzers, and has a full description of the latest Microcomputer Development Systems for the **68HC05** family of Microcontrollers.
- Chapter 13 covers the same real-world applications and interfacing concepts as in the second edition but is expanded and modernized.

- The old Chapter 14 was deleted and the former Chapter 15 is now Chapter 14. It has been reworked, however, to provide an even better understanding of the **68000** family of Microprocessors.
- Chapter 15 (formerly Chapter 16) covers the advanced versions of the **68000** family, and because so much progress has been made by many additions to the family, has many very important additions.
- Finally, Chapter 16 is all new material covering the new high-performance 16- and 32-bit Microcontrollers (the **HC16** and **68300** families). The new system development methods, including use of new 16- and 32-bit Evaluation Boards which use built-in Background Debug Modes are described in detail. The Modular Microcomputer Development Systems are also described briefly.

We want to thank the many people who have helped us prepare this latest edition. That includes, in particular, the many engineers that worked with William C. Wray before his switch to the consulting world. The Austin members are Tim Ahrens, Kellye Prosise, Pete Gilmour, Harley Templeton, Gorden Davies, Chuck McLeavy, and Jim Sibigtroth. In Phoenix, Don Aldridge and Jeff Gorin were most helpful.

We want to acknowledge the kind words and other help from people at Prentice Hall Career & Technology, including Holly Hodder, who suggested the third edition, Adele Kupchik, Melissa Steffens, and others.

Many of the terms used in the text are trademarks of Motorola. These include Minibug, BUFFALO, MMDS, and MCU ToolBox. IBM is a registered trademark of IBM Corporation. Macintosh is a trademark of Apple Computer, Inc. MS-DOS and Microsoft are trademarks of Microsoft Corporation.

William C. Wray
Joseph D. Greenfield

ACKNOWLEDGEMENT

We wish to thank National Semiconductor for the use of their materials in this book, and include here their LIFE SUPPORT POLICY STATEMENT:

NATIONAL'S PRODUCTS ARE NOT AUTHORIZED FOR USE AS CRITICAL COMPONENTS IN LIFE SUPPORT DEVICES OR SYSTEMS WITHOUT THE EXPRESS WRITTEN APPROVAL OF THE PRESIDENT OF NATIONAL SEMICONDUCTOR CORPORATION. As used herein:

1. Life support devices or systems are devices or systems which, (a) are intended for surgical implant into the body, or (b) support or sustain life, and whose failure to perform, when properly used in accordance with instructions for use provided in the labelling, can be reasonably expected to result in a significant injury to the user.

2. A critical component is any component of a life support device or system whose failure to perform can be reasonably expected to cause the failure of the life support device or system, or to affect its safety or effectiveness.

INTRODUCTION TO MICROCOMPUTERS

1-1 ▼ INTRODUCTION

The introduction of the digital computer in the early 1950s revolutionized methods of computing, manipulating data, and controlling other devices and systems. The development of the microcomputer (one or more semiconductor chips with all the functions of a computer) is now revolutionizing the computer industry and many other industries as well. Because of their low cost, small size, and versatility, microcomputers (μCs) are surely destined to play an increasingly important role in the technologies of the future.

A computer, as we will learn, consists of a Central Processing Unit (CPU), some memory devices, capable of storing information, and the Input/Output circuits (I/O) needed to enter or output the data. These functions are implemented using electronic circuits.

In the past three decades electronics has made tremendous strides, progressing from vacuum tubes to transistors to **integrated circuits** (ICs). ICs are very small electronic components that contain miniature transistors and their associated circuits placed on a silicon chip. The science of putting large numbers of these electronic components on a tiny ($\frac{1}{4}$ inch square) semiconductor chip is called *semiconductor technology*. In recent years, highly complex computer circuits have been fabricated on a single chip. Although these chips contained most of the functions, they were not complete computers in one package. These first ICs were known as microprocessors (μPs) and they had to be augmented with several additional IC components to provide all the functions of a μC. Every year as semiconductors improve, more and more of the functions are being incorporated into the main μP, until today the most complex (and most useful) of them are complete enough to be called Microcomputers (μCs). Motorola calls them MicroController Units, or MCUs. Although suitable for many tasks, these MCUs do not incorporate all of the capabilities needed for many uses. Other combinations of μPs, memory, and I/O chips are also required. These combinations of ICs designed to work together, are called *μC families*.

1

The term μC can therefore refer to a single MCU type of IC or to a combination of ICs that form a complete computer. The combination is often the configuration used in Personal Computers such as IBM or Macintosh units.

The purpose of this book is to introduce μC integrated-circuit components and to help the reader understand how they work and how they can be used. This is not a simple task because many μC families of components are available, each with its own *set of instructions* and *unique hardware configuration*. Millions of μCs are now in use to control physical processes. For example, they are used in the electronic control modules that control the operation of an automobile. These μPs include the Intel **8080** family, the Zilog **Z80**, the **6502**, and the Motorola **6800** family.

If we attempted to describe the μC components made by all manufacturers, we could not discuss any one in enough depth to enable the reader to build or use a μC system. A single family, however, containing simple, straightforward μC components can easily be understood and the computer concepts are generally applicable to all other families. Therefore, this book focuses on the popular and extensively used Motorola **6800** μC family with the advanced μCs that have evolved from it. The **6800** μP itself is the original Motorola μP. It is not used in many new designs although it is still available as a replacement part. Because the **6800** CPU core is the heart of all new Motorola designs, the student must understand the **6800** μP, its interfacing, and its programming. The **6800** uses the concepts that are common to most μCs (multibyte instructions, interrupts, stacks, clocks, etc.). The reader who understands how these operations work on the **6800** will have little trouble understanding the operation of other μCs. The basic concepts of the **6800** are used in all the more advanced μPs and μCs in the Motorola family, including **68HC11s, 6805s,** and the even more advanced **68000, 68300** and **68HC16** families.

This introductory chapter presents a preview of μCs, and some material may be difficult for beginners to understand.

After reading this chapter, the student should be able to

1. Understand how μCs are used.
2. Describe the differences between NMOS, PMOS, HMOS and HCMOS technologies.
3. List the differences between a minicomputer and a μC.

A detailed explanation of subjects needed to understand μC operation begins in Chapter 2.

1-2 ▼ SELF-EVALUATION QUESTIONS

Watch for the answers to the following questions as you read the chapter. They should help you to understand the material presented.

1. What are the advantages of a μC over a minicomputer? What are the disadvantages?
2. How does programmability give the μC an advantage over hard-wired electronic controllers?
3. What are the most important characteristics of a μC?
4. Explain why display terminals are not required in many μC applications.
5. Why is it important to design connections for test equipment into a μC system?

6. What is the major cost in developing a μC system?

7. What is the major disadvantage of compilers and high-level languages for a μC in controller applications?

1-3 ▼ COMPUTERS AND MINICOMPUTERS

Large computers [such as those made by IBM or Digital Equipment Corp (DEC) and others], often called *mainframes*, are used to solve highly sophisticated problems or to handle operations that require large volumes of output data. Most corporations, for example, use large computers to print their payrolls and write their bills.

A minicomputer is a scaled-down version of a larger computer with less computational power. It is much smaller and less expensive and is an ideal solution for problems of medium complexity. In the early 1970s, minicomputers were used primarily as general-purpose workstations and to control industrial processes. Now, minicomputers, which are becoming more sophisticated, are taking over some tasks formerly performed by mainframes.

The advent of the semiconductor age has made it possible for μCs to accomplish the tasks of most minicomputers. Microcomputer costs are less than those of most minicomputers, but since minicomputers are sometimes built with expensive high-performance discrete logic (individual transistors or ICs), they can outperform some μCs. Some of the newer μCs are so powerful, however, that the performance gap is rapidly narrowing. Since minicomputers are often less than fully utilized and many applications do not need their speed, μCs have become a good alternative for many uses. Each year, μC costs drop and performance improves, so more and more applications are being found where the μC is able to substitute for larger computers.

1-3.1 ▼ Minicomputers

Many minicomputers and larger computers were built in the 1960s and 1970s using the semiconductor technology that existed at that time: bipolar or Transistor-Transistor Logic (TTL) ICs. Minicomputers were the first step in the miniaturization of computers. They are available from a number of manufacturers as basic general-purpose computers that can be adapted for a variety of uses, usually by plugging in various modular cards. These cards generally include a complete function such as an input module, output module, or memory module. The modules are assembled using discrete components or ICs.

1-3.2 ▼ Minicomputers vs. μCs

A minicomputer is usually equipped with a large-capacity mass storage unit—either a disk, CD, or tape drive—that holds a variety of programs and a large Read/Write semiconductor memory. This type of memory is also known as a Random-Access Memory (RAM). Practically all minicomputers also have a small permanent program based in Read-Only Memory (ROM) which works with the disk to load the operating system (similar to DOS for personal computers) into the RAM. The user then selects the particular application program to be run and also loads it from the disk into the RAM. A minicomputer may include various plug-in accessory modules to interface it to external devices or systems. It is a general-purpose package designed for a variety of uses. The same configuration can be assembled with μC components. Many μCs are being used in this way as personal computers.

1-4 ▼ HOME OR PERSONAL COMPUTERS

One of the prime areas of μC applications has been personal computers (PCs) for the home or office. Modern PCs are as powerful as minicomputers were a decade ago, yet small enough so that many employees of a business have individual PCs on their desks. Because of their increased power, low cost, and small size, millions of PCs are now in use and there has been tremendous growth in the development of all aspects of the PC industry. Not only do PCs use the latest in μPs or μCs and all other semiconductor products, such as memories, but this market has also caused the rapid development of accessory items such as disk drives, cathode ray tube (CRT) terminals (now called video displays or monitors), and printers.

Competition in this business has been fierce, and many companies (e.g., Apple, IBM, and Compaq) have grown dramatically, while others have declined or gone bankrupt. With the growth of home computers there has been a resurgence of time-sharing services, and many systems include a **modem** for communication over telephone lines to other computers. In many cases these are large computers with virtually unlimited information. Communication between home units is also possible. The use of PCs in offices is growing rapidly and they are being networked together via various high-speed communication methods to provide distributed processing and communications systems that approach the performance of mainframes. Some networked business systems interconnect offices in other cities or even internationally.

The information in this book certainly covers the design of personal-type computers, but the emphasis is on the use of MicroController Units (MCUs) for applications where specialized designs are needed. Machinery controllers and robotics are two examples.

1-5 ▼ MICROCONTROLLERS VS. MICROCOMPUTERS

When a μC is configured with large amounts of RAM, a disk storage system, serial Input/Output (I/O) for use with a terminal, and parallel I/O for use with a printer, it is suited for many general-purpose tasks and is properly called a MicroComputer (μC). But by including some of the many special-purpose peripheral functions now available in the μC chip or externally in an integrated circuit, the μC can be configured to control external hardware systems. It will probably have a large ROM with a specialized program and will not require a disk storage system. In this role the system is more correctly called a MicroController Unit or MCU as Motorola calls them.

This book focuses primarily on this aspect of the microcomputer world. There are many fine books on general-purpose or personal computers. The real advantage of the MCU and its companion Integrated Circuit (IC) components is that they can be assembled with as few or as many parts as needed for the task required.

In the early days of the **6800** family, the μP communicated with the external devices it had to monitor and control via a set of special-purpose ICs called *peripheral controllers or interface adapters*. Motorola's **6821** Peripheral Interface Adapter (PIA) and its **6850** Asynchronous Communications Interface Adapter (ACIA) were two examples of these ICs. The required system was formed by assembling the μP, its memories and the interface ICs on a Printed Circuit Board (PCB). Today, however, an MCU IC that internally contains the majority, if not all, of these and the other functions required is selected. These MCUs are available with a variety of built-in peripherals. Sometimes everything needed is not available in one package, but in this case, one or more external IC components can be added to provide a multifunction system.

In many control systems it is not necessary to include displays and entry switches or terminal I/O facilities, because the μC is often built into (or embedded) in machinery where the operator is not skilled in computer discipline or the equipment is unattended in normal operation. The Electronic Control Module (ECM) in an automobile is an example. In these cases, the design, debugging, and maintenance are accomplished by plug-in or transportable test equipment. In some cases, the μC system is designed to accommodate special test equipment. The dedicated μC's memory is often mostly ROM or, as explained later, Programmable ROM (PROM) for program instruction storage with a small RAM for variable data. Since the μC's operating program is in nonvolatile ROM, it is permanent, and restarting the program after power has been off is accomplished quickly and easily. If the RAM is equipped with a *battery-backup* circuit to keep it operational when the power fails, and the necessary software routines are included in the ROMs, the system can recover from a power failure without loss of data. This auto-restart capability is one of the μC's most valuable features.

1-6 ▼ SOFTWARE CONTROL OF ELECTRONIC SYSTEMS

The ability to substitute **software logic** (computer programs) for the actual electronic circuits (i.e., for the **hardware logic**) in an industrial controller is largely responsible for the acceptance of μCs. A μC with an appropriate interface can completely control any system, and its function can easily be modified by changing the software.

Consider a μC built to control a device that includes motors or solenoid-activated valves. The electronic circuitry external to the μC would consist of solid-state relays or power transistor amplifiers, and the TTL-level signals from the μC I/O lines would control them. (A 5-V ON signal could make a motor run or open a valve, and a 0-V OFF signal would halt the action.) The functions of timing, limiting, and interlocking would be provided in software. This is not always safe, so mechanical limit switches or pressure relief valves, for example, could be added to the hardware, provided that the reliability of those electromechanical devices is adequate. These design decisions are often referred to as hardware/software trade-offs and must be made by the system designer.

Mechanical and hydraulic logic devices such as mechanical interlocks or speed-controlling governors are being replaced by appropriately designed μC systems. Electronic control is faster, cleaner, more accurate, and more reliable, and *electronic components do not wear out*. Such systems contain electrical or electronic sensors (transducers) and their outputs are connected to μC input lines so that the information can be processed by the software routines. In the automotive field, for example, ignition spark-advance mechanisms, which have been vacuum controlled, and carburetor controls, which have been universally mechanical, are being replaced by electromechanical devices, which in turn are controlled by μCs. This provides high-speed dynamic adjustments (30 times a second) not previously possible. This increases the gas mileage of the vehicles and still provides maximum power, when needed. These advances are possible today because of the low cost of the μC. They can be justified on the basis of the increased reliability, accuracy, or ease with which a feature can be added to a μC controller.

1-7 ▼ HISTORICAL BACKGROUND OF SEMICONDUCTOR TECHNOLOGY

The complexity of the electronic circuitry that can be incorporated into one integrated circuit chip has been approximately doubling each year for more than three decades. Since the basic raw materials used in ICs are very inexpensive, and high-volume production has made the cost of digital ICs even lower, the performance/price ratio has increased dramatically.

The first ICs used bipolar technology, which eventually resulted in the availability of families of circuits such as the **7400** transistor-transistor logic (TTL) series. These have been described as *Small-Scale-Integration (SSI)* devices. Improvements in this process resulted in bipolar *Medium-Scale-Integration (MSI)* devices, which use many gates on each IC and produce complex circuits such as multiplexers that share the wires and circuits between two functions.

Digital integrated circuits using **Metal-Oxide Semiconductor** (MOS) technology were introduced around 1969. This MOS form of transistor construction is used in many ICs (Section 1-9.2) and has several advantages over bipolar technology.

1. MOS devices require fewer manufacturing steps.
2. MOS gates dissipate less power per gate.
3. MOS gates require less space on the silicon wafer.

Because of these advantages, far more MOS circuitry can be placed on a single IC. Bipolar TTL integrated circuits continue to dominate in SSI and MSI because of their high speed, wide acceptance, and long history of successful applications. Most *Large-Scale-Integration (LSI)* devices, including memories and μPs, which require hundreds or even thousands of gates in a single IC, use MOS rather than bipolar technology.

By 1969, when MOS was introduced, semiconductor technology had progressed to the point where all of the basic μC circuits (gates, registers, arithmetic/logic units, etc.) existed as individual ICs. At about that time, the IC manufacturers started to combine these individual ICs into a single IC to produce a microprocessor. This chip included most, but not all, of the functions of the complete computer.

The first practical IC μP, the Intel **4004**, appeared in 1971. The **4004** is a 4-bit μP that is, by today's standards, slow and difficult to use. Later in the same year Intel also introduced the **8008**, an 8-bit μP with a more sophisticated instruction set.

Two of the most popular μPs in early systems were the Intel **8080** and the Motorola **6800**. They were introduced in 1974, and many are still in use. In 1977 and 1978 several one-chip μCs (which included memory and I/O), such as the Fairchild **F8**, the Texas Instruments (TI) **TMS1000**, and the Motorola **6801** were introduced.

1-8 ▼ MICROCOMPUTER FAMILIES

Any μC system must include a **microprocessor**. The μP may be a separate IC or part of a more complex chip. In either case, the μP contains the control and arithmetic functions of a computer. Microprocessors cannot function by themselves and must be augmented by other functions. Random-access memories (RAMs), read-only memories (ROMs), and peripheral drivers for the input and output of data are necessary to form a complete μC. The original μC families used a separate chip for each function, but newer members of the family include RAM, ROM, and I/O sections on the same chip and therefore some are complete μCs in one package. These μCs are generally suitable for simple applications and must be augmented by additional ROMs, RAMs, or I/O chips for larger jobs.

1-8.1 ▼ Microprocessors and Microcomputers

Figure 1-1 shows the **6800** μP in a Dual In-line Package (DIP) and shows a block diagram of this μP and the other functions necessary to complete a μC. These other functions are in similar packages. Early μC systems used a combination of these DIP packages to assemble an entire computer on a single printed circuit module. Figure 1-2 shows such a module, which contains a **6800** μP plus the associated RAMs, ROMs, clock, and SSI chips required to make a complete functioning μC. Modern technology has advanced to the point where single chips that contain the μP, the clock and the associated RAM, ROM, and I/O are available. These are called *MicroController Units* (MCUs) and are discussed in Chapter 10.

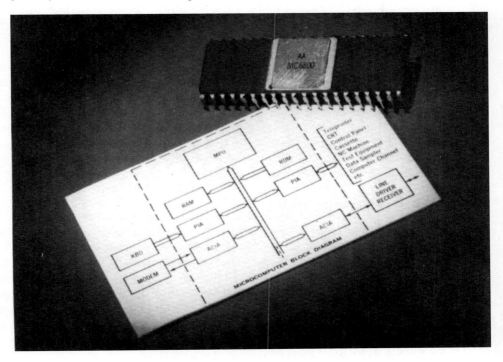

Figure 1-1   6800 μP and its associated family of ICs.

Figure 1-2   6800 μC system on a single card.

1-8.2 ▼ Microcomputer Memories

Computer memories, which were implemented with magnetic cores in early computers, are now fabricated using semiconductors and consist of RAM, factory-programmed Read-Only Memory (ROM), or field-Programmable Read-Only Memory (PROM). Memory is essential to the operation of any computer and is discussed in detail in Chapter 3. The ROM or PROM is used to store the program instructions permanently, and the RAM temporarily saves all variable data used in the course of program operation. In general, the more functions performed by a μC, the more program memory required, but except for a larger ROM, this does not affect the cost of the μP chip, the clock, or even the I/O capabilities. Memory ICs are available in a wide variety of configurations, and several of them in the **6800** family are specifically designed for small μC systems. These and other hardware aspects of the **6800** family are discussed in Chapter 7.

1-8.3 ▼ Testing μC Systems

Because test instruments cannot be connected to circuits inside a μP, special instruments have been developed to "see" the internal contents. Microcomputer manufacturers introduced these specialized instruments, which are used with their family of μC components for both hardware and software troubleshooting. Intel's first **Microcomputer Development System** (MDS) was called the Intellec. Motorola's EXORcisor was developed in 1974. Other manufacturers make similar μC test instruments. A growing number of companies that do not manufacture ICs have introduced a variety of specialized analyzers for general-purpose use in μC system design. The need for these instruments and the techniques for using them are discussed in Chapter 12.

1-9 ▼ MICROCOMPUTER COMPONENT MANUFACTURE

This book is concerned primarily with the *use* of μC components. However, to be aware of performance differences, to plan future products, and to anticipate cost trends and future designs, it is important to have a basic understanding of semiconductor manufacturing processes. Semiconductor technology involves photography, chemistry, materials science, metallurgy, physics, and electronics. Progress is being made rapidly in all these disciplines, resulting in continual improvements in the semiconductors themselves.

The first step in the process of making μC family components is to grow **silicon crystals** and slice them into thin **wafers**. The silicon crystals, which in the early days were less than 5 cm (2 inches) across, are now being grown in sizes up to 8 inches. The electrical circuits are then chemically etched into silicon wafers by treating the wafers with a photosensitive material and exposing the material through a **mask** of the desired pattern. These masks are many feet across when made but are photographically reduced almost 500 times and multiple images are projected onto each wafer. The wafers are subsequently subjected to processes of diffusion or ion implantation and deposition of metal. After many such steps, the wafer is ready to be diced (cut up) into chips, which are usually less than 6 mm ($\frac{1}{4}$ inch) square. Each chip is an IC component such as a memory, an I/O circuit or even a complete μC. The chips are tested to select the good ones, which are then mounted in the familiar plastic or ceramic packages. Using presently available techniques, hundreds of chips are now being cut from each wafer. As the technology improves, the yield of good chips per wafer also increases. This has caused the price of ICs to come down to the point where even μCs are inexpensive. Some of the **6805** family μCs cost less than $1 in large quantities. The **6800** silicon chip is shown in Fig. 1-3.

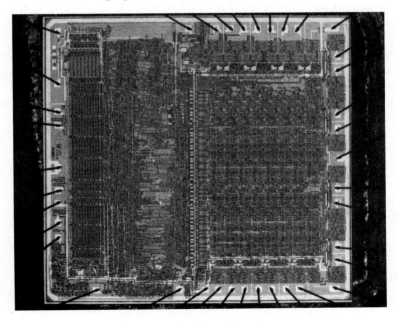

Figure 1-3 **6800** silicon chip.

1-9.1 ▼ Microcomputer Characteristics

Microcomputers are frequently compared on the basis of several main characteristics. Among them are the number of power supplies used, TTL compatibility, and the number of chips needed to form a complete μC. In specialized designs the power dissipation may also be important. How rapidly characters are written to the screen or how quickly calculations are done is one of the most important characteristics of a μP. The operation of most μCs is controlled by a digital clock (see Chapter 7). If the basic semiconductor technology allows high-speed performance, the clock can be run at a higher frequency. This permits the μC to execute more instructions per second, making it more powerful. The speed concept also extends to personal computers. If the clock within the computer is driving the μP at 33 MHz, the processing power is superior to that of slower computers.

1-9.2 ▼ PMOS, NMOS, CMOS, HMOS, and HCMOS Technologies

Metal-oxide semiconductor technology is divided into two basic types: PMOS, which is based on *p*-doped silicon, and NMOS, which is based on *n*-doped silicon. These two types of implementations can be used individually or can be combined to form a third category, known as complementary MOS (CMOS). These technologies have much in common, but each also exhibits some unique characteristics.

PMOS was perfected originally and the first μPs were designed using this process. The Intel **4004** and **8008** are examples of PMOS technology. The circuit speed of PMOS was nearly an order of magnitude (one-tenth) lower than that of bipolar devices, but because of the reduced geometry and lower power dissipation per gate, much more complexity was possible on a chip. However, *n*-type silicon is basically three times faster than *p*-type silicon, because the mobility of electrons is three times that of holes. As a result, and because of its TTL-compatible voltage (5-V), NMOS has emerged as the most popular process for μP production. It is the process used for the **6800**, the **8080**, Fairchild's **F8**, and Zilog's **Z80**. Although Intel's process is called NMOS, it still requires three voltages for the **8080**.

The techniques for producing these circuits on silicon have been continually refined, resulting in smaller designs. A smaller geometry has produced many performance improvements. One process is called high-density NMOS (HMOS). The high speed of HMOS compared to PMOS or other NMOS types provides a very high performance/price ratio. Still another improvement is called HCMOS (High-speed CMOS). This technology has been refined so that gates can be made as small as 0.8 μm. HCMOS is used to make the **68040.**

CMOS represents a major advance in digital technology. It combines an *n*-channel and a *p*-channel MOS transistor in each gate. It has the advantage of extremely low power dissipation when it is static (not being clocked or switched). CMOS has an added advantage of considerable latitude in supply voltage. Consequently, it is advocated as a good choice for battery operation.

CMOS devices have been used for many years in applications where the primary concerns were low power consumption, wide power supply range, and high noise immunity. The drawback to using the **metal-gate** CMOS was the fact that it was too slow for many applications. The logical next step in the CMOS evolution was to introduce a family of devices that are fast enough for most applications and that retain the best features of CMOS. To do this, the **silicon-gate** process with a gate length of 3.5 μm was developed. The resulting high-speed CMOS (HCMOS) device is a little more than half the size of its metal-gate predecessor. In addition, the silicon-gate process eliminates gate overlaps, which significantly lowers the gate capacities, resulting in higher-speed performance, comparable to that of TTL devices.

This HCMOS process is used in a number of inexpensive single-chip μCs in the **M68HC05** family. (The letters HC inside an IC number indicate an HCMOS device.)

New materials such as gallium arsenide are being investigated and under idealized conditions can provide an increase in speed of up to seven times. They have not yet, however, been used in the manufacture of microprocessors.

As a result of HMOS, HCMOS and other techniques, Very Large-Scale Integration (VLSI) μPs such as the **68000**, **68010**, **68020**, **68030**, **68040**, and **68060** have been developed. The **68000** contains about 68,000 transistors, the 32-bit **68020** has nearly 200,000, the **68030** has nearly 300,000, and the **68040** and **68060** have more than 1.2 million transistors (four times that of the **68030**). These are the newest members of the **6800** family (which had about 5000 transistors).

1-10 ▼ MICROPROCESSORS VS. HARD-WIRED LOGIC

Industry has made use of industrial controllers to control machines, manufacturing processes, and appliances. The method of building controllers has progressed from electromechanical devices to electronic (frequently, *analog*) transistors, to digital ICs, and now to μCs. The original controllers were *hard-wired* devices because their operation was determined by the circuits and wires contained within them. As the ICs became more complex with large-scale integration (LSI), the controllers became smaller and yet more sophisticated. They were capable of performing more diverse operations and responding to a larger number of inputs.

The washing machine is a common example of electromechanical control. Relays, solenoids, and timers within the machine determine the sequence of operations (wash, rinse, spin dry, etc.) and control the time of each operation. More recent designs use power transistors and digital ICs to replace the relays and therefore provide more reliable control.

Any function that can be implemented with hard-wired digital ICs can also be implemented or performed by a μC. The μC is a great leap forward in this evolutionary chain. Its operation is determined primarily by its program instead of the way it is wired. Because of this, μCs are rapidly replacing hard-wired logic in most controllers.

Hard-wired logic still maintains the following advantages over MOS μCs

1. It is faster. It can execute a function in perhaps one-tenth of the time required by a MOS μC, because the execution time for computer instructions is much longer than for TTL IC logic.
2. For small devices requiring just a few ICs, the hard-wired approach is less costly, because the more complex (and higher cost) chips and their associated connections are not required.
3. No programming costs are incurred.

As the size and complexity of the devices increase, μCs rapidly become more attractive because the hard-wired approach requires adding ICs and rewiring to perform more complex tasks; μCs usually require only a longer program. Most modifications of a μC system are made simply by changing the program. For example, a modification can frequently be accomplished simply by replacing a ROM, which can easily be done in the field by nontechnical users. Where many decisions or calculations are required, μCs are very useful. It is easier to use the computational power of a computer than to use discrete logic. One example is TV games, where, for example, the controller must keep track of the position of the ball, determine when a point is scored, and keep score. Most of the controllers for these games include a μC, and different games are selected by replacing the plug-in ROM (or PROM).

Microcomputers are now being considered for many new designs in industrial controller applications and are often used to replace existing mechanical or even digital logic designs, because they are far simpler to use than conventional IC logic. Since the μC approach is programmable (i.e., the operation can be changed by changing only the software), many additional features are possible with little or no added cost. **Programmability** makes possible multiple uses of a common computer hardware assembly.

1-11 ▼ FUTURE OF μCs

The technological evolution in microcomputers continues to pack more performance into a smaller space and results in more complex and more powerful semiconductor products. The growth of the **6800** family into the **68HC11** family and on to the 16-bit **68000** family provided outstanding increases in performance, approaching or exceeding that of the mini- and mainframe computer architectures they were originally modeled after.

The performance increase from that of the **68000** (which has a 16-bit data bus) to that of the 32-bit **68020**s, (with their **68881 coprocessors** and **68851 Memory-Management Units** (MMUs) results in remarkable capabilities for microcomputers. The **68030** incorporates the MMU on the chip as well as other features for a further increase. The **68040** includes the MMU and a Floating-Point Unit (FPU) mathematics coprocessor for still another major jump in computing power. These advanced systems will continue to grow, and Motorola has recently brought out two new families of 16- and 32-bit MCUs with the latter based on the **68020**. Last but not least, another new family of *embedded* controllers use simplified **68030** and **68040** CPUs. It should be noted, however, that many (perhaps most) MCU applications do not need the higher speed or 32-bit capability. At present and in the foreseeable future, the market for 8-bit μCs is expected to be much larger than the 16-bit μC market. The 32-bit market will undoubtedly be even smaller. Industrial control (including robotics) does not always need the speed or complexity now possible. Instead, the lower costs due to the reduced **die** size in 8-bit controller-type processors, with the resultant simplifications in the circuit boards and associated hardware, will lead to many more computerized instruments. When controlling large machinery, nanosecond speed is not needed unless many calculations are necessary. Studying 8-bit μCs is not only a good stepping-stone to the 32-bit world but also is very worthwhile in its own right.

1-11.1 ▼ Growing Low-End μC Market

The experience gained during the evolution to 32-bit μCs has greatly enhanced the expertise needed in the semiconductor industry to design more powerful low- and midrange devices. The demanding requirements of the midrange control-oriented microprocessor market, for computer power combined with low cost, has resulted in development of the **6805** HMOS, **146805** CMOS, and the **68HC05** and **68HC11** HCMOS families of μCs and μPs. These families are the first to make the software and hardware capabilities of more advanced computers available to the controller market. Previously, designers and manufacturers were required to choose between no processor at all or a processor that functioned more like a calculator than a computer.

Control-oriented μCs have evolved from two different bases: calculator-based and computer-based. The calculator-based design was at first considered a natural building block for controllers since most often a controller was required to be a completely self-contained unit. However, calculator-based control-oriented μPs use a split memory architecture, with separate data paths between the central processing unit (CPU) and peripherals (memory, and I/O). In addition, calculator-based I/O, display, and keypad were separated from program and data storage memory. Separate address maps were required, which forced the inclusion of many special-purpose instructions and resulted in an irregular architecture. As a result, these calculator-based devices required that hardware and software designers remember and consider many special cases in order to perform any task. The software and hardware for the calculator approach became very random, irregular, and difficult to update.

The computer-based design, on the other hand, led to another group of processors like the **6800**, which has many features of larger computers. These devices contain a single data bus that allows access to a single address map, eliminating the need for split-memory architecture. In this one-address map design, all I/O, program, and data may be accessed with the same instructions; therefore, there are fewer instructions to remember. The actual number of variations on these instructions is increased by additional addressing modes. For example, the load accumulator (LDA) instruction may load the accumulator with data in six different ways, depending on which addressing mode is used. This effectively provides the programmer with more tools to work with but fewer things to remember. These addressing modes generally apply to all memory, or I/O. Because of the regularity of the architecture, the hardware can be implemented more efficiently and it is easier to program.

1-11.2 ▼ Memory Improvements

Progress in size and speed of memory chips is as important in the performance improvements of μCs as is the progress in μPs. It is continuing at a rapid pace with larger and lower-cost RAM and ROM (or PROM) units announced frequently. Today's systems often have up to 128 times as much memory as was commonly used in earlier μC designs, in the same size package (256K vs. 2K bytes). Over the past decade the capacity of memory ICs has quadrupled every three years and it looks like it will continue to do so.

If the future of μCs is based on projections, it appears that the material cost of the ICs themselves will virtually disappear. Since the raw materials are abundant, it can logically be assumed that the cost of each chip will level off at something less than a dollar. As more functions are included in each package, the total material costs become insignificant compared with the design and programming costs. With the switchover from hardware to software, new concepts and techniques are necessary to handle the tasks to be performed, and therefore new methods of cost analysis must be used. Since the price of each system sold is determined by the cost of the hardware plus the cost of development divided by the number of systems sold, high-volume production can result in very low-priced equipment. Many people are alarmed at the rising cost of programming, but it should be recognized that it represents just a shift in costs because software is being substituted for hardware.

Software development costs are one-time costs, but the importance of keeping the development costs low should not be overlooked. Selection of a μP that is easy to program and the use of good systems-development tools are both advisable. Good development tools include not only software editing and debugging aids but also means of troubleshooting the hardware interface between the μC and its peripherals.

Most μP manufacturers provide support tools for software development, but not all of them provide the necessary hardware debugging assistance. FORTRAN, BASIC, C, and other high-level languages are used increasingly, but even though program writing is easier than it was in assembly language, the controversy over which language is best continues. High-level languages, in general, are oriented toward simplifying mathematical calculations and are notoriously poor at *bit manipulations*. Bit handling is needed in most control system applications, which are a large segment of μC uses. Some designers feel that the additional debugging time required with high-level languages in some bit-handling I/O designs may outweigh much of the gain, and because of the inherent coding inefficiencies, may result in excessive memory requirements. High-level languages require the use of compilers instead of assemblers to generate the object codes.

A technique being used more frequently is to write the program using the C high-level language and then to examine the object code and simplify sections of it by replacing them with Assembly Language routines. This is effective where speed can be improved or memory requirements reduced. Improvements in compilers, editors, assemblers, and other development aids continue to be made and should serve to decrease development time and costs.

1-12 ▼ SUMMARY

In this chapter we provided an introduction to μCs, a brief history showing the progress in their development, and a forecast of a bright future for them. The configuration of a μC system and the areas where μCs should and should not be used were discussed.

At this point, you should review the self-evaluation questions (Section 1-2). If any of them seem unclear, you should reread the appropriate sections of the text.

COMPUTER ARITHMETIC AND LOGIC OPERATIONS

2-1 ▼ INSTRUCTIONAL OBJECTIVES

To understand digital circuits and microcomputers (μCs), the reader must first understand the arithmetic they use. In this chapter we introduce the binary number system and give the student some facility in handling binary numbers. The 2s-complement system of arithmetic and the logical operations performed by a computer are also introduced. After reading this chapter, the student should be able to:

1. Convert binary numbers to decimal numbers.
2. Convert decimal numbers to binary numbers.
3. Find the sum and difference of two binary numbers.
4. Convert negative binary numbers to their 2s-complement form.
5. Add and subtract numbers in 2s-complement form.
6. Use hexadecimal numbers instead of binary numbers.
7. Add, subtract, and negate hexadecimal numbers.
8. Complement a word.
9. Find the logical AND, OR, and Exclusive OR of two words.

2-2 ▼ SELF-EVALUATION QUESTIONS

Watch for the answers to the following questions as you read the chapter. They should help you to understand the material presented.

1. What are the advantages of digital circuits?
2. What is the difference between a bit and a decimal digit? How are they similar?
3. How are binary addition and subtraction different from decimal addition and subtraction? How are they similar?
4. How are bits, bytes, and words related?
5. What are the advantages of long word lengths? Why do microprocessors use short words?

6. How is the sign of a 2s-complement number determined by inspection?
7. What is the major advantage of 2s-complement notation?
8. How can the positive equivalent of 2s-complement negative numbers be found?
9. What is the advantage of hexadecimal arithmetic?
10. How can binary numbers be converted to hexadecimal, and vice versa?

2-3 ▼ BINARY NUMBER SYSTEM

Computers and microprocessors (μPs) are built from a large number of digital electronic circuits that are carefully interconnected to perform the operations necessary to execute properly each of the computer's instructions. The instructions that a computer understands are numbers in combinations of 1s and 0s. They are numbers in the **binary number system** (see Section 2-4).

As explained in Chapter 1, a μP contains thousands of tiny digital circuits within its package. The output of a digital electronic circuit is an electrical signal that normally is within one of two possible ranges of voltage. These ranges are designated as either **logic 0** or **logic 1**. For example, in Transistor-Transistor Logic (TTL) circuits, any voltage between 0 and 0.8 V is a *logic 0* and any voltage between 2 and 5.25 V is a *logic 1*. Digital circuits also have a range of *undefined* or *forbidden* voltages that separate logic 1s from logic 0s. For TTL this range is from 0.8 to 2.0 V. If a circuit should produce an output voltage in the undefined range, it is malfunctioning and should be investigated.

Two advantages are gained by restricting the output of an electronic circuit to one of two possible values. First, it is rarely necessary to make fine distinctions. Whether an output is 3.67 or 3.68 V is immaterial; both voltages correspond to a *logic 1*. Well-designed logic circuits produce voltages near the middle of the range defined for 1 or 0, so there is no difficulty in distinguishing between them. In addition, a digital circuit is very tolerant of any drift in the output caused by component aging or changes due to temperature. A change in a component would have to be catastrophic to cause the output voltage to drift from a 1 to a 0 or to an undefined value. The second advantage of digital circuits is that it is far easier to remember a 1 or a 0 than to remember an **analog quantity** such as 3.67. Because computers are required to remember many bits, this is a very important consideration.

The output of a single digital circuit, a single **bit**, defined as a *single digital quantity*, is enough to answer any question that has only two possible answers. For example, a typical job application might ask, "What is your gender?" A "1" could arbitrarily be assigned to a male and a "0" to a female, so that a single bit is enough to describe the answer to this question. A single bit is all the space a programmer needs to reserve in a computer for this answer.

However, another question on the job application might be, "What is the color of your hair?" If the possible answers are black, brown, blonde, and red, a single bit cannot possibly describe them all. Now several bits are needed to describe all possible answers. We could assign 1 bit to each answer (i.e., brown = 0001, black = 0010, blonde = 0100, red = 1000). If there are many possible answers to the given question, many bits are required. The coding scheme presented above is not optimum; it requires more bits than are really necessary to answer the question.

It is most economical to use as few bits as possible to express the answer to a question, or a number, or a choice. So the crucial question arises: *What is the minimum number of bits required to distinguish between n different things?*

Whether these n things are objects, or possible answers, or n numbers is immaterial. To answer this question, we realize that each bit has two possible values. Therefore, k bits would have 2^k possible values. This gives rise to Theorem 1.

Theorem 1

The minimum number of bits required to express n different things is k, where k *is the smallest number such that $2^k \geq n$.*

A few examples should make this clear.

EXAMPLE 2-1

What is the minimum number of bits required to answer the hair color question, and how could they be coded to give distinct answers?

SOLUTION

There are four possible answers to this question; therefore $2^k = 4$. Since 2 is the smallest number such that $2^2 \geq 4$, $k = 2$, and 2 bits are needed. One way to code the answers is 00 = brown, 01 = black, 10 = blonde, 11 = red.

EXAMPLE 2-2

How many bits are needed to express a single decimal digit?

SOLUTION

There are 10 possible values for a single decimal digit (0 through 9); therefore, $2^k > 10$. Since $k = 4$ is the smallest *integer* such that $2^k \geq 10$, 4 bits are required.

EXAMPLE 2-3

A computer must store the names of a group of people. If we assume that no name is longer than 20 letters, how many bits must the computer reserve for each name?

SOLUTION

To express a name, only the 26 letters of the alphabet, plus a space and perhaps a period, are needed. This is a total of 28 characters. Since $2^k > 28$, $k = 5$, and 5 bits are required for each character. Since space must be reserved for 20 such characters, 100 bits are needed for each name.

2-3.1 ▼ Bits and Words

Almost all computers have lines and logic to handle a number of **bits**, or *binary digits*, in *parallel* (i.e., the bits are grouped into **words**). A word is a group of bits that constitute the basic unit of information within the computer. The **word length** of a computer is the *number of bits involved in each data bus transfer* and is always a number equal to a power of 2 (i.e., 4, 8, 16, etc.). While word lengths vary from computer to computer, each computer has a definite word length and its memory or storage locations are built to accommodate words of that length.

Large computers (often called mainframes) generally use long words. The IBM 360/370 series, for example, uses 32-bit words. Minicomputers use intermediate word lengths; 16 bits is the most popular minicomputer word size. Until 1980 almost all μPs used 8-bit words. Since then, 16- and 32-bit μPs have been used in increasing numbers. These include the Intel 16-bit **8086, 80386,** and the Motorola **68000** and **68010,** and 32-bit μPs such as the Intel **80486** and Motorola's **68020, 68030, 68040,** and **68060.**

There are three advantages to using long word sizes:

1. Larger numbers can be accommodated within a single word.
2. Instruction words are more flexible; they allow the instructions to contain more options.
3. With larger instruction words, each instruction is more powerful; it can do more. Consequently, 16-bit μPs tend to execute the same program faster than do 8-bit μPs. Not all 16-bit processors are faster, however, and many other factors are involved.

Presently available μPs can solve complex mathematical problems, such as matrix inversion, but these problems are generally run on large mainframes. Controlling physical processes or handling characters, which do not need the speed of a larger mainframe computer, are the kinds of tasks most often done with μCs. Microcomputers can use shorter word lengths and thus the required hardware is simpler. Data buffers need only be provided for 8 bits, μCs and memories can be simpler, and even Printed Circuit Boards (PCBs) (see Section 13-6.1) require only eight data lines. This selection of word size allows users to adjust their system to fit their job requirements. Shorter word lengths complicate the programming, however, but the additional effort required to program μPs is offset by the low cost of the hardware.

EXAMPLE 2-4

How many numbers can be represented by

(a) A single Motorola **68040** word? (The **68040** uses 32 bits per word.)
(b) An 8-bit μP word?

SOLUTION

(a) Since a **68040** word contains 32 bits, any one of $2^{32} = 4,294,967,296$ numbers may be represented in a single word.
(b) For the μP word of 8 bits, 2^8 or 256 numbers may be represented by a single word.

2-3.2 ▼ Bytes and Nibbles

A group of 8 bits is called a **byte**. This is a convenient size for storing a single **alphanumeric character** (a letter, a number, or a punctuation mark). For the many μPs that have an 8-bit word size, *byte* and *word* are used interchangeably.

Groups of 4 bits are sometimes called a **nibble**. They also constitute a *hexadecimal digit* (see Section 2-8). Other definitions vary depending on whether the computer is an 8-, 16-, or 32-bit type. Thus we have the following conversion table:

4 bits	=	1 nibble
2 nibbles	=	1 byte
2 bytes (16 bits)	=	1 word (16-bit μP) or half-word (32-bit μP)
4 bytes	=	1 long word (16-bit μP) or word (32-bit μP)

2-4 ▼ BINARY-TO-DECIMAL CONVERSION

Because computer operation is based on the *binary* (base 2) number system and people use the *decimal* (base 10) number system, it is often necessary to convert numbers given in one system to their equivalents in the other system. To eliminate any possible confusion, a subscript is used to indicate which number system is employed. Thus 101_{10} is the decimal number whose value is one hundred and one, while 101_2 is a binary number whose decimal value is five. Of course, in considering these two bases, any number containing a digit from 2 through 9 is obviously not a binary number.

The value of a decimal number depends on the *magnitude* of the decimal digits expressing it and on their *position* in the number. A decimal number is equal to the sum $D_0 \times 10^0 + D_1 \times 10^1 + D_2 \times 10^2 + \cdots$, where D_0 is the least significant digit, D_1 the next significant digit, and so on.

EXAMPLE 2-5

Express the decimal number 7903 as a sum to the base 10.

SOLUTION

Here D_0, the least significant digit, is 3, $D_1 = 0$, $D_2 = 9$, and $D_3 = 7$. Therefore, 7903 equals

$$
\begin{aligned}
3 \times 10^0 &= 3 \\
0 \times 10^1 &= 0 \\
9 \times 10^2 &= 900 \\
7 \times 10^3 &= \underline{7000} \\
&\ 7903
\end{aligned}
$$

Similarly, a group of binary bits can represent a number in the binary number system. The binary base is 2; therefore the digits can only be 0 or 1. However, the position of the digits is also important and the total value is equal to the sum of the values designated by each bit, namely $B_0 \times 2^0 + B^1 \times 2^1 + \cdots$, where B_0 is the least significant bit and so on. The powers of 2 are given in the *binary boat* or table of Appendix A. In this table, n is the exponent and the corresponding positive and negative powers of 2 are listed to the left and right of n, respectively.

A **binary number** is a *group of ones (1s) and zeros (0s)*. To find the equivalent decimal number, we simply add the powers of 2 that correspond to the 1s in the number and omit the powers of 2 that correspond to the 0s in the number.

EXAMPLE 2-6

Convert 100011011_2 to a decimal number.

SOLUTION

The first bit to the left of the decimal point corresponds to $n = 0$, and n increases by one (increments) for each position farther to the left. The number 100011011 has **1s** in positions 0, 1, 3, 4, and 8. The conversion is made by obtaining the powers of 2 that correspond to these n values (using Appendix A, if necessary) and adding them.

n	2^n
0	1
1	2
3	8
4	16
8	256
	283

Therefore, $100011011_2 = \mathbf{283}_{10}$.

EXAMPLE 2-7

In the Motorola **68020** μC each word consists of 16 bits; that is, $k = 16$. How many numbers can be represented by each **68020** word?

SOLUTION

Since 16 bits are available, any one of 65,536 (2^{16}) numbers can be expressed. These numbers range from a minimum of sixteen 0s to a maximum of sixteen 1s, which is the binary equivalent of 65,535. Therefore, the 65,536 different numbers that can be expressed by a single word are the decimal numbers 0 through 65,535.

2-5 ▼ DECIMAL-TO-BINARY CONVERSION

It is often necessary to convert decimal numbers to binary numbers. Human beings, for example, supply and receive decimal numbers from computers that work in binary; consequently, computers are continually making binary-to-decimal and decimal-to-binary conversions.

To convert a decimal number to its equivalent binary number, the following **algorithm** (or procedure) may be used:

1. Obtain N (the decimal number to be converted).
2. Determine whether N is odd or even.
3. **a.** If N is odd, write 1 and subtract 1 from N. Go to step 4.
   b. If N is even, write 0.
4. Obtain a new value of N by dividing the N of step 3 by 2.
5. **a.** If $N > 1$, go back to step 1 and repeat the procedure.
   b. If $N = 1$, write 1.

The number written is the binary equivalent of the original decimal number. The number written first is the least significant bit, and the number written last is the most significant bit.

This procedure can also be implemented by following the flowchart of Fig. 2-1. Computer programmers often use **flowcharts** to describe their programs graphically. For the rudimentary flowcharts drawn in this book, the square box is a command, which must be obeyed unconditionally. The diamond-shaped box is a decision box. Within the decision box is a question that must be answered *yes* or *no*. If the answer is yes, the *yes* path must be followed; otherwise, the *no* path is followed. The flowchart of Fig. 2-1 starts with the given number N, and since K equals 0, initially we are writing B_0, the least significant digit. Note that equations in a flowchart are programmer's equations, not algebraic equations. The "equation" $N = N - 1$ makes no sense mathematically. What it means here is that N is *replaced* by $N - 1$.

On the initial pass through the flowchart, B_0, the least significant bit, is written as 0 or 1, depending on whether N is even or odd. Next, N is divided by 2 and K is incremented so that on the following pass B_1, the second **Least Significant Bit** (LSB) will be written. We continue looping through the flowchart and repeating the procedure until $N = 1$. Then the **Most Significant Bit** (MSB) is written as a 1, and the process stops. The bits written are the binary equivalent of the decimal number.

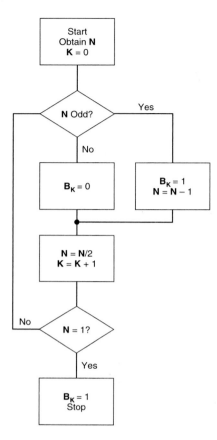

Figure 2-1 Flowchart for decimal-to-binary conversion of whole numbers.

EXAMPLE 2-8

Find the binary equivalent of the decimal number 217.

SOLUTION

The solution proceeds according to the algorithm or flowchart. When an odd number is encountered, a 1 is written as the binary digit and subtracted from the remaining number; when the remaining number is even, 0 is written as the binary digit. The number is then divided by 2. The process continues until the number is reduced to 1.

Remaining Number		Binary Digit or Bit
217	Odd; subtract 1	1
216	Divide by 2	
108	Even; divide by 2	0
54	Even; divide by 2	0
27	Odd; subtract 1	1
26	Divide by 2	
13	Odd; subtract 1	1
12	Divide by 2	
6	Even; divide by 2	0
3	Odd; subtract 1	1
2	Divide by 2	
1	Finish	1

Note that the LSB was written first. Therefore,

$$217_{10} = 11011001_2$$

To check this, convert back from binary to decimal.

$$11011001_2 = 128 + 64 + 16 + 8 + 1 = 217_{10}$$

2-6 ▼ ADDITION AND SUBTRACTION OF BINARY NUMBERS

The binary number system is used by computers in the same way that the decimal system is used by human beings. Mathematical operations such as addition, subtraction, multiplication, and division can also be performed on binary numbers. In this section the most commonly performed arithmetic operations, addition and subtraction, will be discussed. These are the operations performed by a μP or minicomputer. The reader should consult more specialized texts (Section 2-12) for multiplication, division, squares, square roots, and other arithmetic operations.

2-6.1 ▼ Addition of Binary Numbers

The addition of binary numbers is similar to the addition of decimal numbers, except that $1 + 1 = 0$ with a carry out to the next significant place. A carry into a more significant position acts like an additional 1.

EXAMPLE 2-9

Add the binary numbers A = 11101100 and B = 1100110.

SOLUTION

Column	9 8 7 6 5 4 3 2 1	(decimal addition)
A	1 1 1 0 1 1 0 0	(236)
B	1 1 0 0 1 1 0	(102)
	1 0 1 0 1 0 0 1 0	(338)

The addition above proceeded as follows:

Column 1 $0 + 0 = 0$ (least significant digit).

Column 2 $0 + 1 = 1$

Column 3 $1 + 1 = 0$ plus a carry output.

Column 4 $0 + 1 = 1$ plus a carry input from column 3 sums to a 0 and produces a carry out to column 5.

Column 5 $0 + 0 = 0$ but the carry input from column 4 makes the sum 1.

Column 6 $1 + 1 = 0$ and a carry output to column 7.

Column 7 $1 + 1$ plus a carry input results in a sum of 1 and a carry output.

Column 8   B does not have an eighth bit; therefore, a leading 0 can be assumed. Here $0 + 1$ plus a carry input yields a 0 sum plus a carry output.

Column 9   Neither A nor B has a ninth digit, so leading 0s are written for both. In column 9 we have $0 + 0$ plus a carry in from column 8 that gives a sum of 1. Since there is no carry out of column 9, the addition is complete.

The sum of Example 2-9 can be checked by converting the numbers to their decimal equivalent. These numbers are shown in parentheses beside the sums.

2-6.2 ▼ Subtraction of Binary Numbers

The rules for the subtraction of binary numbers are

1. $1 - 1 = 0$
2. $0 - 0 = 0$
3. $1 - 0 = 1$
4. $0 - 1 = 1$ with a borrow out

To borrow, change the next 1 in the minuend to a 0 and change all intervening 0s to 1s. Subtraction of binary numbers is shown in Example 2-10.

EXAMPLE 2-10

Subtract 101101001 from 100011010011.

SOLUTION

Column	12 11 10 9 8 7 6 5 4 3 2 1	(decimal subtraction)
	1 0 0 0 1 1 0 1 0 0 1 1	(2259)
	1 0 1 1 0 1 0 0 1	− (361)
	1 1 1 0 1 1 0 1 0 1 0	(1898)

Column 1	$1 - 1 = 0$	
Column 2	$1 - 0 = 1$	
Column 3	$0 - 0 = 0$	
Column 4	$0 - 1 = 1$	The 1 in column 5 is changed to a 0 due to the borrow out generated in column 4.
Column 5		This is now $0 - 0 = 0$.
Column 6	$0 - 1 = 1$	The 1 in column 7 is changed to a 0.
Column 7		Due to the borrow from column 6, this now becomes $0 - 1$ or 1 with a borrow out that changes the 1 in column 8.
Column 8		This becomes $0 - 0 = 0$.
Column 9	$0 - 1 = 1$	Columns 10 and 11 are 0, so the borrow must be from column 12. Columns 10 and 11 contain intervening 0s, so they change to 1s and column 12 changes to a 0.
Column 10		This is now $1 - 0 = 1$.
Column 11		This is now $1 - 0 = 1$.
Column 12	$0 - 0 = 0$	

The results were checked by converting the binary numbers to their decimal equivalents, which are shown in parentheses beside the numbers.

2-7 ▼ 2s-COMPLEMENT ARITHMETIC

When building hardware such as μCs to accommodate binary numbers, two problems arise:

1. The number of bits in a hardware register* is finite.
2. Negative integers must also be represented.

*A register is hardware circuitry in the μP just like that used in memories. It holds the bits so they can be evaluated.

NOTE: These problems do not arise in conventional pencil-and-paper arithmetic. If additional bits are needed, the number can always be extended to the left and negative numbers can always be represented by a minus sign.

Since a hardware register consists of a finite number of bits, the range of numbers that can be represented is finite. An n-bit register can contain one of 2^n numbers. If positive binary numbers are used, the 2^n numbers that can be represented are 0 through $2^n - 1$ (a string of n 1s represents the number $2^n - 1$).

2-7.1 ▼ 2s-Complement Numbers

As shown in Example 2-11 and 2-12, all modern computers and μCs can use the **2s-complement** number system to allow them to express both positive and negative numbers.

In this system the *MSB of a 2s-complement number denotes the sign* (0 means that the number is positive, 1 means that the number is negative), but the MSB is also a part of the number. In 2s-complement notation, positive numbers are represented as simple binary numbers with the restriction that the MSB is 0. Negative numbers are somewhat different. To obtain the representation of a negative number, use the following algorithm:

1. Represent the number as a positive binary number.
2. Complement it (write 0s where there are 1s and 1s where there are 0s in the positive number).
3. Add 1.
4. Ignore any carries out of the MSB.

EXAMPLE 2-11

Given 8-bit words, find the 2s-complement representation of:

(a) +25
(b) −25
(c) −1

SOLUTION

(a) The number +25 can be written as 11001. Since 8 bits are available, there is room for three leading 0s, making the MSB 0.

$$+25 = 00011001$$

(b) To find –25, complement +25 and add 1.

$$+25 = 00011001$$
$$\overline{(+25)} = 11100110$$
$$+ \underline{\hspace{3em} 1}$$
$$\mathbf{-25 = 11100111}$$

Note that the MSB is 1.

(c) To write –1, take the 2s complement of +1.

$$+1 = 00000001$$
$$\overline{(+1)} = 11111110$$
$$+ \underline{\hspace{3em} 1}$$
$$\mathbf{-1 = 11111111}$$

From this example, we see that a solid string of 1s represents the number –1 in 2s-complement form.

To determine the magnitude of any unknown negative number, simply take its 2s-complement as described in Example 2-11. The result is a positive number whose *magnitude equals that of the original number.*

EXAMPLE 2-12

What decimal number does 11110100 represent?

SOLUTION

This number must be negative because its MSB is a 1. Its positive equivalent is obtained by 2s complementing the given number.

Given Number	11110100
Complement	00001011
Adding 1	+ 1
	00001100

This is the equivalent of $+12_{10}$. Therefore, $\mathbf{11110100_2 = -12_{10}}$.

2-7.2 ▼ Range of 2s-Complement Numbers

The *maximum positive number* that can be represented in 2s-complement form is a single 0 followed by all 1s, or $2^{n-1} - 1$ for an *n*-bit number. The *most negative number* that can be represented has an MSB of 1 followed by all 0s, which equals -2^{n-1}. Therefore, an *n*-bit number can represent any one of $2^{n-1} - 1$ positive numbers plus 2^{n-1} negative numbers plus 0, which is 2^n total numbers. Every number has a *unique* representation.

Other features of 2s-complement arithmetic are:

1. Even numbers (positive or negative) have an LSB of 0.
2. Numbers divisible by 4 have the two LSBs equal to 0.
3. In general, numbers divisible by 2^n have *n* LSBs of 0.

EXAMPLE 2-13

What range of numbers can be represented by an 8-bit word (a byte) using 2s-complement representation?

SOLUTION

The most positive number that can be represented is $2^{n-1} - 1$. Here n = 8, so $2^{n-1} - 1$ is 127_{10}. In 8-bit 2s-complement form it is 0111 1111. The most negative 8-bit number is $10000000_2 = -128_{10}$. Therefore, any number between +127 and −128 can be represented by an 8-bit number in 2s-complement form. There are 256_{10} numbers in this range, as expected, since $2^8 = 256_{10}$. Note also that the seven LSBs of −128 are 0, as required, since −128 is divisible by 2^7.

2-7.3 ▼ Addition of 2s-Complement Numbers

Consider the simple equation $C = A$ plus B. Although it seems clear enough, we cannot immediately determine whether an addition or subtraction operation is required. If A and B are both positive, addition is required. But if one of the operands is negative and the other is positive, a subtraction operation must be performed.

The major advantage of 2s-complement arithmetic is that *if an addition operation is to be performed, the numbers are added regardless of their signs*. The answer is in 2s-complement form with the correct sign. Any carries out of the MSB are meaningless and should be ignored.

EXAMPLE 2-14

Express the numbers 19 and −11 as 8-bit 2s-complement numbers, and add them.

SOLUTION

The number +19 is simply 00010011. To find −11, take the 2s complement of 11.

$$11 = 00001011$$

$$\overline{(11)} = 11110100$$

$$-11 = 11110101$$

Now +19 plus (−11) equals

$$
\begin{array}{ll}
1111\ \ 111 & \text{Carry} \\
00010011 & 19 \\
\underline{11110101} & \underline{-11} \\
00001000 & +8
\end{array}
$$

Note that there is a carry out of the MSB that is ignored. The 8-bit answer is simply the number +8.

EXAMPLE 2-15

Add −11 and −19.

SOLUTION

First −19 must be expressed as a 2s-complement number:

$$19 = 00010011$$

$$\overline{(19)} = 11101100$$

$$-19 = 11101101$$

Now the numbers can be added:

$$111111 \ 1 \quad \text{Carry}$$

$$\begin{array}{r} -19 \ = 11101101 \\ +(-11) = \underline{11110101} \\ \mathbf{-30} \ = \mathbf{11100010} \end{array}$$

Again a carry out of the MSB has been ignored.

2-7.4 ▼ Subtraction of 2s-Complement Numbers

Subtraction of binary numbers in 2s-complement form is also very simple and straightforward. *The 2s-complement of the subtrahend is taken and added to the minuend.* This is essentially subtraction by changing the sign and adding. As in addition, the signs of the operands and carries out of the MSB are ignored.

EXAMPLE 2-16

Subtract 30 from 53. Use 8-bit numbers.

SOLUTION

Note that 30 is the subtrahend and 53 is the minuend.

$$\begin{array}{l} 53 = 00110101 \quad \text{(minuend)} \\ 30 = 00011110 \quad \text{(subtrahend)} \end{array}$$

Taking the 2s complement of 30 and adding, we obtain

$$\begin{array}{r} (\overline{30}) = 11100001 \\ -30 \ = 11100010 \\ +53 \ = \underline{00110101} \\ \mathbf{00010111} = \mathbf{23}_{10} \end{array}$$

EXAMPLE 2-17

Subtract −30 from −19.

SOLUTION

Here

$$\begin{array}{l} -19 = 11101101 \quad \text{(see Example 2-15)} \\ -30 = 11100010 \quad \text{(subtrahend)} \end{array}$$

NOTE: −30 is the subtrahend. 2s complementing −30 gives +30 or 00011110.

$$-19 = 11101101$$
$$+30 = \underline{00011110}$$
$$\mathbf{00001011} = \mathbf{11_{10}}$$

The carry out of the MSB is ignored and the answer, +11, is correct.

2-8 ▼ HEXADECIMAL NOTATION

The binary system uses many 1s and 0s to represent a number, but long strings of 1s and 0s are confusing and unwieldy. To condense the representation of numbers, *hexadecimal notation* is used. The hexadecimal number system is a *base 16* arithmetic system. Since such a system requires 16 different digits, the letters **A** and **F** are added to the 10 decimal digits (0 through 9). The advantage of having 16 hexadecimal digits is that each digit can represent a *unique* combination of 4 bits, and any combination of 4 bits can be represented by a single hex digit.* Table 2-1 gives both the decimal and binary value associated with each **hexadecimal digit**. This notation has been adopted by all μC manufacturers and users.

TABLE 2-1   Hexadecimal-to-Binary
Number Conversions

HEXADECIMAL DIGIT	DECIMAL VALUE	BINARY VALUE
0	0	0000
1	1	0001
2	2	0010
3	3	0011
4	4	0100
5	5	0101
6	6	0110
7	7	0111
8	8	1000
9	9	1001
A	10	1010
B	11	1011
C	12	1100
D	13	1101
E	14	1110
F	15	1111

*The word *hex* is often used as an abbreviation for *hexadecimal*.

2-8.1 ▼ Conversions between Hexadecimal and Binary Numbers

To convert a binary number to hexadecimal, start at the LSB and divide the binary number into groups of 4 bits each. Then replace each 4-bit group with its equivalent hex digit obtained from Table 2-1. See Example 2-18.

EXAMPLE 2-18

Convert the binary number 110000010111111101 to hex.

SOLUTION

We start with the LSB and divide the number into 4-bit nibbles. Each nibble is then replaced with its corresponding hex digit as shown:

$$0011 \quad 0000 \quad 0101 \quad 1111 \quad 1101$$
$$3 \qquad 0 \qquad 5 \qquad F \qquad D$$

When the most significant group has less than 4 bits, as in this example, leading 0s are added to complete the 4-bit nibble.

Example 2-19 shows how to convert a hex number to binary, simply replace each hex digit by its 4-bit binary equivalent.

EXAMPLE 2-19

Convert the hex number 1CB09 to binary.

SOLUTION

We simply expand the hex number

$$1 \qquad C \qquad B \qquad 0 \qquad 9$$
$$0001 \quad 1100 \quad 1011 \quad 0000 \quad 1001$$

Thus the equivalent binary number is

$$11100101100001001$$

It is not necessary to write the leading 0s.

2-8.2 ▼ Conversion of Hex Numbers to Decimal Numbers

The hex system is a base 16 system; therefore, any hex number can be expressed as

$$H_0 \times 1 + H_1 \times 16 + H_2 \times 16^2 + H_3 \times 16^3 + \cdots$$

where H_0 is the least significant hex digit, H_1 the next, and so on. This is similar to the binary system of numbers discussed in Section 2-4.

EXAMPLE 2-20

Convert 2FC to decimal.

SOLUTION

The least significant hex digit (H_0) is C, or 12_{10}. The next digit (H_1) is F, or 15_{10}, and since it is in the second column it must be multiplied by 16, giving 240_{10}. The next digit (H_2) is 2, which is in column 3 and therefore multiplied by 16^2, or 256_{10}. Hence $2FC_{16} = 512 + 240 + 12 = \textbf{764}_{\textbf{10}}$.

An alternative solution is to convert 2FC to the binary number 1011111100 and then perform a binary-to-decimal conversion.

Decimal numbers can be converted to hex by repeatedly dividing them by 16. After each division, the remainder becomes one of the hex digits in the final answer.

EXAMPLE 2-21

Convert 9999 to hex.

SOLUTION

Start by dividing by 16 as shown in the following table. After each division, the quotient becomes the number starting the next line and the remainder is the hex digit with the least significant digit on the top line.

NUMBER	QUOTIENT	REMAINDER	HEX DIGIT
9999	624	15	F
624	39	0	0
39	2	7	7
2	0	2	2

This example shows that $(9999)_{10} = (270F)_{16}$. The result can be checked by converting 270F to decimal, as shown in Example 2-20. By doing so we obtain

$$(2 \times 4096) + (7 \times 256) + 0 + 15 = 9999$$
$$8192 \quad + \quad 1792 \quad + 0 + 15 = 9999$$

2-8.3 ▼ Hexadecimal Addition

When working with μCs, it is often necessary to add or subtract hex numbers. They can be added by referring to hexadecimal addition tables, but we suggest the following procedure:

1. Add the two hex digits (mentally substituting their decimal equivalents).
2. If the sum is 15 or less, express it directly in hex (by mentally converting back to hex).
3. If the sum is greater than or equal to 16, subtract 16 and carry 1 to the next position.

The following example should make this procedure clear.

EXAMPLE 2-22

Add D + E.

SOLUTION

D is the equivalent of decimal 13 and E is the equivalent of decimal 14. Together they sum to 27. This is converted back to hex by subtracting 16 (27 − 16 = 11). The 11 is equal to B and there is a carry. Therefore, **D + E = 1B**.

EXAMPLE 2-23

Add B2E6 and F77.

SOLUTION

The solution is shown below.

Column	4	3	2	1
Augend	B	2	E	6
Addend		F	7	7
Sum	C	2	5	D

Column 1	$6 + 7 = 13 = D$. The result is less than 16 so there is no carry.
Column 2	$E + 7 = 14 + 7 = 21 = 5$ + a carry, because the result is greater than 16.
Column 3	$F + 2 + 1$ (the carry from column 2) $= 15 + 2 + 1 = 18 = 2$ + a carry.
Column 4	$B + 1$ (the carry from column 3) $= C$.

Hex subtraction is analogous to decimal subtraction. If the subtrahend digit is larger than the minuend digit, 1 is borrowed from the next most significant digit. If the next most significant digit is 0, a 1 is borrowed from the next digit and the intermediate digit is changed to an F.

EXAMPLE 2-24

Subtract 32F from C02.

SOLUTION

The subtraction proceeds as follows:

Column	**3 2 1**
Minuend	C 0 2
Subtrahend	3 2 F
Difference	8 D 3

Column 1	Subtracting F from 2 requires a borrow. Because a borrow is worth 16, it raises the minuend to 18. Column 1 is therefore $18 - F = 18 - 15 = 3$.
Column 2	Because column 2 contains a 0, it cannot provide the borrow out from column 1. Consequently, the borrow out must come from column 3, while the minuend of column 2 is changed to an F. Column 2 is therefore $F - 2 = 15 - 2 = 13 = D$.
Column 3	Column 3 can provide the borrow out needed for column 1. This reduces the C to B and $B - 3 = 8$.

As in the decimal addition, the results can be checked by adding the subtrahend and difference to get the minuend.

2-8.4 ▼ Negating Hex Numbers

The negative equivalent of a positive hex number can always be found by converting the hex number to binary and taking the 2s complement of the result (Section 2-7). A shorter method exists, however:

1. Add, to the least significant hex digit, the hex digit that makes it sum to 16.
2. Add to all other digits the digits that make them sum to 15.
3. If the least significant digit is 0, write 0 as the least significant digit of the answer and start at the next digit.
4. The number written is the negative equivalent of the given hex number.

This procedure works because the sum of the original number and the number is always 0.

EXAMPLE 2-25

Find the negative equivalent of the hex number 20C3.

SOLUTION

The least significant digit is 3. To make 16, D must be added to 3. The other digits are 2, 0, and C. To make 15 in each case, we add D, F, and 3, respectively. The negative equivalent of 20C3 is therefore DF3D. This example can be checked by adding the negative equivalent to the positive number. Since X plus −X always equals 0, the result should be 0.

$$
\begin{array}{r}
2\ \ 0\ \mathrm{C}\ \ 3 \\
+\,\mathrm{D}\ \mathrm{F}\ \ 3\ \mathrm{D} \\
\hline
0\ \ 0\ \ 0\ \ 0
\end{array}
$$

The carry out of the most significant digit is ignored.

The procedure described above does not work for numbers that end in 0. For these numbers a 0 is also the least significant nibble of the converted word and then the procedure is applied starting at the first nonzero nibble.

EXAMPLE 2-26

Negate 30B00.

SOLUTION

The two least significant nibbles are 00 and the converted number must also end in 00. The first nonzero nibble is B, so the converted value is 5 (B + 5 = 16). The rest are chosen to add to 15 and the answer is **CF500**.

Check:

$$
\begin{array}{r}
30B00 \\
+\,CF500 \\
\hline
00000
\end{array}
$$

2-9 ▼ LOGICAL OPERATIONS

Besides addition and subtraction, computers must be able to execute a variety of *logical* instructions. These operations are performed between words or bytes, on a bit-by-bit basis. There is no interaction (such as a borrow or a carry) between the bits.

2-9.1 ▼ Logical OR Operation

If two words are ORed together, the result, or output word, has a 1 in each bit position where either or both of the input words had a 1. The logical OR of two operands, A and B, is expressed as $\mathbf{A + B}$. Note that this is different from A *plus* B, which means the arithmetic *sum* of A and B.

EXAMPLE 2-27

Given two words, $A = 10111001$ and $B = 11011010$, find $A + B$.

SOLUTION

The words are lined up as follows:

Bit position	7	6	5	4	3	2	1	0
A	1	0	1	1	1	0	0	1
B	1	1	0	1	1	0	1	0
$A + B$	**1**	**1**	**1**	**1**	**1**	**0**	**1**	**1**

For all bit positions except position 2, either word A or word B or both contain a 1. Therefore, the logical OR ($A + B$) results in a 1 in all bit positions except position 2.

2-9.2 ▼ Logical AND Operation

When two words are ANDed, the output word is a 1 only in those bit positions where both input words are 1. Since the operation is analogous to multiplication, $Y = AB$ means that Y is the logical AND of the two words A and B.

EXAMPLE 2-28

If the two words of Example 2-27 are ANDed, what is the output word?

SOLUTION

The words are ANDed bit by bit:

Bit position	7 6 5 4 3 2 1 0
A	1 0 1 1 1 0 0 1
B	1 1 0 1 1 0 1 0
AB	1 0 0 1 1 0 0 0

A and B are both 1 only in bit positions 3, 4, and 7, as the answer shows.

2-9.3 ▼ Exclusive OR Operation

Another logical operation that has many uses (parity checking is one example) is the *Exclusive OR* (XOR) operation. The symbol for the **XOR** operation is $\oplus$. If two words are XORed, the bits of the output word are 1s if *either, but not both*, of the corresponding bits of the input words is a 1.

EXAMPLE 2-29

Find the XOR of words A and B of Example 2-27.

SOLUTION

The words are XORed on a bit-by-bit basis:

Bit position	7 6 5 4 3 2 1 0
A	1 0 1 1 1 0 0 1
B	1 1 0 1 1 0 1 0
$A \oplus B$	0 1 1 0 0 0 1 1

The output word is seen to be 1 wherever exactly one of the input words contains a 1.

2-9.4 ▼ Complementation

The complement of a word is obtained simply by *inverting each bit of the word*. Because **complementation** is often used in computer arithmetic, most μPs contain a complementation instruction.

EXAMPLE 2-30

Complement word *A* of Example 2-27.

SOLUTION

Complementation is obtained simply by inverting each bit of the word.

$$A = 10111001$$
$$\overline{A}(\text{the complement of } A) = \mathbf{01000110}$$

2-10 ▼ SUMMARY

In this chapter, basic binary arithmetic used in computers was introduced. The binary number system was explained and examples of binary addition, binary subtraction, and binary-to-decimal conversion were presented.

The 2s-complement system, used in most computers, was introduced and arithmetic examples in this system were presented. The hexadecimal system, which is used throughout this book, was demonstrated as an extension and condensation of the binary system.

2-11 ▼ GLOSSARY

Algorithm A standard procedure or method of computation.

Alphanumeric character A character that may be either an alphabetic, numeric, or punctuation character.

Analog quantity A continuously variable quantity; one that may assume any value, usually within a limited range.

Binary number A number containing only 1s or 0s.

Binary system A number system with 2 as the base.

Bit A single binary digital quantity, a 1 or a 0.

Byte A group of 8 bits.

Complementation The process of inverting each bit of a word.

Digital quantity A variable that has one of two possible values.

Flowchart A graphic representation of a procedure or program.

Hexadecimal digit A number (0 to F) that represents the value of a group of 4 binary bits.

Least Significant Bit (LSB) The bit at the right end of a byte. When set, it adds a value of 1 to the byte.

Most Significant Bit (MSB) The bit at the left end of a byte. When set, it adds a value of 128_{10} to the byte.

Nibble A group of 4 bits.

Register A hardware device in the μP or peripheral device that holds a group of related bits usually containing a character, command, or number.

2s-complement The representation of numbers in which negative numbers are obtained by complementing their equivalent and adding 1.

Word A group of bits that constitute the basic unit of information within a computer.

Word length The number of bits involved in each data bus transfer.

2-12 ▼ REFERENCES

GREENFIELD, JOSEPH D., *Practical Digital Design Using ICs,* 3rd ed., Prentice Hall, Englewood Cliffs, N.J., 1994.

HILL, FREDERICK J., AND GERALD R. PETERSON, *Introduction to Switching Theory and Logical Design,* 3rd ed., Wiley, New York, 1979.

KOSTOPOULOS, GEORGE K., *Digital Engineering,* Wiley, New York, 1975.

NASHELSKY, LOUIS, *Introduction to Digital Computer Technology,* 3rd ed., Wiley, New York, 1981.

2-13 ▼ PROBLEMS

2-1. How many bits are required to distinguish between 100 different things?

2-2. A major league baseball team plays 162 games a year. Before the season starts, how many bits must be reserved to express the number of games the team will win and the number of games the team will lose?

2-3. A line printer is capable of printing 132 characters on a single line and each character is one of 64 symbols (26 alphabetic symbols plus 10 numbers plus punctuation). How many bits are needed to print an entire line?

2-4. Express the following decimal numbers as a sum.
   (a) 4507
   (b) 137,659
   (c) 8,897,061

2-5. Convert the following binary numbers to decimal.
   (a) 10111
   (b) 110101
   (c) 110001011

2-6. Convert the following decimal numbers to binary.
   (a) 66
   (b) 252
   (c) 5795
   (d) 106,503

2-7. For each of the following pairs of numbers, find $A + B$ and $A - B$, completing the third and fourth columns.

	A	B	$A + B$	$A - B$
(a)	11011	1001		
(b)	1110011	101010		
(c)	111000111	100101		
(d)	101111011	1000101		

2-8. Find $A + B$ and $A - B$ by converting each number to binary and doing the addition and subtraction in binary. Check the results by converting back to decimal.

	A	B	$A + B$	$A - B$
(a)	67	39		
(b)	145	78		
(c)	31,564	26,797		

2-9. A PDP-11 is a minicomputer with a 16-bit word length. What range of numbers can a single word contain?

2-10. How high can you count in binary using only your fingers?

2-11. Find the 8-bit 2s complement of the following numbers.
   (a) 99
   (b) –7
   (c) 102

2-12. Determine by inspection which of the following 2s-complement numbers are divisible by 4.
   (a) 11011010
   (b) 10011100
   (c) 01111000
   (d) 00001010
   (e) 01000001
   (f) 01010100

2-13. A PDP-8 is a computer with a 12-bit word length that uses 2s-complement arithmetic. What range of numbers can be expressed by a single PDP-8 word?

2-14. Express each of the following numbers in 9-bit 2s-complement form, and add them.

(a) 85
    +37

(b)   85
   +(−37)

(c) −85
   +37

(d) −85
   +(−37)

2-15. Do the following subtractions after expressing the operands in 10-bit 2s-complement notation.

(a)   36
   −(−23)

(b) 835
   −(214)

(c) −450
   −(−460)

(d) 316
   −(−579)

2-16. A number in 2s-complement form can be inverted by subtracting it from − 1. Invert 25 using this procedure and 8-bit numbers.

2-17. Convert the following binary numbers to hexadecimal.

(a) 11111011

(b) 1011001

(c) 10000011111100

(d) 10010101100011101

2-18. Convert the following hex numbers to binary.

(a) 129

(b) 84C5

(c) 5CF035

(d) ABCDE2F

2-19. Perform the following hex additions.

(a) 99
    89

(b) CB
    DD

(c) 15F02
    3C3E

(d) 2CFB4D
5DC98B

2-20. Perform the following hex subtractions.

(a) 59
F

(b) 1CC
DE

(c) 1002
5F8

(d) 3F306
135CF

2-21. Find the negative equivalents of the following hex numbers.

(a) 23
(b) CB
(c) 500
(d) 1F302
(e) F5630

2-22. Given 2 bytes:

$A = 10001101$

$B = 01001011$

find:

(a) $A + B$
(b) AB
(c) $A \oplus B$
(d) $\overline{A}$
(e) $\overline{B}$

After attempting to solve these problems, try to answer the self-evaluation questions in Section 2-2. If any of them still seem difficult, review the appropriate sections of the chapter to find the answers.

3 THE BASIC COMPUTER

3-1 ▼ INSTRUCTIONAL OBJECTIVES

The basic principles of operation of a microcomputer (μC) are identical to those of any larger computer. In this chapter we discuss the basic parts of a computer and how they work together to execute a simple program. Programming is also introduced and some very elementary programs are presented. After reading this chapter, the student should be able to:

1. List each basic part of a computer and describe its functions.
2. Explain the steps involved in reading or writing a memory word.
3. List the registers and flip-flops required by the control section of a computer and explain their operation.
4. Explain the meaning of the symbols used in flowcharts.
5. Construct a flowchart for a problem.
6. Write programs involving branch instructions and loops.

3-2 ▼ SELF-EVALUATION QUESTIONS

Watch for the answers to the following questions as you read the chapter. They should help you to understand the material presented.

1. What are the MAR and MDR? What is their function?
2. Are the contents of a memory location changed when they are written? When they are read?
3. What is the difference between a ROM and a RAM? State an advantage of each.
4. What is the advantage of a PROM over a ROM? When would each be used?
5. What is the PC register? Why is it incremented during each instruction?

6. Is there any distinction between data and instructions when they are in memory? How does the computer tell the difference?

7. What decisions must be made during program planning?

8. What instructions allow a computer to make decisions? How does the computer make a decision?

9. How do loop counting and event detection determine when to end a loop?

3-3 ▼ INTRODUCTION TO THE COMPUTER

A computer consists of four basic hardware sections, as shown in Fig. 3-1:

1. Memory
2. Arithmetic/Logic Unit (ALU)
3. Control unit
4. Input/Output (I/O) system

The difference between digital logic and computer logic is that the former depends on the wiring of the AND and OR gates, whereas the computer logic is controlled by the **bits** in the **instruction register** of the control unit. These instruction bits are brought into the register in the form of a byte from memory, where they are kept. The instructions are part of a **program**. For a computer to perform a given task, a program is prepared and the instructions, in the form of 8-bit bytes (for the basic computer we are discussing), are executed one after another. This program is called **software** since it is easily changed.

The function of each part of the computer shown in Fig. 3-1 is as follows:

1. The **memory** holds the **instructions** of the program to be executed (see Section 3-9), as well as the **data** (which is also in the form of 8-bit bytes) used by the instructions. They are usually kept in separate areas of memory and frequently in different kinds of memory.

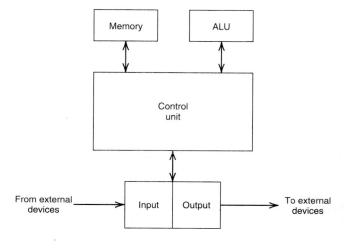

Figure 3-1 Block diagram of a basic computer.

2. The **Arithmetic/Logic Unit** (ALU) is the part of the computer that performs the arithmetic and logic operations required by the program and the ALU *sets* or *resets* the appropriate status bits (condition codes) after each instruction is executed. These status bits are used in the decision-making process of the computer.

3. The **control unit** consists of a group of logic devices and registers that regulate operation of the computer itself. The function of the control unit is to cause the proper sequence of events to occur during execution of each computer instruction. This circuitry and the ALU make up the **Central Processing Unit** (CPU).

4. The **Input/Output** (I/O) function provides communication between the internal registers of the computer and external devices. The computer must receive data and status information from outside hardware, such as temperature or pressure sensors, analog-to-digital (A/D) converters, keyboards, disk drives, or tape units. It must also produce outputs that depend on its program and the data it receives. If the computer is solving a problem, for example, the output is frequently a printout of the results. In this case the CPU must issue commands to a printer to cause the results to be printed for the user to read. If the function of the computer is to control a physical process, however, its output will be electronic signals that are translated into *commands* (open a valve, close a damper to reduce the airflow, etc.) to regulate a process.

Basic microprocessor (μP) chips contains the ALU and control portions of the computer (the CPU), while memory and input/output are frequently handled by auxiliary integrated circuits (ICs). Some of the newer ICs also have memory and I/O capability integrated on the same chip, and thus manufacturers are calling them *single-chip microcomputers* (μCs) or *microcontrollers* (MCUs). They are described in later chapters.

In this chapter the construction and operation of the ALU, memory, and control unit are described in detail. The input/output system is discussed in Chapter 8.

3-4 ▼ MEMORY CONCEPTS

A memory is an electronic circuit that stores or remembers many bits of electronic information. Even the smallest μP or μC system requires a memory of several thousand bits to store its program and data. Large-scale memories for older computers were constructed of magnetic cores, but the first microcomputers used ICs. A block of memory in these early systems typically consisted of one or more semiconductor memory chips each contained in a dual in-line package (DIP) as are the μP and the rest of the semiconductor components of the system. For example, a large section of the motherboard on a personal computer is used to hold the memory ICs.

The binary bits of a block of memory can be organized in various ways. In most μCs, the bits are grouped into *words* of 8, 16, or 32 bits each. As mentioned in Chapter 1, The **6800** is an example of an 8-bit μP. It uses an 8-bit (1-byte word) and its CPU is the *core* of all 8-bit μPs or μCs described in this book. The **68000** and **CPU16** families have a 16-bit ALU and use a 16-bit (2-byte) data word. The **68020** and **68030** and the microcontrollers in the **CPU32** series use 32-bit long words (4 bytes). These μCs are described in detail in later chapters.

Modern computers are *word-oriented* in that they transfer one word at a time by means of the data bus. This bus, the internal computer registers, and the ALU are constructed with *parallel* circuits that handle all the bits of a word *at the same time*.

The memory can be thought of as a post office box arrangement with each location containing a word. The boxes are set up in an orderly sequence so that they can be addressed easily. Each instruction or data word is *written* into a specific location in memory (a word at a selected address) *so that it is preserved* for future use and is *read* at a later time *when the information is needed*. During the interval between writing and reading, other information may be stored or read at other locations.

Eight-bit μC instructions for the **6800** require 1, 2, or 3 bytes (or words), and typical program routines include 5 to 50 instructions. Since IC memories can include thousands of words of data and are physically small and relatively inexpensive, they allow very comprehensive computer programs to be stored and used.

An 8-bit μC can directly address a maximum memory size of 64K words since it has 16 address lines ($2^{16} = 65,536$), but even more memory can be used by employing *bank-select logic* to switch in any number of additional 64K blocks of memory. Only specially written software can use the additional memory, however, and therefore this method is rarely used. In dedicated controller applications, the program memory could be as small as 4 or 8K bytes.

Unlike standard engineering terminology, where K is an abbreviation for kilo (or 1000), $K = 2^{10}$ or 1024 when applied to memories. This value of K is used because normal memory design leads to sizes that are even powers of 2.

Each word in memory has two *parameters:* its **address**, which locates it within memory, and the **data** that is stored at that location. The process of accessing the contents of the memory locations requires two registers (hardware devices that hold a group of related bits), one associated with address and one with data. The **Memory Address Register** (MAR) holds the address of the word *currently being accessed*, and the **Memory Data Register** (MDR) holds the the data *being written into or read out* of the addressed memory location. These registers are usually part of the control unit of a μP (see Section 3-7).

A block diagram of a small 1K-word by 8-bit Random-Access Memory (RAM) is shown in Fig. 3-2. The address information in the MAR selects one of the 1024 words in memory.

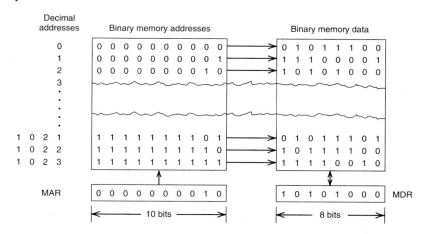

Figure 3-2 Typical 1024-word by 8-bit memory.

EXAMPLE 3-1

The 1K-word by 8-bit memory of Fig. 3-2 is used as part of a μC system with a 16-bit address bus.

(a) How many bits are required to address all locations in this IC?

(b) How many address bits are used for the entire μC system?

(c) How many bits are required in the MDR?

(d) How many data bits are contained in this memory IC?

SOLUTION

(a) A memory specification of 1K × 8 means 1024 (2^{10}) words of 8 bits each. The MAR must hold an address value between 0 and 1023 (1024 total locations) to select any word in this IC. Thus 10 bits are needed to address the memory.

(b) The μC uses 16 address lines (or bits in the MAR). Since 10 address lines are used to select the locations in this memory IC, the other 6 are available to select which memory IC is being accessed.

(c) Each memory location contains 8 bits. Consequently, the MDR must be 8 bits long to accommodate one data word.

(d) A 1K × 8 memory contains 2^{10} words × 2^3 (8) bits per word, which = 2^{13} or 8192 bits. For a μC, this is a relatively small memory.

In Fig. 3-2 the MAR is shown to contain address 2 and the MDR register contains the value that is in that location.

3-4.1 ▼ Reading Memory

Memories operate in two basic modes; READ and WRITE. A memory is read when the information at a particular address is required by the system. To *read* a memory:

1. The location to be read is loaded into the MAR.

2. A READ command is given.

3. The data is transferred from the addressed word in memory to the MDR, where it is accessible to the system.

Normally, the word being read must not be altered by the READ operation, so that the word in a particular location can be *read many times*. The process of reading a location without changing it is called *nondestructive readout*.

3-4.2 ▼ Writing Memory

A memory location is written when the data must be preserved for future use. In the process of writing, the information in the specified location is *destroyed* (overwritten). To *write* into a memory:

1. The address (memory location where the data is to be written) is loaded into the MAR.
2. The data to be written is loaded into the MDR.
3. The WRITE command is then given (by means of the READ/WRITE line), which transfers the data via the data bus from the MDR to the memory location selected.

3-5 ▼ SEMICONDUCTOR MEMORIES

Most semiconductor memories in use today are built of MOS circuits. Until now, most of these have used NMOS technology. Almost all modern memories use CMOS construction. There are two basic types of memories: RAM and ROM. Literally speaking, the term **RAM** means *Random-Access-Memory*,* but that is really a misnomer because ROM is also random access memory. The term RAM is used universally, however, to describe a read/write memory (a memory that can both be read and temporarily changed by being written into). RAMs are also said to be **volatile** because the information in them is lost when the power is turned off or fails. Some sophisticated computer systems use a battery backup circuit to keep voltage on the memories when the main power goes off.

ROMs are *Read-Only Memories* whose data bits are permanently stored during manufacture. Other data cannot be written into them during the normal course of computer operation, and they do not lose the data when the power is removed. They are therefore said to be **nonvolatile**. Information or programs that must be present when the power is turned on are placed in ROM.

In recent years electrically programmable **EPROMs** and **EEPROMs** have been developed. They retain their programs when the power is off and are often substituted for ROMs. They are described in Sections 3-5.6 and 3-5.8. In most μCs, the memory map consists of two parts, a ROM area, used to hold the *program, constants*, and *tables*, and a RAM area, used to hold *variable data*.

In some personal computers and many μP systems, the entire operating system program is stored in ROM, so the computer is ready to execute commands when power is applied. Often, however, and primarily in PCs, only the I/O and disk or tape *loader* routines are in ROM ready to load the rest of the operating system into a large RAM area. The IBM-PC and compatibles are examples. The basic I/O system (BIOS) is stored permanently in the ROM ICs, but it must load the Disk Operating System (DOS) from a disk before it can start. Programs written by the user can be entered into RAM but are lost when power is turned off unless they are preserved (saved on disk). RAMs are discussed in the following section, and ROMs are discussed in Section 3-5.4.

3-5.1 ▼ Static and Dynamic RAMs

RAMs are subdivided into two types, *static* and *dynamic*. Static RAMs store their information on **Flip-Flops** (FFs) inside the memory IC. A flip-flop can be placed in one of two states (SET or RESET) and remains there until commanded to change states. Thus a single FF function is a 1-bit memory. It remembers whether it was last SET or RESET. This information will be lost whenever power goes off.

---

*"Random access" means that any word can be accessed in approximately the same time as any other word. This distinguishes IC memories from nonrandom access memories such as tape or disk, where users must wait until the word they seek is under the read or write head before it can be accessed.

Dynamic memories store their information by charging *capacitors* inside the IC. Unfortunately, the charge on the tiny capacitors tends to leak off and the dynamic RAMs must be *refreshed** periodically to retain their information. The refresh circuits are frequently incorporated within them. Dynamic memories are generally less expensive and contain more bits per IC, but static memories are simpler to use. Most μCs use dynamic memories.

The internal structure of the FFs and gates that make up a memory is not considered in this book. Instead, we concentrate on the I/O characteristics that must be understood if one is to use a memory.

3-5.2 ▼ Interfacing with a RAM Memory

A semiconductor RAM normally has pins for the following:

1. m data bits

2. n address bits (for 2^n words)

3. A READ/WRITE line

4. CHIP SELECT or ENABLE line(s)

To read a location in a memory, the address lines for that location are set to 1s or 0s as required, and the memory chip is then *selected* or *enabled* by means of a decoder chip (explained in the following subsections). The READ/WRITE line is then set to the READ level, which causes the memory contents at the addressed location to be transferred to the data lines and continue to be present until the address, READ/WRITE line, or CHIP SELECT signals change. Reading is *nondestructive* (it does not change the information in the memory cells); the state of the internal memory cells at the address selected is simply brought to the data pins.

EXAMPLE 3-2

The **6810** is a RAM that can be used in very small controller-type **6800** μC systems. It is a 1024-bit memory organized as 128 bytes (128 words by 8 bits). It is seldom used these days because many μPs have at least this much RAM built in. In many cases, however, larger RAMs are needed and their interface is similar. Therefore, the following discussion is appropriate. What input and output lines are required for the **6810**?

SOLUTION

This memory requires

1. Seven address bits to select one of 128 words

2. Eight data lines, one for each bit of the word

3. One read/write line

4. One or more CHIP SELECT or ENABLE lines

5. Power and ground

---

*For a discussion of refresh circuits, see Chapter 15 of Joseph D. Greenfield, *Practical Digital Design Using ICs*, 3rd ed., Prentice Hall, Englewood Cliffs, N.J., 1994.

Writing into a memory requires that the address of the desired location be in the MAR and the data be in the MDR prior to enabling the memory (see Section 3-7). These registers (MAR and MDR) are connected to the memories by means of bus lines and these lines assume the state of the bits in those registers. When the READ/WRITE (R/W) line is switched to WRITE and the memory is enabled, the data on the bus lines is then entered into the memory at the location addressed. One must be careful about changing the input data while in the WRITE mode. Any change of data is gated into the memory and overwrites the previous contents of the memory, which are lost.

The CHIP SELECT and ENABLE inputs are used to turn the memory ON or OFF and, more important, to disconnect it from the bus. This allows the μC designer to multiplex several memory or I/O devices onto a common bus.

In actual systems the upper address lines must be *decoded to select this particular chip* and *to deselect all the other memory ICs* in the system. A decoder IC is used. It is made up of IC logic gates and normally has several address lines coming in and one CHIP SELECT line going out to the RAM. Actually, the **6810** has six CHIP SELECT lines to make the system simpler (the decoder is built in), and the data input and output is done on a common bidirectional data bus. Details of the **6810** are given in Section 7-8 and decoding is explained in Section 7-14.

3-5.3 ▼ Memory Timing

The time relationship between when the signal lines are turned ON or OFF in digital logic is very important. Even though the time is exceptionally small (it is measured in **nanoseconds**), to access a memory to READ or WRITE a byte of data requires a finite time interval. When dealing with memory ICs this is known as memory timing. A READ cycle is limited by the access time of a memory, and a WRITE cycle is limited by the cycle time.*

Access time is the time required for the memory to present valid data after the address and select signals are stable. **Cycle time** or WRITE time is the time the address and data must be held constant in order to write to the memory.

Access time and cycle time are illustrated in Fig. 3-3. Similar figures with specific times are supplied by the manufacturers of IC memories. Figure 3-3a shows the normal

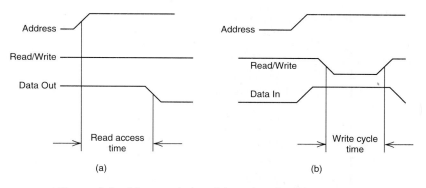

Figure 3-3　Memory timing: (a) read cycle; (b) write cycle.

*A more complete discussion of memory timing is given in Section 9-3 of Gerald Leucke, Jack Mize, and William Carr, *Semiconductor Memory Design and Application*, McGraw-Hill, New York, 1973.

situation where the memory is in READ mode. The output data will change in response to an address change and the time for this response, the *access time,* is clearly visible. Figure 3-3b shows the WRITE cycle. Note that the address and data lines must be stable before the WRITE pulse occurs on the R/W line and must not change while the memory is in WRITE mode. This is necessary to prevent spurious writes that could enter unwanted information into the memory.

3-5.4 ▼ Read-Only Memories

As its name implies, a Read-Only Memory (ROM) is read but cannot be written into during the course of computer operation. Data is *written permanently* into a ROM when it is manufactured. With its program in ROM, a μC can be restarted after a power failure with no need to reload or *boot* its program.

The READ mode of a ROM is identical to the READ mode of a RAM; the μC supplies an address and the ROM provides the data output of the word stored at that address. Like RAMs, ROMs are organized on an *n*-word by *m*-bit basis. Supplying the proper address results in an *m*-bit output. Access time for a ROM is the time between the setting of the address input and the appearance of the resulting data word on the output pins.

EXAMPLE 3-3

A memory has dimensions of 8K words by 8 bits. What input and output lines are required if the memory is:

(a) A RAM?

(b) A ROM?

SOLUTION

(a) A RAM of this size requires
1. Eight data lines
2. Thirteen address lines ($2^{13} = 8192$)
3. A READ/WRITE line
4. CHIP SELECT line(s)

(b) An 8K by 8-bit ROM requires
1. Eight data lines
2. Thirteen address lines
3. CHIP SELECT line(s)

Since a ROM cannot be written into, the READ/WRITE line is not required.

3-5.5 ▼ Programmable Read-Only Memories

Programmable Read-Only Memories (PROMS) are designed to be programmed by users at their facility rather than by the manufacturer. At least two types of PROMs are in use. They are both electrically programmable, but one is electrically erasable and reprogrammable; it is described in Section 3-5.8. The other is described next.

3-5.6 ▼ Erasable PROMs

Some PROMs can be *erased* and *reprogrammed* in the field if users have the proper equipment. These are called Electrically Programmable ROMs (EPROMs). EPROMs are made by a number of manufacturers in a variety of sizes. Typical EPROMs are the **68764** (64K bytes) and **27128** (128K bytes). These EPROMs have a quartz window over the chip and can be erased by exposing the chip to ultraviolet light. Because they are reprogrammable, they are very popular for developing programs for μCs since programming mistakes are common and changes in the program occur frequently. They also are used in small production runs or until the program has been debugged fully, at which time they may be replaced with maskable ROMs to save production costs.

3-5.7 ▼ One-Time Programmable PROMs

Special low-cost versions of many μC chips that contain EPROMs are now available without the quartz window. They are programmable but not erasable, thus the name *One-Time Programmable* (OTP) *PROMs*. They include the letters OTP in the part number and obviously are programmed just like the equivalent EPROM versions.

3-5.8 ▼ Electrically Erasable PROMs

One further step in semiconductor memory technology has been the introduction of *Electrically Erasable PROMs* (EEPROMs). This technique provides a nonvolatile design that can be electrically reprogrammed in the system in less than 9 ms per byte. Many of the single-chip μCs described in later chapters use this technique. Several manufacturers offer separate memory ICs. For μC compatibility, on-chip latches are provided for address, data, and bus controls, allowing the μC to perform other tasks while the EEPROM is erasing or programming (writing) itself. The data is thus protected during power-down and power-up cycles. These devices are very popular because they avoid the need to reconfigure multipurpose systems every time they are turned on.

3-5.9 ▼ FLASH Memory

A newer technique in nonvolatile memories that has evolved from EPROM technology is called **FLASH**. It uses a floating gate structure but with a thinner gate oxide. At the time of this writing, an accepted standard has not been developed. There are at least four varieties currently, although about four companies are following the Intel specifications. As the name implies, the main advantage for FLASH is its speed in programming. Typical device performance is a 160-ns read-access time and a write time of 10 ms for 64 bytes (5 seconds full chip). Because of the small cell size, units having 1-, 2-, and 4-megabyte (Mbyte) density are being developed.

3-6 ▼ ARITHMETIC/LOGIC UNIT

The Arithmetic/Logic Unit (ALU) performs all the arithmetic and logical operations required by the computer. It accepts two operands as inputs (each operand contains as many bits as the basic word length of the computer) and performs the required arithmetic or logical operation on them in accordance with the instruction in process. The ALU function is included within the CPU core of the μP or μC chip.

The ALU included in the **6800** performs the following arithmetic or logical operations:

1. Addition
2. Subtraction
3. Logical OR
4. Logical AND
5. Exclusive OR
6. Complementation
7. Shifting

In all μPs, a *Condition Code Register* (CCR) is associated with the ALU to store the state of the status bits after every instruction executes. These are used by the *conditional branch instructions* in deciding whether or not to branch. The condition code register is discussed in Section 4-6.

Computers are capable of performing sophisticated arithmetic operations such as multiplication, division, extracting square roots, and taking trigonometric functions; however, in most μCs these operations are performed as *software subroutines* (small complete programs). A multiplication command, for example, is translated by the appropriate subroutine into a series of add and shift operations that can be performed by the ALU. A multiplication subroutine is written in Section 5-6.2.

3-7 ▼ CONTROL SECTION

The function of the *control section* is to regulate the operation of the computer. It controls the locations in memory and fetches instructions at the proper time. The instructions are then decoded. A group of registers, FFs, and timing circuits are used to keep track of the processor's operation. The registers are:

1. MAR and MDR. The Memory Address Register and Memory Data Register are used to control memory.

2. Program Counter (PC). This register contains as many bits as does the MAR. *It holds the memory address of the next instruction to be executed.* It is *incremented 1, 2 or 3 bytes* during the execution of an instruction so that it contains the address of the next instruction.

3. Instruction decoder. This register holds the instruction presently being executed and decodes the various bits to determine the functions desired.

4. Accumulators. All computers have one or more accumulator registers, each of which contains as many bits as the MDR. In ALU operations where two operands are required and only one accumulator exists, as in the **8080A** or **Z80** μPs, one of the operands is stored in that accumulator as a result of previous instructions. The other operand is then typically read from memory. The **6800** and many other μPs based on it have two accumulators, called A and B, which greatly simplifies many programming problems. In this case the second operand is typically read from memory into the B accumulator. The two operands form the inputs to the ALU, and the result is normally sent back to the A accumulator.

3-7.1 ▼ Control Unit Flip-Flops

A number of *registers* are included in every μP and peripheral I/O component. A register is frequently implemented as a group of FFs (see Section 3-5.1) that together provide storage for a single unit of information. A single 16-bit number, for example, could be held in a register that consists of 16 FFs. Individual FFs are used where small quantities of data (several bits) must be remembered and changed frequently.

The control unit usually contains a number of FFs. The status bits or condition codes (see Section 4-6) are stored in FFs. Most μPs also have FETCH and EXECUTE FFs. The computer starts by *fetching* an instruction from memory into the instruction register. This is the FETCH portion of the computer's cycle. It then *executes*, or performs the instruction by decoding it. At this time, the computer is in EXECUTE mode. When it has finished executing the instruction, it returns to FETCH mode and reads the next instruction from memory. Thus the computer *alternates* between FETCH and EXECUTE *modes* and the FETCH and EXECUTE FF determines its current mode of operation.

3-8 ▼ EXECUTION OF A SIMPLE ROUTINE

A μP starts to execute instructions by fetching the byte at the address contained in the PC. Most 8-bit μPs use this first byte as an 8-bit operations code or **op code**. The op code tells the μP what to do (e.g., add, subtract, load). Since the **6800** has an 8-bit op code, up to 256 different instructions are possible. Actually, 159 are implemented. (The **6801** has 22 more.) Some of the sophisticated newer 8-bit μPs or μCs such as the **68HC11**, use two bytes for some of the op codes and thus have up to four times as many codes.

The op code includes information on the number of bytes to be used in the instruction. In most cases the μP then executes a second fetch cycle* to get the **operand**, which usually contains an address required by the instruction. It then has both the op code and the address and can execute the instruction. When execution is complete, the μP increments the PC and proceeds to execute the next instruction. The **6800** μP has no HALT instruction as such. Once started, it continues to execute instructions until halted by an external signal. A WAIT instruction can be used to halt the program execution (see Section 9-7.1).

3-8.1 ▼ Sample Problem

As a simple example, let us consider what a **6800** μP must do to add two numbers. Before starting this example, both the numbers to be added and the program must be in memory. Suppose that we are trying to add the numbers 2 and 3. We can arbitrarily set

---

*The number of bytes and cycles required for each instruction depends on the instruction mode. This is discussed thoroughly in Chapter 4.

aside location 30 to hold the number 2 and location 31 to hold the number 3. Location 32 is also set aside to hold the result.

The program, or set of instructions, required to add the numbers would be this:

Location	Op Code	Operand Address	Comments
10	96	30	LOAD A from location 30
12	9B	31	ADD contents of 31 to A
14	97	32	STORE accumulator A in 32
32			

3-8.2 ▼ Hardware Execution of the Routine

The registers and ALU within the core of the μP work together to execute the foregoing program. The instructions must reside at specific locations in memory. As shown in the listing, we have assumed that location 10 is set aside for the start of the program. Thus location 10 contains the op code for the LOAD (96) instruction; location 11 contains the address (30), location 12 contains the op code of the ADD instruction (9B), and so on. The steps in the execution of the program and how the registers and memory contents are affected are shown in Fig. 3-4 and listed in Table 3-1.

Before starting execution, the starting address of the program (10 in this example) must be written into the PC. Table 3-1 shows the contents of the registers at each step in Fig. 3-4. It correlates with the following description of the program's execution:

1. The 10 is transferred from the PC to the MAR and the 96 is read at memory location 10.
2. Since this is the first part of the FETCH cycle, the data read is placed in the instruction register and the instruction decoder determines that it is a LOAD instruction..

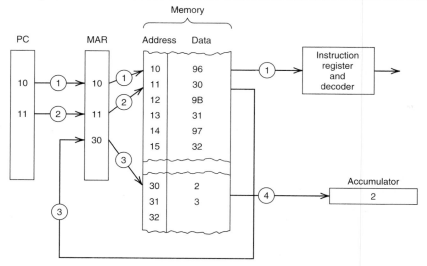

Figure 3-4　Execution of a LOAD instruction of a rudimentary μP.

TABLE 3-1   Register Changes as the Example of Section 3-8.1 Progresses

PC	MAR	MEMORY DATA	ACCUMULATOR CONTENTS	COMMENTS
10	10	96	X	LOAD command
11	11	30	X	Data address
11	30	02	2	Put contents in A
12	12	9B	2	ADD command
13	13	31	2	Data address
13	31	03	5	Add data from 31
14	14	97	5	STORE command
15	15	32	5	Store A in 32

Note that the μP is not actually reading the word LOAD in location 10. It reads a byte of 1s and 0s (10010110_2 or 96_{16}) that are decoded as a LOAD command.

3. The μP then increments the PC and MAR and reads the contents of 11 (30), which it places in the MAR.

4. The μP is now ready to execute the LOAD instruction. It does so by reading the contents of 30, which are already in the MAR, and placing them in the accumulator. The accumulator now contains the contents of 30 (the number 2).

5. The instruction execution is now finished and the FETCH mode for the next instruction is entered. The PC is again incremented to 12 and placed in the MAR.

6. The code for ADD (9B) is fetched from location 12 and decoded.

7. The PC is again incremented and 31 is read from memory and placed in the MAR.

8. The EXECUTE phase of the **ADD** instruction is entered. The contents of 31 (3) are read and added to the contents of the accumulator. This uses the ALU within the μP. The results (5) are written to the accumulator and the ADD instruction is complete.

9. The PC is again incremented and transferred to the MAR. The op code for the STORE instruction (97) is fetched and decoded.

10. The address for the STORED data (32) is fetched from location 15 and placed in the MAR.

11. The STORE instruction (97) is now executed to take the contents of the accumulator (5) and write them to memory at location 32.

3-9 ▼ INTRODUCTION TO PROGRAMMING

A program is a group of instructions that cause the computer to perform a given task. Each instruction directs the computer to do something specific. An extremely simple program might instruct the computer to add two numbers in its data area; another program might command the computer to subtract the same numbers. Obviously, completely different results can be obtained from the same data by applying different programs. As shown in the Section 3-8, each μP instruction consists of an op code (a byte that tells the computer what to do) and usually some additional bytes that are a value or specify the address of an *operand*.

3-9.1 ▼ Machine Language

The op codes (combinations of 1s and 0s) are interpreted by the instruction decoder in the control section of the μP and used to perform the internal functions desired. These bytes are called **machine language** because they are the only thing the machine (computer) understands. These 8-bit binary numbers are usually expressed in hexadecimal notation so that human beings can easily understand them as explained in Chapter 2.

Op codes for a given instruction are not the same in all computers because the control unit hardware is different. The **6800** μP machine language is typical, however, and its use here is the most direct way to explain the operation of μPs.

3-9.2 ▼ Assembly Language

Machine language is generally used by engineers who must troubleshoot and debug hardware systems containing μPs. Machine language, however, makes programming slow and cumbersome and **assembly language**, which uses mnemonics and is thus easier for human beings to understand, has been developed. Programmers prefer to write in assembly language or a higher-level language such as BASIC, FORTRAN, or C.

In assembly language programming, **mnemonics** are used for op codes, addresses, and labels. Instead of writing 96   30, an assembly language programmer might write

```
LDAA    SAM
```

where LDAA means *load the A accumulator* and SAM becomes the symbol for an address, 30 in this case. Assembly language programming is used because the programmer does not have to remember the numeric values of op codes and because it is easier to keep track of variables when calling them by symbolic names.

Assembly language programs cannot be executed directly. The mnemonic program must first be converted to machine language. This is done by using an **assembler** program in another computer. The programmer's mnemonics, called the **source program**, are translated into the 1s and 0s that make up the machine language. This **object program**, as it is also called, can then be loaded directly into the μP's memory.

During development, these programs usually must be changed many times, and they are therefore loaded into RAM for debugging. Once the programs are fully developed and not expected to change, they are usually put into PROMs or a custom-built ROM may be ordered. The manufacturer of the ROM must be given the code each word is to contain. The manufacturer then makes a mask that is used to produce the ROM. Because of the custom programming involved, a mask costs more than $1000. Users should be sure of their inputs before they incur the masking charge, because the ROM is normally useless if a single bit is wrong. Once the mask is made, identical ROMs can be produced inexpensively.

Because individual μPs have different machine language op codes as well as different mnemonics, each μP has an assembler written specifically for it. After deciding which μP to use, the engineer should investigate the assemblers available for that μP.

High level
language
Compiler to

3-9.3 ▼ High-Level Languages

In an effort to simplify the programming task, a number of other languages, such as BASIC, FORTRAN, Pascal, and C, have been developed. With them, it is not necessary to worry about registers and other specific computer details, and *one* high-level language statement can generate *several* machine language instructions. Using them makes it easier for a programmer to write a program. The program necessary to translate these high-level languages to machine code is called a compiler. Many μPs do not have compilers for all languages.

There are some objections to using high-level languages with μPs. Some languages are not good when bit manipulation is required or cannot be used to generate precise time delays, and the execution of their code is generally slower than with assembly language. They are, however, the most convenient way to write programs. In general, programs written to get answers to problems are written in higher-level languages, whereas programs to control processes and devices, which must operate in **real time,** are written in assembly language.

3-10 ▼ FLOWCHARTS

Flowcharts are used by programmers to show the progress of their programs graphically. They are a clear and concise method of presenting the programmer's approach to a problem. They are often used as a part of programming documentation, where the program must be explained to those unfamiliar with it. Since good documentation is essential for proper use of any computer, the rudiments of flowcharts are presented in this section.

3-10.1 ▼ Flowchart Symbols

The flowchart symbols used in this book are shown in Fig. 3-5.

1. The *oval* symbol is either a *beginning* or a *termination* box. It is used simply to denote the start or end of a program.

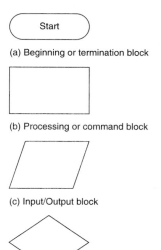

(a) Beginning or termination block

(b) Processing or command block

(c) Input/Output block

(d) Decision block

Figure 3-5 Most common standard flowchart symbols: (a) beginning or termination block; (b) processing or command block; (c) input/output block; (d) decision block.

2. The *rectangular block* is the *processing* or *command block*. It states what must be done at that point in the program.

3. The *parallelogram* is an *input/output block*. Such commands as READ and WRITE, especially from an external device such as a disk or printer, are shown on the flowchart by using these boxes.

4. The *diamond box* is a *decision box.* It usually contains a question. There are typically two output paths, one if the answer to the question is yes and the other if the answer is no. When a comparison between two numbers is made, there might be three exit paths corresponding to greater than, less than, and equal.

EXAMPLE 3-4

Draw a flowchart to add the numbers 1, 4, 7, and 10.

SOLUTION

The solution is shown in Fig. 3-6. It consists simply of a start box, four command boxes, and a stop box. This is an example of straight-line programming since no decisions were made. It was also assumed that the numbers 1, 4, 7, and 10 were available in the computer's memory and were not read from an external device.

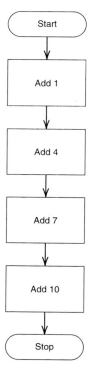

Figure 3-6 Flowchart for Example 3-4.

TABLE 3-2 Program for the Flowchart
of Fig. 3-6

LOCATION	INSTRUCTION/OPERAND	MNEMONIC
10	96	LOAD
11	30	
12	9B	ADD
13	31	
14	9B	ADD
15	32	
16	9B	ADD
17	33	
18	97	STORE
19	34	
1A	3E	WAIT

3-11 ▼ ELEMENTARY PROGRAMMING

To introduce the concepts of programming, we use simple **6800** instructions. The instructions are really binary data words stored in various memory locations. Each instruction is assumed to consist of words that contain the op code and the address of the data. The op codes used in this section are ADD, SUBTRACT, LOAD, and STORE.

For example, consider the problem of writing instructions for the flowchart of Fig. 3-6. The first problem is to allocate memory areas for the instructions and the data. All these words must be in memory before the program can be started.

To illustrate, we will use the **6800** μP instructions where the first byte is the op code and the next byte is the address of the data. Again we arbitrarily decide to start the program at location 10 and the data at 30. The program is shown in Table 3-2.

Operation of the LOAD, ADD, and STORE instructions was explained in Section 3-8.1. The data might then be as follows:

LOCATION	CONTENTS
30	1
31	4
32	7
33	10
34	Reserved for result

Once the data areas and all the required constants are written in memory, the op code can be executed by starting at location 10. Note that the data could be changed and the same program executed any number of times.

3-11.1 ▼ Branch Instructions and Loops

The program of the preceding section is extremely simple; indeed, users can compute the answer faster than they can write the program. Suppose, however, the program is expanded so that we are required to add the numbers 1, 4, 7, 10, . . . , 10,000.* Conceptually, this could be done by expanding the flowchart of Example 3-4 and the program of Table 3-2. However, the program and data areas would then require 3333 locations each, and just writing them would become very tedious. Obviously, something else must be done.

3-11.2 ▼ Branch Instructions

Branch instructions provide the solution to the problem outlined above. A **BRANCH** instruction or **JUMP** instruction alters the normal sequence of program execution and can be used to create loops that allow the same sequence of instructions to be executed many times.

As we saw in Section 3-8, in the normal course of program execution, the PC is incremented during the execution of each instruction and contains the location of the next instruction to be executed. Assume, however, that the next instruction is

```
BRA $500
```

where BRA is the mnemonic (for branch) and $500 is the branch address (the $ designates hex). This instruction causes the branch address to be written into the PC. Thus the location of the next instruction to be executed is the branch address ($500 in this case) rather than the next sequential address. A **branch instruction** can therefore be used to cause the program to **loop** back and execute the same instructions again.

There are two types of branch instructions, unconditional and conditional. The **unconditional branch** always causes the program to go to the specified address. In the **6800** the mnemonic is **BRA**, which stands for BRANCH ALWAYS. The **conditional branch**, which is explained in the next section, causes the program to branch only if a specified condition is met.

3-11.3 ▼ Computer Decisions

As you will recall in Section 3-6, we described the arithmetic/logic unit (ALU) and the condition code register (CCR). The bits of the CCR (also called status bits or flags) are SET (made equal to 1) or RESET (made equal to 0) by the ALU of the **6800** as each instruction is executed. For example, when one number is subtracted from another, the resulting number is either positive, negative, or zero and the ALU will SET or RESET the bits of the CCR accordingly. They can then be used to control the program flow by including the proper **conditional branch instruction**.

Probably the easiest way to introduce conditional branch instructions is to examine the two instructions that *test* the zero or Z bit. These are **BEQ** (**B**ranch if **EQ**ual) and **BNE** (**B**ranch if **N**ot **E**qual to zero). One of these might be used, for example, if the program is deciding whether a number entered is equal to a certain value. That value would be subtracted from the number entered and then tested with one of these instructions. If the test is true, the program branches or jumps to another part of the program. If it is *not* true, the program continues in sequence. Therefore, when the subtraction instruction

---

*Since the object of this section is to teach programming and not mathematics, we ignore the fact that this is an arithmetic progression whose sum is given by a simple formula.

mentioned previously is followed by one of these *conditional branch instructions*, the state of the **Z** bit will determine the path to be taken by the program. This decision-making action is an example of the primary function of a computer and is frequently depicted in flowcharts of programs by a diamond-shaped box with an arrow out of the bottom to show the in-line sequence or out of one side to show a branch.

There are 14 *decision-making* instructions in the **6800**. Each of the 4 least significant bits of the CCR (N, Z, V, and C) has two associated branch instructions.

EXAMPLE 3-5

A computer is to add the numbers 1, 4, 7, 10, . . . , 10,000.*
Draw a flowchart for the program.

SOLUTION

The flowchart is shown in Fig. 3-7. We recognize that we must keep track of two quantities. One is the number to be added. This has been labeled N in the flowchart and progresses 1, 4, 7, 10, ... The second quantity is the sum S, which progresses 1, 1 + 4, 1 + 4 + 7, . . . or 1, 5, 12, ...

The first box in the flowchart is an *initialization* box. It sets N to 1 and S to 0 at the beginning of the program. The next box ($S = N + S$) sets the new sum equal to the old sum plus the number to be added. The number to be added is then increased by 3. At this point the flowchart shows that the program must loop around to repeat the sequence. This is accomplished in this example by placing an unconditional branch instruction in the program. The quantities S and N will then progress as specified.

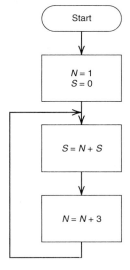

Figure 3-7 Flowchart for Example 3-5.

*For the introductory problem of this section, we have ignored the fact that decimal 10,000 cannot be contained within a single byte.

3-11.4 ▼ Decision Boxes and Conditional Branches

The reader has probably already realized that there is a serious problem with Example 3-5; the loop never terminates. Actually, putting a program into an endless loop is one of the most common programming mistakes.

There are two common ways to determine when to end a loop: *loop counting* and *event detection*. Either method requires the use of decision boxes in the flowchart and corresponding conditional branch instructions in the program.

Loop counting is considered first. Loop counting is done by determining the number of times the loop should be traversed, counting the actual number of times through and comparing the two.

EXAMPLE 3-6

Improve the flowchart of Fig. 3-7 so that it terminates properly.

SOLUTION

The program should terminate not when $N = 10,000$ but when 10,000 is added to the sum. For the flowchart of Fig. 3-7, N is increased to 10,003 immediately after this occurs. At the end of the first loop $N = 4$, the second loop $N = 7$, and so on. It can be seen here that $N = 3L + 1$, where L is the number of times through the loop. If N is set to 10,003, $L = 3334$. The loop must be traversed 3334 times. The correct flowchart is shown in Fig. 3-8. The loop counter L has been added and set initially to −3334. It is incremented each time through the loop and tested to see if it is positive. After 3334 loops, it becomes 0. Then the YES path from the decision box is taken and the program halts

---

Event detection terminates the loop when an *event* occurs. In Example 3-7 that event could be the fact that N is greater than 10,000. Using event detection, locations 1C through 21 could be replaced by

1C,1D	96 32	(LOAD 32)
1E,1F	90 35	(SUBTRACT 35)
20,21	01 01	not needed (NOP)
22,23	2B 10	(BMI 10)

where location 35 contains 10,001. This program branches back until $N = 10,003$. In this problem the use of event detection is conceptually simpler and saves one instruction.

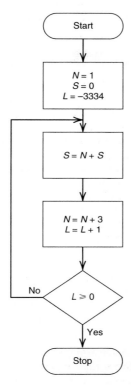

Figure 3-8 Flowchart for Example 3-6.

TABLE 3-3 Program for the Flowchart of Fig. 3-8

LOCATIONS	INSTRUCTIONS		COMMENTS
10,11	96 31	LOAD 31	
12,13	9B 30	ADD	} S = N + S
14,15	97 31	STORE 31	
16,17	96 30	LOAD 30	
18,19	9B 33	ADD 33	} N = N + 3
1A,1B	97 30	STORE 30	
1C,1D	96 32	LOAD 32	
1E,1F	9B 34	ADD 34	} L = L + 1
20,21	97 32	STORE 32	
22,23	2B 10	BMI 10	
24	3E	WAIT	

EXAMPLE 3-7

Write the code for the flowchart of Fig. 3-8.

SOLUTION

As in Table 3-2, the program is started at location 10 and the data area is at location 30. In the data area, three variables, N, S, and L, are needed. These should be initialized to 1, 0, and −3334, respectively, before the program starts. In addition, two constants, 1 and 3, are needed during the execution of the program. Initially, the data area should look like this:

LOCATION	TERM	INITIAL VALUE
30	N	1
31	S	0
32	L	−3334
33	Constant	3
34	Constant	1

The program can now be written directly from the flowchart (Table 3-3). Each instruction takes 2 bytes (except the last), as it could in a typical μP such as the **6800**. Two locations are therefore assigned to each instruction and the addresses are in hex.

Note that the instructions follow the flowchart. The decision box has been implemented by the **BMI** (**B**ranch if **MI**nus) instruction. The program loops as long as L remains negative.

Check: As a check on the program, we can write the contents of N, S, and L at the end of each loop as in the following table.

TIMES THROUGH LOOP	N	S	L
1	4	1	−3333
2	7	5	−3332
3	10	12	−3331
⋮	⋮	⋮	⋮

The chart shows that each time around the loop

$$\frac{N-1}{3} + |L| = 3334$$

Therefore, when N = 10,003, L indeed equals 0 and the loop terminates.

3-12 ▼ SUMMARY

In this chapter the operation of a basic computer was described. First, the major parts of the computer were listed and the function of each was explained briefly. Then the operations of the memory, ALU, and control sections were described in detail.

Elementary programming was explored further. Flowcharts and their uses were introduced, and simple problems involving loops and branches were presented. Finally, an example of the execution of a simple program was given. We showed how the hardware and software work together in a step-by-step manner to solve a simple problem.

3-13 ▼ GLOSSARY

Access time The time required for a memory to provide valid data after the address and control lines are stable.

Accumulator A register in a computer that holds an operand used by the instructions.

Address A memory location where data is stored.

Arithmetic/logic unit (ALU) The part of the computer that performs the required arithmetic and logic operations and indicates the processor status by setting the bits of the condition code register.

Assembler A computer program to translate the programmer's mnemonics to machine language and to provide a program listing.

Assembly Listing A program listing of the mnemonics and machine language produced by an assembler.

Branch instruction An instruction that alters the normal sequential course of a program by causing it to skip over or jump to another instruction.

Bus A group of wires; generally a bus carries a set of signals from one group of digital devices to another.

Conditional branch An instruction that branches or transfers the program flow to an address other than the next sequential location but only when a specified condition of bits is met.

Control unit The internal part of a computer that control and organize its operations.

Cycle time The time required to complete a Write cycle in a memory.

Destructive readout Readout of data in which the data is destroyed.

EEPROM Electrically erasable and programmable read-only memory.

EPROM Erasable (by UV light) and electrically programmable read-only memory.

Event detection Using the occurrence of an event to terminate a loop or program.

EXECUTE The portion of an instruction cycle where the instruction is executed.

FETCH mode The portion of an instruction cycle where the instruction is brought from memory to the instruction register.

Flip-flop (FF) An electronic circuit that functions as a 1-bit memory.

Flowchart A graphic method used to outline or show the action of a program.

Increment To add 1 to a number.

Initialization Clearing or presetting of RAM locations and the programming of the peripheral adapters (see Chapter 8) prior to program execution.

Input/output (I/O) system The part of a computer that communicates with external devices.

Instruction A command that directs the computer to perform a specific operation.

Instruction register A register in a computer that holds the instruction currently being executed.

LOAD An instruction that causes data to be brought from memory into an accumulator register.

Loop A programming technique to return to the start of a sequence of instructions so that the same instructions may be repeated.

MAR Memory address register. It contains the address of the memory location currently being accessed.

Memory The part of a computer used to hold the program or temporary storage of data.

MDR Memory data register. It contains the data going to or coming from the memory.

Object program A machine language program of 1s and 0s understood by the computer.

Operation code (op code) The first byte of an instruction that specifies the operation to be performed by the CPU.

Program A group of instructions that control the operation of a computer.

Program counter (PC) A register in a computer that contains the address of the next instruction to be executed.

RAM Random-Access Memory. Memory capable of both READ and WRITE operations.

Restart The act of starting up the computer. A restart is performed when the computer is first turned on and after most power failures.

ROM Read-Only Memory. Memory with a permanent program that can only be read.

Software Programs used to control a computer that are easily changed.

Source program A program written by the programmer using mnemonics.

STORE An instruction that causes data in the accumulator to be moved to memory or a peripheral register.

Subroutine A small program of a complete function.

Unconditional branch An instruction that always jump the program to an address other than the next sequential location.

Volatility The inability of a memory to retain data when power is interrupted.

3-14 ▼ REFERENCES

BARTEE, THOMAS C., *Digital Computer Fundamentals,* 5th ed., McGraw-Hill, New York, 1981.

GREENFIELD, JOSEPH D., *Practical Digital Design Using ICs*, 3rd ed., Prentice Hall, Englewood Cliffs, N.J., 1994.

BOILLOT, MICHEL H., GARY M. GLEASON, AND L. WAYNE HORN, *Essentials of Flowcharting,* WILLIAM C. BROWN, Dubuque, Iowa, 1975.

3-15 ▼ PROBLEMS

3-1. The dimensions of a memory are 16K words by 32 bits. How many bits are:
  (a) In the MAR?
  (b) In the MDR?
  (c) In the memory?

3-2. Repeat Problem 3-1 for an 8K by 24-bit memory.

3-3. In Problems 3-1 and 3-2, list the input and output lines required for the memory if
  (a) The memory is a RAM.
  (b) The memory is a ROM.

3-4. Explain how a memory can be addressed sequentially.

3-5. Write a program to add 50 and 75 and then subtract 25. Select memory areas for your data and instructions. Describe the progression of your program and list the contents of each pertinent memory location before and after its execution.

3-6. Write a program to add 25, 35, 45, and 55 and then shift the results 2 bits to the right. Explain the significance of your answer.

3-7. Prepare a chart similar to Fig. 3-7 for the programs of Problems 3-6 and 3-7.

3-8. Your alarm clock always goes off at 8:00 A.M. You get up, except on Tuesdays, when you can sleep an extra hour. You then eat breakfast. If it's raining, you take an umbrella. If your car starts, you go to work; otherwise, you go back to bed. Draw a flowchart showing this portion of your day's activities.

3-9. Your friends are Alice, George, Cindy, and Arthur in that order. You ask one of them to the ballgame. If it's raining or if none of your friends can make it, you stay home and watch television. Draw a flowchart to show this portion of your activities.

3-10. Write a program to add the numbers 1, 6, 9, 13, . . . , 20,001.

3-11. The number N is in location 40. Write a program to put $N!$ in location 41.

3-12. There are 101 numbers in locations 100 to 200. Some of them are 5. Write a program to count the number of times that 5 appears in these locations.

After attempting to solve these problems, try to answer the self-evaluation questions in Section 3-2. If any of them still seem difficult, review the appropriate sections of the chapter to find the answers.

4 | ACCUMULATOR AND MEMORY REFERENCE INSTRUCTIONS

4-1 ▼ INSTRUCTIONAL OBJECTIVES

In this chapter we introduce the software features of the **6800,** the mnemonics or assembly language concept, and the accumulator and memory referencing instructions. After reading this chapter, the student should be able to:

1. Explain the function of each register in the **6800** μP.
2. Realize the need for mnemonics and assembly language.
3. Write and use instructions that use the immediate, direct, extended, indexed, and implied addressing modes.
4. List each bit in the Condition Code Register and explain its function.
5. Perform multibyte additions and subtractions using the carry bit.
6. Use all the BRANCH instructions to provide computer decisions.
7. Write programs to add and subtract BCD numbers.
8. Use logic instructions.
9. Use SHIFT and ROTATE instructions.
10. SET or CLEAR specific bits in a register.
11. Test specific bits in a register.

4-2 ▼ SELF-EVALUATION QUESTIONS

Watch for the answers to the following questions as you read the chapter. They should help you to understand the material presented.

1. Why are mnemonics easier to use than machine language?
2. What is one advantage of having two accumulators?

3. Which memory locations can be accessed by direct instructions? Why can't *all* memory locations be accessed by direct instructions?

4. What is the difference between an ADD and an ADD-WITH-CARRY instruction? Give an example of the proper use of each.

5. Why is it necessary to worry about overflow or underflow?

6. What is the significance of the H bit? Why is it used only in BCD operations?

7. Why doesn't the carry bit have any effect on logic operations?

8. Why do INCREMENT, DECREMENT, and CLEAR instructions require many memory cycles?

9. What are the advantages of using the carry bit in conjunction with SHIFT and ROTATE instructions?

4-3 ▼ PROGRAMMING THE 6800 MICROPROCESSOR

The **MC6800,** Motorola's first μP, was introduced in 1974. Millions of them have been used. In Chapter 3 we used the simpler **6800** instructions to illustrate how the basic functions of a computer work. The **6800** is a powerful computer but is also the easiest μP for a student to learn. All of the instructions that can be executed by a **6800** can also be executed identically by most of Motorola's more advanced 8-bit computers, and the *computer concepts* such as addressing modes and stacks as well as hardware bus techniques carry over to the 16- and 32-bit μCs as well. Figure 4-1 shows the registers contained within the **6800** and identifies the status bits in the *Condition Code Register* (CCR).

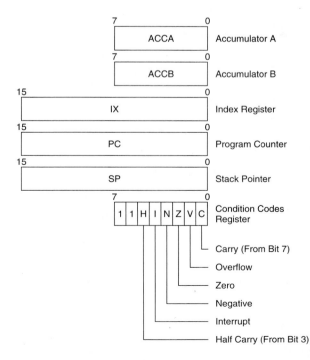

Figure 4-1 Programming model of the **6800** microprocessors.

Internally, the **6800** has three 8-bit registers and three 16-bit registers. Two of the 8-bit registers are the A and B *accumulators*. Any arithmetic operation must involve one of them. These are almost identical in operation. The accumulator to be used is generally specified by the op code. For example, an op Code of 8B specifies an ADD IMMEDIATE to accumulator A, and an op code of CB specifies an ADD IMMEDIATE to accumulator B. The 8-bit Condition Code Register contains the *condition codes* or *flags*. It is described in Section 4-6. The three 16-bit registers in the **6800** are:

1. **Program Counter (PC).** This is the standard 16-bit PC found in 8-bit μPs. It contains the address of the next instruction to be executed.

2. **The Stack Pointer (SP).** This register points to an area in memory called the *Stack* that is used with PUSHes, PULLS, JUMPs to SUBROUTINEs and Interrupts. The Stack Pointer is discussed in Section 5-4.

3. **Index Register (X).** This register is used in indexed instructions (see Section 4-5.4).

Most of the functions necessary for total system operation are included in the **6800** IC itself. At this point the features of the **6800** μP that determine the software characteristics will be described; the hardware aspects are discussed in later chapters.

4-3.1 ▼ Arithmetic/Logic Unit

As a complete processor, the **6800** contains within it all of the registers necessary for the operation of a computer, such as the instruction register and decoder, the input and output buffers, and the Arithmetic/Logic Unit (ALU). These are shown in the expanded block diagram of Fig. 4-2. The **6800** ALU performs the arithmetic operations of addition, subtraction, complementation, negation, and shifting. Multiplication and division for the **6800** are performed by programs (subroutines) that use these functions (shifts with additions or subtractions). The ALU also performs the Boolean algebra functions of AND, OR, and Exclusive OR.

The *Condition Code Register* (CCR) is a part of the ALU and its bits are altered as a result of each arithmetic or logic instruction. The bits of this register are then used by the *conditional branch instructions* to select alternative paths for the program. These are the decision-making functions that distinguish a computer and are described in Section 4-7.

4-3.2 ▼ Registers and Accumulators

The registers and accumulators within the **6800** are all 8 bits wide and, as shown in Fig. 4-2, are interconnected by an 8-bit internal bus. Those registers in the μP that are associated with addresses [program counter (PC), index (X), and stack pointer (SP)] use two bytes each and therefore have a high (H) and a low (L) byte. The **6800** is thus able to generate a 16-bit address, and as a result, 65,536 (2^{16}) bytes of memory can be addressed.

As explained in Chapter 3, the PC keeps track of the location in memory where the next instruction byte is to be fetched. The bytes are then loaded into the instruction register and the instructions are executed. All **6800** instructions consist of 1, 2, or 3 bytes.

4-3.3 ▼ 6800 Instruction Set

The first byte of each instruction is called the *operation code* (op code) because its bit combination determines the operation to be performed. The second and third bytes of the

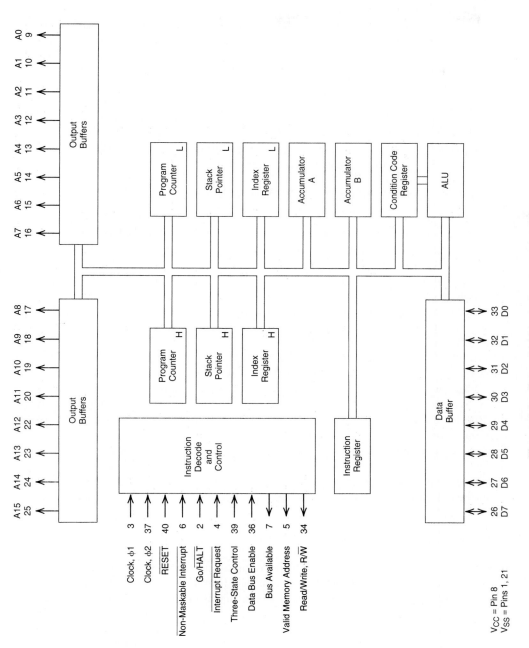

Figure 4-2 Expanded block diagram of the **6800**.

V_{CC} = Pin 8
V_{SS} = Pins 1, 21

73

instruction (if used) contain address or data information. They are the *operand* part of the instruction. The op code also tells the μP logic how many additional bytes to fetch for each instruction. There are 197 unique instructions in the **6800** instruction set. Since an 8-bit word has 256 combinations, a high percentage of the possible op codes are used.

When an instruction is fetched from the location in memory pointed to by the program counter (PC) register, and the first byte is moved into the instruction register, it causes the logic to execute the instruction. If the bit combination is 01001111 (or 4F in hex), for example, it CLEARs the A accumulator (RESETs it to all zeros), or if the combination is 01001100 (4C), the processor increments accumulator A (adds 1 to it). These are examples of *1-byte* instructions that involve only one accumulator. An instruction byte of 10110110 (B6) is the code for the *extended addressing mode* of LOAD A (see Section 4-5.3) It also commands the logic to fetch the *next 2 bytes* and use them as the *address* of the data to be loaded into accumulator A.

4-3.4 ▼ Understanding the 6800 Instructions

When the op codes for each instruction are expressed in their binary or hex format, as in Section 4-3.3, they are known as *machine language instructions*. The bits of these op codes must reside in memory and be moved to the instruction decoder for analysis and action by the μP.

Writing programs in machine language is very tedious, and trying to follow even a simple machine language program strains the ability of most people. As a result, various techniques have evolved in an effort to simplify the program documentation. The first step in this simplification is the use of *hexadecimal notation* to express the codes. This reduces the number of digits from eight to two (10100011 = A3, for example), or in the case of an address, from 16 binary digits (bits) to 4 hex digits. Even this simplification, however, is insufficient, and the concept of using *mnemonic language* to describe each instruction has therefore been developed. A *mnemonic* is defined as a *device to help people remember*. For example, the mnemonics LDA A (load A) and STA A (store A) are used for the LOAD and STORE instructions instead of the hex op codes of 86 and B7 because the mnemonics are *descriptive* and *easier to remember*.

Programs and data can be entered into the memory or registers of a μP in machine language using data switches. It is easier however, as explained in Chapter 11, to use a μP development system that has a memory access routine and a data terminal to type in the hexadecimal forms of the instructions or data.

4-4 ▼ ASSEMBLY LANGUAGE

Not only are mnemonics easy to remember, but the precise meaning of each one makes it possible to use a computer program to translate them to the machine language equivalent that can be used by the computer. A program for this purpose is called an *assembler* and the mnemonics that it recognizes constitute an *assembly language program*. It is possible to have any number of different assemblers for the **6800,** each with its own mnemonics, but the mnemonics described here are used by Motorola for the **6800** μP instruction set. The mnemonics for each machine language instruction code and its hexadecimal equivalent are shown in Table 4-1.

TABLE 4-1 Mnemonics and Hexadecimal Values for the 6800 Machine Codes

Hex	Mnem	Acc	Mode	Hex	Mnem	Acc	Mode	Hex	Mnem	Acc	Mode	Hex	Mnem	Acc	Mode
00	·			40	NEG	A		80	SUB	A	IMM	C0	SUB	B	IMM
01	NOP			41	·			81	CMP	A	IMM	C1	CMP	B	IMM
02	·			42	·			82	SBC	A	IMM	C2	SBC	B	IMM
03	·			43	COM	A		83	·			C3	·		
04	·			44	LSR	A		84	AND	A	IMM	C4	AND	B	IMM
05	·			45	·			85	BIT	A	IMM	C5	BIT	B	IMM
06	TAP			46	ROR	A		86	LDA	A	IMM	C6	LDA	B	IMM
07	TPA			47	ASR	A		87	·			C7	·		
08	INX			48	ASL	A		88	EOR	A	IMM	C8	EOR	B	IMM
09	DEX			49	ROL	A		89	ADC	A	IMM	C9	ADC	B	IMM
0A	CLV			4A	DEC	A		8A	ORA	A	IMM	CA	ORA	B	IMM
0B	SEV			4B	·			8B	ADD	A	IMM	CB	ADD	B	IMM
0C	CLC			4C	INC	A		8C	CPX	A	IMM	CC	·		
0D	SEC			4D	TST	A		8D	BSR		REL	CD	·		
0E	CLI			4E	·			8E	LDS		IMM	CE	LDX		IMM
0F	SEI			4F	CLR	A		8F	·			CF	·		
10	SBA			50	NEG	B		90	SUB	A	DIR	D0	SUB	B	DIR
11	CBA			51	·			91	CMP	A	DIR	D1	CMP	B	DIR
12	·			52	·			92	SBC	A	DIR	D2	SBC	B	DIR
13	·			53	COM	B		93	·			D3	·		
14	·			54	LSR	B		94	AND	A	DIR	D4	AND	B	DIR
15	·			55	·			95	BIT	A	DIR	D5	BIT	B	DIR
16	TAB			56	ROR	B		96	LDA	A	DIR	D6	LDA	B	DIR
17	TBA			57	ASR	B		97	STA	A	DIR	D7	STA	B	DIR
18	·			58	ASL	B		98	EOR	A	DIR	D8	EOR	B	DIR
19	DAA			59	ROL	B		99	ADC	A	DIR	D9	ADC	B	DIR
1A	·			5A	DEC	B		9A	ORA	A	DIR	DA	ORA	B	DIR
1B	ABA			5B	·			9B	ADD	A	DIR	DB	ADD	B	DIR
1C	·			5C	INC	B		9C	CPX		DIR	DC	·		
1D	·			5D	TST	B		9D	·			DD	·		
1E	·			5E	·			9E	LDS		DIR	DE	LDX		DIR
1F	·			5F	CLR	B		9F	STS		DIR	DF	STX		DIR
20	BRA		REL	60	NEG		IND	A0	SUB	A	IND	E0	SUB	B	IND
21	·			61	·			A1	CMP	A	IND	E1	CMP	B	IND
22	BHI		REL	62	·			A2	SBC	A	IND	E2	SBC	B	IND
23	BLS		REL	63	COM		IND	A3	·			E3	·		
24	BCC		REL	64	LSR		IND	A4	AND	A	IND	E4	AND	B	IND
25	BCS		REL	65	·			A5	BIT	A	IND	E5	BIT	B	IND
26	BNE		REL	66	ROR		IND	A6	LDA	A	IND	E6	LDA	B	IND
27	BEQ		REL	67	ASR		IND	A7	STA	A	IND	E7	STA	B	IND
28	BVC		REL	68	ASL		IND	A8	EOR	A	IND	E8	EOR	B	IND
29	BVS		REL	69	ROL		IND	A9	ADC	A	IND	E9	ADC	B	IND
2A	BPL		REL	6A	DEC		IND	AA	ORA	A	IND	EA	ORA	B	IND
2B	BMI		REL	6B	·			AB	ADD	A	IND	EB	ADD	B	IND
2C	BGE		REL	6C	INC		IND	AC	CPX		IND	EC	·		
2D	BLT		REL	6D	TST		IND	AD	JSR		IND	ED	·		
2E	BGT		REL	6E	JMP		IND	AE	LDS		IND	EE	LDX		IND
2F	BLE		REL	6F	CLR		IND	AF	STS		IND	EF	STX		IND
30	TSX			70	NEG		EXT	B0	SUB	A	EXT	F0	SUB	B	EXT
31	INS			71	·			B1	CMP	A	EXT	F1	CMP	B	EXT
32	PUL	A		72	·			B2	SBC	A	EXT	F2	SBC	B	EXT
33	PUL	B		73	COM		EXT	B3	·			F3	·		
34	DES			74	LSR		EXT	B4	AND	A	EXT	F4	AND	B	EXT
35	TXS			75	·			B5	BIT	A	EXT	F5	BIT	B	EXT
36	PSH	A		76	ROR		EXT	B6	LDA	A	EXT	F6	LDA	B	EXT
37	PSH	B		77	ASR		EXT	B7	STA	A	EXT	F7	STA	B	EXT
38	·			78	ASL		EXT	B8	EOR	A	EXT	F8	EOR	B	EXT
39	RTS			79	ROL		EXT	B9	ADC	A	EXT	F9	ADC	B	EXT
3A	·			7A	DEC		EXT	BA	ORA	A	EXT	FA	ORA	B	EXT
3B	RTI			7B	·			BB	ADD	A	EXT	FB	ADD	B	EXT
3C	·			7C	INC		EXT	BC	CPX		EXT	FC	·		
3D	·			7D	TST		EXT	BD	JSR		EXT	FD	·		
3E	WAI			7E	JMP		EXT	BE	LDS		EXT	FE	LDX		EXT
3F	SWI			7F	CLR		EXT	BF	STS		EXT	FF	STX		EXT

When a program is written in mnemonic or assembly language it is called a *source program*. After being assembled (or translated) by the computer, the machine language codes that are produced are known as the *object program*. An assembler also produces a *program listing* that lists the addresses, object codes, and the mnemonics, and is used for debugging the program, and kept as a record of the design.

TABLE 4-2 Accumulator and Memory Instructions

OPERATIONS	MNEMONIC	IMMED OP	~	=	DIRECT OP	~	=	INDEX OP	~	=	EXTND OP	~	=	IMPLIED OP	~	=	BOOLEAN/ARITHMETIC OPERATION (All register labels refer to contents)	H (5)	I (4)	N (3)	Z (2)	V (1)	C (0)
Add	ADDA	3B	2	2	9B	3	2	AB	5	2	BB	4	3				A + M → A	↕	●	↕	↕	↕	↕
	ADDB	CB	2	2	DB	3	2	EB	5	2	FB	4	3				B + M → B	↕	●	↕	↕	↕	↕
Add Acmltrs	ABA													1B	2	1	A + B → A	↕	●	↕	↕	↕	↕
Add with Carry	ADCA	89	2	2	99	3	2	A9	5	2	B9	4	3				A + M + C → A	↕	●	↕	↕	↕	↕
	ADCB	C9	2	2	D9	3	2	E9	5	2	F9	4	3				B + M + C → B	↕	●	↕	↕	↕	↕
And	ANDA	84	2	2	94	3	2	A4	5	2	B4	4	3				A · M → A	●	●	↕	↕	R	●
	ANDB	C4	2	2	D4	3	2	E4	5	2	F4	4	3				B · M → B	●	●	↕	↕	R	●
Bit Test	BITA	85	2	2	95	3	2	A5	5	2	B5	4	3				A · M	●	●	↕	↕	R	●
	BITB	C5	2	2	D5	3	2	E5	5	2	F5	4	3				B · M	●	●	↕	↕	R	●
Clear	CLR							6F	7	2	7F	6	3				00 → M	●	●	R	S	R	R
	CLRA													4F	2	1	00 → A	●	●	R	S	R	R
	CLRB													5F	2	1	00 → B	●	●	R	S	R	R
Compare	CMPA	81	2	2	91	3	2	A1	5	2	B1	4	3				A − M	●	●	↕	↕	↕	↕
	CMPB	C1	2	2	D1	3	2	E1	5	2	F1	4	3				B − M	●	●	↕	↕	↕	↕
Compare Acmltrs	CBA													11	2	1	A − B	●	●	↕	↕	↕	↕
Complement, 1's	COM							63	7	2	73	6	3				M̄ → M	●	●	↕	↕	R	S
	COMA													43	2	1	Ā → A	●	●	↕	↕	R	S
	COMB													53	2	1	B̄ → B	●	●	↕	↕	R	S
Complement, 2's	NEG							60	7	2	70	6	3				00 − M → M	●	●	↕	↕	①	②
(Negate)	NEGA													40	2	1	00 − A → A	●	●	↕	↕	①	②
	NEGB													50	2	1	00 − B → B	●	●	↕	↕	①	②
Decimal Adjust, A	DAA													19	2	1	Converts Binary Add. of BCD Characters into BCD Format	●	●	↕	↕	↕	③
Decrement	DEC							6A	7	2	7A	6	3				M − 1 → M	●	●	↕	↕	④	●
	DECA													4A	2	1	A − 1 → A	●	●	↕	↕	④	●
	DECB													5A	2	1	B − 1 → B	●	●	↕	↕	④	●
Exclusive OR	EORA	88	2	2	98	3	2	A8	5	2	B8	4	3				A ⊕ M → A	●	●	↕	↕	R	●
	EORB	C8	2	2	D8	3	2	E8	5	2	F8	4	3				B ⊕ M → B	●	●	↕	↕	R	●
Increment	INC							6C	7	2	7C	6	3				M + 1 → M	●	●	↕	↕	⑤	●
	INCA													4C	2	1	A + 1 → A	●	●	↕	↕	⑤	●
	INCB													5C	2	1	B + 1 → B	●	●	↕	↕	⑤	●
Load Acmltr	LDAA	86	2	2	96	3	2	A6	5	2	B6	4	3				M → A	●	●	↕	↕	R	●
	LDAB	C6	2	2	D6	3	2	E6	5	2	F6	4	3				M → B	●	●	↕	↕	R	●
Or, Inclusive	ORAA	8A	2	2	9A	3	2	AA	5	2	BA	4	3				A + M → A	●	●	↕	↕	R	●
	ORAB	CA	2	2	DA	3	2	EA	5	2	FA	4	3				B + M → B	●	●	↕	↕	R	●
Push Data	PSHA													36	4	1	A → MSP, SP − 1 → SP	●	●	●	●	●	●
	PSHB													37	4	1	B → MSP, SP − 1 → SP	●	●	●	●	●	●
Pull Data	PULA													32	4	1	SP + 1 → SP, MSP → A	●	●	●	●	●	●
	PULB													33	4	1	SP + 1 → SP, MSP → B	●	●	●	●	●	●
Rotate Left	ROL							69	7	2	79	6	3				M	●	●	↕	↕	⑥	↕
	ROLA													49	2	1	A	●	●	↕	↕	⑥	↕
	ROLB													59	2	1	B	●	●	↕	↕	⑥	↕
Rotate Right	ROR							66	7	2	76	6	3				M	●	●	↕	↕	⑥	↕
	RORA													46	2	1	A	●	●	↕	↕	⑥	↕
	RORB													56	2	1	B	●	●	↕	↕	⑥	↕
Shift Left, Arithmetic	ASL							68	7	2	78	6	3				M	●	●	↕	↕	⑥	↕
	ASLA													48	2	1	A	●	●	↕	↕	⑥	↕
	ASLB													58	2	1	B	●	●	↕	↕	⑥	↕
Shift Right, Arithmetic	ASR							67	7	2	77	6	3				M	●	●	↕	↕	⑥	↕
	ASRA													47	2	1	A	●	●	↕	↕	⑥	↕
	ASRB													57	2	1	B	●	●	↕	↕	⑥	↕
Shift Right, Logic	LSR							64	7	2	74	6	3				M	●	●	R	↕	⑥	↕
	LSRA													44	2	1	A	●	●	R	↕	⑥	↕
	LSRB													54	2	1	B	●	●	R	↕	⑥	↕
Store Acmltr.	STAA				97	4	2	A7	6	2	B7	5	3				A → M	●	●	↕	↕	R	●
	STAB				D7	4	2	E7	6	2	F7	5	3				B → M	●	●	↕	↕	R	●
Subtract	SUBA	80	2	2	90	3	2	A0	5	2	B0	4	3				A − M → A	●	●	↕	↕	↕	↕
	SUBB	C0	2	2	D0	3	2	E0	5	2	F0	4	3				B − M → B	●	●	↕	↕	↕	↕
Subtract Acmltrs.	SBA													10	2	1	A − B → A	●	●	↕	↕	↕	↕
Subtr. with Carry	SBCA	82	2	2	92	3	2	A2	5	2	B2	4	3				A − M − C → A	●	●	↕	↕	↕	↕
	SBCB	C2	2	2	D2	3	2	E2	5	2	F2	4	3				B − M − C → B	●	●	↕	↕	↕	↕
Transfer Acmltrs	TAB													16	2	1	A → B	●	●	↕	↕	R	●
	TBA													17	2	1	B → A	●	●	↕	↕	R	●
Test, Zero or Minus	TST							6D	7	2	7D	6	3				M − 00	●	●	↕	↕	R	R
	TSTA													4D	2	1	A − 00	●	●	↕	↕	R	R
	TSTB													5D	2	1	B − 00	●	●	↕	↕	R	R

| | | | | | | | | | | | | | | | | | | H | I | N | Z | V | C |

To write a program, the programmer must understand the differences between each mnemonic. The following sections and chapters are devoted to describing these differences. A detailed description of an assembler is given in Chapter 6, and debugging is described in Chapter 11.

4-4.1 ▼ Numerical Identifications

The Motorola **6800** assembler described here uses several symbols to identify the various types of numbers that occur in a program. These symbols are:

1. A blank or no symbol indicates that the number is a *decimal* number.
2. A $ immediately preceding a number indicates that it is a *hex* number. ($24, for example, is 24 in hex or the equivalent of 36 in decimal.)
3. A # sign indicates an *immediate* operand (see Section 4-5.1).
4. A @ sign indicates an *octal* value.
5. A % sign indicates a *binary* number (e.g., 01011001).

4-5 ▼ ADDRESSING MODES

The accumulator and memory instructions available in the **6800** are given in Table 4-2.* The leftmost columns indicate the operations and the mnemonic for each instruction. The accumulator and memory instructions can be broken down roughly into the following categories:

1. Transfers between an accumulator and memory (LOADs and STOREs)
2. Arithmetic operations: ADDITION, SUBTRACTION, DECIMAL ADJUST ACCUMULATOR
3. Logical operations: AND, OR, XOR
4. Shifts and rotates
5. Test operations: bit test and compares
6. Other operations: CLEAR, INCREMENT, DECREMENT, and COMPLEMENT

To reduce the number of instructions required in a typical program and, consequently, the number of memory locations needed to hold a program, the **6800** features several ways to address them. They are called *addressing modes* and many of them only use 1 or 2 bytes. The following paragraphs and examples illustrate how and when each mode is used.

The instructions of Table 4-2 can be addressed in one or more of the following modes: *immediate, direct, indexed, implied*, or *extended*. Each mode occupies a column in Table 4-2, and the instructions that can be executed in each mode are listed in the appropriate column. The listing contains the op code, the number of cycles, and the number of bytes required for the instruction. The number of cycles is listed under the ~ symbol and gives the number of *clock cycles* that each instruction uses. This information is used when analyzing the timing of the μP (Section 9-10). The number of *bytes* is listed under the # symbol and indicates the number of memory locations required by each instruction.

*The complete **6800** instruction set is given in Appendix B.

EXAMPLE 4-1

How many cycles and bytes are required by:

(a) A LOAD IMMEDIATE instruction?

(b) A LOAD EXTENDED instruction?

SOLUTION

(a) Looking at the load accumulator instructions (LDAA means *load* accumulator A and LDAB means *load* accumulator B) in the IMMED column, we find that a LOAD IMMEDIATE takes **two cycles** and requires **2 bytes.**

(b) Moving over to the EXTND column, we see that a LOAD EXTENDED takes **four cycles** and the instruction occupies **3 bytes.**

These modes are explained in the following paragraphs and illustrated in Fig. 4-3, where each instruction is assumed to start at location 10. The figure shows the op code at location 10 and the following bytes. It explains the function of each byte and gives a sample instruction for each mode.

4-5.1 ▼ Immediate Addressing Instructions

All the *immediate instructions* in Table 4-2 require 2 bytes. The first byte is the op code and the second byte contains the *operand* or *information to be used*. For example, assume that the accumulator contains the hex number 2C and the following instruction occurs in a program:

ADD A #$23

The # indicates that the hex value $23 is to be added to accumulator A. The immediate mode of the instruction is indicated by the # sign. After the instruction is executed, A contains 4F (23 + 2C).

EXAMPLE 4-2

What does the following instruction do?

LDA B #$FF

SOLUTION

The action of this instruction is shown in Fig. 4-4, where the op code for the instruction LOAD B IMMEDIATE (C6) is in $40 and the immediate operand (FF) is in $41. The instruction places or LOADs the operand into accumulator B.

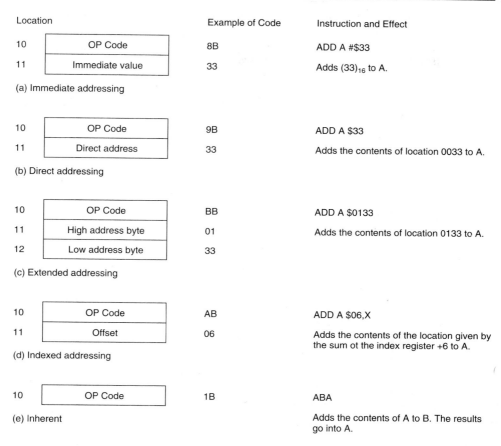

Location		Example of Code	Instruction and Effect

10 | OP Code | 8B | ADD A #$33
11 | Immediate value | 33 | Adds $(33)_{16}$ to A.

(a) Immediate addressing

10 | OP Code | 9B | ADD A $33
11 | Direct address | 33 | Adds the contents of location 0033 to A.

(b) Direct addressing

10 | OP Code | BB | ADD A $0133
11 | High address byte | 01 | Adds the contents of location 0133 to A.
12 | Low address byte | 33 |

(c) Extended addressing

10 | OP Code | AB | ADD A $06,X
11 | Offset | 06 | Adds the contents of the location given by the sum ot the index register +6 to A.

(d) Indexed addressing

10 | OP Code | 1B | ABA | Adds the contents of A to B. The results go into A.

(e) Inherent

Figure 4-3 Examples of the various addressing modes of the **6800**.

4-5.2 ▼ Direct Instructions

Immediate instructions are used if the variable or operand is *known* to the programmer when he or she is coding. For example, if the programmer knows that he or she wants to add 5 to a variable, it is more efficient to add it *immediately* than to store 5 in memory and do a direct or extended ADD. When one of the operands must reside in *memory*, however, *direct* or *extended* instructions are required.

Like immediate instructions, *direct instructions* require 2 bytes. The *second byte*, in this case, contains the *address of the operand* used in the instruction. Since the op code

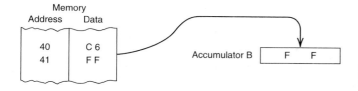

Figure 4-4 Action of a LOAD IMMEDIATE instruction.

identifies this as a 2-byte instruction, only 8 address bits are available. The μP contains 16 address lines, but for direct instructions, the 8 MSBs of the address are effectively set to 0. The memory locations that can be addressed by a direct instruction are therefore restricted to 0000 to 00FF.

EXAMPLE 4-3

What happens when the instruction

LDAA $55

is encountered in a program? Assume that location $55 contains CA.

SOLUTION

This is a direct instruction. The second byte of this 2-byte instruction is the address ($0055). The LDAA $55 instruction causes the μP to read location 0055 and load its contents into A. At the end of the instruction, accumulator A contains CA.

The action of this instruction is shown in Fig. 4-5. The op code for the LOAD A DIRECT (96) is again in memory location $40 and the operand (55) is in $41. Because this is a direct instruction, the operand is an address ($0055) and the contents of that address (CA) are loaded into accumulator A.

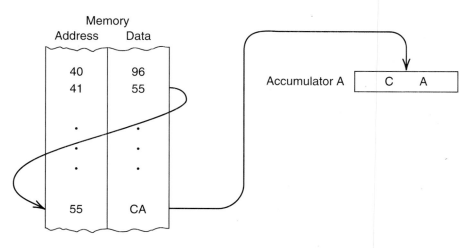

Figure 4-5   Action of a LOAD DIRECT instruction.

In extended it loads the 8 LSB of the address first
& then the 8 MSB

EXAMPLE 4-4

If location $55 contains CA and accumulator B contains 13, what does B contain after execution of the following instructions?

(a) ADDB #$55   13+65 = 68

(b) ADDB $55   dd

SOLUTION

(a) The # indicates the IMMEDIATE mode. Thus ADDB #$55 causes $55 to be added to $13 and the result is 55 + 13 = **68.**

(b) Since the address of $55 is less than $100, this is a DIRECT mode instruction. It causes the contents of 55 to be added to B and the result stored in the B register. Since location 55 contains CA, the result stored is CA + 13 = **DD.**

4-5.3 ▼ Extended Instructions

Extended instructions are 3-byte instructions. The op code is followed by 2 bytes that specify the address of the operand used by the instruction. The second byte contains the 8 high-order bits of the address. Because 16 address bits are available, any one of the 65,536 memory locations in the **6800** μP can be selected. Thus extended instructions have the advantage of being able to select *any* memory locations, but direct instructions require only 2 bytes in the program instead of 3. Direct instructions also require one less cycle for execution, so they are somewhat faster than the corresponding extended instructions. It is often wise to place variable data in memory locations below $100 because this data is usually referenced frequently throughout the program. The programmer can then make maximum use of 2-byte direct instructions instead of 3-byte extended instructions and reduce memory requirements by up to 25% in a typical program.

EXAMPLE 4-5

What occurs when the instruction

                    STAA $13C

appears in a program?

SOLUTION

Since this operand is a hex address greater than $100, this is an EXTENDED mode instruction. This 3-byte instruction causes the contents of accumulator A to be *stored* or written into location $013C.

4-5.4 ▼ Indexed Instructions

As its name implies, an indexed instruction makes use of the *index register* (X)* in the **6800** μP. There are two types of instructions and the reader must be able to distinguish between them.

The first form of indexed instructions uses the contents of the X Register to calculate the address of the instruction. *These instructions do not change the contents of the Index Register.* For any indexed instruction, the address referred to is the *sum* of the number (called the OFFSET) in the second byte of the instruction, plus the contents of X.

The second type of instructions are those that *do affect* or change the contents of X. Table 4-3 is a list of instructions that affect the index register and stack pointer. Notice that the **6800** provides instructions to LOAD, STORE, INCREMENT, and DECREMENT the stack pointer (SP), as well as X. Under some conditions, the SP can be used as a second index register.

EXAMPLE 4-6

What does the following program accomplish?

```
LDX #$0123
SUBA $A0,X
```

SOLUTION

The first instruction is an immediate LOAD of the index register. It causes the number $0123 to be loaded into X. The second instruction is an INDEXED SUBA. In executing this instruction, the μP adds the second byte (A0) to the contents of X ($0123) to get the data address. Thus *the contents of memory location $01C3 are subtracted from accumulator A.*

Note that because the X register is 16 bits wide, an immediate load of the index register (LDX #) requires 2 bytes following the op code, whereas an immediate load of an accumulator (LDAA #) requires only 1 byte (plus the op code).

Index registers are useful for scanning tables or *relocating* a table or block of data.

EXAMPLE 4-7

A data list that starts at memory location $1000 is to be moved or relocated to start at location $2000. Write a program to accomplish this.

---

*Referred to as the X register or simply X.

TABLE 4-3 Index Register and Stack Pointer Instructions

POINTER OPERATIONS	MNEMONIC	IMMED OP	~	#	DIRECT OP	~	#	INDEX OP	~	#	EXTND OP	~	#	IMPLIED OP	~	#	BOOLEAN/ARITHMETIC OPERATION	H (5)	I (4)	N (3)	Z (2)	V (1)	C (0)
Compare Index Reg	CPX	8C	3	3	9C	4	2	AC	6	2	BC	5	3				$X_H - M, X_L - (M+1)$	●	●	①	↕	②	●
Decrement Index Reg	DEX													09	4	1	$X - 1 \rightarrow X$	●	●	↕	↕	●	●
Decrement Stack Pntr	DES													34	4	1	$SP - 1 \rightarrow SP$	●	●	●	●	●	●
Increment Index Reg	INX													08	4	1	$X + 1 \rightarrow X$	●	●	↕	↕	●	●
Increment Stack Pntr	INS													31	4	1	$SP + 1 \rightarrow SP$	●	●	●	●	●	●
Load Index Reg	LDX	CE	3	3	DE	4	2	EE	6	2	FE	5	3				$M \rightarrow X_H, (M+1) \rightarrow X_L$	●	●	③	↕	R	●
Load Stack Pntr	LDS	8E	3	3	9E	4	2	AE	6	2	BE	5	3				$M \rightarrow SP_H, (M+1) \rightarrow SP_L$	●	●	③	↕	R	●
Store Index Reg	STX				DF	5	2	EF	7	2	FF	6	3				$X_H \rightarrow M, X_L \rightarrow (M+1)$	●	●	③	↕	R	●
Store Stack Pntr	STS				9F	5	2	AF	7	2	BF	6	3				$SP_H \rightarrow M, SP_L \rightarrow (M+1)$	●	●	③	↕	R	●
Indx Reg → Stack Pntr	TXS													35	4	1	$X - 1 \rightarrow SP$	●	●	●	●	●	●
Stack Pntr → Indx Reg	TSX													30	4	1	$SP + 1 \rightarrow X$	●	●	●	●	●	●

COND. CODE REG.

① (Bit N) Test: Sign bit of most significant (MS) byte of result = 1?

② (Bit V) Test: 2's complement overflow from subtraction of ms bytes?

③ (Bit N) Test: Result less than zero? (Bit 15 = 1)

83

SOLUTION

In this program it is necessary to read a byte from $1000, write it in $2000, read a byte from $1001, write it in $2001, and so on. Before starting the program, two *pointers*, one for the read addresses and one for the write addresses, must be set up. Let us assume that locations $30 through $33 are unused and set them aside for the pointers. Note that we are dealing with extended addressing, so the pointer requires 2 bytes to hold its 16 bits. The program is shown in Table 4-4.

The program proceeds by loading pointer 1 into X, doing an indexed LOAD, incrementing X, and restoring the incremented pointer. This leaves the data word in the accumulator. It then loads pointer 2 into X, stores the data in its new location, increments X, and restores pointer 2. It then branches back to get the second data word, and so on. Of course, this routine, as written, never ends. Methods used to terminate loops should be used and are discussed in Sections 3-11.3 and 4-7.

This program is complex because it really needed two index registers, one to point to the source of data and one for the destination, but only one index register is available in the **6800.** This resulted in frequent data swapping. More advanced μPs, such as the **6809** and **68HC11,** have two index registers, which greatly simplifies this type of problem.

The index register is often used by programs that are required to perform *code conversions*. Such programs might convert one code to another (ASCII to EBCDIC, for example) or might be used for trigonometric conversions where the sine or cosine of a given angle may be required.

TABLE 4-4 Program for Example 4-7

CODE		MNEMONICS	COMMENTS
CE 1000		LDX #$1000	Load pointer 1
DF 30		STX $30	Store pointer 1
CE 2000		LDX #$2000	Load pointer 2
DF 32		STX $32	Store pointer 2
DE 30	START	LDX $30	Get pointer 1
A6 00		LDAA 0,X	Get data at X into A
08		INX	Update pointer 1
DF 30		STX $30	Store pointer 1
DE 82		LDX $32	Get pointer 2
A7 00		STAA 0,X	Store data in new
table			
08		INX	Update pointer 2
DF 32		STX #$32	Store pointer 2
20 F0		BRA START	Loop back for next byte

EXAMPLE 4-8

If the number in A represents an angle from 0 to 360° in 2° intervals [such that $(01)_{10} = 2°$, $(15)_{10} = (0F)_{16} = 30°$, up to $(179)_{10} = (B3)_{16} = 358°$],* write a program to obtain the sine of the angle to the nearest hundredth.

SOLUTION

To solve this program, a rudimentary sine table must first be written into memory. The base or beginning address is written into X. The sine of any angle can be obtained by going to that location whose address is the sum of the base address plus the angle in A and loading that location with the sine of the corresponding angle. Since 8 bits are available, the values between +127 and −128 can be represented. The numbers +100 and −100 can represent 1.00 and −1.00, and the sine of each angle can be expressed to the nearest 0.01.

To illustrate the use of the table, note that the sine of 60° = 0.866 = 0.87 to the nearest 0.01. If the base address of the table is $500, the 60° value occupies the thirtieth entry, or location $51E. Since the sine is scaled between + 100 and −100, the number 0.87 becomes $(87)_{10} = (57)_{16}$. Therefore, the contents of location $51E must be $(57)_{16}$. The table in memory is illustrated in Fig. 4-6.

Once the sine table is in memory, a program for taking an angle in A and producing its sine in B can be written as follows:

ADDR	CODE		MNEMONIC	COMMENTS
C000	CE 04 FF		LDX #$04FF	Place pointer to table in X
C003	08	LOOP	INX	Increment index register
C004	80 01		SUBA #1	Decrement angle in A
C006	24 F8		BCC LOOP	Branch if carry clear to LOOP
C008	E6 00		LDAB 0,X	Load B from address in X (+0)

This program uses a common technique of searching a table by incrementing X while simultaneously decrementing the value in A. Numbers larger than $7F in A will use bit 7 and thus we cannot use a conditional branch decision that depends on the negative bit. We must carry the bit (i.e., BRANCH IF CARRY CLEAR). In this type of program, DECA is usually used, but it does not set the carry bit, and therefore our program must use a SUBA #1 instruction instead.

*Two-degree intervals were used so that all angles from 0 to 360° degrees could be represented within a single byte.

Memory address	Memory data	
500	00	sine of 0°
501	04	sine of 2°
502	07	sine of 4°
503	0A	sine of 6°
•	•	
•	•	
•	•	
50F	32	sine of 30° = 0.5 = 50 = $(32)_{16}$

Figure 4-6 Sine table in memory.

To illustrate further, if the sine of 210° is required, A must contain $(105)_{10} = (69)_{16}$. Location \$0569 should contain $(-0.5) = -50$ (on our scale) $= (-32)_{16} = CE$. The program then loads the contents of \$0569, or CE, into B.

Modifications and improvements to the foregoing program are certainly possible. One obvious possibility is to limit the angle to 90° or less, which could improve the resolution. This example was presented primarily to show how tables can be constructed and used in a **6800** μP.

4-5.5 ▼ Implied Addressing

Implied instructions are used when *all* the information required for the instruction is already within the CPU and *no external operands* from memory or from the program (in the case of immediate instructions) are needed. Since no memory references are needed, implied instructions only require 1 byte for their op code. Examples of implied instructions that affect the accumulators are CLEAR, INCREMENT, DECREMENT, SHIFT, ROTATE, ADD, and SUBTRACT.

EXAMPLE 4-9

What does the following instruction do?

SBA

SOLUTION

This is a 1-byte instruction. SBA is the mnemonic for SUBTRACT ACCUMULATORS. Table 4-2 shows that the operation is (A)-(B) → (A). Thus the number in accumulator B is subtracted from accumulator A and the results are stored in A. At the end of the instruction, A contains the result (difference), while B contains the original subtrahend and its value is unchanged.

4-6 ▼ CONDITION CODES

The **6800** uses six *condition codes* (also called *status bits*). They are labeled H, I, N, Z, V, and C. These bits reside in the Condition Code Register (CCR). As shown in Fig. 4-1, the 1s in the two MSBs of the CCR are merely to fill it out to 8 bits.

The function of most of the condition codes is to retain information about the *results of the last arithmetic or memory operation* for use by the conditional branch instructions. This is how the computer makes its decisions, and the programmer must select the proper conditional branch instruction to get the desired results. The effect of an instruction on each condition code is shown in the six rightmost columns of Table 4-2. Two symbols dominate this part of the table; the dot (·) means that the instruction does not affect the condition codes, and the ↕ symbol indicates that the condition code is SET or CLEARED as a result of the instruction execution.

The I condition code bit is set or cleared to enable the μP to be *interrupted*. Its action is discussed in Chapter 9. None of the accumulator and memory instructions affect the I bit, but CLI and SEI will clear or set it.

4-6.1 ▼ Z Bit

The Z (for zero) bit in the CCR is SET whenever an instruction results in a 0 being entered into the destination register or memory location. The Boolean algebra equation for the Z bit is

$$Z = \overline{R_7}\,\overline{R_6}\,\overline{R_5}\,\overline{R_4}\,\overline{R_3}\,\overline{R_2}\,\overline{R_1}\,\overline{R_0}$$

which means that Z is 1 only if all 8 bits of the result are 0.

The major function of the *compare instruction* is simply to set the Z bit. Compare instructions internally subtract an operand from an accumulator but *do not* change the contents of either. They simply change the bits of the CCR. A μP can determine if two operands are equal by comparing them. If the Z bit is SET after execution of the compare instruction, it indicates that the two operands are indeed equal. This information is often used by branch instructions (see Section 4-7).

4-6.2 ▼ C Bit

The C or carry bit in the CCR is mainly set in one of four ways.

  1. It is SET during *add instructions* when the result of the addition produces a *carry* output.
  2. For subtraction and comparison instructions, it is SET when the absolute value of the subtrahend is larger than the absolute value of the minuend. Generally, this implies a borrow.
  3. It is changed when executing SHIFT and ROTATE instructions. For these instructions the bit shifted out of the accumulator becomes the carry bit and is not lost.
  4. It is SET when an SEC instruction is executed.

Some other instructions, such as CLEAR and TEST, affect the carry bit. The careful programmer should consult the notes attached to Table 4-2 when there is any doubt about how an instruction affects the carry bit.

Two instructions, ADD WITH CARRY and SUBTRACT WITH CARRY, use the carry bit as part of the instruction. This simplifies the addition or subtraction of numbers that are longer than 8 bits. If, for example, the least significant bytes are added and produce a carry output, an ADC (add with carry) instruction is used to add the more significant bytes and also adds 1 if the sum of the least significant bytes produced a carry output.

> **NOTE:** For a proper understanding of the actions of the Condition Codes (or any program instruction) it has been found desirable to use some type of test system. These can vary from a simple **6800** system with a Monitor ROM such as MINIBUG3 (now obsolete) to a μP Development System (MDS), as described in Chapter 11. It is recommended that a practical solution is to use the Motorola EVBU or EVB evaluation modules described in Section 11-5. All these systems, as a minimum, provide a way to write the program into memory and to step through it, an instruction at a time, while observing the resultant changes in the registers.
>
> If one of the EVBs is available to the student, it is recommended that time be taken to study the sections in Chapter 11 that describe these evaluation tools. It will help immensely to understand the material if the EVB is used as we suggest from here on.

EXAMPLE 4-10

The 16-bit number in memory locations $22 and $23 is to be subtracted from the 16-bit number in $20 and $21. The result is to be stored in $24 and $25. Assume that location $20 contains the MS byte of the minuend and $22 contains the MS byte of the subtrahend.

(a) Write a program to subtract the numbers.

(b) Show how the program operates if the minuend is +4 and the subtrahend is –5.

SOLUTION

(a) The program is shown in Fig. 4-7a. First, the least significant bits (LSBs) or LS byte, of the minuend must be loaded into an accumulator; then the LS byte of the subtrahend is subtracted. *This may produce a borrow even if the final result is a positive number.* The result is stored and the MSBs of the minuend are loaded into an accumulator. The MSBs of the subtrahend are then subtracted from the accumulator, *with carry*, so that if a borrow had set the carry bit to 1, it is now subtracted from the more significant result.

(b) To check this problem the machine language was written into the memory of a **68HC11EVB** evaluation system (see Section 11-5) equipped with a BUFFALO monitor program. The data was written into locations $20 through $25, which are not used by BUFFALO.

After the program has been entered in memory, starting at $C000 (using the ASM command) and is listed, it appears as shown in Fig. 4-7a. The data have been entered, starting at $20 as shown at the top of Fig. 4-7b. Note that –5 is entered in its 2s-complement form (FFFB).

We start the evaluation by using the RM command to preset the register display and using the MM command to verify the data as shown in the top lines of Fig. 4-7b. The space bar is used after the first byte is displayed to increment to the following locations, as described in Section 11-6.3. The T (trace) command is then entered and BUFFALO displays the op code of the instruction just executed and the contents of all the registers as shown on the next two lines of Fig. 4-7b.

An ASCII display has been added at the end of each register line as an interpretation of the Condition Codes (or C register). If a codes status is 0, a period is displayed, and if it is SET, the code letter is displayed. Note that the two MSBs of the CCR are always 1. Using this ASCII representation, the status of each flag can easily be determined. For example, if the C register contained $FF, the display would be 11HINZVC, meaning that all bits are set. In the first register line of Fig. 4-7b, all the condition codes, including Carry, are 0s at this point.

The first step of the debugger program executes the 96 op code and it loads the Least Significant byte (04) from 21 into accumulator A as shown in the first register line of Fig. 4-7b. It also increments the PC to $C002. The Condition Codes are not changed because the N bit is already clear. The data movement is shown pictorially in Fig. 4-7c. The second step subtracts the contents of 23, which is the LS byte of the subtrahend. The result (09) is left in accumulator A. This can produce a borrow, as in this case, and if the C1 in the C register is translated, as shown by the ASCII display, it will be seen that the Carry bit is SET. Step 3 stores the contents of A into location $25 (LS byte of the result). This cannot be seen unless the MM command is used to display this memory location, as shown. The Most Significant byte (MS byte) of the Minuend is loaded into accumulator A (setting the Z bit), and the MS byte of the subtrahend is then subtracted as shown in steps 4 and 5, but this time the carry is included. Step 5 subtracts FF from 00, which is the same as subtracting −1 from 0 and will give +1. This is a subtract with carry (borrow), however, and since the carry bit is SET, a 1 is subtracted from the result. Thus the MS byte of the final result is 00 and the entire result is 0009, which is correct. The action of this example is seen more clearly if the bytes are placed in proper order, as shown in Fig. 4-7d. Note that the carry bit is also SET at the end of the fifth instruction, but this has no effect on this problem. This program works because the carry bit that is SET in step 2 is not affected by the STAA and LDAA instructions (instructions 3 and 4), so it can be used in instruction 5.

As the program progresses it is instructive to follow the Condition Codes, especially the C and Z flags, which are important here. At the beginning the CCR contains C0, indicating that both C and Z are 0. The first subtraction SETs C, which changes the CCR to C1. The load of the contents of 20, which contains 00, SETs Z, and changes the CCR to C5.

4-6.3 ▼ N Bit

The N (negative) bit of the CCR is SET whenever the results of an operation are negative; that is, the N bit is SET whenever the MSB of the result is a 1 (an MSB of 1 indicates a negative number in 2s-complement arithmetic). The Boolean equation for the N bit is $N = R_7$. Note that all accumulator and memory instructions except PSH and PUL affect the N bit.

STEP	ADDR	OBJECT	MNEMONICS	COMMENTS
1	C000	96 21	LDAA $21	Load LS byte of minuend into A
2	C002	90 23	SUBA $23	Subtract [23] from A
3	C004	97 25	STAA $25	Store result in 25
4	C006	96 20	LDAA $Z0	Load MS byte of minuend into A
5	C008	92 22	SBCA $22	Subtract [22] from A w/ borrow
6	C00A	97 24	STAA $24	Store MS byte of result

(a) Subtraction Program Listing

```
P-C000 Y-FFFF X-FFFF A-FF B-FF C-C0 S-C100
>mm 20

0020 00 04 FF FB FF FF
>t

Op- 96
P-C002 Y-FFFF X-FFFF A-04 B-FF C-C0 S-C100 11......
>

Op- 90
P-C004 Y-FFFF X-FFFF A-FF B-09 C-Cl S-C100 11.....C
>

Op- 97
P-C006 Y-FFFF X-FFFF A-09 B-FF C-C1 S-C100 11.....C
>mm 25

0025 09
>t

Op- 96
P-C008 Y-FFFF X-FFFF A-00 B-FF C-C5 S-C100 11...Z.C
>

Op- 92
P-C00A Y-FFFF X-FFFF A-00 B-FF C-C5 S-C100 11...Z.C
>

Op- 97
P-C00C Y-FFFF X-FFFF A-00 B-FF C-C5 S-C100 11...Z.C
>mm 20
```

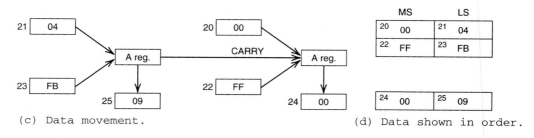

(c) Data movement.

(d) Data shown in order.

Figure 4-7 Subtraction Program for Example 4-10.

EXAMPLE 4-11

The numbers $03A4 and $123F are in locations $20, $21, $22, and $23, respectively.

(a) Write a program to add them and store the results in $24 and $25.
(b) What instructions in the program set the N bit?

SOLUTION

(a) The program is shown in Fig. 4-8a. First the LS bytes are added and the result stored. Then the MS bytes are added (with carry) and stored.

(b) The object program was loaded into memory using the BUFFALO debug program that is provided with the **68HC11EVB** Evaluation Board, as described in Example 4-10, and was executed a step at a time, as shown in Fig. 4-8b. Again the ASCII display of the CCR is shown at the end of each register display line of Fig. 4-8b and shows the state of the condition codes (Register C) for each register line of Fig. 4-8b. The data movement is also shown in Fig. 4-8c. Figure 4-8d shows these data locations in proper order. These four figures show the following:

1. The N bit is set by the first instruction because a negative number ($A4) is loaded into A.
2. The second step adds the $3F from $23. The result in A is seen to be $E3, which also SETs the N bit because bit 7 of that byte is a 1.
3. The result is stored in step 3. The N bit remains SET.
4. The fourth step CLEARs the N bit because a positive number is loaded into A.
5. The N bit remains CLEAR during the fifth and sixth steps because the sum (in A) is a positive number.

Note that the N bit was SET by the first addition. Since this is an intermediate step in the summation, however, the N bit has no significance. At the end of the addition, the N bit is CLEAR, indicating a positive result. Note also that the carry bit was never SET by the numbers used in this program. If it had been SET initially, it would have been cleared by the first addition (instruction 2).

4-6.4 ▼ V Bit

The V or overflow bit is SET when an arithmetic operation results in a *2s-complement* overflow or underflow. In this case the sign bit is involved and thus only 7 bits remain to express the magnitude of the number. **Overflow** occurs when the result of an arithmetic operation produces a number *larger* than the register can accommodate (i.e., $>127_{10}$), and thus the sign bit is affected. **Underflow** occurs when the result produces a

STEP	ADDR	OBJECT	MNEMONIC	COMMENTS
1	C000	96 21	LDAA $21	Load LS byte of Augend
2	C002	9B 23	ADDA $23	Add LS byte of Addend
3	C004	97 25	STAA $25	Store result in 25
4	C006	96 20	LDAA $20	Load MS byte of Augend in A
5	C008	99 22	ADCA $22	Add W/C MS byte of Addend
6	C00A	97 24	STAA $24	Store MS byte of result

(a)   Addition Program Listing

```
P-C000 Y-FFFF X-FFFF A-15 B-FF C-C0 S-C100
>mm 20

0020 03 A4 12 3F 00 00
>t

Op- 96
P-C002 Y-FFFF X-FFFF A-A4 B-FF C-C8 S-C100 11..N...
>

Op- 9B
P-C004 Y-FFFF X-FFFF A-E3 B-FF C-E8 S-C100 11H.N...
>

Op- 97
P-C006 Y-FFFF X-FFFF A-E3 B-FF C-E8 S-C100 11H.N...
>mm 25

0025 E3
>t

Op- 96
P-C008 Y-FFFF X-FFFF A-03 B-FF C-E0 S-C100 11H.....
>

Op- 99
P-C00A Y-FFFF X-FFFF A-15 B-FF C-C0 S-C100 11......
>

Op- 97
P-C00C Y-FFFF X-FFFF A-15 B-FF C-C0 S-C100 11......
>mm 20

0020 03 A4 12 3F 15 E3
>
```

(b) Execution by steps using EVB

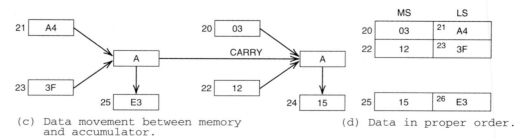

(c) Data movement between memory
    and accumulator.

(d) Data in proper order.

Figure 4-8   Program analysis for Example 4-11

number *more negative* than the register can accommodate (less than −128); this also affects the sign bit.

The limitations on the numbers that can be handled by an *n*-bit register are $2^{n-1}-1$ positive numbers, and 2^{n-1} negative numbers. A single 8-bit byte is thus restricted to numbers between $+127_{10}$ and -128_{10}.

To illustrate overflow, consider the number 100_{10} expressed as an 8-bit binary number, 01100100_2. If an attempt is made to add 100_{10} plus 100_{10}, the result is 200_{10} (11001000_2). Unfortunately, considered as a 2s-complement number, it equals −56. This ridiculous result occurred because the answer, $+200_{10}$, was *beyond the range* of numbers that could be handled by a single byte ($+200_{10}$ is greater than $+127_{10}$).

There are two criteria for overflow and underflow in the **6800**.

1. For *addition* instructions the basic Boolean equation for overflow is

$$V = \overline{A_7}\,\overline{B_7}\,R_7 + A_7\,B_7\,\overline{R_7} \tag{1}$$

where it is assumed that the operation is A plus B → R and A_7 is the MSB of A (the augend), B_7 is the MSB of B (the addend), and R_7 is the MSB of the result. The plus sign in the equation indicates the logical OR.

If the first term of the equation is 1, it indicates that two positive numbers have been added (because A_7 and B_7 are both 0) and the result is negative (because $R_7 =$ 1). This possibility has been illustrated in the preceding paragraph. The second term indicates that two negative numbers have been added and have produced a positive result.

EXAMPLE 4-12

Show how the hex numbers $80 and $C0 are added.

SOLUTION

$80 + $C0 = $40 plus a carry (see Section 2-8.3). Note that 80 and C0 are both negative numbers, but their sum (as contained in a single byte) is positive. This corresponds to the second term of equation (1). Fortunately, this addition sets the V bit to warn the user that overflow (in this case underflow) has occurred.

---

2. For subtraction operations, the Boolean equation is

$$V = A_7\,\overline{B_7}\,\overline{R_7} + \overline{A_7}\,B_7\,R_7 \tag{2}$$

The assumption here is that A − B → R. The first term indicates that a positive number has been subtracted from a negative number and produced a positive result. The second term indicates that a negative number has been subtracted from a positive number and produced negative result. In either case, the overflow bit is set to warn the user.

EXAMPLE 4-13

If the numbers \$23C4 and \$FDAB are added by the program of Example 4-11, what flags are set after the:

(a) LS bytes are added?
(b) MS bytes are added?

SOLUTION

(a) First the μP adds the least significant bytes, C4 and AB, to obtain \$6F. This addition sets the C and V bits. The V bit is set because two negative numbers were added and the result, \$6F, is positive. This positive result also clears the N bit.
(b) The next part of the program adds the MS bytes, \$23 and \$FD, and the 1 in the C bit. The result is \$21. The C bit is SET, but both N and V are CLEAR. Because numbers of unlike sign were added, overflow is impossible and V is CLEAR.

The significance of the overflow bit depends on the program. In Example 4-13 the V bit was set after the first addition, but because this was an intermediate step, the V bit could be ignored. After the final addition the V bit was CLEAR, indicating that the result was correct.

4-6.5 ▼ Manipulations of the Condition Code Register

Table 4-5 shows those instructions that affect the CCR.

1. Although the Condition Codes are normally controlled by the ALU, specific instructions exist to SET or CLEAR the C, V, and I bits.

TABLE 4-5   Condition Code Register Instructions

						COND. CODE REG.					
		IMPLIED				5	4	3	2	1	0
OPERATIONS	MNEMONIC	OP	~	=	BOOLEAN OPERATION	H	I	N	Z	V	C
Clear Carry	CLC	0C	2	1	$0 \rightarrow C$	●	●	●	●	●	R
Clear Interrupt Mask	CLI	0E	2	1	$0 \rightarrow I$	●	R	●	●	●	●
Clear Overflow	CLV	0A	2	1	$0 \rightarrow V$	●	●	●	●	R	●
Set Carry	SEC	0D	2	1	$1 \rightarrow C$	●	●	●	●	●	S
Set Interrupt Mask	SEI	0F	2	1	$1 \rightarrow I$	●	S	●	●	●	●
Set Overflow	SEV	0B	2	1	$1 \rightarrow V$	●	●	●	●	S	●
Acmltr A → CCR	TAP	06	2	1	$A \rightarrow CCR$	———————— ① ————————					
CCR → Acmltr A	TPA	07	2	1	$CCR \rightarrow A$	●	●	●	●	●	●

R = Reset
S = Set
● = Not affected
① (ALL) Set according to the contents of Accumulator A.

2. The CCR can be transferred to the A accumulator by a TPA instruction. This would be done if the program had to preserve the present contents of the CCR for future use. The CCR could be transferred to A and then saved in RAM by a STORE A or PUSH A instruction.

3. The contents of accumulator A can be transferred to the CCR by a TAP instruction. This would be done when the contents of the CCR are being restored from memory.

EXAMPLE 4-14

At a point in a program the H, I, and C bits of the CCR should be SET and the N, V, and Z bits should be CLEAR. Write a sequence of instructions to set the bits accordingly.

SOLUTION

According to Fig. 4-1, the CCR should look like this:

$$11110001$$

It can be forced into this configuration by the following instructions:

CODE	MNEMONIC	COMMENTS
86 F1	LDAA #$F1	Load desired contents of CCR into A
06	TAP	Transfer A to CCR

4-7 ▼ BRANCH INSTRUCTIONS

The major use of the condition codes is with CONDITIONAL BRANCH instructions. As explained in Section 3-11, a BRANCH instruction directs the PC to another address.

Table 4-6 is a partial table of the BRANCH instructions used with the **6800** μP. The first instruction, BRA, is an *unconditional* branch. The program always jumps or branches when the BRA (Branch Always) instruction occurs. The remaining instructions are *conditional* branches; they take the branch only if the condition codes are set properly. The table shows that there are conditional branches for the N, V, C, and Z condition codes and gives the op code and condition for each BRANCH instruction. These instructions allow the computer to make the decisions necessary to control the program (see Section 3-11.2).

Each BRANCH instruction is accompanied by an *offset*, a number that is added to the current value of the Program Counter to determine where the μP will go if it branches. Thus BRANCH instructions skip over a part of the program to a location that is *relative* to the program counter. They typically command the PC to "move up 6 locations" or "go back 10 locations."

TABLE 4-6 Partial List of BRANCH Instructions Used with the **6800** μP

Instruction	Mnemonic	Op Code	CC
Branch Always	BRA	20	– – –
Branch if carry SET	BCS	25	C = 1
Branch if carry CLEAR	BCC	24	C = 0
Branch if zero	BEQ	27	Z = 1
Branch if not zero	BNE	26	Z = 0
Branch if minus	BMI	2B	N = 1
Branch if plus	BPL	2A	N = 0
Branch if overflow SET	BVS	29	V = 1
Branch if overflow CLEAR	BVC	28	V = 0

4-7.1 ▼ Calculating Offsets

Branches were originally used in the **6800** and are now used in the same way by many μPs. A BRANCH instruction for the **6800** consists of the BRANCH op code in one byte and an 8-bit offset in the following byte. The offset is a 2s-complement number that is added to the address.

If N is the location of the BRANCH instruction and T is the target address (the address the program will jump to), the following formula can be used to calculate the offset:

$$\text{Offset} = T - (N + 2) \qquad (3)$$

Note that both forward and backward branches can be accommodated. Backward branches have negative offsets. The 2 in the formula indicates where the PC would be if a branch did not take place (i.e., at the start of the next instruction).

EXAMPLE 4-15

The op code of the BRANCH instruction is in $011A. What should the offset be if the program must jump to $0150?

SOLUTION

From Equation (3) we obtain

$$\$011A + 2 = \$011C$$
$$\text{Offset} = \$0150 - \$011C = \$34$$

Thus the program segment would be as follows:

```
011A      XX       (branch op code)
011B      34       (offset)
```

EXAMPLE 4-16

The op code of the BRANCH instruction is in $011A. What should the offset be if the program must jump to $00EA?

SOLUTION

From the formula

$$\$011A + 2 = \$011C$$
$$\text{Offset} = \$00EA - \$011C = \$FFCE$$

For an 8-bit negative offset the $FF is discarded and the program is as follows:

```
011A     XX     (branch op code)
011B     CE     (offset)
```

Note that the offset is a negative number ($CE) and the program branches backward from $11C to $EA.

EXAMPLE 4-17

(a) If the offset for the BRANCH instruction in $011A is $39, where will the program branch to?

(b) Repeat if the offset is $93.

SOLUTION

(a) Formula (3) can be transposed to read

$$T = (N + 2) + \text{offset}$$

Because the op code is in $011A, $N + 2 = \$011C$. Therefore, $T = \$011C + \$39 = \$0155$.

(b) The procedure can be repeated but $93 is a negative offset. Negative 8-bit offsets should be preceded by $FF to convert them to 16-bit numbers.

$$T = \$011C + \$FF93 = \$00AF$$

In this case the program will branch backward to $AF.

4-7.2 ▼ Long and Short Branches

The maximum positive number that can be represented in one byte is $7F_{16}$ (or 127_{10}), and the most negative number is 80_{16} (or -128_{10}). Thus the program can branch forward no more than 127 bytes or backward no more than 128 bytes from where it would be if it did not branch (i.e., the start of the next instruction). This range is often sufficient since the destination of most branches is usually nearby. This is a constraint as the programs become larger. In the **6800,** branches to more remote locations must use jumps (see Section 5-3).

Some newer 8-bit µPs, such as the **6809,** and all the 16-bit µPs permit long branches by allowing the use of a 16-bit offset. This allows the programmer to branch to any location within a 64 K-byte memory.

4-8 ▼ BCD ADDITION AND THE H BIT

Although programmers and readers of this book can use hex fluently, most people prefer to communicate with their computers using ordinary *decimal numbers*. Normal input devices such as CRT terminals or hand calculator keyboards have keys only for the numbers 0 through 9. The outputs, whether displayed on a terminal, printed on paper, or shown on a seven-segment calculator display, are usually in decimal form.

In applications that deal with money, such as cash registers, it is preferable to keep the numbers in decimal form rather than converting them to binary or hex. The use of the H bit of the CCR and the DAA (Decimal Adjust Accumulator) instruction makes decimal arithmetic possible.

TABLE 4-7 BCD Code Conversions

DECIMAL DIGIT	BINARY-CODED DECIMAL (BCD) REPRESENTATION
0	0000
1	0001
2	0010
3	0011
4	0100
5	0101
6	0110
7	0111
8	1000
9	1001
X	1010
X	1011
X	1100
X	1101
X	1110
X	1111

4-8.1 ▼ Expressing Numbers in BCD*

Decimal numbers are usually entered into a computer in BCD (binary-coded decimal) form. The BCD code uses 4 binary bits called a *decade* to represent a single decimal digit (0 to 9). Since numbers greater than 9 are *not* used, the numbers from 10 to 15, which are also possible with 4-bit representation, should *never* appear in a BCD output. The BCD code conversion table is shown in Table 4-7. When a number consisting of several decimal digits is to be represented in BCD form, each digit is represented by its own group of 4 bits. Therefore, there are four times as many bits in the representation as there are decimal digits in the original number.

EXAMPLE 4-18

Express the decimal number 6309_{10} in BCD form.

SOLUTION

From the code conversion table, we find that

$$6 = 0110$$
$$3 = 0011$$
$$0 = 0000$$
$$9 = 1001$$

The number 6309 is expressed by stringing these bits together:

$$(6309_{10}) = \underbrace{0110}_{6}\ \underbrace{0011}_{3}\ \underbrace{0000}_{0}\ \underbrace{1001}_{9}$$

Numbers given in BCD form can be converted into decimal numbers simply by dividing them into 4-bit decades, starting at the least significant bit, and assigning the correct decimal digit to each decade.

EXAMPLE 4-19

Find the decimal equivalent of the BCD number.

$$0001\,0101\,1000\,0111\,0100$$

---

*Readers familiar with BCD may omit this section.

SOLUTION

The given number is divided into groups of 4 bits each and the decimal digit for each decade is identified.

$$0001 \; 0101 \; 1000 \; 0111 \; 0100$$
$$1 \quad 5 \quad 8 \quad 7 \quad 4$$

The decimal equivalent of the BCD number is **15,874.**

4-8.2 ▼ Adding BCD Numbers

Since each **6800** memory location contains 8 bits and each BCD decade contains 4 bits, it is natural to store two BCD digits in a single memory location. This is sometimes called *packing*, or *packed BCD*, and is a function of the input/output routine.

Addition and subtraction of BCD numbers is possible, but since all addition and subtraction instructions in the **6800** assume *binary* numbers, the *binary results must be manipulated to convert them to BCD*. This is done by using the H bit and the DDA instruction.

Table 4-2 shows that the H bit is changed only by addition instructions. *It is SET when the addition produces a carry out of bit position 3 and into bit position 4*. For BCD numbers the H bit is SET whenever the sum of the two digits, plus carry, is equal to or greater than $(16)_{10}$. Because this carry occurs midway through the byte, the H bit is sometimes called the *half-carry* bit.

EXAMPLE 4-20

Accumulators A and B contain the decimal numbers 48 and 79, respectively. They are added by an ADD accumulator (ABA) instruction. What is the result, and what are the conditions of the C and H bits after the addition?

SOLUTION

The **6800** adds 48 and 79 as though they were hex digits, placing the sum, C1, in accumulator A. The results of entering these values into an EVB system and executing the instruction are shown in Fig. 4-9. At the end of the addition the H bit is SET (because the sum of 8 and 9 produces a carry), but the carry bit is CLEAR because the sum of the two most significant digits is less than 16.

```
P-C000 Y-FFFF X-FFFF A-48 B-79 C-D0 S-004A

>mm c000

C000 1B
>t

Op- 1B
P-C001 Y-FFFF X-FFFF A-C1 B-79 C-EA S-004A 11H.N.V.
>_
```

Figure 4-9   EVB Screen Display for Example 4-20

4-8.3 ▼ DAA Instruction

The result of Example 4-20 (48 + 79 = C1) is unsatisfactory if decimal arithmetic is being used. This instruction must be followed by a *decimal adjust accumulator* (DAA) instruction to convert the hex result to the correct BCD result.

The DAA instruction modifies an answer as shown in Table 4-8. It examines four parts of the result.

1. The lower half-byte
2. The upper half-byte
3. The H bit
4. The C bit

It then adds 00, 06, 60, or 66 to the answer. This transforms the result to BCD.

TABLE 4-8 Action of the DAA Instruction

State of C Bit Before DAA	Upper Half-Byte (Bits 4-7)	Initial Half-Carry H Bit	Lower Half-Byte (Bits 0-3)	Number Added by DAA	State of C Bit After DAA
0	0-9	0	0-9	00	0
0	0-8	0	A-F	06	0
0	0-9	1	0-3	06	0
0	A-F	0	0-9	60	1
0	9-F	0	A-F	66	1
0	A-F	1	0-3	66	1
1	0-2	0	0-9	60	1
1	0-2	0	A-F	66	1
1	0-3	1	0-3	66	1

EXAMPLE 4-21

What happens if a DAA instruction is added to Example 4-20?

SOLUTION

In Example 4-20, the sum was C1. The DAA notes that:

1. The lower half-byte is 0–3.
2. The H bit is SET.
3. The upper half-byte is A–F.
4. The C bit is CLEAR.

These conditions occur on line 6 of Table 4-8. The table shows that the DAA adds 66 to the result and SETs the C bit. After the DAA, A contains C1 + 66 = 27 and the carry bit is SET, which indicates a carry (a weight of 100 in decimal arithmetic). Therefore, the BCD sum is 127, which is correct. The progress of the program is illustrated in Fig. 4-10.

EXAMPLE 4-22

The decimal numbers 2946 and 4957 are in locations $20, $21 and $22, $23, respectively. Write a program to add them and store the BCD result in locations $24 and $25.

SOLUTION

The program and its analysis are shown in Fig. 4-11. Figure 4-11b is the result of executing one instruction at a time with the debug program BUF-FALO of the EVB evaluation system (see step b of the solution to Example 4-10.) As in Example 4-10, the ASCII display of the CCR follows each register display line for each step. The first addition SETs the N and V bits. These bits are both RESET and the carry is SET by the DAA instruction. The last instruction shows how the two adjacent bytes containing the answer can be fetched as a 16-bit or four decimal-digit number for further manipulation by the program. The result in the X register is the correct answer.

4-8.4 ▼ Subtracting BCD Numbers

BCD subtraction in the **6800** μP can be accomplished by complementation. *Subtraction by complementation,* a method of performing subtraction by addition, works well for decimal numbers. In subtraction by complementation, the subtrahend must be replaced by its

```
P-C000   Y-FFFF   X-FFFF   A-48   B-79   C-C0 S-004A
>mm c000

C000 1B
C001 19
>t

Op- 1B
P-C001 Y-FFFF X-FFFF A-C1 B-79 C-EA S-004A 11H.N.V.
>t

Op- 19
P-C002 Y-FFFF X-FFFF A-27 B-79 C-E1 S-004A 11H....C
>
```

Figure 4-10 Program execution using EVB for Example 4-21.

9s complement, which is obtained by taking each decimal digit and replacing it with the difference between itself and 9. The 9s complement of 2, for example, is 7, and the 9s complement of 0 is 9.

EXAMPLE 4-23

Find the 9s complement of the decimal number 399704.

SOLUTION

The 9s complement is obtained by replacing each digit with its 9s complement as shown:

$$399704 \quad \text{(original number)}$$
$$600295 \quad \text{(9s complement)}$$

Note that each digit plus its 9s complement adds to 9.

Decimal subtraction can be performed by using the following procedure:

1. Take the 9s complement of the subtrahend and add it to the minuend.
2. Remove the most significant 1 and add it to the least significant digit. This is known as an *end-around-carry*.

Step	Addr	Object	Mnemonics	Comments
1	C000	96 21	LDA $21	Load LS byte of Augend
2	C002	9B 23	LDDA $23	Add LS byte of Addend
3	C004	19	DAA	Adjust for half carry, if any
4	C005	97 25	STAA $25	Store results in 25
5	C007	96 20	LDAA $20	Load MS byte of Augend in A
6	C009	99 22	ADCA $22	Add W~C MS byte of Addend
7	C00B	19	DAA	Adjust result
8	C00C	97 24	STAA $24	Store MS byte
9	C00E	DE 24	LDX $24	Load 16-bit answer into X

(a)   BCD Addition Program Listing

```
P-C000   Y-FFFF   X-FFFF   A-FF   B-FF   C-C0   S-004A
>mm 20

0020 29   46   49   57   FF   FF
>t

OP- 96
P-C002 Y-FFFF X-FFFF A-46 B-FF C-C0 S-004A 11......
>

Op- 9B
P-C004 Y-FFFF X-FFFF A-9D B-FF C-CA S-004A 11..N.V.
>

Op- 19
P-C005 Y-FFFF X-FFFF A-03 B-FF C-C1 S-004A 11.....C
>

Op- 97
P-C007 Y-FFFF X-FFFF A-03 B-FF C-C1 S-004A 11.....C
0025 03
>t

Op- 96
P-C009 Y-FFFF X-FFFF A-29 B-FF C-C1 S-004A 11.....C
>

Op- 99
P-C00B Y-FFFF X-FFFF A-73 B-FF C-E0 S-004A 11H.....
>

Op- 19
P-C00C Y-FFFF X-FFFF A-79 B-FF C-E0 S-004A 11H.....
>

Op- 97
P-C00E Y-FFFF X-FFFF A-79 B-FF C-E0 S-004A 11H.....
>mm 20

0020 29   46   49   57   79   03
 >t

Op- DE
P-C010 Y-FFFF X-7903 A-79 B-FF C-E0 S-004A 11H.....
>_
```

(b) Execution by Steps using the EVB

Figure 4-11   Program and results of execution for Example 4-22.

EXAMPLE 4-24

Subtract 19,307 from 28,652.

SOLUTION

The 9s complement of 19,307 is 80,692. Adding this to the minuend, we obtain

(minuend)	28,652	(original number)
(subtrahend)	80,692	(9s complement)
	109,344	

Removing the most significant 1 and adding it to the least significant digit yields

$$109,344$$
$$+\qquad 1 \qquad \text{(end-around carry)}$$
$$\mathbf{9,345}$$

This is the correct result.

In the **6800** the H bit is *not* set by subtraction instructions but BCD subtraction can be accomplished by complementing and adding, because addition sets the H bit (if the digit total exceeds 9). The **6800** can be programmed for BCD subtraction as follows:

1. Load accumulator A with 99.
2. Subtract the subtrahend (to obtain the 9s complement).
3. Add 1 (to make the 10s complement).
4. Add the minuend (BCD addition).
5. Decimal adjust the accumulator.

In this method each digit can be subtracted from 9 without "borrows," and thus binary subtraction instructions can be used.

EXAMPLE 4-25

Subtract 35 from 82 using the method described above. Assume that 82 is in $20 and 35 is in $22.

SOLUTION

The program is shown in Fig. 4-12a and the progress of the program as it is executed in the EVB is shown in Fig. 4-12b. The status of the CCR bits is shown at the end of each register display line as explained in Example 4-10. The correct answer, 47, appears in A at the end of the program. Some adjustments are required in the program if multiple byte subtraction or the possibility of negative results are to be allowed.

ADDR	OBJECT	MNEMONICS		COMMENTS
C000	86 99	LDAA	#$99	Make 9s Complement
C002	90 22	SUBA	$22	Get Subtrahend
C004	4C	INCA		Make 10s Complement
C005	9B 20	ADDA	$20	Add other number
C007	19	DAA		Decimal Adjust

(a) Program Listing

```
P-C000   Y-FFFF   X-FFFF   A-FF   B-FF   C-C0   S-004A
>mm 20

0020 82
0021 FF
0022 35
>t

Op- 86
P-C002 Y-FFFF X-FFFF A-99 B-FF C-C8 S-004A 11..N...
>

Op- 90
P-C004 Y-FFFF X-FFFF A-64 B-FF C-C2 S-004A 11....V.
>

Op- 4C
P-C005 Y-FFFF X-FFFF A-65 B-FF C-C0 S-004A 11......
>

Op- 9B
P-C007 Y-FFFF X-FFFF A-E7 B-FF C-C8 S-004A 11..N...
>

Op- 19
P-C008 Y-FFFF X-FFFF A-47 B-FF C-C1 S-004A 11.....C
>
```

(b) Execution by steps using EVB

Figure 4-12 Program and step execution for Example 4-25.

4-9 ▼ SHIFT AND ROTATE INSTRUCTIONS

Microprocessors can perform a variety of SHIFT and ROTATE instructions. Minicomputers and mainframes have a minor advantage over 8-bit μCs because they can command a multiple shift in a single instruction. For example, it only takes one instruction in a mainframe to shift a register or accumulator 4 bits, whereas it would take four instructions in an 8-bit μP. This advantage does not exist for 16- or 32-bit μCs, however, since they also have multibit shifts (see Chapter 10).

4-9.1 ▼ Shift Operation

The ALU used in the **6800** performs shift and rotate operations. The ASL (Arithmetic Shift Left), ASR (Arithmetic Shift Right), and LSR (Logical Shift Right) instructions are shown in Fig. 4-13. Note that the Carry bit that is part of the CCR (see Section 4-6.2) is

Bit positions

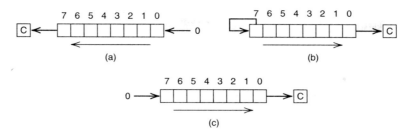

Figure 4-13 6800 shift instructions: (a) arithmetic shift left (ASL);
(b) arithmetic shift right (ASR); (c) logical shift right.

used in the shift operations. In the ASL operation, the MSB is shifted out of the data word and into the Carry bit. The LSB is filled with a 0.

The ASR operation shifts each bit to the right and moves the LSB into the Carry bit. The MSB, however, is retained and also shifted into bit 6. If the bits in the register are considered as a 2s-complement number, this method of shifting *preserves the sign of the number*. The ASR is equivalent to dividing the number in the register by 2, regardless of the sign of the number.

The LSR operation simply shifts each bit one position to the right. The MSB becomes a 0 and the LSB goes into the Carry bit.

EXAMPLE 4-26

An 8-bit word contains the bit pattern 10011010 (hexadecimal 9A).

(a) What is the contents of the word after two shifts to the right (ASR, ASR)?
(b) What is its contents after three arithmetic shifts to the left (ASL, ASL, ASL)?
(c) What is its contents after two logic shifts to the right (LSR, LSR)?

SOLUTION

(a) Here every bit is moved two places to the right, except bit 7. Since the rightmost bits are shifted through the carry register, bit 0 is lost and bit 1 becomes the carry bit. After execution of these two instructions, the word is

11100110

Note that bits 7, 6, and 5 are 1s because bit 7 was originally 1.

(b) The bits are shifted three positions to the left and the two most significant bits are lost. Since bit 5 was 0, the carry is now 0. The least significant bit positions are filled with 0s; the word is now

11010000

(c) After two LSRs the word becomes

$$00100110$$

and the carry is a 1. Note that 0s are shifted into the MSBs in an LSR.

EXAMPLE 4-27

(a) If the number in an accumulator is 50_{10}, show that an ASR is equivalent to a division by 2.

(b) Repeat for -50_{10}.

SOLUTION

(a) Since $+50 = 00110010$, an ASR causes the accumulator to become 00011001, or $+25$.

(b) Since $-50 = 11001110$, an ASR causes the accumulator to become 11100111, or -25. Again, division by 2 has occurred. This would not have been so if a 0 had been shifted into bit 7 instead of a 1.

4-9.2 ▼ Rotations

Two additional shifting instructions are ROL (rotate left) and ROR (rotate right), shown in Fig. 4-14. These are special forms of circular shifting where the bits coming off one end of the word are inserted into the carry bit, while the contents of the Carry bit are transferred into the vacated bit position.

(a) Rotate left (ROL)   (b) Rotate right (ROR)

Figure 4-14   6800 rotate instructions.

EXAMPLE 4-28

If a computer word is 11011100, what is it after the following commands?

(a) Rotate right three times (ROR, ROR, ROR). Assume that the Carry bit is CLEAR.

(b) Rotate left twice (ROL, ROL). Assume that the Carry bit is SET.

SOLUTION

(a) In response to three ROR instructions, the three LSBs are moved through the Carry bit to the other end of the word. The word becomes

00011011

and the Carry bit contains the 1 that was originally in bit 2.

(b) In rotating left twice, the carry now contains the original bit 6 (1) and the 1 that was bit 7 is now the LSB of the word. The result is

01110011

The 1 that was originally in the carry bit has been shifted through bit 0 and appears in bit 1 of the result.

There are many uses for ROTATE instructions. One application is to determine the **parity** of a byte. If the bits of the byte are successively shifted into the carry bit, the number of 1s can be counted and the parity can be determined as an ODD or EVEN number (see Section 8-8).

4-10 ▼ LOGIC INSTRUCTIONS

The **6800** contains AND, OR, and Exclusive OR instructions. They allow the programmer to perform Boolean algebra manipulations on a variable and to SET or CLEAR specific bits in a byte. They can also be used to test specific bits in a byte, but other logic instructions, such as BIT, TEST, or COMPARE, may be more useful for these tests.

Since logic operations are performed on a *bit-by-bit* basis, the C bit has no effect. It is unchanged by all logic operations. The V bit is cleared by logic operations. The N and Z bits are set in accordance with the result.

4-10.1 ▼ Setting and Clearing Specific Bits

AND and OR instructions can be used to SET or CLEAR a specific bit or bits in an accumulator or memory location. This is very useful in systems where each bit has a specific meaning rather than being part of a number. In the control and status registers of the peripheral interface adapter (PIA) or the asynchronous interface adapter (ACIA) (see Chapter 8), for example, each bit has a distinct meaning.

EXAMPLE 4-29

Bit 3 of accumulator A must be SET, while all other bits remain unchanged. How can this be done?

SOLUTION

If A is ORed with 08, which contains a 1 in bit position 3, bit 3 of the result will be SET and all other bits will remain as they were. The instruction ORAA #08 (8A 08) accomplishes this.

EXAMPLE 4-30

Bits 3, 5, and 6 of A are to be cleared while all other bits remain unchanged. How can this be done?

SOLUTION

If A is ANDed with 97, which contains 0s in positions, 3, 5, and 6, these bits of the result are 0 and the rest are unchanged. The instruction 84 97 (AND A #$97) accomplishes this.

4-10.2 ▼ Testing Bits

In addition to being able to SET or CLEAR specific bits in a register, it is also possible to test specific bits to determine whether they are 1 or 0. In the PIA, for example, a 1 in the MSB of the control register indicates that some external event has occurred. The μP can test this bit and react appropriately. Typically, the result of the test sets the Z or N bit. The program then executes a conditional branch and takes one of two different paths depending on the result of the test.

Accumulator bits can be tested by the AND and OR instructions, but this modifies the contents of the accumulator. If the accumulator is to remain unchanged, the BIT TEST instruction is used. This ANDs memory (or an immediate operand) with the accumulator without changing either.

EXAMPLE 4-31

Without changing B, determine whether bit 5 of accumulator B is a 1 or a 0.

SOLUTION

The instruction BIT B #$20 (C5 20) is a BIT TEST immediate. It ANDs the contents of B with 20, since 20 contains a 1 only in the bit 5 position. The result is 00 if bit 5 of B is 0, and 20 if bit 5 of B is 1. The Z bit is CLEARed or SET accordingly and retains the result of this test.

4-10.3 ▼ COMPARE Instructions

A COMPARE instruction essentially subtracts a memory or immediate operand from an accumulator, leaving the *contents of both memory and accumulator unchanged.* The actual results of the subtraction are discarded; the function of the COMPARE is to SET the Condition Code bits.

There are two types of COMPARE instructions: those that involve accumulators and those that use the index register. Effectively, the two numbers that are being compared are subtracted, but neither value is changed. The subtraction serves to SET the condition codes. In the case of the COMPARE accumulator (CMPA or B) instruction, the carry, negative, zero, and overflow bits are affected and allow us to determine whether the operands are equal or which is greater. The **6800** COMPARE INDEX REGISTER (CPX) instruction sets the Z bit properly, but in the **6800,** the N and V bits are often set *incorrectly* and the reader is warned *not* to depend on the N or V after a CPX instruction. This is not true for the **6801** μC described later. These instructions are often used to terminate loops (Section 4-7).

EXAMPLE 4-32

Determine if the contents of location $CB are equal to the number $F2.

SOLUTION

One program that does this is

```
C6 F2        LDAB #$F2        Load B Immediate
D1 CB        CMPB $CB         Compare B Direct
```

The first instruction loads $F2 into B. The second instruction compares the contents of B ($F2) with the contents of $CB. The Z bit is SET if they are equal, since the result of the subtraction is 0.

EXAMPLE 4-33

Determine if the contents of $80C0 are greater than, equal to, or less than $2A.

SOLUTION

A program that does this is

```
86 2A        LDAA #$2A        Load B Immediate
B1 80C0      CMPA $80C0       Compare B extended
```

Three possibilities exist:

1. $2A is greater than the contents of $80C0. In this case, N = Z = 0 after the compare, indicating that the result is not 0 and not negative.
2. The contents of $80C0 equal $2A. In this case, the Z bit is SET.
3. The contents of $80C0 are greater than $2A. Here the subtraction gives a negative result and N is set.

4-10.4 ▼ TEST Instruction

The TEST (TST) instruction subtracts 0 from an operand and therefore does not alter the operand. Its effect, like that of compares or bit tests, is to set the N and Z bits. It differs in that it always CLEARs the overflow and carry bits. It is used to set the condition codes in accordance with the contents of an accumulator or memory location.

EXAMPLE 4-34

Determine if the contents of location $F0 are positive, zero, or negative.

SOLUTION

This problem is solved by using the TEST instruction. Since $F0 is below $FF it is generally addressed in direct mode, but this mode is not available with the test instruction (see Table 4-2). We can, however, use extended addressing. The instruction

```
              TST $F0      7D 00F0
```

sets the N and Z bits and allows us to determine the sign of the number in $F0.

4-11 ▼ OTHER 6800 INSTRUCTIONS

The remaining **6800** instructions listed in Table 4-2 are well described by their name and mnemonics.

4-11.1 ▼ CLEAR, INCREMENT, and DECREMENT Instructions

These allow the user to alter the contents of an accumulator or memory location as specified. Those instructions referring to memory locations can be executed in extended or indexed modes only. They are simple to write but require six or seven cycles for execution because the contents of a memory location must be brought to the CPU, modified, and rewritten to memory.

4-11.2 ▼ Accumulator Transfer Instructions

The TAB and TBA instructions allow the transfer of data from A to B and B to A, respectively. These instructions help the user make use of both accumulators, which simplifies the programming of the **6800**.

4-11.3 ▼ COMPLEMENT and NEGATE Instructions

The COMPLEMENT instructions invert all bits of a memory location. They are useful as logic instructions and in programs requiring complementation, such as the BCD subtraction program.

The NEGATE instruction takes the 2s-complement of a number and therefore negates it. The negate instruction works by subtracting the operand from 00. Since the absolute value of the operand is always greater than the minuend, except when the operand itself is 00, the negate instruction SETs the carry flag for all cases, except when the operand is 00.

EXAMPLE 4-35

There is a 16-bit number in $F0 (MS byte) and $F1. Write a program to negate the 16-bit number.

SOLUTION

The general method of negating a number is to complement all the bits and add 1. Alternatively, it can be subtracted from zero as the NEGATE instruction does. The simple solution to this problem, negating both $F0 and $F1, fails because it effectively adds 1 to both bytes (i.e., if $F0 and $F1 contain $C1D2 and both are negated, the result is $3F2E, which is *not* $C1D2). Negating the LS byte and complementing the MS byte works in all cases *except* if the LS byte is 00.

A program that works for all cases is

```
CLRA
NEG    $F1
SBCA   $F0
STAA   $F0
```

The NEGATE instruction produces a carry for all cases except when $F1 contains 00. Now the SBC subtracts out the carry, complementing the MS byte. If $F1 contains 00, there is no carry and the SBC instruction negates the MS byte as required (see Problem 4-26).

4-12 ▼ SUMMARY

In this chapter the accumulator and memory instructions available in the **6800** μP were introduced. Five modes of addressing were discussed and examples using each mode were given.

The function of each bit of the CCR was explained and the way in which instructions CLEAR and SET these bits was discussed. The addition and subtraction instructions were introduced, and examples of multibyte arithmetic using the Carry bit were presented. The effect of the Carry bit in Shift and Rotate instructions was described. Finally, logical instructions and miscellaneous instructions, such as transfers, compares, increments, and decrements, were discussed to complete this introduction to **6800** programming.

4-13 ▼ GLOSSARY

ADD instruction An instruction used to add the contents of two locations. The locations can be either a register or a memory.

Binary-Coded Decimal (BCD) The use of 4 binary bits to represent a single decimal digit (a number from 0 to 9).

Clock cycles The number of transitions of the square-wave clock signal used to synchronize operation of the μP.

Code conversion The process of changing the coding of data from one system to another. For example, to change the alphanumeric characters from the ASCII code to IBM's EBCDIC code.

Compare instruction An instruction used to determine whether two operands are the same or whether one is larger. Instructions are provided for either 8 or 16 operations.

Condition code The status or flag bit in the condition code register that are SET or RESET by the ALU as each instruction is executed.

Condition Code Register (CCR) A register that contains the ALU status bits or condition codes as set by the last instruction executed. They indicate whether the result was zero, negative, and so on. In the **6800** the CCR contains six flags (H, I, N, Z, V, C) and two unused bits (always 1).

Decimal Adjust Accumulator (DAA) An instruction that adjusts a binary addition to make the results appear as BCD.

End-around carry The process of adding the most significant 1 to the least significant digit during subtraction by complementation.

Extended instruction An instruction that includes a full 16-bit address as well as the op code. A 3-byte instruction.

Flags Bits within a μP that retain information about the results of previous operations. Condition codes are also called flags.

Immediate operand The data used by the op code.

Indexed instruction An instruction that uses the contents of the index register plus an offset to calculate the address of the operand.

Index register A sixteen-bit register in the μP. During indexed instructions an offset (sometimes zero) is added to the instruction address specified to obtain the memory address actually used.

Mnemonic An abbreviated form of a word used as an instruction and designed to be easy to remember.

Overflow A result that is too large to be contained in a single 7-bit word or byte.

Parity An error-checking technique where the number of 1s in a 7-bit byte are counted. Depending on whether odd or even parity is to be used, the MSB is made a 1 or a 0.

Program Counter (PC) A sixteen-bit register in the μP used to hold the address of the next instruction to be executed.

Stack Pointer (SP) A sixteen-bit register in the μP used to hold the address pointer to the next available location in the stack area of memory.

Subtraction instruction An instruction to subtract the contents of one location from another.

Underflow A result that is too negative to be contained in a single 7-bit word or byte.

4-14 ▼ REFERENCES

GREENFIELD, JOSEPH, *Practical Digital Design Using ICs*, 3rd ed., Prentice Hall, Englewood Cliffs, N. J., 1994.

LEVANTHAL, LANCE, ***6800** Assembly Language Programming*, Adam Osborn & Associates, Berkeley, Calif., 1978.

MOTOROLA, *6800 Programming Reference Manual*, M68PRM/D, Phoenix, Ariz., first edition, 1976, currently 1984 reprint.

————, *M6800 Microcomputer System Design Data,* Phoenix, Ariz., 1976.

SOUTHERN, BOB, *Programming the 6800 Microprocessor,* Motorola, Phoenix, Ariz., 1977.

4-15 ▼ PROBLEMS

4-1. Why doesn't the instruction set include a STORE IMMEDIATE instruction?

4-2. If A contains $45 initially, what will it contain after the following instructions?

(a) 8A	77	ORA A	#$77	**(f)** 4F	CLR A	
(b) 80	23	SUB A	#$23	**(g)** 43	COM A	
(c) 84	77	AND A	#$77	**(h)** 4A	DEC A	
(d) 8B	77	ADD A	#$77	**(i)** 40	NEG A	
(e) 88	77	EOR A	#$77			

4-3. Assume that each location in memory between $40 and $4F contains three more than its own address (i.e., $40 contains $43, $41 contains $44, etc.). If A contains $21 and the index register contains $20, what does A contain after executing each of the following instructions?

(a) 88   42   EOR A #$42

(b) 9B   42   ADD A $42

(c) AB   23   ADD A $23,X

4-4. How many cycles and bytes do subtract instructions take in each of the following modes?

(a) Immediate mode

(b) Direct mode

(c) Indexed mode

(d) Extended mode

(e) Implied mode

4-5. Show that the instruction 88 FF is equivalent to the instruction 43.

4-6. Show how the program of Example 4-8 operates if the angle is:

(a)   44°

(b)   144°

(c)   244°

(d)   344°

What memory locations are accessed, and what do they contain?

4-7. Write a program to add the 32-bit number in $F3–$F0 to the 24-bit number in $F6–$F4. Place the results in $FF–$FC.

4-8. If the two numbers in Problem 4-7 are F35C2472 and CC8142, show the results in the accumulator and the state of the H, V, Z, N, and C bits after each step in your program.

4-9. Show that 20   00 is a NOP.

4-10. The instruction in locations $012D and $012E is BRA XX. Where will the program branch to if XX equals:

(a) F2?

(b) E5?

(c) 26?

(d) 05?

4-11. The op code of a BRANCH instruction is located in 0110. What offset is needed for the following destinations?

(a) C0

(b) D5

(c) 0153

4-12. Write a program to add the decimal numbers 4972 and 3729. Use BCD arithmetic. Show the status of the accumulator and H, V, N, Z, and C after each instruction.

4-13. Write a program to subtract 016359 from 242214. Use BCD arithmetic. Show the status of the accumulator and H, V, N, Z, and C after each instruction.

4-14. Write a program to SET bits 2, 4, 6, and 7, leaving all other bits unchanged.

4-15. A 16-bit computer contains the following word in its accumulator:

$$1011100111000111$$

What will the accumulator contain after the following instructions?

(a) Shift left 2 bits.

(b) Shift right 4 bits.

(c) Rotate left 5 bits.

(d) Rotate right 3 bits.

4-16. Write a program to add 50 and 75 and then subtract 25. Select memory areas for your data and instructions. Describe the progression of your program and list the contents of each pertinent memory location before and after its execution.

4-17. Write a program to add 25, 35, 45, and 55 then shift the results 2 bits to the right. Explain the significance of your answer.

4-18. Write a program to CLEAR bits 2, 4, 6, and 7, leaving all other bits unchanged.

4-19. Compare the bytes in F0 with F1 to determine if they are equal.

(a) Use the COMPARE instruction.

(b) Use the Exclusive OR (XOR) instruction.

4-20. Test the contents of F3 to determine if bit 4 is a 1.

(a) Use an AND instruction.

(b) Use a BIT TEST instruction.

How do the condition codes indicate whether the bit is a 1 or a 0?

4-21. (a) What does each instruction of the following program do?

```
96 40      C9 00      97 42
D6 41      8B 05      98 43
48         C9 00
```

      (b) If the numbers in 40 and 41 initially are 7E and 23, what numbers appear in 42 and 43 at the end of the program?

4-22. Suppose that Y is an integer ($0 < Y < 10$) in accumulator A and we must calculate $20Y^3 - 10Y^2 + 5$. This is to be done by table lookup rather than making the μP do the calculations. Construct the table and a program to write the correct result into locations D0 and D1.

4-23. When two numbers are added, the result is positive when the N bit and V bit are both CLEAR or both SET. Explain. Give an example of each case using numbers.

4-24. Explain why the N and V bits are SET in Fig. 4-7.

4-25. A 16-bit number is in location F0 (MS byte) and F1. Write a program to shift it 2 bits to the left. Bring 0s into the vacated positions. Ignore the two MSBs.

4-26. Consider the three programs

```
NEG $F1          NEG $F1          CLR A
NEG $F0          COM $F0          NEG $F1
                                  SBC A $F0
                                  STA A $F0
```

What is the result of each program if F0 and F1 contain:

(a) 1357?

(b) 1300?

In which cases do each of these programs correctly negate the number?

After attempting to solve these problems, try to answer the self-evaluation questions in Section 4-2. If any of them still seem difficult, review the appropriate sections of the chapter to find the answers.

5 STACKS, SUBROUTINE, AND OTHER INSTRUCTIONS

5-1 ▼ INSTRUCTIONAL OBJECTIVES

In this chapter we continue the presentation of the **6800** instruction set by introducing the STACK and the BRANCH and JUMP instructions that allow the use of subroutines. After reading this chapter, the student should be able to:

1. Use any BRANCH or JUMP instructions in a program.
2. Compare numbers in signed or absolute form and branch accordingly.
3. Use instructions involving stacks, such as PUSH, PULL, and JUMP to Subroutine.
4. Use indirect jumps.
5. Write programs using subroutines and preserve the contents of the main program's registers during subroutine execution.
6. Write multiply and divide routines.

5-2 ▼ SELF-EVALUATION QUESTIONS

Watch for the answers to the following questions as you read the chapter. They should help you to understand the material presented.

1. Explain why BRANCH instructions are said to be in the relative mode. What are they relative to?
2. What is the difference between a jump and a branch?
3. Why must a JUMP instruction be used when the object of the jump is more than +129 or –126 locations away?
4. What is the difference between a BRANCH Greater Than OR Equal instruction and a BRANCH if Plus instruction?

5. What is the function of the stack pointer (SP) register? Why must it be initialized if it is going to be used?

6. Explain why instructions that write to the stack (i.e., PUSH), decrement the SP, while instructions that read from the stack (i.e., PULL), increment the SP.

7. In a jump or branch to subroutine, how and why are the program counter (PC) contents preserved?

5-3 ▼ BRANCH AND JUMP INSTRUCTIONS

Some of the basic **6800** BRANCH instructions were introduced in Section 4-7. Table 5-1 shows *all* the JUMP and BRANCH instructions available in the **6800** μP. They complete the **6800** instruction set and allow programs requiring *decisions, branches,* and *subroutines* to be written. Table 5-1 also contains several other instructions that will be discussed later. RTS is discussed in Section 5-5.2; RTI, SWI, and WAI are discussed in Chapter 9.

5-3.1 ▼ JUMP Instructions

One of the simplest instructions in Table 5-1 is the **JUMP** instruction. It loads the PC with a new address that causes the program to fetch the next instruction from a location that is not in sequence. The JUMP instruction can be specified in one of two modes, indexed or extended. The JUMP Indexed (JMP 0,X) is a 2-byte instruction; the second byte or *offset* is added to the Index Register and the sum is loaded into the PC.

EXAMPLE 5-1

What does the following program accomplish?

```
LDX   #$5234    CE 5234
JMP   $2D,X     6E   2D
```

SOLUTION

The functioning of the two modes of the JUMP instruction is shown in Fig. 5-1. Figure 5-1a shows the indexed mode. In this example the first instruction, LDX #$5234, is an immediate load and loads $5234 into the Index Register (X). The second instruction is an indexed jump. It adds the second byte, $2D, to the contents of X and loads the sum, $5261, into the PC. Thus the next op code to be executed is in location $5261. If the offset byte had been zero (0,X), the destination of the jump would have been the same as the address in the Index Register.

Extended jumps are 3-byte instructions, where the last 2 bytes are a 16-bit address. Their action is shown in Fig. 5-1b. Since a 16-bit address is available, they allow the program to jump to any location in memory. They are very easily understood because they require no calculations.

TABLE 5-1 Jump and Branch Instructions

OPERATIONS	MNEMONIC	RELATIVE OP	~	#	INDEX OP	~	#	EXTND OP	~	#	IMPLIED OP	~	#	BRANCH TEST	5 H	4 I	3 N	2 Z	1 V	0 C
Branch Always	BRA	20	4	2										None	•	•	•	•	•	•
Branch If Carry Clear	BCC	24	4	2										C = 0	•	•	•	•	•	•
Branch If Carry Set	BCS	25	4	2										C = 1	•	•	•	•	•	•
Branch If = Zero	BEQ	27	4	2										Z = 1	•	•	•	•	•	•
Branch If ≥ Zero	BGE	2C	4	2										$N \oplus V = 0$	•	•	•	•	•	•
Branch If > Zero	BGT	2E	4	2										$Z + (N \oplus V) = 0$	•	•	•	•	•	•
Branch If Higher	BHI	22	4	2										$C + Z = 0$	•	•	•	•	•	•
Branch If ≤ Zero	BLE	2F	4	2										$Z + (N \oplus V) = 1$	•	•	•	•	•	•
Branch If Lower Or Same	BLS	23	4	2										$C + Z = 1$	•	•	•	•	•	•
Branch If < Zero	BLT	2D	4	2										$N \oplus V = 1$	•	•	•	•	•	•
Branch If Minus	BMI	2B	4	2										N = 1	•	•	•	•	•	•
Branch If Not Equal Zero	BNE	26	4	2										Z = 0	•	•	•	•	•	•
Branch If Overflow Clear	BVC	28	4	2										V = 0	•	•	•	•	•	•
Branch If Overflow Set	BVS	29	4	2										V = 1	•	•	•	•	•	•
Branch If Plus	BPL	2A	4	2										N = 0	•	•	•	•	•	•
Branch To Subroutine	BSR	8D	8	2										} See Special Operations	•	•	•	•	•	•
Jump	JMP				6E	4	2	7E	3	3					•	•	•	•	•	•
Jump To Subroutine	JSR				AD	8	2	BD	9	3					•	•	•	•	•	•
No Operation	NOP										01	2	1	Advances Prog. Cntr. Only	•	•	•	•	•	•
Return From Interrupt	RTI										3B	10	1		①					
Return From Subroutine	RTS										39	5	1	} See Special Operations	•	•	•	•	•	•
Software Interrupt	SWI										3F	12	1		•	②	•	•	•	•
Wait for Interrupt*	WAI										3E	9	1		•	②	•	•	•	•

*WAI puts Address Bus, R/W, and Data Bus in the three-state mode while VMA is held low.

① (All) Load Condition Code Register from Stack. (See Special Operations)

② (Bit 1) Set when interrupt occurs. If previously set, a Non-Maskable Interrupt is required to exit the wait state.

121

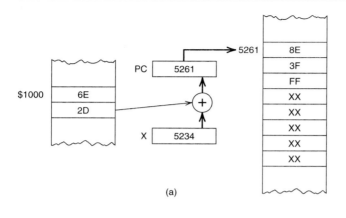

(a)

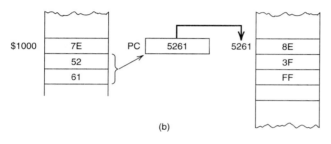

(b)

Figure 5-1 The two modes of the JMP instructions. (a) Indexed mode. (b) Extended mode.

5-3.2 ▼ Indirect Jumps

Many programmers make use of **indirect jumps,** where the program must jump to an address that is stored in a memory location rather than to the memory location itself.

EXAMPLE 5-2

Assume that the address to which we wish to jump is contained in locations 40 and 41. How can an indirect jump be performed in the **6800** μP?

SOLUTION

First the 2 bytes are placed in the X register with an LDX direct instruction (LDX $40). Then the JMP 0,X indexed instruction is used, which transfers X to the PC, effectively completing the indirect jump while using only 4 bytes.

5-3.3 ▼ BRANCH Instructions

BRANCH instructions have been explained in Sections 3-11 and 4-7. Both BRANCH and JUMP instructions cause the program to start executing instructions at the branch or jump address rather than continuing to the next sequential location. (As explained in Sections 3-11 and 4-7, conditional branches are taken only when the condition is true.)

In the **6800,** although conditional BRANCH instructions can *branch* only within the range of a 1-byte 2s-complement offset (+129 or −126 from the location of the BRANCH instruction), a combination of BRANCH and JUMP instructions can be used effectively to branch conditionally anywhere in the 64K map. For example, consider the following two program segments:

```
1.  26 xx     BNE    START
    .. ..      ...    .....

2.  27 03     BEQ    *+5
    7E xxxx    JMP    START
    .. ..      ...    .....
```

The programs will both go to the next instruction in sequence when the condition is true (Z = 1). When Z = 0, they will go to the location of START, which in the first program must be within branching range. In the second program, START can be anywhere in memory. The assembler interprets * as the *current* location (of the BEQ) and thus, *+5 jumps over the next 3 bytes.

Branches are often preferred because they use only 2 bytes and can be used in **relocatable programs,** where the entire program can be moved to a different area of memory without changing the BRANCH instructions. In addition, assemblers calculate branch values (see Section 6-7) and relieve the programmer of the task.

5-3.4 ▼ Other Conditional BRANCH Instructions

The unconditional BRANCH instruction BRA and the conditional branch instructions that depend on the C, V, N, and Z bits were discussed in Section 4-7. When writing programs it often happens that two numbers are compared and a branch must be taken, depending on which number is greater. The term *greater* may also depend on whether we are using *unsigned numbers* (all numbers considered positive) or *signed* (2s-complement) *numbers*. Table 5-1 shows that the **6800** has six additional BRANCH instructions (not shown in Table 4-6) that can be executed after a COMPARE instruction to compare numbers in signed or absolute form and to branch accordingly.

1. **Branch if Greater than or Equal to zero (BGE).** We have already seen that it is possible to add two positive numbers and get a negative result if overflow occurs (Section 4-6.4). The BGE instruction takes the branch if the result of the last operation was positive or 0, *even if the N bit is 1.* It is often used after subtraction or compare instructions and branches only if the minuend is greater than or equal to the subtrahend. The logic equation is $N \oplus V = 0$.

2. **Branch if Greater Than zero (BGT).** This instruction is very much like BGE. It branches only if the result of the last operation was positive and not equal to 0. The logic equation is $Z + N \oplus V = 0$.

3. **Branch if Higher (BHI).** This instruction is meant to be executed after a COMPARE or SUBTRACT instruction (CBA, CMP, SBA, or SUB). It branches if the minuend, considered as an unsigned binary number, is greater than the subtrahend. The logic equation is $C + Z = 0$, so the instruction will not branch if C is 1 (indicating that the result of the subtraction is negative; see Section 4-6.2) or if Z is 1 (indicating that the minuend and subtrahend are equal and the result of the subtraction is 0).

4. **Branch if Less than or Equal to zero (BLE).** This instruction branches if the result of the last operation is less than or equal to 0. It allows for the possibility that $N = 0$ due to overflow.

5. **Branch if Less Than zero (BLT).** Similar to the BLE, but no branch is taken if the last result is 0.

6. **Branch if Lower or the Same (BLS).** This instruction complements the BHI. It is also meant to be executed after a COMPARE or SUBTRACT instruction and causes a branch if the subtrahend is greater than or equal to the minuend. Since the logic equation is $C + Z = 1$, the branch is taken if the result of the subtraction is negative $(C = 1)$ or 0 $(Z = 1)$.

The BGE, BGT, BLE, and BLT instructions treat the numbers as *signed numbers*, but BHI and BLS are for *absolute numbers*.

EXAMPLE 5-3

Assume that accumulator A contains 60 and B contains 90.

(a) Which number is higher?

(b) With which of the following programs will it branch?

    1. CBA
       BHI
    2. CBA
       BGT
    3. CBA
       BPL

SOLUTION

(a) Considered as unsigned numbers, B > A; but if signed numbers are being used, the 60 is positive and 90 is negative, therefore, A > B.

(b) CBA is the mnemonic for COMPARE accumulators. The result of the compare is $60 - 90 = D0$, with the C, N, and V bits all SET. The contents of accumulators A and B remain 60 and 90, however, because they are not affected by a COMPARE instruction.

Program 1 will not branch because 90 is higher (in absolute value) than 60, and the subtraction SETs the C bit so that $C + Z = 1$. Program 2 will branch because the BGT considers signed numbers and A > B. Note that the logic equation $Z + N \oplus V = 0$ is satisfied because $Z = 0$ and both N and $V = 1$. Program 3 will not branch because the result SETs the N bit and the **6800** considers the result as negative.

The results of this program show that the BHI instruction should be used when comparing *absolute* numbers, but when comparing 2s-complement signed numbers, the BGE or BGT instructions are correct.

EXAMPLE 5-4

If the following program is executed, what numbers must be in the accumulator B for the program to branch?

```
LDAA    #$FD
CBA
BHI
```

SOLUTION

The first instruction loads $FD into A and the second instruction compares the accumulators. Unless B contains $FF, $FE, or $FD, the minuend is higher than the subtrahend and the program will branch.

5-4 ▼ STACKS

In **6800** μPs and many larger computers, memory is divided into three distinct areas: the program and data areas, which we have already considered, and the stack. *The stack is an area of memory used for the temporary storage of important information or data that is changed frequently.* Subroutines (see Section 5-5) and interrupts (see Chapter 9) make use of the stack. Since it must be written to as well as read, the stack must be in RAM.

5-4.1 ▼ The Stack Pointer

The system designer must determine the area of memory allocated to the stack during initialization. The **Stack Pointer** (SP) is a register within the μP that contains the *address of the next location available for the stack.* The **6800** internal logic causes the SP to decrement automatically when data or return addresses are stored in the stack and to increment when they are removed. Therefore, the SP must initially be set to the highest address in the stack area. This location is often called the *top of the stack* and is pointed to when nothing is stored in the stack. The instructions shown in Table 5-2 pertain to the stack pointer.

EXAMPLE 5-5

The stack is to occupy locations $0200 to $02FF. What instructions are required at the beginning of the program to initialize the SP?

SOLUTION

The SP points to the highest vacant location in the stack. At the beginning of the program the entire stack is empty, so the SP must point to $02FF. The single instruction

LDS #$2FF   (8E 02FF)

is a LOAD IMMEDIATE that loads $02FF into the SP Register. This instruction is said to *initialize* the stack so that it starts at $02FF. Whenever the stack is used, the SP is decremented. The stack must not be allowed to become so large that it invades memory area set aside for programs or data, or it will overwrite them. One common programming mistake is to do something that causes the stack pointer to decrement and to fail to increment it later. This can cause the stack to overflow and destroy the program.

TABLE 5-2 Stack Pointer Instructions

MNEMONIC	DESCRIPTION
DES	Decrement stack pointer.
INS	Increment stack pointer.
LDS	Load stack pointer. (This instruction can be executed in the immediate, direct, indexed, or extended mode.)
STS	Store stack pointer. (This instruction can be executed in the direct, indexed, or extended mode.)
TXS	Transfer the contents of the index register (minus 1) to the stack pointer register.
TSX	Transfer the contents of the stack pointer register (plus 1) to the index register (see Table B-2 in Appendix B).

5-4.2 ▼ PUSH and PULL

Two memory instructions that were not discussed in Chapter 4 because they involve the stack are PUSH and PULL.* These are implied instructions that refer to accumulators A and B.

A PSHA (or B) takes the contents of the specified accumulator and *writes* it in the stack at the SP location. It then *decrements* the SP because the original stack location is no longer vacant; it contains the *pushed byte*.

*The word "POP" instead of "PULL" is often used by other manufacturers.

EXAMPLE 5-6

If A contains $CB, what do the following instructions accomplish?

```
LDS    #$2FF
PSHA
```

SOLUTION

The first instruction loads $02FF into the SP, as in Example 5-5. The second instruction pushes A onto the stack. After execution, location $02FF contains $CB and the SP contains $02FE, which points to the highest vacant location in the stack.

A PULL instruction first *increments* the SP, then *transfers* the contents of the stack at the new address of the SP to the accumulator. Note that once the contents of a stack location have been pulled, the location is considered vacant, although the byte is still there. It will be overwritten by the next PUSH or other use of the stack.

EXAMPLE 5-7

If the SP contains $200, location $200 contains $CB, and $201 contains $CC, what happens in response to a PULB instruction?

SOLUTION

The SP is incremented to $201 and the stack is read. At the end of the instruction, B contains $CC and the SP contains $201. Now $200 and $201 are both considered to be vacant.

Note that the stack acts as a Last-In, First-Out (LIFO) register. *A PULL retrieves the information that was last PUSHed onto the stack.*

5-5 ▼ SUBROUTINES

When the same function is required more than once in a program, it is frequently written as a **subroutine,** that is, a subprogram that can be used any number of times by the main program. This capability is provided by three of the instructions listed in Table 5-1: JSR, BSR, and RTS. Subroutines to do multiplications, 16-bit adds, and square roots are typical. In Section 4-5.4 a program to obtain the sine of an angle was given. If the sine had to be calculated more than once during execution of the main program, the sine program would surely be a subroutine.

Figure 5-2 illustrates use of the same subroutine by two different parts of the main program. The subroutine located at $200 can be entered from either location $0011 or $00CC by placing a JUMP to Subroutine (JSR) (op codes of $AD, $BD, or $8D, depend-

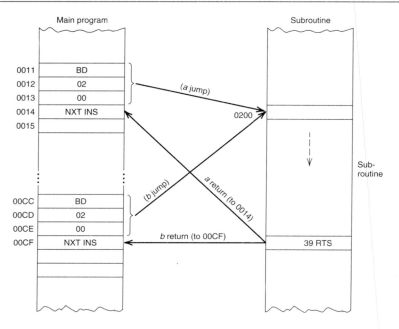

Figure 5-2   Use of a subroutine.

ing on the mode) in these addresses. The PC actions that result from the subroutine jump at $0011 are identified by the *a* in Fig. 5-2, and *b* identifies jumps from $00CC.

After the subroutine is complete, the program resumes from the instruction following the location where it called the subroutine (see Section 5-5.2). Because the subroutine must return to one of *several* locations, depending on which one caused it to be entered, the *original contents of the PC must be preserved* so that the subroutine knows where to return.

5-5.1 ▼ Jumps to Subroutines

The JSR (Jump to SubRoutine) instruction remembers the 16-bit address of the next main instruction by *writing it to the stack* before it takes the jump. The JSR can be executed in the indexed or extended mode. There is a BSR (Branch to SubRoutine) instruction that can be used if the starting address of the subroutine is within +129 to –126 locations of the program counter. The advantage of the BSR is that it uses an 8-bit offset and therefore needs one less byte in the main program.

The actions of the subroutine instructions are illustrated in Fig. 5-3. In each case they store the address of the next instruction on the stack before taking the jump.

5-5.2 ▼ Return from Subroutine

The JSR and BSR instructions preserve the contents of the PC on the stack, but an RTS (ReTurn from Subroutine) instruction is required to return properly. The RTS is the last instruction executed in a subroutine. Its action is shown in Fig. 5-4. It places the contents of the stack in the PC and causes the SP to be incremented twice. Because these bytes contain the address of the next main instruction in the program (put there by the JSR or BSR that initiated the subroutine), the program resumes at the place where it left off before it entered the subroutine.

SPECIAL OPERATIONS

JSR, JUMP TO SUBROUTINE:

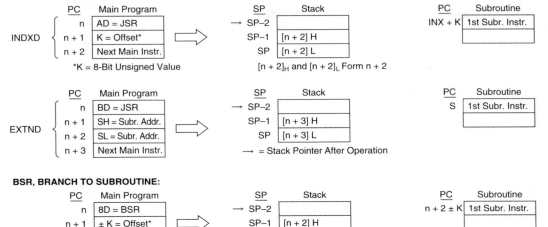

Figure 5-3 Jumps and branches to subroutine in the **6800** μ.p.

EXAMPLE 5-8

If the SP and X registers both contain $0200, what happens when the instruction

```
JSR $20,X
```

in location $30 is executed?

SOLUTION

This is the indexed mode of the instruction JSR. Since the op code for the JSR ($AD) occupies location $30, and $20 (the offset) occupies location $31, the address of the next instruction, $0032, is written to the stack. Location $0200 then contains $32 and location $01FF contains 00. The SP has been decremented twice and contains $01FE. The program then jumps to $0220 (the sum of the contents of X and the offset), which should be the starting location of the subroutine.

RTS, RETURN FROM SUBROUTINE:

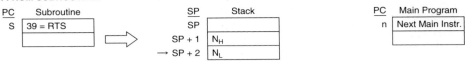

Figure 5-4 Action of the return-from-subroutine (RTS) instruction.

5-5.3 ▼ Nested Subroutines

In some sophisticated programs the main program may call a subroutine, which then calls a second subroutine. The second subroutine is called a **nested subroutine** because it is used by and returns to the first subroutine.

The situation is shown graphically in Fig. 5-5. The main program does a JSR extended at address $40. This puts $0043 on the stack. The first subroutine does a JSR at $01C3, placing $01C6 on the stack and jumping to the second subroutine. When the second subroutine is complete, an RTS returns it to $01C6 and increments the SP twice. Now the first subroutine picks up where it left off. When the first subroutine finishes, it ends with an RTS that causes a return to the main program. By making use of the stack as shown, there can be any number of nested subroutines, limited only by the stack size.

5-5.4 ▼ Use of Registers during Subroutines

During the execution of a subroutine, the subroutine will use the accumulators; it may use X and it changes the contents of the CCR. When the main program is reentered, however, the contents of these registers must often be as they were before the jump to the subroutine.

The most commonly used method for preserving register contents during execution of a subroutine is to write the subroutine so that it PUSHes those registers it must *preserve* onto the stack at the beginning of the subroutine and then PULLs them off at the end of the subroutine, thus *restoring their contents* before returning to the main program.

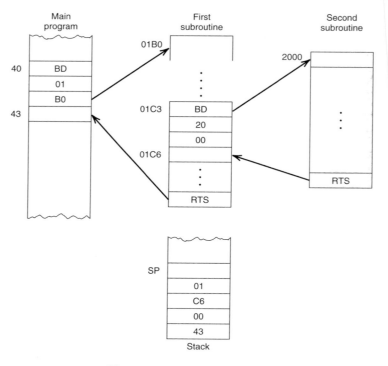

Figure 5-5   Nested subroutines.

EXAMPLE 5-9

A subroutine uses accumulators A and B and the CCR. How can the main program contents of these registers be preserved?

SOLUTION

To preserve the contents of these registers for the main program, the first four instructions of the subroutine should be

Op Code	Mnemonic
36	**PSHA**
37	**PSHB**
07	**TPA**
36	**PSHA**

This puts the contents of A, B, and the CCR on the stack as shown in Fig. 5-6.
    To restore these registers before returning to the main program, instructions that are converse to those at the beginning must be executed in *reverse* order. The last five instructions of the subroutine must be

Op Code	Mnemonic
32	**PULA**
06	**TAP**
33	**PULB**
32	**PULA**
39	**RTS**

Note that the Register A had to be preserved. It is also used by the TPA and TAP instructions. Thus its contents are overwritten and will be lost unless it is first pushed onto the stack.

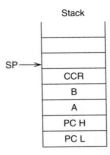

Figure 5-6 Contents of the stack after entering the subroutine of Example 5-9 and executing the first four instructions.

5-6 ▼ MULTIPLICATION

In a μC, multiplication and division are performed far less often than addition, subtraction, and logical operations. There are no multiply and divide instructions in the **6800** μP, and therefore these operations must be done using software subroutines. In this section a subroutine for multiplying 2 bytes is developed.

5-6.1 ▼ Multiplication Algorithm

Multiplication starts with a multiplier, multiplicand, and product register. The product register, which is initially 0 and eventually contains the product, must be as long as the number of bits in the multiplier and multiplicand added together. In computers, the multiplier and multiplicand are typically one *n*-bit word each, and two *n*-bit words must be reserved for the product.

Multiplication can be performed in accordance with the following algorithm:

1. Examine the least significant bit of the multiplier. If it is 0, shift the product register 1 bit to the right. If it is 1, add the multiplicand to the MSB of the product register and then shift.

2. Repeat step 1 for each bit of the multiplier.

At the conclusion the product should be in the product register.

It is common to shift the multiplicand 1 bit left for each multiplier bit and then add it to the product register. This is analogous to multiplication as taught in grade school. The algorithm presented here, however, holds the position of the multiplicand constant by shifting the product register right. This algorithm is more easily implemented in a μP.

EXAMPLE 5-10

Multiply 22 × 26 using the above algorithm outlined above.
(*Note:* All numbers are decimal.)

SOLUTION

The solution is shown in Fig. 5-7. The multiplier bits are listed in a column with the Least Significant Bit (LSB) on top. The multiplication proceeds in accordance with these bits, as the leftmost column shows.

Consider line 5 as an example. Since the multiplier bit is 1, the 5-bit multiplicand (26) is added to the 5 Most Significant Bits (MSBs) of the product register, which appear on line 4 as 13. The result, 39, appears on line 5. The product moves steadily to the right. The final product appears on line 9 and is a 10-bit number in this case. Note that the MSB of the product register is reserved for carries that may result from the additions.

Multiplier = 22 = 1 0 1 1 0

Line Number	Multiplicand = 26 =	1 1 0 1 0				Multiplier Bit	
1		0 0 0 0					Initial product
2		0 0 0 0	0			0	Shift product register
3		1 1 0 1 0	0			1	Add multiplicand
4		0 1 1 0 1	0 0				Shift product register
5	1	0 0 1 1 1	0 0			1	Add multiplicand
6		1 0 0 1 1	1 0 0				Shift product register
7		0 1 0 0 1	1 1 0 0			0	Shift product register
8	1	0 0 0 1 1	1 1 0 0			1	Add multiplicand
9		1 0 0 0 1	1 1 1 0 0				Shift – final product

Figure 5-7 Multiplying 22 × 26.

5-6.2 ▼ Multiplication Subroutines

Multiplication can be performed in accordance with the algorithm above by using the **6800** μP. A routine for a 1-byte by 1-byte multiplication is shown in Figure 5-8. Before the program starts, three assumptions are made:

1. The multiplicand is in location $80.
2. Locations $82 and $83 are reserved for the 16-bit product. Actually, the partial products will be in accumulator A and location $83. At the end of the program, A, which contains the MS byte of the product, is stored in $82.
3. Location $84 contains the multiplier.

   NOTE: If this program is to be verified using the EVB (described in Section 11-5), it will be necessary to change the locations to avoid interfering with BUFFALO's RAM location. Addresses $20 through $24 are suggested for the data and $C000 for the program.

   The program starts by storing the required number of shifts into $81 and storing the multiplicand into B. It then shifts the multiplier right. If the bit of the multiplier that is shifted into the carry FF is a 1, the multiplicand is added to the product register (A). The reader may have noticed that a 1 is sometimes carried out of the product register in the illustrative example. Fortunately, this 1 goes into the carry FF and is preserved.

   The two ROR instructions then shift A and location $83. This is essentially a 16-bit shift of the product register. Location $81 keeps track of the number of shifts and the program halts when it decrements to a 0. Multiplying larger numbers requires 16-bit adds and 32-bit shifts but can proceed in accordance with the same general algorithm.

5-6.3 ▼ Parameter Passing in Subroutines

To use subroutines correctly, several conditions must be observed:

1. If any constants change during execution of the subroutine, they must be *reinitialized* whenever the subroutine is used again. In the multiplication subroutine, loca-

ADDR	CODE	MNEMONIC		COMMENTS
20	C6 08	LDAB	#8	Put 8 in B register
22	D7 81	STAB	$81	Save shift count in $81
24	D6 80	LDAB	$80	Load multiplicand into B
26	4F	CLRA		Clear A
27	74 0084	LSR	$84	Shift multiplier right
2A	24 01	BCC	$2D	Skip to $2D if carry clear
2C	1B	ABA		Add accumulators
2D	46	RORA		Shift product MS byte Rt.
2E	76 0083	ROR	$83	Shift product reg LS byte
31	7A 0081	DEC	$81	Decrement count
34	26 F1	BNE	$27	Branch back to 27 if not 0
36	97 82	STAA	$82	Is 0. Done. Store MS byte
38	20 FE	BRA	$38	HALT program by looping
		END		

Reserved locations

```
80 Multiplicand
81 Count
82 Product Register (MS byte)
83 Product Register (LS byte)
84 Multiplier
```

Figure 5-8   Multiplication Program.

tion $81, the shift count, is an example. It is decremented to zero during the course of the subroutine. Therefore, it must be reinitialized every time the subroutine is started. This is done by the first two instructions of the subroutine.

2. The calling routine must know where to put the parameters. In the multiplication subroutine the calling routine must place the multiplicand in location $80 and the multiplier in $84 before it can call the subroutine.

3. The calling routine must know where to find the result of the subroutine. In the multiplication subroutine the results are always stored in $82 and $83.

The last two conditions are called **parameter passing.** The calling routine must provide the subroutine with the proper input parameters (i.e., multiplier and multiplicand) and the subroutine must make its results available to the calling program (i.e., store them in locations $82 and $83).

EXAMPLE 5-11

There are numbers in $A1, $A2, $B1, and $B2. Describe a program to find the sum of the two products:

$$S = (A1)(B1) + (A2)(B2)$$

Store S in $C1 and $C2.

SOLUTION

The first decision is to use the multiply routine of Section 5-6.2 as a subroutine to obtain both of the products required. Once this decision is made, the program can start at location $100, for example, to keep out of the way of the multiply subroutine and the data. The stack can start at $200 to keep it out of the way of everything else. The program then proceeds as follows:

1. Load the stack pointer. Whenever a program requires use of the stack (and subroutines use the stack) the SP must be initialized before it is used. Otherwise, the SP may be pointing to a random location and the jump or branch to subroutine's return address may overwrite the program or data.
2. Move $A1 to $80 and $B1 to $84. This sets up the multiplier and multiplicand for the subroutine. This is an example of parameter passing.
3. Jump to $20 to enter the multiply subroutine.
4. Move the product in $82 and $83 to $C1 and $C2.
5. Move $A2 and $B2 to $80 and $84, for the second product.
6. Jump to the multiply subroutine again.
7. Add the contents of $82 and $83 with $C1 and $C2 to get the sum of the two products. Store the results in $C1 and $C2. This completes the program.

5-7 ▼ BCD-TO-BINARY CONVERSION PROBLEM

As a final practical example that uses lists, indexed instructions, subroutines, and stacks, let us consider the problem of converting BCD information to binary. BCD was introduced in Section 4-8. BCD information can be entered into a μC system from the terminal keyboard. Each ASCII (see Section 8-7.1) number must be ANDed with a $0F to remove the four MSBs. This leaves a BCD digit. Other peripherals may also supply BCD information.

BCD numbers must often be converted to binary before computations can be made using the number. One way to convert from BCD to binary* is to assign a weight to all the BCD bits and then add the weights for all bits that are 1 in the BCD representation of the number. The weights are assigned in accordance with the value represented by each BCD bit, that is, 1, 2, 4, 8, 10, 20, 40, 80, 100, 200, ... A table of the decimal numbers and binary weights corresponding to each BCD bit is given in Table 5-3.

*A thorough discussion of BCD-to-binary and binary-to-BCD conversion is given in Joseph D. Greenfield, *Practical Digital Design Using ICs,* 3rd ed., Prentice Hall, Englewood Cliffs, N.J., 1994.

EXAMPLE 5-12

Convert the decimal number 169 to binary using the add algorithm.

SOLUTION

The number 169 is expressed in BCD form as

$$0001 \quad 0110 \quad 1001$$
$$\underbrace{\quad}_{1} \quad \underbrace{\quad}_{6} \quad \underbrace{\quad}_{9}$$

where the LSB is on the right. There are 1s in positions 1, 4, 6, 7, and 9. The weights corresponding to these numbers are (from Table 5-3)

$$0001$$
$$1000$$
$$10100$$
$$101000$$
$$1100100$$

Simple addition of these binary numbers yields 10101001, which is the binary equivalent of decimal 169.

Computers, which generally have binary adders, often use the add algorithm to convert from BCD to binary. Now that the method of converting from BCD to binary has been explained, a conversion program using the **6800** can be written.

EXAMPLE 5-13

A four-digit BCD number is in locations $F0 and $F1, with the least significant digit in $F1, bits 3 through 0, and the most significant digit in $F0, bits 7 through 4. Write a routine to convert this number to binary.

SOLUTION

We start with a vague general idea of how to perform the conversion; add the proper number wherever a 1 appears in the given BCD number. Each bit can be tested by performing a shift right and testing the carry bit.

We also realize now that the list of Table 5-4 must be placed in memory so that the proper number can be added to the sum. Table 5-4 shows that smaller binary values can be included in 1 byte but the larger values need 2 bytes. For uniformity, it is wise to allocate 2 bytes for each binary entry. It will soon become clear that this simplifies the programming. The list is arbitrarily started at location $100, so $100 and $101 contain the binary equivalent of 1 (hex 0001); the list continues to $11F, where locations $11E and $11F contain the binary equivalent of 8000_{10}, which is $1F40_{16}$, or

$$
\begin{array}{cccc}
 & 1 \quad F & & 4 \quad 0 \\
11E & \overbrace{0001\ 1111} & 11F & \overbrace{0100\ 0000}
\end{array}
$$

The result can be no larger than $(9999)_{10}$, which means that it can be represented by a 14-bit binary number. Let us reserve $F2 and $F3 for this number. We also assume that the addition is done by a subroutine, so the stack pointer is arbitrarily initialized to $200. The flowchart can now be drawn and is shown in Fig. 5-9.

The flowchart assumes that the list and the numbers to be converted are already in memory. The program proceeds in the following way.

1. The sum is initialized to 0, the index register (X) to $100, and the SP to $200.

2. The first word (two least significant digits) is loaded into accumulator A and shifted out. After each shift, the carry bit is tested.

TABLE 5-3 Weights for BCD-to-Binary Conversion

Bit Position	Decimal Number	Binary Number
1	1	1
2	2	1 0
3	4	1 0 0
4	8	1 0 0 0
5	1 0	1 0 1 0
6	2 0	1 0 1 0 0
7	4 0	1 0 1 0 0 0
8	8 0	1 0 1 0 0 0 0
9	1 0 0	1 1 0 0 1 0 0
10	2 0 0	1 1 0 0 1 0 0 0
11	4 0 0	1 1 0 0 1 0 0 0 0
12	8 0 0	1 1 0 0 1 0 0 0 0 0
13	1 0 0 0	1 1 1 1 1 0 1 0 0 0
14	2 0 0 0	1 1 1 1 1 0 1 0 0 0 0
15	4 0 0 0	1 1 1 1 1 0 1 0 0 0 0 0
16	8 0 0 0	1 1 1 1 1 0 1 0 0 0 0 0 0

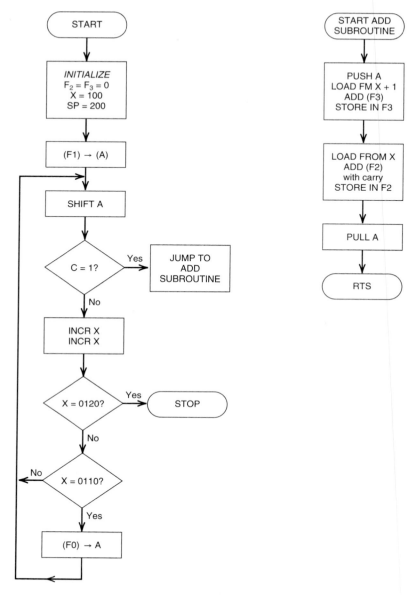

Figure 5-9 Flowchart for Example 5-13.

3. The X register is then incremented twice to point to the next 2-byte numbers in the list. It should now be apparent that if the list contained both 1- and 2-byte entries, additional programming would have been required to determine the starting address of the next item. This is why 2 bytes were allocated to each item in the list whether they were required or not.

4. X is tested for the HALT condition. The program should halt after 16 shifts or when the list is exhausted. Since the list contains 16 two-byte numbers, it is exhausted when X equals $(120)_{16}$.

5. The second word to be converted must be loaded into A after eight shifts or 16 increments of X. This occurs when the number in X = $0110. Note that in this program register X is performing the dual function of selecting the appropriate number in the list and determining whether or not branches are to be taken.

6. When C = 1 the add subroutine is entered. Since accumulator A is used by both the main program and the subroutine, it is immediately pushed onto the stack to save it for the main program.

7. The proper number in the list (as determined by X) is added to the LSBs of the sum in $F3.

8. The MSBs of the list are added (with carry) to $F2. This completes a 16-bit addition.

9. Accumulator A is restored to its original value and the main program is reentered.

Using the detailed flowchart of Fig. 5-9, the coding is straightforward and is shown in Fig. 5-10. Before coding can begin, a starting address must be assigned arbitrarily to the main program ($20) and the subroutine ($80). These addresses will need to be changed if the EVB is to be used (see Section 11-5). The only other caution is that these areas must not overlap each other, the data, the list, or the stack area.

The reader may have observed that this program is not optimum. There is no real need for a subroutine (it could have been included in the main program) and some instructions could have been saved by using accumulator B. The program was used because it demonstrates many of the features available in the **6800** software.

5-8 ▼ SUMMARY

In this chapter we introduced the BRANCH and JUMP instructions available in the **6800** μP. The conditions that caused the branches were explained, as were the methods of calculating the branch locations.

The stack was then introduced. Its use in conjunction with PUSH and PULL instructions and subroutines was explained. Finally, a multiplication program and a BCD-to-binary conversion program were presented as examples that used many of the features of the **6800.**

5-9 ▼ GLOSSARY

BRANCH A jump where the location jumped to can be specified by a 1-byte offset from the current value of the PC.

Indirect jump A jump to an address stored in memory rather than directly to the memory location itself.

JUMP An instruction that loads the PC with a new address that causes the program to fetch the next instruction from a location that is not in sequence.

ADDR	CODE	MNEMONICS		COMMENTS
		* MAIN PROGRAM		
20	4F	CLRA		Clear A
21	97 F2	STAA	$F2	Clear F2
23	97 F3	STAA	$F3	Clear F3
25	8E 0200	LDS	#$200	Initialize Stack Pointer
28	CE 0100	LDX	#$100	Initialize Index Register
2B	96 F1	LDAA	$F1	Load LS BCD digit into A
2D	47	ASRA		Shift A right
2E	24 02	BCC	$32	Skip to $32 if C = 0
30	8D 4E	BSR	$80	To Add subroutine if C = 1
32	08	INX		Increment X twice to
33	08	INX		point to next entry
34	8C 0120	CPX	#$120	Reached end of list ?
37	27 09	BEQ	$42	Yes - branch to HALT at $42
39	8C 0110	CPX	#$110	Is word 1 finished ?
3C	26 EF	BNE	$2D	No, loop back & shift again
3E	90 F0	LDAA	$F0	Yes, load MS digits into A
40	20 EB	BRA	$2D	Loop to $2D & shift MS digit
42	20 FE	BRA	$42	Repeat and HALT prog.
		* ADD SUBROUTINE		
80	30	PSHA		Save A on stack
81	A6 01	LDAA	1,X	Load fron list-LS byte
83	9B i3	ADDA	$F3	Add LS byte of sum
85	97 F3	STAA	$F3	Update LS byte of sum
87	A6 00	LDAA	0,X	Load MS byte from list
89	99 F2	ADCA	$F2	Add MS byte w/ carry
8B	97 F2	STAA	$F2	Update MS byte of sum
8D	32	PULA		Restore A
8E	39	RTS		Return to main program

Figure 5-10 Program for Example 5-13.

Nested subroutine A subroutine called by another subroutine. It is used by the first subroutine, and when completed, the program returns to the first subroutine.

Parameter passing A placing of data in prescribed locations so that they can be shared by the subroutine and main program.

PULL An instruction that copies into an accumulator the contents of the location in the stack pointed to by the SP.

PUSH An instruction that copies the contents of the accumulator to the stack at the current SP location.

Relocatable program A program of instructions containing only relative branching. Thus the program can be located anywhere in memory (i.e., it is relocatable).

Stack An area of memory reserved for subroutine return addresses and saving register contents during an interrupt. Also, other parameters can be saved and retrieved.

Stack Pointer (SP) A register that contains the address of the highest vacant location in the stack.

5-10 ▼ REFERENCES

BISHOP, RON, *Basic Microprocessors and the 6800,* Hayden, Rochelle Park, N.J., 1979.

GREENFIELD, JOSEPH D., *Practical Digital Design Using ICs,* 3rd ed., Prentice Hall, Englewood Cliffs, N.J., 1994.

LEVENTHAL, LANCE, *6800 Assembly Language Programming,* Adam Osborn & Associates, Berkeley, Calif., 1978.

MOTOROLA, *M6800 Programming Reference Manual,* M68PRM(D), Phoenix, Ariz., 1976.

5-11 ▼ PROBLEMS

5-1. Write a program to write the number $C2 into all locations between $0250 and $02FF.

5-2. Write a program to transfer the contents of locations $0100 to $0120 to locations $0110 to $0130. (*Hint:* Start by moving $120 to $130, then $11F to $12F, etc.)

5-3. The Boolean equation for BGE is $(N \oplus V) = 0$. Explain what it implies.

5-4. If the SP contains $021C and X contains $022C, write the contents of the stack and the starting address of the subroutine if the instruction in location $40 is:

   (a) JSR $30,X   AD 30

   (b) JSR $C2,X   AD C2

   (c) JSR $15F   BD 015F

   (d) BSR * + $25   8D 23

   (e) BSR * – 6   8D F8

5-5. Write a program to convert a 13-bit binary number to BCD. The algorithm is to subtract from the given number the highest number in Table 5-3 that is less than the given number, and write it in all positions where these subtractions are performed.*

5-6. Your receivables are positive numbers in locations $0100 through 01FF. Your expenses are positive numbers in locations $0200 through 02FF. Write a program to determine your net worth.

5-7. Describe in words what the following program does.

   *A more complete description is given in Chapter 10 of Joseph D. Greenfield, *Practical Digital Design Using ICs,* 3rd ed., Prentice Hall, Englewood Cliffs, N. J., 1994.

LOCATION	MACHINE CODE	MNEMONIC
40	CE 0130	LDX #$130
43	8E 01D0	LDS #$1D0
46	A6 00	LDAA 0,X
48	36	PSH A
49	09	DEX
4A	8C 0100	CPX #$100
4D	26 F7	BNE $46
4F	20 FE	BRA $4F

5-8. Using the multiplication routine of Figure 5-8, multiply 127_{10} by 75_{10}. Show the contents of the accumulator after each step.

5-9. Write a divide routine. Reserve 1 byte for the quotient and 1 byte for the remainder.

5-10. Write the code for Example 5-11.

5-11. A business deals in a series of items. If the price of each item is listed in locations $A0 to $BF and the corresponding number of items sold is in locations $C0 to $DF, write a program to determine the gross receipts.

After attempting to solve these problems, try to answer the self-evaluation questions in Section 5-2. If any of them still seem difficult, review the appropriate sections of the chapter to find the answers.

6 ASSEMBLY LANGUAGE FOR THE 6800 FAMILY

6-1 ▼ INSTRUCTIONAL OBJECTIVES

The purpose of this chapter is to acquaint the **6800** family system designer with standard methods of writing and documenting software and to expand on the use of mnemonics for ease of programming. Assembler and Editor programs are presented to demonstrate the mechanics of program development. After reading this chapter, the student should be able to:

1. Translate flowcharts or program notes into the assembly language mnemonic statements of a source program.
2. Write a program and save it on disk.
3. Specify the Assembler directives needed to assemble the program properly.
4. Assemble and reedit the source program until it assembles without syntax errors.
5. Obtain the Program Listing and Object Code output files needed to load the program into memory for testing.
6. Use Macros and Substitutable Arguments in Assemblers.

6-2 ▼ SELF-EVALUATION QUESTIONS

Watch for the answers to the following questions as you read the chapter. They should help you to understand the material presented.

1. How are mnemonics used to express addressing modes and addresses?
2. What is the difference between a source program and an object program?
3. What is an Assembler program?
4. What is the function of the program comments?
5. What is the difference between an instruction and an Assembler directive?

6. What steps are required to assemble a source program using a Personal Computer?

7. Why does the Assembler/Editor program object code have to be different for an IBM-PC (or clone) and an Apple Macintosh system?

8. What is a Substitutable Argument? How is it identified?

6-3 ▼ ASSEMBLY LANGUAGE PROGRAMMING

Computers can only understand *machine language*, where each instruction contains a numerical value of 1s and 0s for the op code and the operand. Writing programs directly in machine language, however, is awkward, unwieldy, and unwise. Assembly language programming, which substitutes mnemonics for numerical values, was described briefly in Chapter 4. It greatly simplifies program writing.

Modern programs are originally written in an Editor program as a series of assembly language instructions and directives (see Section 6-6). This is called a *source code program.* Source code programs are then put into a computer along with another program called an *Assembler.* The assembler operates on the source code program, translates its instructions into machine language, and generates program listings and error messages that help the programmer. In this chapter we show how to write source code programs and how **Assembler** and **Editor programs** are used to translate the source code programs to machine language programs that a μP can use.

The mnemonic Operator (op) codes of all the Motorola **6800** Assembly Language instructions (shown in Table 4-1) use three letters for the basic instruction. If either accumulator is involved, an A or B is added. The op codes may be followed by an Operand (or dual Operand). The machine code for a given mnemonic depends on the addressing mode. The type of information placed in the operand field depends on the particular mnemonic operator. The addressing mode is determined by the mnemonic operator combined with the information in the operand field. The various addressing modes and some examples of how they apply to the LDA instruction are shown below.

ADDRESSING MODE	MNEMONIC	MACHINE CODE	
1. Extended addressing	LDAA $A0F3	B6	A0F3
2. Direct addressing	LDAA $F3	96	F3
3. Immediate addressing	LDAA #$F3	86	F3
4. Indexed addressing	LDAA 3,X	A6	03

The instructions above are in *assembly language format* (see Section 6-3.2). The $ sign denotes a hexadecimal value, and the # sign indicates an immediate operand.*

In analyzing these instructions, the following points should be noted:

1. To match the capabilities of the **6800** μP, the **6800** μP assembler recognizes addresses below $100 [which is $(256)_{10}$], as **direct addresses,** and as shown in line

*Early versions of Assemblers optionally permitted a space between the mnemonic and the accumlator letter. They permitted instructions such as LDA A $F3, for example. The Personal Computer cross-assemblers in current use do not allow for a space.

2 of the table, the Assembler generates instructions that are 2 bytes in length (the op code plus one 8-bit address byte). Three-byte **extended addressing** instructions, as shown in line 1, are used to reference addresses above $00FF.

2. The **immediate** instruction of line 3 loads the value F3 into accumulator A, instead of loading the *contents* of location $F3 as would be the case for the direct mode shown in line 2 above.

3. The 3 shown in the **indexed** instruction (line 4) is an example of an **offset** value that is added to the index register when this instruction is executed. The offset is limited to 1 byte and is considered to be positive. It is expressed in machine language as the second byte of that instruction (03 in this case).

Below are several other addressing modes that were not shown because they are not applicable to the LDA instruction.

Addressing Mode	Mnemonic	Machine Code
5. Relative addressing	BPL *+5	2A 03
6. Inherent addressing	ABA	1B
7. Accumulator addressing	ASLA	48

Instruction 5 is an example of relative addressing, which applies to BRANCH and JUMP instructions. Here the ★ is interpreted as the value of the PC at the *beginning* of the instruction, and the second byte adjusts the PC *relative* to the value it would have after this instruction is executed.

EXAMPLE 6-1

The instruction BPL *+A is at location $C000. What will the machine language instruction be, and where does the program branch to?

SOLUTION

Assuming that the N flag is 0, the program will go to *+A. Because * (= to the current location) is $C000, the program will go to $C00A. The code will be 2A 08 because 8 must be added to the *address of the following instruction* ($C002), which is where the PC will be after the instruction is executed. It will branch to $C00A.

For backward branches a minus sign must be used, and the second byte is the 2's-complement of the minus number, also adjusted by the 2 bytes of the instruction. The second byte can therefore represent a maximum offset of $+127_{10}$ ($7F) or -128_{10} ($80) bytes relative to the address of the first byte of the *following* instruction.

Instructions 6 and 7 are **inherent** instructions. They need only *one* byte because all the information required for their execution is already within the μP and no memory locations or immediate operands are required.

6-3.1 ▼ Use of Mnemonics to Express Addresses

Mnemonics can be used to express *addresses* as well as op codes. When used in this way they are called **labels.** For example, a program to add three numbers and then branch back to itself might be:

```
BEGIN   LDAA   FIRST
        ADDA   SECOND
        ADDA   THIRD
        STAA   SUM
        BRA    BEGIN
```

Here the operands that represent addresses were given the **symbolic** names FIRST, SECOND, THIRD, BEGIN, and SUM. These are the names of the locations in memory from which the contents are fetched in the first three instructions, and to which the results (in A) are stored in the fourth. The **labels** or **symbols** chosen are usually whatever pops into the programmer's mind and are therefore considered to be **mnemonic** because they usually give some clue as to what they represent. Note that the program starts with a label called BEGIN and it is referenced in the operand of the branch instruction.

6-3.2 ▼ Source Programs

When several mnemonic or assembly language statements are written to perform a task, as in the BEGIN routine above, it is known as a **source** or **assembly language** program. The program consists of a number of lines of **source statements.** Each line can have one or more mnemonics and possibly a comment, terminated by a carriage return. All lines must consist of printable ASCII characters.

To use this source program in a μC, it must be processed by an **Assembler program.** This is a program that runs in the Host computer. The main purpose of an assembler program is to convert the source program into the machine language **Object Program.** Each source statement must be written in a *specific format* (or in the proper **syntax**) so that it can be interpreted by the Assembler.

6-3.3 ▼ Assembler Operation

Although a programmer need not be concerned with the details of Assembler operation, we suggest that he or she try to understand them. The assembler reads the program twice, or makes two *passes* through the program. When an Assembler is invoked, it first executes pass 1. It reads the first line from the source file, which has been previously saved on the Host's disk, into its buffer. It then scans the buffer and converts each mnemonic instruction to the proper machine language code in hex. These codes are stored temporarily. During pass 1 the labels and their addresses are stored away in the Symbol Table. Nothing is printed unless an error is detected.

When the Assembler begins pass 2 it will read the first source statement again. The Assembler writes the line number, program counter, and machine codes stored in pass 1 on this line of the file it is creating. The line number and addresses are incremented as required. The Assembler looks up all references in the symbol table (see Section 6-4.8) and inserts the proper values for each label. It formats these properly (inserting the necessary spaces) and then copies the contents of the line buffer, which was read from the source file, exactly as the programmer wrote it (except for added spaces). Any comments that follow on the same line are also written on the remainder of the line. Each line of source code is read and processed in this way until the end of the program is reached. This file created during pass 2 is called the *Program Listing* or *list file*. It is generally written to the system's development disk.

At the same time, the Assembler also generates a separate *Object File*. As each source line is converted, it sends the hexadecimal codes to the Object File, which is also being assembled on the disk. The Object File (see Section 6-7) is **6800** machine language, in hexadecimal codes, of the instructions to be executed by the program. The Object File can later be loaded into the **6800**'s memory and executed. When desired the Program Listing can be printed (see Section 6-6.4) and the Object File can be downloaded to the target system as described in Chapter 10.

Many different Assembler programs are available specifically for the **6800** family of μCs. Some are written or provided by Motorola, but many are from third-party vendors. They all have certain basic features, but they may differ in how they respond to the command line. All will provide a **Program Listing,** and some provide **Symbol Tables** or **Cross-Reference lists** (see Sections 6-4, 6-4.8, and 6-4.9).

6-3.4 ▼ Cross-Assemblers

When the **6800** was introduced, assembler programs were designed to run on a system using a **6800** μP. Today, however, the programs for the **6800** are developed using a **Microcomputer Development System** (MDS) or a Personal Computers (PC) that undoubtedly has a different type of μP. PCs are used more often because of their wide availability and relatively lower cost. Also, they usually include printers and hard disks. These systems will require the use of a **Cross-Assembler.** Cross-Assemblers are assembler programs that run in one computer, the IBM-PC for example, and generate code for a different computer, the **6800** in this case.

Cross-assemblers are available for many types of computers, including IBM-compatible and Macintosh personal computers (PCs). Source programs can be written on the Host computer using any text editor (in the nondocument mode; i.e., using no control codes). They are written to a file on the Host's disk and then assembled using a Cross-Assembler.

Simplified Cross-Assemblers for PCs are available from Motorola on their Bulletin Board System (BBS). This bulletin board can be reached by dialing Motorola in Austin, Texas, at 512-891-3733. These assemblers are not as powerful as Macro Assemblers (see Section 6-9.5), but they do produce a list file and an S-record or object code file. One example is the IBM-compatible AS11 program, written as an Assembler for the **68HC11** microcontroller and available from Motorola.*

---

*This Assembler is discussed in *The 68HC11 Microcontroller* by J. D. Greenfield, Saunders College Publishing, Philadelphia, 1992.

EXAMPLE 6-2

If the program of Sec. 6-3.1 were assembled and the addresses assigned to
the labels as FIRST = 40, SECOND = 41, THIRD = 42, SUM = 43, and BEGIN
= 20, what would the Assembler produce as an object program?

SOLUTION

A simplified listing for this program is shown below:

ADDR	OBJECT	LABEL	MNEMONIC	COMMENTS
20	96 40	BEGIN	LDAA FIRST	Load A from 40
22	9B 41		ADDA SECOND	Add contents of 41 to A
24	9B 42		ADDA THIRD	Add contents of 42 to A
26	97 43		STAA SUM	Store A to 43
28	20 F6		BRA BEGIN	Branch back to BEGIN

Note that the Assembler substitutes the appropriate machine code or address
for each part of the mnemonic statement [i.e., 96 = LDAA (direct), 40 = FIRST,
etc.]. In the last statement the Assembler program calculated the offset value
for the branch (−10 = $F6). This is not a practical program because it results
in an endless loop, but it could be used as a test program. When using
Assemblers, the programmer is not required to calculate the offset values for
branch instructions. The Assembler will do it.

6-4 ▼ PROGRAM LISTINGS

A **Program Listing** is generated when the program is being assembled, *if* requested on
the command line. This file shows the mnemonics and machine code for each instruction
in the program. It can also report any errors that prevent the program from assembling
(see Section 6-6.5). Other aids for the programmer, such as a Symbol Table (see Section
6-4.8) and/or a Cross-Reference List (Section 6-4.9), can also be generated during assembly. These listings will be appended to the program listing file on the disk. They can also
be displayed on the operator's terminal of the software development system, or printed
later on a line printer which is part of that system. The object file is displayable also since
it is stored in an ASCII–hex format known as the **S-record** file (see Section 6-7).

To illustrate how a program listing displays all its information, a *list* file for a sample program is shown in Fig. 6-1. This is *not* a real program. This listing was produced by
one of the Freeware Assemblers currently available on the Motorola Bulletin Board
System (BBS). Different Assembler versions may format the listing slightly differently.

LINE 1	ADDR 2	CODE 3	LABEL 4	OP 5	OPERAND 6	COMMENTS 7
0001			* Sample program to illustrate the formatting			
0002			* provided by the Assembler program.			
0003			*			
0004				OPT	cre	X-Ref Listing option
0005	0100			ORG	256	
0006	000a		COUNT	EQU	@12	@ indicates Octal
0007	0100	8e 01 32	START	LDS	#STACK	Load stack pointer
0008	0103	fe 01 36		LDX	ADDR	Load X extended
0009	0106	c6 0a		LDAB	#COUNT	Immediate addressing
0010	0108	96 0a	BACK	LDAA	10	Direct addressing
0011	010a	a1 02		CMPA	2,X	Indexed addressing
0012	010c	27 05		BEQ	FOUND	Relative addressing
0013	010e	09		DEX		Inherent addressing
0014	010f	5a		DECB		Accumulator only addr
0015	0110	26 f6		BNE	BACK	Label reference
0016	0112	3e		WAI		Wait for interrupt
0017						
0018	0113	bd 01 19	FOUND	JSR	SUBRTN	Jump to subroutine
0019	0116	7e 01 00		JMP	START	Extended addressing
0020			* Comment Statement			
0021	0119	16	SUBRTN	TAB		Comment field
0022	011a	ba 01 33		ORAA	BYTE	Set MST Sgnficnt byte
0023	011d	39		RTS		Return from subroutine
0024						
0025	011e			RMB	20	Area for stack
0026	0132		STACK	RMB	1	Start of stack
0027	0133	80	BYTE	FCB	$80	Form constant byte
0028	0134	10 97		FCB	$10,%10010111% is for binary	
0029						
0030	0136	01 38	ADDR	FDB	DATA	Form double byte
0031	0138	53 45 54	DATA	FCC	"SET"	Form constant characters
0032						
0033				END		

- a -

ADDR	0136		ADDR	0136	*0030	0008
BACK	0108		BACK	0108	*0010	0015
BYTE	0133		BYTE	0133	*0027	0022
COUNT	000a		COUNT	000a	*0006	0009
DATA	0138		DATA	0138	*0031	0030
FOUND	0113		FOUND	0113	*0018	0012
STACK	0132		STACK	0132	*0026	0007
START	0100		START	0100	*0007	0019
SUBRTN	0119		SUBRTN	0119	*0021	0018

- b -   - c -

Figure 6-1 List File of Sample Program.

This Assembler listing is used only to demonstrate the many features of this type of file and to show the distinctions between the various mnemonic expressions. The comments on each line explain the feature involved. Examples of several useful programs are given later in this chapter.

Figure 6-1a shows that the assembler formats the listing into seven columns or fields:

1. Line numbers
2. Addresses
3. Object codes
4. Labels
5. Operators
6. Operands
7. Comments

The mnemonic expressions in columns 5 and 6 are translated by the assembler into the machine code shown in column 3. This code resides at the addresses in column 2. Some of the lines (4, 5, 6, 25, 26, 27, 28, 30, 31, and 33) of Fig. 6-1a include statements that are not listed as instructions in Table 4-1. These mnemonic statements are Assembler **directives** and are listed in Table 6-1 (see Section 6-5). Some of these directives produce object code (lines 27, 28, 30, and 31 of Fig. 6-1a), but those that do not are used to control the Assembler or to format the listing. Each column of Fig. 6-1a will now be described.

6-4.1 ▼ Line Numbers (Column 1)

Each line in this listing is numbered and the line numbers appear in column 1. When the programmer writes source statements, **line numbering** is *optional*. If the source program has line numbers, they will be printed as each line is assembled. If numbers were not originally used, some Assemblers will provide them, if requested. Line numbers are decimal, and 65536 is the highest number possible.

Line numbers are not generally part of a list file but are very helpful in debugging because the Assembler identifies the errors by the line number. They are also added automatically, for example, when the Cross-Reference List (shown in Fig. 6-1c) is requested. They are used here to identify those lines that are referred to in the explanation of the Assembler Listing.

6-4.2 ▼ Addresses (Column 2)

The addresses correspond to the location in memory for each byte. Addresses are listed as four-digit hexadecimal numbers and are incremented automatically by the number of bytes required for each instruction by the assembler. The starting address is determined by the ORG statement (described in Section 6-5.1) specified by the programmer.

6-4.3 ▼ Object Codes (Column 3)

Each instruction is translated into machine language and the codes are printed on each line in hexadecimal format. These instructions can be 1, 2, or 3, bytes in length depending on the instruction and addressing mode involved. In Section 6-7 we give details on the Object Code output of the assembler.

6-4.4 ▼ Labels (Column 4)

In Section 6-3.1 we explained that mnemonics could be assigned to **addresses** as well as **op codes.** Mnemonics that apply to addresses are called **labels** (or symbols). They are placed in this column by the programmer to name this location. They can also be used in the operand column when they refer to the named location.

Specific rules apply when writing labels. The **6800** family assemblers have the following requirements:

1. A label consists of from one to six alphanumeric characters.
2. The first character of a label must be alphabetic.
3. A label must begin in the first character position of a statement.
4. All labels within a program must be unique.
5. A label must not consist of any one of the single characters A, B, or X. (These characters are reserved for special syntax and refer to accumulator A, accumulator B, and the index register X, respectively.)

The EQU directive is used to assign *values* to labels. Line 6, for example, reads COUNT EQU @12. This sets the value of COUNT to octal 12 (or hex 000A). Here are some typical labels:

```
START   START2   E3   W   B120   SUBRTN
```

Labels (or symbols) are used in the source program (they print in column 4 of the program Listing) to identify the starting address of a routine or the location of a constant. Labels are also used in the operand field to reference those locations.

Both program location and operand labels are used on lines 7 and 18 of Fig. 6-1. The label START in column 4 of line 7 refers to the starting address of the program. Column 2 shows that the starting address of the program is 0100 or that START = 0100.

Line 7 also contains the label STACK, whose address is loaded into the SP by the **immediate** LDS instruction. Note that the second and third bytes of column 3 are 0132, which is the value of STACK. STACK is used as a label on line 26, where it is defined further (see Example 6-8).

EXAMPLE 6-3

   a. What is the address of the instruction on line 9?

   b. How can it be expressed symbolically?

SOLUTION

a. The location of the LDAB instruction in line 9 is at $0106 as given on the assembler printout (column 2). It could have been calculated by realizing that this instruction occurs after two 3-byte instructions from START ($0100).
b. This location can be expressed symbolically as START+6.*

Labels must be used for program locations that are the objects of branch instructions. In Fig. 6-1a the labels FOUND and BACK are used this way. The branch instruction on line 15 (BNE BACK), for example, returns the program to BACK (location $0108) if the branch is taken. The use of labels here eliminates the problem of *calculating offsets*. The Assembler calculates the proper value for the second byte of the branch instruction on line 15 and inserts it into the offset (F6 in this case).

6-4.5 ▼ Operators (Column 5)

The Operation codes (op codes) appear in column 5. Mnemonics that are not in Table 4-1 are assembler directives; these are discussed in Section 6-5.

6-4.6 ▼ Operands (Column 6)

The Operand field of an instruction contains a *value*, an address, or a label that references one of them. Inherent instructions do not need an Operand (see line 13).

Numbers can be expressed in several ways in all Operands, but except for decimal, each number must be preceded by a symbol as follows:

1. Hexadecimal $
2. Octal   @
3. Binary   %
4. Decimal   (none)

Operands can also reference a label. In line 6 of Fig. 6-1a a numerical value of octal 12, which translates to hex A, is assigned to the label COUNT. COUNT is used by the assembler on line 9. This instruction is an example where the label is preceded by the # sign to indicate the *immediate* mode of addressing. An Operand can also contain an expression such as *+5 (see Example 6-1), which will be evaluated algebraically by the assembler.

Examples of statements with various operands are:

```
LDAA #$F3       Immediate load of hex value F3
LDX SUZY,X      "X" indicates that indexed instruction
                    offset equals the value of SUZY
JMP $1200       Jump to 1200 (hex)
```

*Note, however, that this is not a good programming practice because subsequent editing could result in a change in the number of statements between START and location 0106. It is always best to assign a label to each address referenced in the program.

```
BRA EXIT          Branch to label called EXIT
BEQ *+5           Branch to the PC +5
LDAA #100         Immediate load of decimal 100
```

EXAMPLE 6-4

What do the instructions on lines 10 and 11 of Fig 6-1a do?

SOLUTION

Line 10 contains LDAA 10. It loads the contents of location 10 ($A in hex) into register A. Line 11 compares the contents of A with the contents of the address in the index register+2. Since X contains $138 (see lines 8 and 30), the contents of location $0A are compared with the contents of address $013A, which are seen to be 54 (see line 31). Thus the instruction in line 11 compares the contents of register A with 54 and sets the flags.

6-4.7 ▼ Comments (Column 7)

Comments are used to *explain* what each line or each section of the program is doing. They can be added to any statement by separating it from the operand (or operator if no operand is used) by one or more spaces. A comment can also be used on a line by itself if the line starts with an * in the first character position. Comments do not generate machine code but are simply copied from the source to the program listing (verbatim). *Comprehension* of the program is aided immeasurably when proper comments are used. Comments are *required* if the program is to be understood by someone other than the programmer.

Good comments should indicate the function of the instruction in the program. For example, the comments "JUMP TO SUBROUTINE AT LOC 20" and "STORED EXTENDED" are poor comments because they do not tell what the instruction is doing in the *context* of the program. The program flow can be understood more readily if these comments are replaced by comments such as "JUMP TO MULTIPLICATION SUB-ROUTINE" and "STORE ADDEND."

The comments in Fig. 6-1a are poor because this is not a normal program that does something useful. They can be contrasted with Fig. 6-3, which contains good comments.

6-4.8 t Symbol Table

Figure 6-1b is the *Symbol Table*. This table is generated at the end of the program listing when *OPT s* is specified on the command line. The symbol table lists each Symbol used by the program and the address or value of that Symbol. In a large program this can be very helpful in locating a particular Symbol (or label) location. The Symbols are listed in alphabetical order. In Fig. 6-1b nine symbols are used.

EXAMPLE 6-5

In the assembly of Fig. 6-1a, what is the starting address of the subroutine?

SOLUTION

We find that the label for the subroutine is SUBRTN. Its address can be found by examining the code, but in a long program, it can be found more easily by going directly to the Symbol Table, which in this case shows that SUBRTN equals $0119.

6-4.9 ▼ Cross-Reference Lists

Figure 6-1c is the *Cross-Reference List*. It lists the Symbols and their addresses as in the Symbol Table, but in addition, all the lines where the Symbols are used are also shown. The first location is marked with an asterisk to indicate where the Symbol is defined. This list is very valuable in debugging the program. The Assembler can be commanded to write a Cross-Reference List by including an *OPT cre* directive in the source program as shown on line 4 in Fig. 6-1a or a *cre* can be entered on the command line. Either will cause the Assembler to append a Cross-Reference List of Symbols to the Program Listing. Obviously, both *Opt s* and *OPT cre* are not needed for the same program because they contain redundant information.

6-5 ▼ ASSEMBLER DIRECTIVES

When writing a program, Assembler options exist that enable the programmer to reserve memory bytes for data, specify the starting address of the program, and select the format of the assembler output. These options are called **assembler directives.** They are instructions to the Assembler. Essentially, directives organize the output listing.

Directives are different for different Assemblers. The basic directives are common to all Assemblers, but more sophisticated Assemblers frequently have additional directives. The directives used in the listing of Fig. 6-1a are shown in Table 6-1. These assembler directives are all three-letter mnemonics (with the exception of PAGE). They are written into the source program like instructions and are interpreted by the Assembler during the assembly process. Three of the directives generate object code in the form of data, but others control only the Assembler. Table 6-1 shows that the **assembler directives** are divided into four major categories.

1. **Assembly control.** These directives define the starting address of each section of the program, and tell the Assembler when to stop processing the source program.
2. **Symbol (or label) definition.** These denote an address or a value that is assigned to a label.
3. **Data definition.** These directives specify the type of data and where it will be stored in memory.

TABLE 6-1 Assembler Directives

Assembly control

ORG	Set Program Counter
END	Stop assembling

Symbol definition

EQU	Assign permanent value

Data definition/storage allocation

BSZ	Block Storage of Zeroed single bytes
FCB	Form Constant Byte
FCC	Form Constant Character string
FDB	Form Double Byte
FILL	Initialize a block of memory to a constant
RMB	Reserve Memory; single Bytes
ZMB	Zero Memory Bytes; same as BSZ

Listing control

OPT c	Enable cycle counting
OPT cre	Print Cross-Reference Table
OPT l	Print source listing from this point
OPT nol	Inhibit printing of source listing from this point
OPT s	Print Symbol Table
PAGE	Print subsequent statements on top of next page

4. **Listing control.** These directives specify the output format of the assembly and which options are to be used.

The Program Listing of Fig. 6-1a shows how some of the directives are used.

6-5.1 ▼ Assembly Control Directives

The two assembly control directives listed in Table 6-1 are ORG and END. The ORG directive sets the program counter to its initial value and is used to put the program in the proper place in memory. The ORG directive should always be used before code is entered, as it was in line 5 of Fig. 6-1a. If the ORG directive is omitted, the code will default to starting at 0000. This is usually not what the programmer intended.

EXAMPLE 6-6

A program consists of a main loop and a subroutine. If the code for the main loop is to start at $C000 and the subroutine is to start at $D100, how can this be arranged?

SOLUTION

The code for the main loop should be preceded by the directive ORG $C000. At the end of this code the programmer should enter the directive ORG $D100 and then follow with the code for the subroutine. It is good form to leave blank lines before and after the second ORG statement, to separate the different parts of the program.

The END directive is intended to tell the Assembler when to stop assembling. Many Assemblers can sense the end of the source and therefore do not need an END statement.

Older Assemblers provided a NAM directive. NAM was in the operator field and was followed by the name of the program in the operand field. It had to be the first line of the program. The name used (up to eight characters) was printed at the start of the assembly. This directive has not been very popular and is not used by the current simplified Freeware Assemblers. We have found the NAM directive to be useful because it is printed in the list file and can be used to identify the disk file that it came from. This can be helpful if the user is wondering where the file can be found. This could be a good reason to purchase a more capable third-party Assembler.

6-5.2 ▼ EQU Directive

The only symbol definition directive used in Table 6-1 is the EQU Directive, used to assign a permanent value to a label. For example, the statement on line 6 of Fig. 6-1a,

```
COUNT EQU @12
```

assigns the value octal 12 (000A in hex) to the label COUNT, and that value is used in line 9. This directive is used to assign absolute values to a label. The addresses of the registers in the hardware peripheral devices used in a system are absolute numbers and the EQU directive is used to identify them (see Chapter 8).

6-5.3 ▼ Data Definition/Storage Allocations Directives

The data definition/storage allocation directives in Table 6-1 are outlined below.

BSZ. This directive is used to clear a block of memory when the program is loaded.

EXAMPLE 6-7

How would the programmer assure that the memory between $C000 and $C127 is clear of data (has zeros in all locations)?

SOLUTION

The source listing must include an ORG and a BSZ directive as follows:

```
            ORG $C000
(<Label>) BSZ $127 (<comments>)
```

The parentheses in the BSZ directive indicate that the label and comments are optional. The BSZ (and ZMB) directives cause the assembler to allocate a block of bytes, and each byte is given the initial value of zero. The number of bytes allocated is given by the expression in the operand field. The ORG directive preceding the BSZ positions the block in memory.

FCB (Form Constant Byte). FCB is used to define a 1-byte constant. The byte on line 27 of Fig. 6-1a is labeled BYTE and used by the instruction on line 22. The FCB is also used on line 28. Note that on line 28 two operands are defined, one written in hex and one written in binary. They occupy locations 134 and 135 in memory.

FDB (Form Double Byte). FDB defines a 2-byte constant. In Fig. 6-1a, a constant, labeled ADDR, is defined by the FDB directive on line 30. The operand of the FDB is the label DATA. The Assembler assigned address 136 to DATA and placed the number 138, the value of DATA, in it as required by the FDB directive.

FCC (Form Constant Characters). This directive (used on line 31) is used to format ASCII expressions or messages that are to be printed or displayed by a program. This directive generates the machine language equivalents for the ASCII characters included between the delimiters (apostrophes in this case). Here the word SET is translated to its hex equivalent of 53, 45, and 54, respectively.

The FCB and FDB mnemonics must be followed by a decimal, hex, octal, or binary number, or a label. Many bytes can be defined by a single FCB or FDB provided that the data values are separated by commas and don't overflow the line.

FILL. The FILL directive causes the Assembler to initialize an area of memory with a constant value. It is defined as follows:

```
(<label>) FILL <expression>,<expression>
```

The label is optional. The first expression must evaluate to the range of 0 to 255 and signifies the 1-byte value to be placed in the memory, and the second expression indicates the total number of successive bytes to be initialized. Again, the ORG directive often precedes the FILL directive to indicate the starting address of the area to be FILLed. Expressions in the FILL directive cannot contain forward references or undefined symbols.

RMB (Reserve Memory Byte). This directive reserves a location in memory or a group of locations where data is to be stored. If several areas are required for different types of data, several RMBs can be used. As shown in lines 25 and 26 of Fig. 6-1a, labels can precede the RMB and the value of the expression that follows determines the number of locations assigned.

EXAMPLE 6-8

In Fig. 6-1a, where is the stack located, and how is it specified by the assembler?

SOLUTION

Since the stack decrements when used, the RMB directive on line 25 specifies that 20 decimal or 14 hex locations are to be reserved for the stack. The RMB on line 26 reserves 1 byte and specifies the top or start of the stack. Line 26 includes the label STACK. STACK is referred to by the LDS instruction on line 7. In this example the assembler has thus assigned 21 locations from $011E to $0132 inclusive, for the stack.

6-5.4 ▼ Listing Control Directives

The listing control directives are also shown in Table 6-1. The various OPT directives are followed by a statement that explain the functions of each of the OPT directives except that OPT c or cycle counting needs more explanation. This is an assembler option that includes the number of cycles used by each instruction. This is shown in Fig. 6-2. Frequently, the number of cycles (or time) required to complete an external action is

```
0001                              * Test program to show cycle counting
0002                              * Written in 6800 codes
0003 c000                         org $C000
0004                              OPT c
0005 c000 8e c1 00     [ 3 ]      lds #$C100
0006 c003 ce 56 78     [ 3 ]      ldx #$5678
0007 c006 86 02        [ 2 ]      ldaa #2
0008 c008 4a           [ 2 ] t1   deca
0009 c009 26 fd        [ 4 ]      bne t1
0010 c00b bd c0 11     [ 9 ]      jsr t2
0011 c00e 7e c0 00     [ 3 ]      jmp $C000
0012
0013 c011 ce 00 00     [ 3 ] t2   ldx #0
0014 c014 39           [ 5 ]      rts
0015                              *
0016                              end
```

Figure 6-2 Program showing the number of cycles used by each instruction.

important in a MCU design. This assembler option allows the designer to optimize it. Appendix C includes a table of cycle-by-cycle operation for each **6800** instruction.

Examples of OPT s and OPT cre can be seen in Fig. 6-1b and c. OPT s was entered on the command line to generate the symbol table of Fig. 6-1b.

6-6 ▼ WRITING A PROGRAM

As an example of Assembly Language programming, let us write a source program (using an editor on a personal computer (PC) for a routine to convert BCD numbers to binary. The source program is shown in Fig. 6-3. This is basically the same program as used for Fig. 5-9, but the directives required by the assembler have been added. The program was written to a file called BCDBIN.S, which is a descriptive name for the program.

6-6.1 ▼ Source Code File

The source file starts with the NAME on a comment line. We recommend that all programs start with a name line, for two reasons:

1. The name line can indicate what the program does.
2. The name of the source file can be made the same.

Thus if a programmer is looking at the list and needs to know where the source file is on the disk, he or she can look at the name line. Here it would be BCDBIN, which would tell the person to look for the source file as BCDBIN.S.

The name line is followed by several other lines of comments to introduce the program. BCDBIN.S does not include line numbers, but we had the Assembler add them in the assembly listing for clarity of explanation.

The source program was written as follows:

1. The program starts with six lines of comments (plus a blank line). They name and date the program and explain what the program is doing, so that someone other than the original programmer might understand it.
2. The ORG directive starts the program at $C020.
3. Memory areas are set aside for the number to be converted and the result using the FCB directives.
4. The code starts at START1 and continues until HALT.
5. The subroutine, referenced in the code, starts at the label START2.
6. A list of 16-bit numbers is required to convert from BCD to binary. The list starts at $C100 and is defined by the FDB directives.

There are several other things to be aware of when writing a source code file:

1. All Labels must start at the leftmost column of the line. SHIFT2 and INCR are examples of labels that are used in Fig. 6-3.
2. All lines that do not define labels must have a space in the leftmost column of the line. This space tells the assembler that the line does not take a label and the next character starts the operator field. LDX #LIST is an example in Fig. 6-3.

```
* BCDBIN Program

* Used to convert a 4-digit BCD number to binary
* WORD1 & WORD2 contain the BCD words.
* SUM1 & SUM2 contain the binary equivalent.
* Rewritten by J. D. Greenfield 1-30-92.
* The program starts here.

          ORG    $C020
WORD1     FCB    0          MSB of packed BCD number.
WORD2     FCB    0          LSB of packed BCD number.
SUM1      FCB    0          MSB of binary output.
SUM2      FCB    0          LSB of binary output.

START1    LDS    #$C200     Set Stack
          LDX    #LIST
          CLR    SUM1
          CLR    SUM2
          LDAA   WORD2      Get LSB of word to be converted.
SHIFT2    ASRA              Shift it to see if LSB is a 1.
          BCC    INCR       If no, skip the subroutine.
          BSR    START2     If yes, go to the ADD subroutine.
INCR      INX
          INX               Increment X twice for each bit.
          CPX    #$C120     List completed?
          BEQ    HALT       Yes. Halt.
          CPX    #$C110     WORD2 finished?
          BNE    SHIFT2     No. Loop for next bit.
          LDAA   WORD1      Yes. Get WORD1
          BRA    SHIFT2

HALT      BRA    *

* Add algorithm subroutine.

START2    PSHA              Save A
          LDAA   1,X        Load LSB from list.
          ADDA   SUM2       Add LSB of sum.
          STAA   SUM2       Store updated sum.
          LDAA   0,X        Load MSB from list.
          ADCA   SUM1       Add MSB of sum.
          STAA   SUM1       Store updated sum.
          PULA              Retrieve A
          RTS

          ORG    #$C100
LIST      FDB    1,2,4,8,10,20,40,80,100,200,400,800
          FDB    1000,2000,4000,8000
          END
```

Figure 6-3 Source Program BCDBIN.ASM

3. The object of all BRANCH or JUMP instructions must be a label, and this label must be defined on another line. BCC INCR is an example in Fig. 6-3.

6-6.2 ▼ List File

The list file, BCDBIN.LST, was created by assembling BCDBIN.S. It is shown in Fig. 6-4 and lists all the locations, the op codes, and data they contain. Observe how the 2-byte decimal numbers in the LIST statement were converted to hex numbers by the Assembler.

The first four statements after the ORG statement (lines 11 through 14) are FCBs that reserve memory locations to hold the binary number to be converted (In WORD1 and WORD2) and the results (in SUM1 and SUM2). The ORG directive in line 10 causes the Assembler to assign locations $C020 through $C023 to these addresses.

Line 18 is LDX #LIST. For this instruction the assembler must be able to determine the value of LIST. Here the value of LIST is assigned in line 50. The ORG statement on line 49 causes the list to start at $C100.

6-6.3 ▼ Running the Program

To run the program, the user must first insert the four-digit BCD number to be converted into WORD1 and WORD2. After the program is run, the results will appear in SUM1 and SUM2. An evaluation system with its Monitor program as described in Section 11-5 can be used to do this, or it can be tested by running it in a *simulator* program (see Section 11-7).

6-6.4 ▼ Assembling the Program

Before writing a source program the user should have a current Assembler available and should consult the manual for that Assembler. The user must understand the directives and rules that apply to the Assembler actually being used, or statements may be written that cause errors. Section 6-13 contains references to several such manuals.

Assemblers for many of Motorola's μPs are available on the *Freeware BBS*, an electronic bulletin board that can be reached at 512-891-3733. Motorola provides this BBS to give its users current information on their μPs. Assemblers are available to run on IBM-PCs or compatibles or on Apple's Macintosh computers.

An example of such an Assembler is the AS11 Assembler for the **68HC11** MCU. It will also Assemble **6800** code which is a subset of the **68HC11.** (The **68HC11** is discussed in more detail in Section 10-7.) To use this Assembler, the programmer must:

1. Download a copy of AS11 from the Freeware BBS, or obtain it from another source.

2. Write a source code file on the same computer that contains the Assembler program. We recommend that source code files be given the name <filename>.S, where <filename> is the name the user is assigning to the program. Because we do not have a NAM directive in these Freeware Assemblers, the programmer should place the same name in a comment line at the start of the source file. The .S extension can be used to identify the file as a source file.

3. The Assembler can be invoked by typing the command

```
AS11 <filename>.S -l (lower case L)
```

```
00001                     * BCDBIN Program
00002
00003                     * Used to convert a 4-digit BCD number to binary
00004                     * WORD1 & WORD2 contain the BCD words.
00005                     * SUM1 & SUM2 contain the binary equivalent.
00006                     * Rewritten by J. D. Greenfield 1-30-92.
00007
00008                     * The program starts here.
00009
00010  c020                          ORG    $C020
00011
00012  c020    00    WORD1   FCB    0           MSB of packed BCD number.
00013  c021    00    WORD2   FCB    0           LSB of packed BCD number.
00014  c022    00    SUM1    FCB    0           MSB of binary output
00015  c023    00    SUM2    FCB    0           LSB of binary output
00016
00017  c024 8e c200  START1  LDS    #$C200      Set Stack
00018  c027 ce c100          LDX    #LIST
00019  c02a 7f c022          CLR    SUM1
00020  c02d 7f c023          CLR    SUM2
00021  c030 b6 c021          LDAA   WORD2       Get LSB of word to be con-
   verted.
00022  c033 47       SHIFT2  ASRA               Shift it to see if LSB is a 1.
00023  c034 24 02            BCC    INCR        If no, skip the subroutine.
00024  c036 8d 13            BSR    START2      If yes, go to the ADD subrou-
   tine
00025  c038 08       INCR    INX
00026  c039 08               INX                Increment X twice for each bit.
00027  c03a 8c c120          CPX    #$C120      List completed?
00028  c03d 27 0a            BEQ    HALT        Yes. Halt.
00029  c03f 8c c110          CPX    #$C110      WORD2 finished?
00030  c042 26 ef            BNE    SHIFT2      No. Loop for next bit.
00031  c044 b6 c020          LDAA   WORD1       Yes. Get WORD1
00032  c047 20 ea            BRA    SHIFT2
00033
00034  c049 20 fe    HALT    BRA    *
00035
00036                     * Add algorithm subroutine.
00037
00038
00039  c04b 36       START2  PSHA               Save A
00040  c04c a6 01            LDAA   1,X         Load LSB from list.
00041  c04e bb c023          ADDA   SUM2        Add LSB of sum
00042  c051 b7 c023          STAA   SUM2        Store updated sum.
00043  c054 a6 00            LDAA   0,X         Load MSB from list.
00044  c056 b9 c022          ADCA   SUM1        Add MSB of sum.
00045  c059 b7 c022          STAA   SUM1        Store updated sum.
00046  c05c 32               PULA               Retrieve A
00047  c05d 39               RTS
00048
00049  c100                          ORG    $C100
00050  c100 00010002 LIST    FDB    1,2,4,8,10,20,40,80,100,200,400,800
00051  c118 03e807d0         FDB    1000,2000,4000,8000
```

Figure 6-4 Program Listing, BCDBIN.LST

On an IBM-PC this will cause the *list file* (see Section 6-4) to appear on the screen. If it is more than a few lines, it probably will contain errors. If it contains **fatal errors,** which are errors that prevent the program from assembling, only they will be shown and the program will terminate. If the errors are less serious, the listing will be displayed with the error messages inserted above each statement that caused an error.

4. After the errors have been corrected, the user should preserve the file. We recommend that the user issue the command

```
AS11 <filename>.S -l > <filename>.LST
```

The > redirects the screen output and will store the list file into the file named (with the .LST extension) on the disk. This allows it to be displayed or printed.

5. AS11 will also produce a file called <filename>.S19 every time it is invoked. This is the *Object* File in S-Record form (see Section 6-7).

6. To sum up, the user must start with AS11 and the source (.S) file. When he or she is finished, two more files will have been created, the list (.LST) file and the object (.S19) file.

6-6.5 ▼ Errors

Assemblers will display errors that prevent a program from assembling correctly. This is very helpful because these errors indicate syntax errors made by the programmer. Figure 6-5 is a source program that contains many of the most common types of errors. It does nothing

```
0001                    NAM      ERROR1
0002
0003                    ORG      $C020
0004         START      LDAA     $C100
0005                    ADDA     C101
0006                    ADDA     #FF
0007                    STOA     $C102
0008                    BCC
0009                    ADD      JANE
0010                    BNE      BAMBI
0011                    JSR      MIKE
0012
0013                    BRA      *
0014
0015                    ORG      $C200
0016         MIKE       LDAA     $C103
0017                    ADDA     $C104
0018         BAMBI      TAB
0019
0020                    END
```

Figure 6-5 Source file containing syntax errors.

```
0001                          *       NAME      ERROR1
0002 c020                             ORG       $C020
0003
0004 c020 b6 c1 00   START    LDAA      $C100
5: symbol Undefined on pass 2
0005 c023 bb 00 00            ADDA       C101
6: symbol Undefined on pass 2
0006 c026 8b 00              ADDA       #FF
0007 c028 b7 c1 02            STAA      $C102
8: Branch out of Range
0008 c02b 24 fe              BCC
9: symbol Undefined on pass 2
0009 c02d bb 00 00           ADDA      JANE
10: Branch out of Range
0010 c030 26 fe              BNE       BAMBI
0011 c032 bd c2 00           JSR       MIKE
0012 c035 20 fe              BRA       *
0013
0014 c200                    ORG       $C200
0015 c200 b6 c1 03   MIKE     LDAA      $C103
0016 c203 bb c1 04            ADDA      $C104
0017 c206 16         BAMBI    TAB
0018                          END
```

Figure 6-6 Listing of ERROR1 file showing second pass errors (for Example 6-9)

useful and makes many mistakes doing it. It was written to illustrate the reaction of the Assembler to errors.

The first time an assembly was attempted, pass 1 printed out two errors and stopped. They were unrecognized mnemonics on lines 7 and 9. Examining the file, we see that both lines contain nonexistent op codes. Line 7 should read STAA. On line 9, ADD is not an op code; it must be ADDA or ADDB.

Once the op code errors were corrected, the Assembler attempted pass 2 and printed out a list file that indicated where it found additional errors. The results are shown in Fig. 6-6. The error messages apply to the line below them.

```
S00600004844521B
S1130000285F245F2212226A000424290008237C2A
S11300100002000800082629001853812341001813
S113002041E900084E4223430018234200082 4A952
S113003000144ED492
S9030000FC
```

Figure 6-7 Typical S-Record Object file.

EXAMPLE 6-9

Explain the errors made in Fig. 6-6.

SOLUTION

Pass 2 found five errors. They are:

- **Line 5:** The assembler thinks that C101 is a symbol and cannot find it. The line should have read ADDA $C101.
- **Line 6:** The Assembler is looking for the symbol FF. The line should have read ADDA #$FF.
- **Line 8:** There is no target specified for the BCC.
- **Line 9:** JANE is nowhere to be found. She should have been defined by an FCB.
- **Line 10:** Location BAMBI is too far away from the branch instruction because of the second ORG directive. This is a genuine branch out of range.

Even if a program assembles with no syntax errors, there still may be logic errors that the Assembler will not catch. If all the syntax errors of Example 6-9 were corrected, the program would still have the following errors.

1. The Stack Pointer has not been defined. In this case the assembler may put it at location 0. What happens when it tries to decrement it?
2. Subroutine Mike does not end in an RTS.

Of course, there are many other possible errors. The manuals on each assembler often include error messages and explain their meaning.

6-7 ▼ OBJECT CODE OUTPUT

The Motorola Assembler programs, whether resident in Personal Computers (PCs), on a mainframe, or in a μP Development System (MDS), produce Object Files in an ASCII–hex format. A sample Object file in S-Record format is shown in Fig. 6-7. This is a Motorola standard and is universally used for downloading object code to Motorola systems (see Chapter 11). The machine language or data file is encoded into ASCII characters so that it can be transported through the serial ports of the development and evaluation systems by standard communications programs. The path can include modems as well.

S-Records are character strings that can be divided into five fields: record type, record length, address, code/data, and checksum. The record length and checksum provide a method to ensure accuracy of transmission. Table 6-2 shows the composition of these five fields.

TABLE 6-2 S-Record Field Composition

Field	Printable Characters	Contents
Type	2	S-record type: S0, S1, etc.
Record length	2	Number of character pairs in the record, excluding type and record length pairs.
Address	4, 6, or 8	The 2-, 3-, or 4-byte address at which the data field is to be loaded into memory.
Code/data	0–n	From 0 to n bytes of executable code, memory-loadable data, or descriptive information. for compatibility with teletypewriters, some programs may limit the number of bytes to as few as 28 (of 56 printable characters in the S-record).
Checksum	2	The least significant byte of the 1s complement of the sum of the values represented by the pairs of characters making up the record's length, address, and code/data fields.

These methods were first developed for 8-bit μPs and all the data was handled using three types of records: S0, S1, and S9. A record is a one-line string of characters, and one of these pairs of characters comprises the first two characters in each record. The S0 record simply contains the name of the file, as specified by the NAM directive. Many modern assemblers ignore the NAM directive and no longer create an S0 record. The S1 records contain the data or machine code for the program that was assembled and the S9 line is a terminating line.

Today, assemblers must be able to handle 16- and 32-bit word lengths for the newer MCUs. For this purpose the S-Record concept was expanded to include S2, S3, S7, and S8 records. Table 6-3 explains the record types currently in use. Because we are dealing only with 8-bit systems at this time, we need only understand the S1 or *data* line and the S9 or *terminating* line.

6-7.1 ▼ S1 Line

The S-Record file for the BCDBIN program of Fig. 6-4 is shown in Fig. 6-8. It consists of only S1 lines and an S9 line. The S1 lines contain the object codes of the program. There may be many S1 lines because the number of data bytes for each line is limited to a specific number. This number varies with different assemblers (or monitor ROMs, which also generate this format). Some programs provide 16 bytes on a line as in Fig. 6-6 or 32 as in Fig. 6-8. The last S1 line can be anything less, even only 1 byte of data.

For 8-bit μPs, each line starts with either S1, which identifies it as a data line, or S9, which makes it the last line in the assembly or the terminating line. As explained in Table 6-2, the S1 or S9 type is followed by a *byte count* or *record length* (two hexadecimal characters) that defines the number of bytes in the remainder of the line (including the address and the checksum). The third field in the record is the *address*, indicating where the data will go. This is followed by the data bytes themselves. The line ends with a checksum byte. The checksum is used by the loader routine to verify that no errors were

TABLE 6-3 S-Record Types

TYPE	DESCRIPTION
S0	The header record for each block of S-records. The code/data field may contain any descriptive information identifying the following block of S-records. The address field is normally zeros.
S1	A record containing code/data and the 2-byte address at which the code/data is to reside.
S2	A record containing code/data and the 3-byte address at which the code/data is to reside.
S3	A record containing code/data and the 4-byte address at which the code/data is to reside.
S7	A termination record for a block of S3 records. The address field may optionally contain the 4-byte address of the instruction to which control is to be passed. There is no code/data field.
S8	A termination record for a block of S2 records. The address field may optionally contain the 3-byte address of the instruction to which control is to be passed. There is no code/data field.
S9	A termination record for a block of S1 records. The address field may optionally contain the 2-byte address of the instruction to which control is to be passed. If such an address is not specified, the first entry point specification encountered in the object module input will be used. There is no code/data field.

made in reading the file from the disk or in transmitting it to the user's system. As Table 6-2 shows, *the checksum is the 1s complement of the summation of all of the data, byte count, and address bytes*. It is calculated by the Assembler and is written to the disk as the last byte of each line. The loading function of the monitor program used in the development system (see Chapter 11) recalculates the sum as it loads the program and prints an error message if it is wrong. This avoids wasting time with a faulty program.

6-7.2 ▼ S9 Line

The S9 line signifies the end of the Object Code. The byte count and checksum for this terminating line are calculated in the same way as for the other type lines. Most assemblers place 0000 in the address field of the S9 line. Some versions have an option to include the starting address for the program in the S9 line.

```
S123C020000000008EC200CEC1007FC0227FC023B6C0214724028D1308088CC120270A8C7C
S121C040C11026EFB6C02020EA20FE36A601BBC023B7C023A600B9C022B7C0223239E0
S123C1000001000200040008000A001400280050006400C80190032003E807D00FA01F40C6
S9030000FC
```

Figure 6-8 S-Record Object file for the BCDBIN program.

EXAMPLE 6-10

The S-Record file for the BCDBIN program is shown in Fig. 6-8. Explain the first few bytes of the file.

SOLUTION

The first byte is S1, which identifies it as an S1 line. The second byte is $23. This is the byte count for the remainder of the line and indicates that there will be 35 (decimal) bytes following on this line. The next 2 bytes are $C020. This is the address where the code in this line is to be written to memory. The next 4 bytes are 00s. They are written into the locations reserved for WORD1, WORD2, SUM1, and SUM2. Then the instruction code starts as 8E C2 00 CE . . . . The last two characters in the line, $7C, are the checksum for this line.

6-8 ▼ ASSEMBLERS FOR VARIOUS HARDWARE CONFIGURATIONS

Various Assembler programs are provided by Motorola and other companies to generate **6800** family system software. Most are designed to be used with one of the standard MDSs (see Chapter 11) or with a Personal Computer. The function of these systems is to serve as a software development station to write, edit, and assemble **6800 family** programs. (**6800, 6801, 6805, 68HC11,** etc. are supported).

While developing software, the resulting object programs must also be debugged by running them in a system with the same processor and I/O ports as the system under development. A number of **Evaluation Modules** are available from Motorola (and others) for this purpose. They are also described in Chapter 11.

While Motorola now provides a complete line of Cross-Assemblers for the **6800 family** that run on IBM-PC and Apple Macintosh computers, many other Assemblers with various capabilities are supplied by third-party vendors. Versions are available to run on IBM mainframes, DEC PDP-11s, and even Z80 microcomputers. Information on these is provided in Section 6-13.

6-9 ▼ ADVANCED ASSEMBLERS

The Motorola Freeware Assemblers available on the BBS are suitable for developing programs up to approximately 2K bytes of object code with relative ease. But because more modern MCUs are using large and more complex programs, several more powerful assemblers for these 8- and 16-bit μCs have been developed. These assemblers are generally known as **Macro Assemblers.** They are a dramatic improvement over the simple Freeware Assemblers provided on the BBS. They have advanced capabilities such as:

1. Relocation
2. Linking
3. Macro operations
4. Conditional Assembly

6-9.1 ▼ Relocation and Linking

Very large programs can be developed more quickly by having several programmers working on different parts of the program simultaneously and then linking all the parts together. Each part or subsection of a large program is called a *module*. When the module is translated to machine language by the assembler, it is called an object module.

A large program consists of several modules, which, in turn, have *sections*. Each section contains a specific type of code or data and is defined in the following paragraphs. The program sections provide the basis of the relocation and linking procedure. The sections are passed on to the linker. From the modules to be linked, the linker collects all sections of the same type together and assigns a memory area to each section in order to create the load module. As a result, the **absolute load module** produced by the linker will contain one continuous memory area for each section type encountered during the linking process.

The concept of generating *relocatable* modules and *linking* them was developed for use with large computers, but it is now applicable to μCs also. It provides the following capabilities:

1. Parallel program development by a team
2. Easy development of programs for RAM/ROM environment
3. Easy specification of any addressing mode

6-9.2 ▼ Program Sections

Macro Assemblers partition the μC's memory into several sections. These sections are defined by the following directives:

1. **ASCT (absolute section).** This is a nonrelocatable section. This section is used to allocate or initialize memory locations that are assigned by the programmer rather than by the linker. For example, ASCT can be used to define the locations of PIAs, ACIAs, or any other interface IC that must, because its hard-wired, occupy a specific address in memory.
2. **BSCT (base section).** This is a relocatable section. The linker assigns portions of the base section to each module that requires space in BSCT. The base section is generally used for variables that are accessed using the direct addressing mode. BSCT is restricted to memory locations 0 through 255 (the direct addressing range).
3. **CSCT (blank common section).** This is a relocatable section. CSCT is similar to blank common used in FORTRAN. The blank common section is an unnamed scratch pad area and cannot be initialized (set to specific values).
4. **DSCT (data section).** This is a relocatable section. The linker assigns portions of this section to each program that requires space in DSCT. DSCT is generally used

to contain data or variables in RAM and is usually accessed with the extended addressing mode.

5. **IDSCT (initialized data section).** This is a relocatable section. The IDSCT can be used to contain initial values to initialize RAM areas at startup time in a controller environment by moving a block of initialized data from ROM (IDSCT) area to RAM (DSCT) area.

6. **IPSCT (initialized program section).** This is a relocatable section. It can contain the code for initializing IDSCT areas. The IPSCT code is generally written in ROM.

7. **PSCT (program section).** This is a relocatable section. PSCT is similar to DSCT; however, it is generally used to contain program instructions. The use of PSCT allows creation of programs that reside in ROM.

6-9.3 ▼ Common Areas of Memory

The CSCT contains an uninitialized blank common area of memory. At times, however, it is convenient to have several common areas, each of which may be initialized. Therefore, the concept of *named common* was included in the **6800** family Macro Assembler relocation and linking scheme. Named common can be specified in either BSCT, DSCT, or PSCT sections. The size of the named common area that is allocated is the largest of the named common sizes from the program modules that reference it. A named common block must reside wholly within a single section.

6-9.4 ▼ Relocation

Using this type of Assembler, Relocatable Modules are produced when assembling the various subprograms written by the programmers. The term *relocatable* means that the data in the module has not yet been assigned to absolute addresses in memory; instead, each different section of the program is assembled or compiled as though it started at relative address 0. The exception to this is an **absolute section** of the final program, which is assigned to an *absolute* starting address at assembly time. The absolute section provides the fixed addresses of the I/O ports and memory as determined by the hardware configuration.

After a group of these modules have been generated they are *linked* together by a program called a **Linkage Editor** or **Linker.** Linking is necessary so that the independently programmed modules are not assigned overlapping addresses in memory, and they can address each other properly. The linker then combines the modules to create an **Absolute Load Module.** While this output module contains all of the data at the proper addresses, it is formatted in **Common Object File Format** (COFF). COFF is used by large computers, particularly in the UNIX environment. The COFF standard is documented in the Motorola *SYSTEM V/68 Support Tools Guide* cited in Section 6-13. A utility program provided with this software reads the COFF file and writes a Motorola S-record file suitable for loading into the system under development. This, of course, is the final object module that is installed in the system ROM after it is fully debugged.

When creating an absolute load module, the Linker reads in all the relocatable object modules that comprise a program and assigns each section to an absolute memory address. The inputs to the Linker are relocatable object modules produced by the Assembler, by a Compiler, such as CC11 (see Section 6-11), or by the Linker itself. Then, in the process of actually putting the code and data read from each object module into the proper location in the load module, the linker must fill in the correct address for such items as absolute loading addresses and referencing across sections. This is the process of relocation.*

Along with relocation, the Linker performs **reference resolution** between modules, which allows one module to reference symbols defined in a different module. This is accomplished in the following manner. At the time of compilation or assembly, the referencing module does not know where the symbol it is referencing is to be located in the final load module. Therefore, the compiler or assembler places information in the symbol table of the relocatable object module to indicate that an external symbol is referenced in this module. The location referenced by the symbol is stored in the module's relocation table. This is called an *external reference* (XREF). Also, the relocatable object module in which the symbol is defined identifies the symbol definition information. The symbol definition, which includes the symbol and the relative address of the symbol in the module, is called an *external definition* (XDEF). When the two modules are read by the linker, an address is assigned to each symbol defined with an XDEF, and the correct address of the symbol is inserted wherever it is referenced (by an XREF).

The user can break up a large program into smaller, more manageable modules that can be assembled or compiled separately. Using relocation and linking, the Linker can **link edit** these modules to produce a final object file. If a problem is encountered, only the module that contains the problem has to be edited and recompiled or reassembled. Then the user can perform *reference resolution* between the new relocatable object module and the other object modules created previously.

6-9.5 ▼ Macros

A **Macro** is a set of instructions that can be called by a simple name (like a Symbol). Programming applications frequently involve repeating the same group of instructions. If they are defined once as a Macro, and given a name, the name becomes the mnemonic and it is only necessary to substitute the name of the Macro as a source statement each time this same routine is needed. The Macro can also be invoked with different parameters each time it is called.

A Macro can be called from anywhere in the program. The programmer can use the Macro as many times as needed, substituting different parameters for the designated variable portions of the statements. These are called *Substitutable Arguments*.

Invoking a Macro. To invoke a Macro, the macro mnemonic must appear in the op code field of a source statement. Any arguments are placed in the operand field. By suitably selecting these arguments, the programmer then causes the Assembler to produce in-line coding variations of the macro definition. The effect of a macro call is the same as that of an open subroutine call, except that the macro produces in-line code to perform the macro function. The code is inserted in the normal flow of the program so that the generated instructions are executed in-line with the rest of the program each time the macro name is encountered. Once a Macro is debugged, it simplifies coding, just as a modular subroutine does.

*Relocatable and position-independent codes are different. A position-independent program uses relative branches and runs correctly when the machine code is positioned arbitrarily in memory. On the other hand, the output of the **6800** family Portable Cross-Assemblers (PASMs) is relocatable (i.e., it can be assigned to any location because the jumps and branches are then calculated correctly by the assembler).

Substitutable Arguments. When a Macro statement is used it causes source statements to be generated by the Assembler. The statements may contain *Substitutable Arguments*. A substitutable argument is a *Symbol* that stands for a number. The number to be used is substituted in the operand field of the macro. Substitutable Arguments can be used with any processor instruction, almost any Assembler directive, or any previously defined Macro.

The following example of Substitutable Arguments applies to all **6800 family** assemblers except for the **M6805** Macro Assembler (because it does not have an accumulator B).

EXAMPLE 6-11

The following three code patterns are used in a program:

```
ADDA  LA+5        ADDA  LU          ADDA  LW+LX
ADCB  LB+5        ADCB  LV          ADCB  LY+LZ
SUBA  LC          SUBA  ALPHA       SUBA  GAMMA
SBCB  LD          SBCB  BETA        SBCB  DELTA
```

Write a single macro that can be used with arguments.

SOLUTION

The following macro definition could be used:

```
LDM      MACR
         ADDA  \0
         ADCB  \1
         SUBA  \2
         SBCB  \3
         ENDM
```

The symbols \0, \1, \2, and \3 are the Substitutable Arguments. Each code pattern could be replaced as follows:

```
LDM      LA+5,LB+5,LC,LD
         •
LDM      LU,LV,ALPHA,BETA
         •
LDM      LW+LX,LY+LZ,GAMMA,DELTA
```

The LDM operator calls the Macro, and the substitutable arguments are the operands that follow. They substitute in the Macro for the appropriate backslash character: \0, \1, and so on. The Assembler recognizes these substitutable arguments by the presence of the backslash (\) character.

An example showing all the detail of a macro and its expansion is too complex to show here. The student is referred to the Macro Assembler and Linker manuals listed in Section 6-13 for examples.

Conditional assembly. The **conditional assembly** feature of an assembler makes it possible to have one source file that will accommodate any number of different hardware *conditions* or applications. Having one file makes it easier to keep the performance the same for all conditions of the target system.

Different assembly conditions may then be specified through the use of arguments in the case of macros, and through definition of symbols via the SET and EQU directives. Both of these directives assign a value to their label, but while the EQU value is permanent, the SET value can be redefined by subsequent SET directives. Inserting a new SET value will then cause assembly of only those parts necessary for the specified conditions.

The **absolute expression comparison** form of the conditional assembly directive compares an expression to zero and assembles code when a specified relationship is true. Otherwise, it skips over that code. The following table shows values of XX that are accepted by the assembler and their significance.

IFXX	ASSEMBLE CODE IF:
IFEQ	<expression> = 0
IFNE	<expression> <> 0
IFLT	<expression> < 0
IFLE	<expression> <= 0
IFGT	<expression> > 0
IFGE	<expression> >= 0

The *absolute expression comparison* compares the <expression> to zero. The XX letter pair specifies the result. The conditional assembly structure is terminated by an ENDC directive. The alert reader will notice that these are like branch instructions and must be preceded by an expression that needs to be evaluated.

For example, suppose that a system is equipped with a disk and a tape drive. A variable called DEVTYP could be defined to tell the assembler whether to use disk or tape. The coding might be

```
*
* DEVTYP SET = 0    MEANS DISK I/O
* DEVTYP SET = 1    MEANS TAPE I/O     (OR NOT 0)
*

        .
        IFEQ DEVTYP
        .
        .     DISK I/O STATEMENTS
        .
        .
        ENDC
        IFNE DEVTYP
        .
        .     TAPE I/O STATEMENTS
        .
        ENDC
```

When the program is assembled, one of the I/O sections will be included and one will be excluded based on the assembly time value of the symbol "DEVTYP."

If the statement DEVTYP SET = 0 is placed into the source file prior to any references, the disk I/O will be included. If it is DEVTYP SET = 1, the disk I/O will be excluded and the tape I/O will be included. Other conditional expressions could have been used (e.g., "greater than" or "less than").

Modern Macro Assemblers. The features just described are included in a number of assembler programs that are available to develop assembly language programs for Motorola **6800, 6801, 6804, 6805, 6809,** and **68HC11** microprocessors.

The *M6800 Family Portable Cross Assembler (PASM) Reference Manual* contains rules, examples, and guidelines to help programmers, system designers, analysts, and software engineers to develop the assembly language programs for the **6800** family of μCs. The information contained in the manual pertains only to operation of the assemblers.

Motorola has produced a number of Macro Assemblers. They differ slightly in specific details. We will not attempt to cover the details here because they can be found in the user's manuals. They are listed in Section 6-13.

A growing number of third-party vendors are providing assemblers and other development tools for these Motorola MCUs. Many of them have features similar to those we have described. Motorola has issued a catalog of third-party vendors called the *MCU Toolbox*. It includes descriptions of features as well as names and telephone numbers. See Section 6-13 for details.

6-10 ▼ COMPILERS

Throughout this chapter we described Assemblers that translate Assembly Language statements into machine language. Compilers are an alternative tool for program development in MCU applications. A **Compiler** is a program similar to an assembler that translates High-Level language statements into machine language. Languages such as BASIC, FORTRAN, Pascal, and others have been used for years in other computers. In recent years the C language has become very popular.

Compilers must be written for a specific language and for a specific CPU. C Compilers have been written for IBM-PCs, Apple Macintoshes, and many other computers that use UNIX. The C programs can thus be transported or *ported* from one computer to another with little or no change in the C source program. This, of course, is true for general-purpose computers and does not apply to application specific MCUs.

Growing use of the C language has prompted the development of the **68HC11** Cross C Compiler, described in Motorola manual **M68HCC11** listed in Section 6-13. The high-level languages, such as BASIC and the others, are considered to be much easier to use than Assembly Language. Various estimates indicate that programming can be done at least 25% faster in C than in assembly language. However, experienced MCU designers tell us that C does not produce as efficient code as Assembly Language. That is, it uses more bytes of memory and is therefore slower than an Assembly Language version. But because larger ROMs are now available and not all routines suffer from the slower execution speed, C can be used in many cases without a problem.

A new technique is to write the program in C and then replace any troublesome sections with assembly language modules. This, of course, is easily done using the relocatable assemblers and linkers just described. The CC11 compiler produces relocatable modules compatible with the Motorola Cross Linkage Editor described in Section 6-9.4. Many third-party vendors also provide C compilers and linkers.

6-11 ▼ SUMMARY

Because of its mnemonic nature and easy correlation with I/O hardware features, Assembly Language is used for most program development of MCU systems. In this chapter we have explained how to write an Assembly Language source program and how to translate it to machine language. Detailed printouts of assembler program listings were shown and their features presented in detail. Directives, symbol tables, and error messages were demonstrated to help the user write and debug programs.

We then described more advanced Assemblers, and the techniques of Linking, Relocation, and Conditional Assembly and the use of Macros were covered. These features are now used in the Assemblers for the **6800** family of μPs and μCs. Finally, use of the C language with its Compiler was described as an alternative for program development.

6-12 ▼ GLOSSARY

Assembler directive An instruction-like mnemonic that controls the assembler. Some directives produce object code, but others affect the formatting of the listing.

Checksum byte A byte calculated by the assembler to be the 1s complement of the sum of the bytes on each line and appended to each line of the object program. It is checked by the loader to verify that no error occurred in loading.

Common Object File Format (COFF) The object file format used by many Macro Assemblers and UNIX systems.

Compiler A program like an Assembler that translates High-Level language statements into machine language.

Conditional Assembly An assembler feature that includes, or excludes, certain instructions at will.

Cross-assembler An assembler program that runs on one type of computer and generates object code for a different type of computer. It also produces a program listing.

Cross-reference listing An optional listing of the symbols used in an assembly, showing the line numbers where the symbols were referenced.

Direct address An address below $100 that permits 2-byte instructions to be used.

Directive A statement in a source file that controls the assembler.

Editor A program used to write or edit source programs and save them on disk.

Evaluation module A small test system for use in debugging programs or testing hardware interfaces.

Extended addressing The instruction addressing mode that references addresses above $FF using 3-byte instructions.

Immediate addressing The instruction mode that uses the value of the second byte of an instruction instead of treating it as an address as is done for the *direct addressing mode*. In some cases it uses the value of the second and third bytes as a 16-bit operand.

Indexed addressing The addressing mode that uses the address in the index register (X) for the operand. In some cases it uses this address plus an *offset*.

Inherent instructions Instructions that require only one byte because all the information needed for their execution is already within the μP and no memory locations or immediate operands are required.

Initialize To assign values to memory locations or registers that allow the program to start up properly.

Label A mnemonic word used to reference an address or value.

Link edit A term used to describe the process of combining relocatable object modules.

Linker A program to combine relocatable object modules into an absolute load module (for a specific address).

Macro instruction An instruction-like mnemonic that the macro assembler replaces with a sequence of assembly language statements.

Monitor A control program, usually in ROM, which provides routines to load or dump programs and to test them. Monitors also allow memory and register contents to be viewed or changed.

Offset A value in the second byte of indexed mode instructions that is added to the index register to get the address of the operand.

Program Listing A printout produced by an assembler or compiler showing the addresses and object code associated with each mnemonic statement of the source program.

Relocatable object module An object code module produced by an assembler intended for use with a Linking Loader.

Source program A list of mnemonic statements written by the programmer.

S-records The standard Motorola format for object files.

Symbol table A list of each symbol used by a program and the address or value of that symbol. Symbols are also called labels.

Syntax A format of source statements required by the Assembler or Compiler.

6-13 ▼ REFERENCES

MOTOROLA, *Freeware PC Compatible 8-Bit Cross-Assembler User's Manual,* M68FCASS/AD1, Phoenix, Ariz., March 1990.

————, *The MCU Toolbox for M68HC05, 68HC11, M68HC16, M68300,* Phoenix, Ariz., September 1991.

————, *M6800 Family Portable Cross Assembler (PASM) Reference Manual,* M68HASM/D1, Phoenix, Ariz., June 1989.

————, *M6800 Family Portable Cross Linkage Editor Reference Manual for MS-DOS/PC-DOS,* M68HLINK/D2, Phoenix, Ariz., August 1990.

————, *M6800 Programming Reference Manual,* M68PRM(D), Phoenix, Ariz., November 1976.

————, *68HC11 Family Cross C Compiler User's Manual,* M68HCC11/D2, Phoenix, Ariz., January 1990.

————, *SYSTEM V/68 Support Tools Guide,* Phoenix, Ariz., 1986.

————, *Toolware Macro Assembler User's Manual,* M68HCASM/D1, Phoenix, Ariz., September 1991.

————, *Toolware Linker User's Manual,* MC68HLINK2/D3, Phoenix, Ariz., September 1991.

6-14 ▼ PROBLEMS

6-1. In Fig 6-4, what is the location of:
   (a) SUM1?
   (b) START1?
   (c) LIST?
   (d) SHIFT2?

6-2. In Fig. 6-4, why are 0s shown on lines 11 through 14?

6-3. Which of the following are satisfactory labels:
   (a) SAM
   (b) SUZY Q
   (c) SUZYQ
   (d) 2SUZY
   (e) SUZY2
   (f) BILLANDJOE
   (g) X
   (h) Y
   (i) Z

6-4. Verify the relative offset value in location $C048 of Fig. 6-4.

6-5. Write an assembly language source program for the program of Table 5-2.

6-6. Write an assembly language source program for the program of Problem 5-11.

6-7. What would have happened to the listing of Fig. 6-4 if line 9 (the ORG) had been omitted?

6-8. Is ADDA #115 a legitimate instruction? Is ADDA #$115 legitimate?

6-9. Explain how each byte of the S9 line in Fig. 6-8 was obtained.

6-10. The following instructions are located at $C200:

```
C200      BNE   -2A
C202      BRA   *+5C
```

Where does each instruction branch to? Write the code for each instruction.

After attempting to solve these problems, try to answer the self-evaluation questions in Section 6-2. If any of them still seem difficult, review the appropriate sections of the chapter to find the answers.

THE HARDWARE CONFIGURATION OF THE 6800 SYSTEM

7-1 ▼ INSTRUCTIONAL OBJECTIVES

In this chapter we introduce the hardware components of the **6800** system and examine some of the problems encountered when interconnecting them. After reading the chapter, the student should be able to:

1. List each component of the **6800** system and explain its function.
2. Explain the functions of the address and data buses and each line of the **6800** control bus.
3. Determine the number of clock cycles and the number of data bytes required by each instruction.
4. Determine the exact data that appears on the address and data buses at the end of each instruction.
5. Allocate memory space to the various components of a system.

7-2 ▼ SELF-EVALUATION QUESTIONS

Watch for the answers to the following questions as you read the chapter. They should help you to understand the material presented.

1. What are the three states of a three-state driver?
2. Why do memories need three-state driver/receivers on their data lines but only receivers on their address lines?
3. Are the μP data bus drivers enabled when the R/W line is in READ or WRITE mode? Explain.
4. Explain why BA does not go HIGH as soon as HALT goes LOW.
5. What is the relationship between the access time of the memory used and the clock frequency? Why is it important?
6. Why is it advantageous to have many Chip Select lines on a component?

7-3 ▼ INTRODUCTION TO THE 6800 SYSTEM

When introduced in 1974, the basic **6800** family of microcomputer (μC) components consisted of five parts:

1. The **MC6800** microprocessor (μP)
2. The **MC6830** masked programmable Read-Only Memory (1024-byte ROM)
3. The **MC6810** static Random-Access Memory (128-byte RAM)
4. The **MC6820** Peripheral Interface Adapter (PIA) for parallel data Input/Output (I/O)
5. The **MC6850** Asynchronous Communications Interface Adapter (ACIA) for serial data I/O

The original **6800** family system using these components is shown in Fig. 7-1. All the ICs except the μP had only one function per chip.

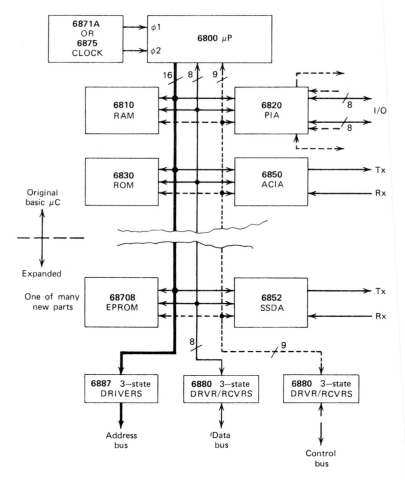

Figure 7-1 **6800** family components.

Since these components were introduced, there have been dramatic improvements in technology which have greatly increased the amount of circuitry that can be included in MOS ICs, particularly microprocessors and memories. Because of these advances, denser and higher-speed circuits are more easily manufactured. The **6830** ROM and the **6820** PIA are now obsolete and have been superseded by later designs. It is noteworthy, however, that over 18 years later the other basic components are still used in many systems.

In the years since 1974, many new components have been added to the **6800** family. These are primarily microcontrollers (MCUs) rather than new μPs. A MCU contains a μP within it, but it also contains memory and I/O capabilities inside the same IC. MCUs follow the same basic **6800** system concepts, but many of the individual ICs shown in Fig. 7-1 have been eliminated because their functions have been incorporated in the MCU IC. The memories inside each chip might include various combinations of RAM, ROM, EPROM, or EEPROM. The I/O capabilities included in the MCU allow it to connect to external circuits using parallel or serial data transmission (see Section 8-3.1).

Many complete single-chip MCUs are now available. The reason for having different MCUs is to provide different combinations of I/O functions and types of memory. The choices include RAM, ROM, EPROM, and EEPROM. Then the user can select the μC that has the best combinations for his particular task.

Because unused circuitry adds unnecessary cost, the best approach in designing a new μC system is to select an MCU that has the necessary basic functions and then add external ICs that have the capabilities the μC lacks. The designer must therefore know how to interface these external ICs to the selected MCU. For that reason we describe the features and interfacing standards of the Motorola **6800** family, with which all components must be compatible.

7-3.1 ▼ The 6800 IC

The original **6800** IC was strictly a μP and had no memory or I/O capabilities; these were provided by the other ICs in the system. The instruction set of the **6800,** however, forms the basis for the instruction sets of the newer 8-bit MCUs. The **6800** μP is still manufactured and is in use in many existing systems, but it is not used in new designs primarily because the newer and more powerful components currently available make it possible to build simpler and less expensive μC systems.

One limitation of the **6800** μP is that it does not include the *clock circuit* needed for digital systems of this type. To use the **6800,** an external clock circuit must be used to control the timing of the system. Several clock ICs, such as the **MC6871A** and the **MC6875,** were popular when the **6800** was first used. These *crystal-controlled* clock circuits provide the necessary two phase nonoverlapping timing pulses and are equipped with output circuits suitable for driving the MOS circuitry in the **6800.**

If we wanted to build a basic system today, similar to Fig. 7-1, we could specify the **6802** μP, which has the identical CPU core but includes a 128-byte RAM (equivalent to the **6810**) and a clock circuit similar to the **6875,** within the chip. Replacing these three ICs with the **6802** simplifies the system significantly and thereby reduces its cost. The **6802** cannot be classified as an MCU because it has no I/O or ROM. It and other enhanced μCs are described in Chapter 10. They are, however, all based on the **6800** instruction set and bus structure described in the remainder of this chapter.

7-4 ▼ 6800 SYSTEM HARDWARE FEATURES

For a group of ICs to function as a microcomputer system, as shown in Fig. 7-1, the components must satisfy several requirements. First, *all elements of a computer must be present*, and second, they must be partitioned into the various packages so that they are *modular* and a variety of useful configurations can easily be assembled. Finally, there must be a simple way to interconnect them.

In the system of Fig. 7-1, the program instructions for the system would typically be stored in an EPROM such as the **2764,** and all variable data would be written into, or read from, a RAM similar to the **6810.** Other *bytewide* RAMs with up to 32K bytes are available and might be substituted. The I/O of data for the system would be done by way of the PIA, ACIA, SSDA, or one of several other peripheral devices currently available.

To understand how these units work together, it is necessary to be familiar with the hardware features of each part. Figure 7-1 shows that the system components are interconnected via a 16-wire address bus, an 8-wire data bus, and a 9-wire control bus. For a component to be a member of the **6800** μC family and to ensure compatibility, it must meet specific **system standards.** These standards make it convenient for external devices to interface (or communicate) with the **6800** μP. These standards, which apply to all **6800** components, are as follows:

1. 8-bit bidirectional data bus
2. 16-bit address bus
3. Three-state bus switching techniques
4. TTL/DTL level compatible signals (see Section 7-4.4)
5. 5-Volt N-channel MOS silicon gate technology
6. 24-, 28-, and 40-pin packages
7. Clock rate 100 kHz to 2 MHz
8. Temperature range 0° to 70°C

7-4.1 ▼ Data Bus

Because the basic word length of the **6800** μP is 8 bits (1 byte) it communicates with other components via an 8-bit data bus. The data bus is *bidirectional*, and data is transferred into or out of the **6800** over the same lines. A read/write line (one of the control lines) is provided to allow the μP to control the direction of data transfer in exchanges with external devices.

An 8-bit data bus is a convenient size since it can accommodate ASCII (American Standard Code for Information Interchange) characters and/or packed BCD (see Section 4-8).

7-4.2 ▼ The Address Bus

A 16-bit address bus was chosen for these reasons:

1. For programming ease, the addresses should be multiples of 8 bits.
2. An 8-bit address bus would provide only 256 addresses, but a 16-bit bus provides 65,536 distinct addresses, which is adequate for most controller applications.

7-4.3 ▼ Three-State Bus Concepts

A typical digital line normally can be in one of two possible states. It is either HIGH (at a "1" level) or LOW (at a "0" level). When ICs such as a μP and its memory or peripherals must communicate with each other on a common bus, all of these components must have their outputs connected to the common bus using *three-state gates*. These gates can be switched to a third state that presents a *high impedance* to the bus. In this way *one, and only one, component is* selected to drive the bus at any time. The **6800** system component selected causes a 1 or 0 to be placed on each line of the bus in accordance with the data word being transmitted. *All unselected components* must place their bus drivers in the *high-impedance* state. Simultaneously, one of the other components on the bus is enabled to read the data, thus transferring or transmitting it in one direction. This three-state switching of direction is controlled by the μPs read/write (R/W) line. The transfer of information via the data bus can therefore be *bidirectional* over the same eight-line bus. All components of the **6800** family include this three-state capability in their data output circuits.

External memory or I/O devices, which are not part of the family, can be connected to the bus via three-state driver/receivers packages as shown in Fig 7-1. This is unnecessary today because all modern memory and peripheral ICs have a *chip enable* (CE) input. If the CE input is HIGH, the IC is deselected or disabled; it will not respond to commands from the μP and will not put data on the bus. The state of CE is derived from the address bus, by means of an address decoder, so the μP selects a particular memory or peripheral by sending out its address (see Section 7-14). Most modern memory ICs (including ROMs, EPROMs, and EEPROMs) have two control lines: a *Chip Enable* (CE) and an *Output Enable* (OE). CE is the chip power control. OE is the output control and is used to disconnect the IC from the Data Bus. If either of these signals is HIGH, the IC is disabled. The OE pin, which is normally connected to the R/W line, controls the state of the output circuits. When OE is HIGH, the data bus is in the high impedance state.

Many RAMS also have OE, but may have Write or Write Enable pins. Generally, the stored data is available at the output when the R/W line is HIGH (READ) and the CE is LOW. When the CE is High, the outputs will be in the high-impedance state.

In a **6800** system with external ICs, the R/W line controls the RAM or other peripherals so that either the μP or the peripherals data output circuits are ON, depending on whether the μP is writing or reading.

EXAMPLE 7-1

Which component drives the bus when:

a. The μP is reading memory?

b. The μP is writing to memory?

SOLUTION:

a. When the μP is *reading* memory it must receive information that is in memory. The memory must drive the data bus with that information so that the μP can read it. All other devices must be in their *high-impedance state*.

> **b.** When *writing*, the μP is sending information to the memory. Therefore, the μP bus drivers are active. The memory receivers must be ON and all other bus drivers (including the receiving memory) must be in the *high-impedance state.*

7-4.4 ▼ TTL Signal Compatibility

The **6800** components are designed to be compatible with available digital circuitry. At present, the **7400** TTL (Transistor-Transistor Logic) series dominates the field of digital ICs. Consequently, the design standard chosen for the **6800** series of components requires that each output will drive one standard TTL load (defined as 1.6 mA at 0.4 V) plus a capacitive load of 130 pF (at 1 MHz).

7-4.5 ▼ 5-Volt N-Channel MOS Silicon Metal Gate Technology

The **6800** was one of the first μPs to use NMOS technology that requires only +5 volts for its operation. The use of a single standard voltage gave it a significant advantage over other μPs and MOS devices which required several different voltages for their operation. Most of those devices are now obsolete. Today, NMOS is slowly being replaced by CMOS or HCMOS devices but they retain the 5-V and TTL interface standards.

7-4.6 ▼ 24-, 28-, and 40-Pin Packages

The **6800** μP uses a 40-pin DIP package. This allows for 38 input/output connections (plus power and ground) so that it can present the information simultaneously on its 16 address lines, 8 data lines, and the various control lines. Other components in the **6800** series (the ACIA and memories) do not require full 16-bit addressing and use a smaller 24-pin DIP package. Some of the newer large memory devices, such as the **68764** EPROMs, use 28 pins to allow for the increased number of address lines needed.

7-4.7 ▼ Clock Rate

The clock rate determines the speed at which the μP executes instructions. Many **6800** family parts were originally available in three clock rates. The **6800** can be driven by a clock up to 1 MHz, the **68A00** up to 1.5 MHz, and the **68B00** up to 2 MHz (see Section 7-7).

7-4.8 ▼ Temperature Range

Because most μPs operate in a controlled environment, (comfortable rooms or laboratories) they are not subjected to extreme temperature variations. The temperature range chosen for the plastic-cased **MC6800P** (0 to 70°C) is adequate for almost all industrial and commercial applications. This temperature range is also the same as the standard TTL temperature range. The **MC6800CP** has a wider range, −40 to +85°C. Military versions are also available for operation from −55 to +125°C.

It should be recognized that all operating temperatures are measured at the device location in the housing. The system must not generate so much heat that it causes the temperature in the vicinity of any of the components to exceed specifications. If necessary, cooling fans can be placed in a system housing to dissipate excessive heat.

7-5 ▼ THE 6800 MICROPROCESSOR UNIT

Figure 7-2 shows the block diagram of a **6800** microprocessor (μP). An 8-bit internal bus interconnects the various registers with the instruction decode and control logic. The nine control lines that communicate with the external devices can be seen on the left, with the address bus at the top and the data bus at the bottom of the figure.

7-5.1 ▼ Hardware Aspects of the 6800 ALU and Registers

The arithmetic is performed in the **6800** CPU core by an 8-bit, parallel-processing, 2s-complement Arithmetic/Logic Unit (ALU). It includes the Condition Code Register (CCR). The functions of the ALU and the various registers have been described in Sections 4-3.1 and 4-3.2. The clock hardware is described later in Section 7-7. Interrupt functions, Direct Memory Access (DMA), and various hardware design features are described in later chapters.

7-5.2 ▼ Registers and Accumulators

As explained in Section 4-3.2, the **6800** system has a 16-bit address bus, but as seen in Fig. 7-2, the internal bus is 8 bits wide. The 16-bit registers, the address bus, the index register and the stack pointer are implemented with a high (H) and a low (L) byte. The two 8-bit accumulators, A and B, speed up program execution by allowing two operands to remain in the μP. Instructions that can be performed using both accumulators (e.g., ABA and SBA) are very fast because they do not require additional cycles to fetch the second operand.

7-5.3 ▼ Other Features of the 6800

Five of the six condition codes (H, N, Z, V, and C in Fig. 4-1) have been described in Section 4-6. The action of the sixth condition code register bit (I) or interrupt mask is discussed in Chapter 9. The clock hardware and HALT modes are discussed in Sections 7-6.6 and 7-7.

7-5.4 ▼ Vectored Interrupts

An *interrupt* is a signal to the μP that causes it to stop execution of the normal program and to branch (or jump) to another location that is the beginning address of an **interrupt service routine.** These routines are written to provide whatever action is necessary to respond to the interrupt. Four types of interrupts are provided in the **6800**, and each has its unique *interrupt service routine* and *vector*.

1. Restart (RST)
2. NonMaskable Interrupt (NMI)
3. SoftWare Interrupt (SWI)
4. Interrupt ReQuest (IRQ)

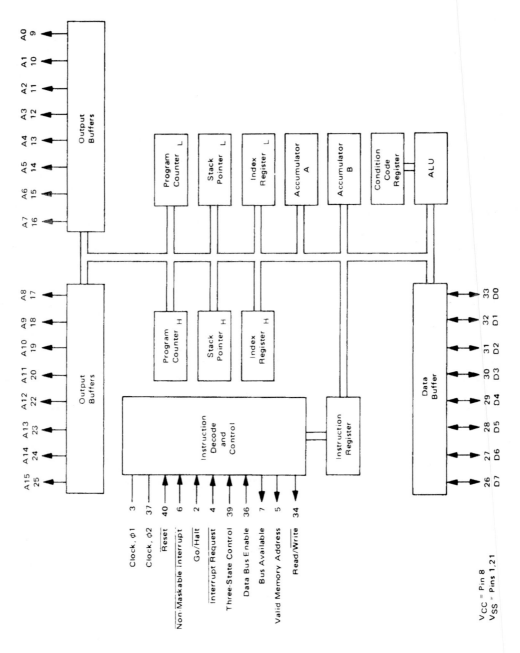

Figure 7-2 Block diagram of **6800** microprocessor.

Three of them also are implemented by pins on the **6800.**

For the program to be branched to the appropriate routine, the eight locations of the ROM or PROM that are highest in memory (addresses $FFF8 to $FFFF) are reserved for these interrupt vectors. The contents of these locations contain the 16-bit addresses where the service routines begin. When activated, the program is *vectored* or pointed to the appropriate address by the μP logic. This is called a *vectored interrupt*. The details of these interrupts are discussed in Chapter 9.

7-6 ▼ 6800 CONTROL LINES AND THEIR FUNCTIONS

The components of a μC system must be connected so that data is properly transferred between them and to any external hardware that is being used. In addition to the obvious requirement for power and ground to each component, the address bus, the bidirectional data bus, and numerous control signal lines are required. These control lines are, in effect, a third bus called the **control bus**. These lines are shown in Fig. 7-1 and are identified in Fig. 7-2, which also shows their pin numbers.

To design a system that performs properly, it is necessary to understand each signal's characteristics and function. These are described in the following paragraphs.

7-6.1 ▼ Read/Write (R/W)

The Read/Write (R/W) output line is used to signal all external devices that the μP is in a READ state (R/W = HIGH) or a WRITE state (R/W = LOW). The normal standby state of this line is HIGH. This line is three-state. When Three-State Control (TSC) (see Section 7-6.8) goes HIGH, the R/W line enters the high-impedance mode.

7-6.2 ▼ Valid Memory Address

The **6800**'s Valid Memory Address (VMA) output line (when in the HIGH state) tells all devices external to the μP that there is a valid address on the address bus. During execution of certain instructions, the address bus may assume a random address because of internal calculations. VMA goes LOW to avoid enabling any device under those conditions. Note also that VMA is held LOW during HALT, TSC, or during the execution of a WAIT (WAI) instruction. VMA is not a three-state line and therefore Direct Memory Access (DMA) cannot be performed unless VMA is externally opened (or gated).

Some other μCs such as the **6801** and **68HC11** do not have a VMA pin. Instead, they force the address bus to all 1s when performing a read cycle anytime that VMA would normally be low on the **6800.**

7-6.3 ▼ Data Bus Enable

The Data Bus Enable (DBE) signal enables the data bus drivers of the μP when it is in the HIGH state. This input is normally connected to the phase 2 (φ2) clock but is sometimes delayed to assure proper operation with some memory devices. When HIGH, it permits the μP to place data on the bus during a WRITE cycle. During a μP READ cycle, the data bus drivers within the μP are disabled internally. If an external signal holds DBE LOW, the μP data bus drivers are forced into their high-impedance state. This allows other devices to control the I/O bus (as in DMA).

7-6.4 ▼ Interrupt Request, Nonmaskable Interrupt, and Reset

An active signal on the IRQ, NMI, or RESET lines initiates an interrupt sequence. The action of these lines is discussed in Chapter 9, where interrupts are considered in detail.

7-6.5 ▼ Phase One (φ1) and Phase Two (φ2) of the Clock

The φ1 and φ2 are used for a two-phase, nonoverlapping clock which is required for the **6800** μP (see Section 7-7). This clock runs at a frequency up to 1 MHz for the **M6800** and up to 2 MHz for the depletion load versions of the **6800 (MC68B00).**

7-6.6 ▼ HALT and RUN Modes

When the HALT input to the **6800** is HIGH, the μP is in the RUN mode and is continually executing instructions. When the HALT line goes LOW, the μP halts after completing its present instruction. At that time the μP is in the HALT mode. Bus Available (BA) goes HIGH, VMA (Section 7-6.2) becomes a 0, and all three-state lines enter their high-impedance state. Note that the μP does not enter the HALT mode as soon as HALT goes LOW but does so only when the μP has finished execution of its current instruction. It is possible to stop the μP while it is in the process of executing an instruction by stopping or "stretching the clock" as described in Section 7-7.

7-6.7 ▼ Bus Available

The bus available (BA) signal is a normally LOW signal generated by the μP. In the HIGH state it indicates that the μP has stopped executing instructions and that the address and data buses can be controlled by external devices, as required for Direct Memory Access (DMA) circuits. This occurs if the μP is in the HALT mode or in a WAIT state as the result of the WAI instruction.

7-6.8 ▼ Three-State Control

Three-State Control (TSC) is an externally generated signal that effectively causes the μP to disconnect itself from the address and control buses. This allows an external device to assume control of the system. When TSC is HIGH, it causes the address lines and the READ/WRITE line to go to the high-impedance state. The VMA and BA signals are forced LOW. The data bus is not affected by TSC and has its own enable (DBE). TSC is used in DMA applications discussed in Chapter 9.

7-7 ▼ CLOCK OPERATION

The **6800** μP requires an external clock circuit to drive its internal MOS circuitry, but all of the newer members of the **6800** family of μC components have a clock circuit within the chip. This internal circuit includes everything needed for the clock except for an external quartz crystal that sets the frequency of the clock and two small capacitors. An internal divide-by-4 circuit is also provided so that a 4-MHz (or 8-MHz) crystal can be used. Because the physical size of a quartz crystal determines its frequency, the 4- or 8-

MHz crystal is much smaller and cheaper than the 1-MHz crystal needed for the **6800.** The **6802,** for example, is one of these newer μPs with the internal clock circuit. It has a processor (or CPU core), that is identical to the **6800** (see Chapter 10 for details).

Because the clock is integrated into the chip in all of the newer MCUs, it is not necessary for MCU developers to understand the internal clock circuitry. Unless the student wants to know about the internal design, he or she can safely skip to Section 7-7.3.

7-7.1 ▼ External Clocks for the 6800

The **6800** uses an external *two-phase* clock to control its operation. The waveforms and timing of the clock are critical for proper operation of the μP and the other components of the family. The timing requirements are shown in the waveforms and table of Fig. 7-3. The two phases of the clock must be nonoverlapping and conform to the timing table (Fig 7-3b).

The **6800** μP is a dynamic IC that must be refreshed periodically by its own clocks. Phase 1 should not be stopped longer than 9600 ns (PW_{OH}), or the μP may lose some of its internal data. The clock synchronizes the internal operations of the μP, as well as all external devices on the bus. The program counter, for example, is advanced on the falling edge of φ1 and data is latched into the μP on the falling edge of φ2. All operations necessary for the execution of each instruction are synchronized with the clock.

Certain components and functions of the system affect the clock requirements. If dynamic memories are used, slow memories are involved, or DMA is required, the clock may have to be stopped momentarily, or stretched. If the memory is slow, for example, phase 2 has to be long enough to allow the memory to complete its READ or WRITE operation. Since a memory that is too slow to operate with a 1-MHz clock (such as an Intel 1702A EPROM) may only be addressed periodically, there is no need to slow the clock for the entire system, provided that a "memory ready" feature can be included in the clock.

The **MC6875** shown in Fig. 7-4 is a 16-pin IC which includes all the features necessary to control the timing of a **6800** system. It includes an internal oscillator whose frequency can be determined by an external crystal or RC network connected to pins X1 and X2. (An inexpensive 3.59-MHz crystal made for color TV sets can be used.) Alternatively, an external timing signal can be connected to the Ext. In pin. The oscillator frequency is divided by 4 and shaped to provide φ1 and φ2, the two-phase nonoverlapping clock required by the **6800** μP. If the system contains slow memories, φ2 can be stretched by holding Memory Ready low until the data is transferred. The **6875** also contains a Schmitt trigger input that controls RESET. A capacitor to ground (power ON reset) and/or a reset switch may be used. DMA or dynamic memory refresh can also be accommodated. These are discussed in Chapter 9.

7-7.2 ▼ Optional Clock Circuits

The unique two-phase clock signals required for the **6800** can be provided by other means, such as the **6871A** hybrid clock circuit or even by a simple oscillator followed by a number of discrete components to provide the two nonoverlapping phases.

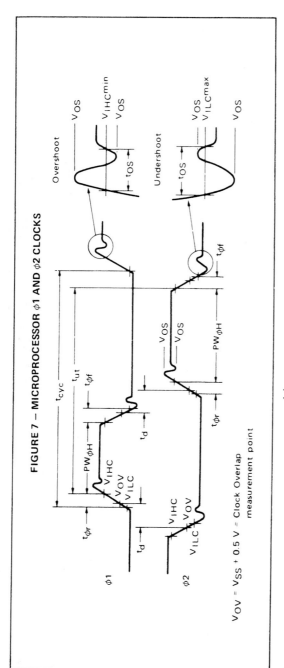

FIGURE 7 – MICROPROCESSOR φ1 AND φ2 CLOCKS

$V_{OV} = V_{SS} + 0.5\ V$ = Clock Overlap measurement point

(a) Waveforms

	Symbol	Min	Typ	Max	Unit
Frequency of Operation	f	0.1	—	1.0	MHz
Clock Timing (φ1 and φ2)					
Cycle Time	t_{cyc}	1.0	—	10	µs
Clock Pulse Width (Measured at V_{CC} - 0.3 V) φ1	$PW_{\phi H}$	430	—	4500	ns
φ2		450	—	4500	ns
Clock Up Time	t_{ut}	940	—	—	ns
Rise and Fall Times φ1, φ2 (Measured between V_{SS} + 0.3 V and V_{CC} - 0.3 V)	$t_{\phi r}, t_{\phi f}$	5.0	—	50	ns
Delay Time or Clock Separation (Measured at V_{SS} + 0.5 V)	t_d	0	—	9100	ns
Overshoot Duration	t_{OS}	0	—	40	ns

(b) Timing table

Figure 7-3   6800 clock timing: (a) waveforms; (b) timing table.

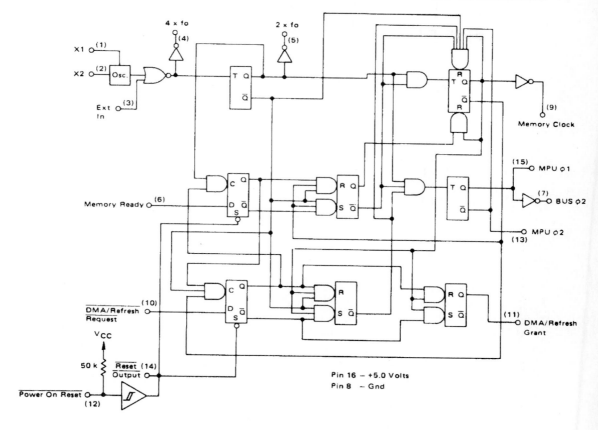

Figure 7-4 **6875** block diagram.

7-7.3 ▼ Instruction Bytes and Clock Cycles

Whether the clock is internal or external, the instructions are *clocked* through the digital logic of the CPU in the same way. The **6800** instruction table (Appendix B) lists the number of bytes and clock cycles for each instruction. The number of bytes for each instruction determines the amount of memory required to hold the program, and the number of cycles determines the time required to execute the program. The instruction LDAA $1234 (which is in the extended addressing mode), for example, requires 3 bytes, one to specify the operation (op) code and two to specify the address, but requires four cycles to execute. Often, an instruction requires the processor to perform internal operations in addition to the fetch cycles. Consequently, for any instruction the number of cycles is generally larger than the number of bytes.

Note that Chapter 11 describes the **6801** μC with an augmented instruction set (22 additional op codes) that uses one less cycle for most instructions, yet these instructions are compatible with the **6800.** Thus some instructions will execute faster.

EXAMPLE 7-2

How long does it take to execute a LDAA 0,X (indexed) instruction if a 1-MHz oscillator is used as the system clock?

SOLUTION

From Appendix B we find that a LDAA 0,X instruction requires 2 bytes—the op code and the offset address—and five cycles. The μP must add the offset to the contents of its index register. This accounts for the large number of clock cycles required for this instruction. Since the instruction takes five cycles, it takes 5 μs to execute at a clock rate of 1 MHz.

7-8 ▼ MEMORIES

Memory concepts were described in Sections 3-4 and 3-5. At this point we discuss some of the possible memory types that could be included in a **6800** family system. The system's memory could be made up of discrete components, as shown in Fig. 7-1, or it might be fully integrated into the MCU. Motorola does not manufacture some classes of memories, such as separate ROMs, EPROMs, or EEPROMs. Usable versions are available from other suppliers, however, and a few will be described. We will discuss static and dynamic RAMs as well as the several nonvolatile types of memory (ROM). Because we are dealing only with **6800** systems we are concerned only with memories smaller than 64K bytes.

All 8-bit μPs use byte-sized (8-bit) words on their data bus. Some ICs are available with byte-sized data words, but many are made in 4- or 1-bit configurations. In these cases either two or eight ICs must be assembled as an array to provide the byte-sized data storage required. Also, when considering RAM, either static or dynamic devices must be selected (see Section 3-5.1). Although the dynamic RAMs provide more bits in a given space, the possibility of needing additional components for refreshing the dynamic units must be taken into account.

Any external component attached to a μP or μC must work on a bidirectional data bus without additional interface components. Thus the output circuits must be able to present a high impedance when not sending data to the bus. This is done by using three-state gates on the component's outputs.

Last, but not least, is the need to match the speed of the IC to the clock speed. Access and cycle times are important, as discussed in the next section. It is not difficult to find suitable memory ICs these days because memory designs have improved, but a component that is much too fast may be more expensive than needed.

7-8.1 ▼ 6810 Random Access Memory

The **6810** is an older Random Acess Memory (RAM) IC that can hold 128 bytes of memory. All of the μPs or MCUs described in Chapter 10 include at least 128 bytes of internal RAM, so the **6810** is not needed in new designs, unless, perhaps, 256 bytes are needed. It is discussed here because it is a simple device that meets all of the conditions described in the preceding section and is representative of the circuitry provided in the μCs discussed later in this book.

Figure 7-5 shows the **6810.** It is a 1024-bit (128 words by 8 bits/word) memory in a 24-pin package. It provides 128 bytes of read/write memory and is designed for use in the **6800** system. The 8-bit word organization makes it uniquely applicable for small μP systems because many such systems only need 128 or 256 bytes of RAM.

The **6810** bus interface of Fig. 7-6 shows how a typical IC would be connected to the address, data, and control buses. The pins on the **6810** include:

1. Eight data lines (D0–D7): Three-state bidirectional lines for compatibility with the **6800** data bus.
2. Seven address lines
3. Six Chip Select lines
4. A R/W line

The **6810** is a static RAM, which requires only one power supply (+5 V). It has four LOW-level and two HIGH-level Chip Select pins. The proper voltage level must be present on each of these pins for the IC to be selected. The pins can be connected directly to address lines or voltage levels as shown in Fig. 7-6 to select the chip without additional decoders. When selected and R/W is HIGH (the memory is being READ), the output buffers are turned ON to drive the data bus. Otherwise, they present high impedance to the data bus (see Section 7-14 for details). The use of E and VMA connected to the CS lines is discussed in Section 7-14.

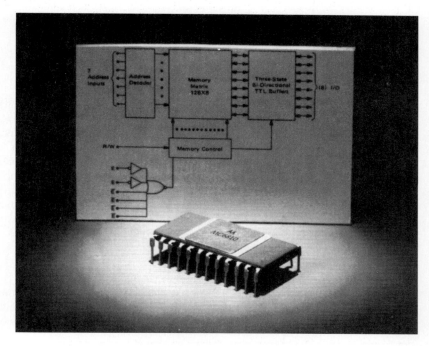

Figure 7-5 **6810** random access memory (128 8-bit words).

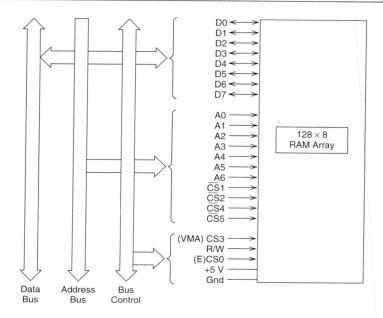

Figure 7-6 **6810** RAM bus interface.

EXAMPLE 7-3

What is the maximum memory access time that a **6810** component may have when used in a **6800** system with a 1-MHz clock?

SOLUTION

where is Section 7.17.

Reference to the **6810** data sheet (see Section 7-17) indicates that the time from the point in the cycle where the *address* lines become stable (all 1s are above 2.0 V, and all 0s are less than 0.8 V) until the *data* becomes stable is defined as the *memory read access time* (T_{acc}) and that the data will remain stable a minimum of 10 ns after the end of the cycle. The **6800** data sheet READ timing figure shows that the time from the beginning of the cycle until all address, R/W, and VMA lines are stable is a maximum of 300 ns, and the minimum length of time that the data must be available (on the bus) is 100 ns. The clock timing waveform shows that at 1 MHz, the total time from where $\phi1$ starts setting the address until $\phi2$ cuts off the data (T_{uT}) is 940 ns. Therefore, the access time for the memory is:

$$T_{acc} = 940 - (300 + 100) = 540 \text{ ns}$$

The data sheet shows that all the newer **6810**s meet the requirements. These calculations assume that a minimum configuration system is involved, and therefore no additional delays are incurred in bus drivers or TTL decoders.

7-8.2 ▼ Other RAM Choices

In some cases, system requirements may dictate a larger RAM. Perhaps a 2K by 8-bit, or possibly even an 8K by 8-bit memory, as used in the EValuation Board (EVB) described in Chapter 11, could be selected. Of course, the basic system design must be analyzed to be sure that the room exists in the memory map for the size selected. The **MCM2018A,** which is a 2K by 8-bit HCMOS static RAM, is a possible choice. The student should refer to the latest MOS memory update listings or Memory Data books available from the Motorola sales offices or to those listed in the Section 7-17, for suitable choices.

where is Section 7-17

7-9 ▼ READ-ONLY MEMORIES

The three types of read-only memories (ROMs)—masked ROMs, EPROMs, and EEPROMs—were introduced in Section 3-5.4. They can only be read, and not written to, during computer operation. Also, they will not lose their information when power is turned off. They are therefore *nonvolatile*. Nonvolatile memory is normally required in all microcontroller systems to hold the entire user's application program. The startup program in all Personal Computers (PCs) are in ROM, so they will start properly when power is applied. They can then load whichever application program they want to run into RAM. When an IBM-PC (or clone), for example, is first turned on, it executes the BIOS (Basic Input/Output System) program, which is retained in ROM. This program tests the computer and then loads DOS (the Disk Operating System) into RAM. DOS then takes control and runs the user's programs.

Different methods are used to write information into the three types of ROMs. The manufacturer effectively writes the bits into **mask**-programmed ROMs when they are manufactured by creating a *mask* that leaves connections open for a 1, but closes them where a 0 must appear. EPROMs store charges on *floating gates* to preserve a 1 or a 0. They usually require a special PROM programmer, which is a piece of hardware designed to write the program electrically into the chip. EPROMs can be either a separate chip or part of a MCU chip. They usually are removed from the MCU socket and put into the programmer in order to install the program. EEPROMs can also be separate or part of the MCU. In this case, however, they are frequently programmed while in place inside the μC.

If a program is to be considered permanent and placed in one of the three types of ROM, it must first be developed and tested to be sure that it is free of bugs. If the masked ROM is selected, the engineer can then place an order for a planned number of units with the desired pattern of instructions and data to be programmed into the ROM. The semiconductor manufacturer then translates this pattern into a photographic mask to be used during processing of the silicon wafers. A small batch is then produced for verification. After verification by the customer, full production of these custom ROMs begins.

Some MCUs have a separate internal ROM that is used to program EPROMs, EEPROMs, or possibly FLASH memory. This ROM contains the *bootloader program*. All of the considerations mentioned in Section 7-8 apply.

Motorola provides many MCUs that include ROMs, but they do not market separate ROMs at the time of this writing. There are situations where a separate ROM may be desirable, however. For example, suppose that a product must be released before the designer is sure that the program is fully debugged, or the program is expected to change at a later time. Then it might be cost-efficient to provide an external EPROM in a socket for the first units produced and to replace it with a ROM later. Like separate RAMs, ROMs are available from IC suppliers such as AMD (American Microdevices, Inc.) or Intel. They all feature three-state outputs capable of driving the data bus.

7-10 ▼ PROMs AND EPROMs

PROMs (Programmable Read-Only Memory) or EPROMs (Erasable Programmable ROM) can also be added to a μC system, where required. When external components are required, it frequently is necessary to provide separate decoders or other **glue parts** (small-scale TTL ICs) to interface the external I/O or memory IC's to the μP.

An EPROM can be erased by ultraviolet light and reprogrammed any number of times. They contain a quartz window, so the ultraviolet light can enter and erase the memory. In normal operation this window should be covered over so that ambient light cannot enter and inadvertently erase the memory.

EPROMs are extremely valuable for program and system development. They make it possible for the designer to build the hardware in final form (with sockets for memories) so that testing and program revisions can continue, using EPROMs, even after the first models of the product are shipped. Ultimately, a One-Time-Programmable (OTP) ROM can be installed, either in the field or in future production. This would be done in high volume production systems because the OTP ROMs (without the quartz window) are significantly less expensive.

7-10.1 ▼ External EPROMs

The **27C64** is an example of a popular and widely used EPROM. It is manufactured by both Intel and Texas Instruments and contains 8192 bytes. It is an ultraviolet erasable EPROM available in a 28-pin windowed or in an OTP package. When used, it behaves like a ROM.

The bus organization of the **27C64** is shown in Fig. 7-7. Note that there are 13 address lines, 8 data lines, and 2 Chip Select lines. Because this is a ROM, no read/write line is needed. If this IC is selected, the byte at the addressed location will appear on the data bus. When the IC is *not* selected, its output drivers are in the high-impedance state, allowing another device to drive the I/O bus.

7-11 ▼ 6821 PERIPHERAL INTERFACE ADAPTER

The **6821** Peripheral Interface Adapter (PIA), shown in Fig. 7-8, provides a simple means of interfacing peripheral equipment on a parallel or byte-wide basis to the **6800** μC system. This IC is compatible with the **6800** bus interface on the μP side, and provides up to 16 I/O lines and 4 control lines on the peripheral side, for connection to external units. The **6821** is an NMOS device, but its outputs are TTL and CMOS compatible and can drive two TTL loads on all A and B side buffers. The **6821** is capable of static operation (no clocking required). The PIA is described in detail in Sections 8-4, 8-5, and 8-6.

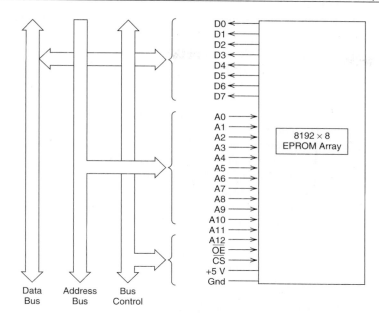

Figure 7-7 **27C64** EPROM bus interface.

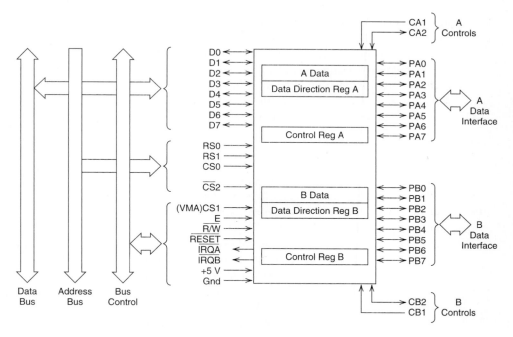

Figure 7-8 PIA bus interface and registers.

7-12 ▼ ASYNCHRONOUS COMMUNICATIONS INTERFACE ADAPTER

The **6850** Asynchronous Communications Interface Adapter (ACIA) is a 24-pin IC similar to all the others in the **6800** family. It is also an NMOS device and provides the circuitry to connect serial asynchronous data communications devices, such as a modem or a CRT terminal, to bus-organized systems such as the **6800** μC system.

The bus interface of a **6850** includes select, enable, read/write, and interrupt signal pins in addition to the 8-bit bidirectional data bus lines. The parallel data of the **6800** system is serially transmitted and received (simultaneously) with proper ASCII formatting and error checking. The Control Register of the ACIA is programmed via the data bus during system initialization. It determines word length, parity, stop bits, and interrupt control of the transmit or receive functions. The operation of the **6850** is discussed in detail in Sections 8-8 through 8-10.

The PIA and ACIA have been the most widely used I/O components in the **6800** family. Many users are switching to equivalent CMOS components. Table 7-1 shows other ICs that are currently available for 8-bit systems. Readers should consult the manufacturers' literature for information on these products.

7-13 ▼ MEMORY SPACE ALLOCATION

The I/O devices in the **6800** system (e.g., the PIA, ACIA, etc.), all have internal registers that contain the I/O data or control the operation of the device. Each of these registers is allocated a unique address on the address bus and is communicated with just as if it were memory. This technique is called *memory-mapped* I/O. The programmer no longer needs to remember special I/O instructions, and all the **6800** memory referencing instructions can be used with the registers in the peripheral ICs.

The process of addressing a particular IC includes not only selecting a location in that IC but also selecting that chip from among all those on the same bus. *The low-order address lines are generally used to address registers within the chips, and the high-order lines are available to single out the desired chip.* These high-order lines could be connected to a **decoder** circuit which has one output line used to enable each chip, but since

TABLE 7-1   6800 Family Peripherals

6821	Peripheral Interface Adapter (PIA)
6840	Programmable Timer Module (PTM)
6844	Four channel Direct Memory Access (DMA)
6845	CRT Controller (CRTC)
68488	General Purpose Interface Adapter (IEEE488)
6850	Asynchronous Communications Interface Adapter (ACIA)
6852	Synchronous Serial Data Adapter (SSDA)
6854	Advanced Data Link Controller (ADLC)
68HC24	Port Replacement Unit (PRU)
R62C52	Dual Asynchronous Communications Interface Adapter (DACIA) Made by Rockwell

many of the **6800** family devices have several Chip Select pins available, these are frequently connected directly to the high order address lines (A15, A14, A13, etc.) and separate decoders are not needed, particularly in simple systems (see Section 7-14).

A component is selected only if *all its CS lines are satisfied.* The **6810,** for example, is enabled only if it sees a HIGH level on both its two positive select lines (CS0, pin 10 and CS3, pin 13) and at the same time a LOW level on its four negative select pins (CS1, CS2, CS4, and CS5). Negative select pins are generally denoted by an overbar above the pin designation. When deselected, a component places its outputs in a high-impedance state and is effectively disconnected from the data bus.

Data should only be available when the φ2 clock on the **6800** is HIGH. This pin is often connected to a peripheral IC, either as a select line or as the E clock input. The component will never be selected when this clock is LOW.

Table 7-2 shows the number of addresses required and the number of Chip Select (CS) pins available for typical **6800** family components. When setting up a **6800** system, each component must be allocated as much memory space as it needs and must be given a *unique* address so that *no address selects more than one component.* In addition, one component (usually a ROM) must respond to the highest addresses ($FFFF) because it contains the vector interrupt addresses (see Chapter 9).

7-14 ▼ ADDRESSING TECHNIQUES

Most systems do not use all 64K bytes of available memory space. Therefore, not all of the address lines need to be used to select the various components. This simplifies the addressing of the components, but it allows *redundant addresses* to occur. This means that some components will respond to two or more addresses. It is important, however, to chose the lines used so that no two components can be selected by the same address. Since the Chip Selects serve to turn ON the bus drivers (for a μP READ), only *one* component should be ON at any time or an IC may be damaged.

When allocating memory in a **6800** family system, it is wise to place the **scratch pad RAM** at the bottom of the memory map (below $100), because it is then possible to use the direct address mode instructions throughout the program when referencing these RAM locations. Because 2-byte instead of 3-byte instructions are used, for addresses below $100, a savings (in a typical program) of up to 25% in total memory requirements is possible.

TABLE 7-2 Addresses and Chip Selects for **6800** Family Devices

Component		Addresses Required	Positive CS Pins	Negative CS Pins
6810	RAM	128	2	4
6821	PIA	4	2	1
6850	ACIA	2	2	1
6852	SSDA	2	0	1
6264C	RAM	8192	1	1

In summary, the following rules should govern the assignment of address bus lines to the various Chip Select pins:

1. Not all address bus lines need to be used for chip selection. Partial decoding is acceptable provided that precautions are taken to avoid two or more chips responding to the same address.

2. The clock must be included in the selection so that the bus drivers in each chip are only ON at the proper time.

3. In **6800** or **6802** systems, VMA must be included to avoid chip selection by the chance state of the address bus during nonmemory referencing cycles.

4. When an address line is used as a positive enable on one chip, the same line should go to negative enables on all other chips, if possible. This prevents any two chips from being selected at the same time regardless of the state of the address bus.

5. One ROM (or PROM) should contain the interrupt vector addresses and should respond to $FFF8 through $FFFF either directly or redundantly. (It can also respond to other redundant addresses.)

6. One RAM should respond to addresses $0000 through $00FF (256 bytes) to permit Direct Addressing Mode instructions to be used.

7. ACIAs are dynamic parts and must have the clock connected directly to E (the enable pin) in order to respond properly to interrupts. **682l**s do not require this since they are static parts.

EXAMPLE 7-4

How Many address lines are available to select:

(a) A **6810**?
(b) A **27C128** (16K by 8-bit EPROM)?

SOLUTION

(a) A **6810** is a 128-word RAM that requires 7 bits to select a specific address ($2^7 = 128$). Thus the seven LSB address lines are connected to the **6810** address pins for word selection, leaving 9 bits available for chip selection.

(b) A **27C128** is a 16,384 (16K)-byte EPROM. It requires 14 bits ($2^{14} =$ 16,384) to select a word, which leaves 2 bits available to select the chip.

The solution to part (a) of Example 7-4 shows that there are more address lines for chip selection than there are CS pins on some components. For large systems where most of the available 64K of memory is used, it may be necessary to use all of the lines and some address decoding to provide a unique location in the memory map for each device. Most systems, however, use only a fraction of the available memory space. For these smaller systems, a judicious choice of memory locations to avoid interference between redundancies reduces the need for added decoding.

EXAMPLE 7-5

(a) Which address does each component in the system configuration of Fig. 7-9 respond to?

(b) Which component must contain the Restart and other vector addresses?

SOLUTION

Figure 7-9 shows a small system using a **6802** μP and some of the memory and I/O components described previously. Only address lines 14 and 15 are used to select the chips. Because the **27C128** 16K by 8-bit EPROM and **6264C** 8K by 8-bit RAM have only one or two Chip Select lines, additional external decoding is necessary. The **74HC00** quad NAND gate IC is used. This is a CMOS IC that is equivalent to the **7400** in the TTL family of chips and has replaced the standard TTL ICs in most recent designs. Because seven gates are needed, we require two **74HC00**s. In addition to address lines A14 and A15, VMA and E are also used in decoding for all of the components being addressed. The EPROM is selected when all four of these signals are HIGH. Valid Memory Address (VMA) is combined with the clock signal (E) in gates 3 and 4 to create a signal that contributes to the selection of the component that has the right combination of A14 and A15. It can be seen that the EPROM contains one negative CS input and is connected to the output of NAND gate 1. Address lines A14 and A15 are connected directly to the inputs of that gate. Therefore, the EPROM responds to any address of the binary form 11XX XXXX XXXX XXXX, (X means either 1 or 0) or any address whose most significant hex digit is C, D, E, or F.

The **6264C** 8K by 8-bit RAM is not selected until both Chip Selects (or enables) are satisfied. Note that line A15 is connected to the positive enable (E). Thus a LOW on A14 and a HIGH on A15 will result in the **6264C** RAM being selected. It therefore responds to binary 10XX XXXX XXXX XXXX or any address whose most significant hex digit is 8, 9, A or B.

Address line A13 is not used in the decoding. The RAM will therefore appear redundantly in the memory map. It will be selected when A13 is 0 as in an MSD of 8 or 9 and again when the MSD is A or B.

The **6810** RAM has two of its negative CS bits connected to A14 and A15. However, you will notice that it also has CS3 connected to A7. It therefore responds to 00XX XXXX 1XXX XXXX or any address whose most significant hex digit is 0, 1, 2, or 3 and whose lower bits are in the range from 0080 through 00FF. Thus this external RAM is located just above the internal 128 bytes of RAM in the **6802**. It therefore extends the *scratch pad* to 00FF (or 255 decimal), which doubles the locations that can be addressed with direct addressing instructions.

The PIA input requires A14 (CS1) to be a 1 and A15 (CS2) to be a 0. It responds to any address of the form 01XX XXXX XXXX XXXX or any address that has a most significant digit of 4, 5, 6, or 7. This determines the chip selection. The registers in the PIA are then addressed by the A0 and A1 connections to RS0 and RS1.

This addressing scheme satisfies two major requirements:

(a) Each component in this system has a set of addresses that pertain uniquely to itself, since each responds to a different set of most significant digits of the address.

(b) The EPROM must contain the restart and other interrupt vector addresses since this is the only component that responds to addresses whose most significant digit is F.

7-14.1 ▼ Using a Memory Map

A memory map, shown in Fig. 7-10, helps keep track of the memory space allocations. For convenience the total space that can be addressed is shown divided into 64 blocks of 1K (1024) bytes each. A **27C128** occupies 16 blocks, but eight **6810**s can fit into one block. If, for example, we assign a **27C128** EPROM to address \$C000, the memory will occupy locations \$C000 through \$FFFF or blocks 49 through 64. The required binary states of the two most significant address lines are 11, as shown in Example 7-5. If, on the other hand, these MSB address bits are 10, as shown in the depiction of the address register at the bottom of Fig. 7-10, addresses with an MSB of 8, 9, A, or B will select the

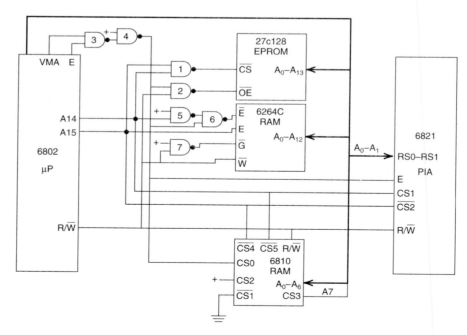

Figure 7-9   The System for Example 7-5.

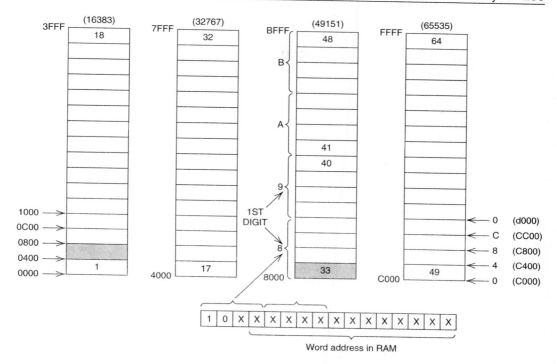

Figure 7-10 Typical **6800** system 64K memory map.

6264C RAM. Two redundant areas of memory of eight blocks each are selected because address line A13 is not used in the decoding. Blocks 33 through 40 are selected when A13 is 0, or the MSB is 8 or 9, and blocks 41 through 48 are selected when it is a 1. The 13 LSBs of the address which select the location in the 8K by 8-bit RAM are shown as "X" since they may take on a value of either 1 or 0, depending on which word in the RAM is selected.

7-15 ▼ SUMMARY

In this chapter we introduced the hardware components of the **6800** system and described the **6800** system standards. The μP, clock, and various types of memory were discussed in detail. The function of each signal on the μP was explained so that external components can be properly interfaced. Finally, we explained methods of allocating memory space among the system components and gave an example.

7-16 ▼ GLOSSARY

Bus Available (BA) A signal generated by the μP to tell an external device when the μP is halted.

Bus driver/receiver An Integrated circuit (IC) capable of driving and receiving information from a bidirectional I/O bus.

Chip Select pins Signal lines (or pins) that enable (or disable) a memory or peripheral IC.

Clock oscillator A component or circuit that provides the two-phase nonoverlapping timing pulses suitable for driving the MOS circuits of the **6800** μP.

Crystal control The use of a small quartz crystal that has been ground precisely to the proper thickness to provide a stable fixed frequency for the timing pulses.

Data Bus Enable (DBE) A signal to the μP allowing it to activate its data bus drivers.

Direct Memory Access (DMA) The ability of external devices to communicate directly with memory without using the μP.

HALT mode The mode in which the processor has stopped executing instructions.

Interrupt A signal from an external device that causes the processor to stop executing its program and branch to a routine that will service the interrupt.

Memory-mapped I/O A technique whereby I/O device registers are treated just like memory. It eliminates the need for special I/O instructions as used in other μPs (i.e., the **8085**).

Memory-ready signal A line to the clock circuit that stops the clock with phase 1 LOW and phase 2 HIGH to permit operation with slow memory devices without slowing the system all the time.

Partial decoding A technique where not all address lines are used but it is acceptable if precautions are taken to avoid two or more chips responding to the same address.

PROM programmer An electronic device that will change the bits in the PROM from all 1s to 1s and 0s as required to correspond to the machine language program being installed.

Redundant addresses The addresses that are the same except for some bits (or lines) that are not connected to the memory chip (IC) involved.

Reset An interrupt that causes the program to restart.

RUN mode The mode where the processor is continually and normally executing instructions.

Scratch pad RAMs The RAM memory used for miscellaneous calculations or storage by various routines in a program.

Three-state bus A bus made possible by data bus driver/receivers capable of a third high-impedance state as well as the normal TTL levels of 1 and 0. This permits many devices to be placed on the same bus and bidirectional transmission to be possible over the same 8 lines.

Three-State Control (TSC) A signal to the processor that, when HIGH, causes it to disconnect the address bus and R/W line drivers.

Transistor-Transistor Logic (TTL) The standard method of construction for internal circuits of **7400** family IC logic components.

Two-phase clock Two nearly identical clock signals called φ1 (phase 1) and φ2 (phase 2) but one is the inverse of the other and they are nonoverlapping. Used to drive the logic inside the **6800** μP.

Valid Memory Address (VMA) A signal generated by the processor which indicates that there is a valid address on the address bus.

Vectored interrupt An interrupt that sets the program counter to the address of the appropriate service routine.

7-17 ▼ REFERENCES

GREENFIELD, JOSEPH D., *Practical Digital Design Using ICs,* 3rd ed., Prentice Hall, Englewood Cliffs, N.J., 1994.

MOTOROLA, *Motorola Programming Manual,* M68PRM(D), Phoenix, Ariz. 1976, reprinted 1984.

———, *8/16/32-Bit Microcontrollers from Motorola,* BR261/D Rev. 2, Phoenix, Ariz., 1991.

———, *MC6800 8-Bit Microprocessing Unit (MPU) Data Sheet,* DS9471-R2, Phoenix, Ariz., 1984.

———, *MC6810 128 x 8-Bit Static Random Access Memory,* DS9487-R3, Phoenix, Ariz., 1984.

———, *MC6821 Peripheral Interface Adapter,* DS9435-R5, Phoenix, Ariz., 1985.

———, *MC6850 Asynchronous Communications Interface Adapter,* DS9493-R4, Phoenix, Ariz., 1985.

7-18 ▼ PROBLEMS

7-1. How many bytes and how many cycles are required for each of the following instructions?

(a) AND IMMEDIATE

(b) LOAD EXTENDED

(c) STORE DIRECT

(d) STORE INDEXED

(e) ROTATE LEFT EXTENDED

(f) JSR EXTENDED

7-2. What information appears on the address and data buses at the conclusion of each instruction of the following program? Make a table as shown for Problem 7-5.

ADDRESS	PROGRAM
20	96
21	C2
22	8B
23	AB
24	97
25	C3
26	20
27	F8

7-3. How long does it take to execute each loop in the program of Problem 7-2?

7-4. A system using several **EPROM**s should only have one that responds to all 1s on the address lines. Explain why this is so.

7-5. A **6802** system like Fig. 7-9 but using 8K by 8-bit EPROMs and RAMs has its components selected when the address levels are as shown by the following table.

ADDRESS BITS	EPROM1	EPROM2	RAM1	RAM2	PIA1
A15	1	1	0	0	0
A14	1	1	1	1	0
A13	1	0	1	0	1
A7				1	

Which addresses does each component respond to? Which component contains the vector addresses?

7-6. A **6802** system consists of four 4K by 8-bit ROMs, four 1K by 8-bit RAMs, two PIAs, and an ACIA. Allocate the memory space for each IC. Give the addresses that affect each component. Use **74HC00** series ICs as required as in Example 7-5.

7-7. If a **6802** system's memory space is to be filled entirely with **6810**s, how many **6810**s can be accommodated? How many **6810**s can be accommodated without resorting to external decoding?

After attempting to solve these problems, try to answer the self-evaluation questions in Section 7-2. If any of them still seem difficult, review the appropriate sections of the chapter to find the answers.

8 | INPUT/OUTPUT

8-1 ▼ INSTRUCTIONAL OBJECTIVES

The object of this chapter is to introduce those components that control the Input/Output (I/O) operations of the **6800** system. After reading this chapter, the student should be able to:

1. Explain how a μC can control an external device using PIAs, and/or Digital-to-Analog (D/A) and Analog-to-Digital (A/D) converters.
2. Explain the function of each signal connected to the PIA.
3. Explain the function of each bit in the PIA's Control and Direction Registers.
4. Utilize the PIA to transmit data.
5. Utilize the PIA to communicate with a peripheral by using CB1 and CB2 lines to control the data flow.
6. Explain the function of each register and I/O line in the ACIA.
7. Write a program to transmit asynchronous serial data using the ACIA.
8. Explain the lines needed to connect an ACIA to a data terminal or modem.

8-2 ▼ SELF-EVALUATION QUESTIONS

Watch for the answers to the following questions as you read the chapter. They should help you to understand the material presented.

1. What are the two basic methods of digital I/O?
2. Explain the difference between control words and status words.
3. What is the function of A/D and D/A converters?
4. What is initialization?
5. What is the difference between the control lines and the other I/O lines on the PIA?
6. Why is the B side of the PIA better suited for outputting data and the A side better suited for receiving data?
7. What is the function of START and STOP bits?

8. Explain the interaction in an **6850** ACIA between the Transmit Data Register and the Transmit Shift Register, and the interaction between the Receive Shift Register and the Receive Data Register.

8-3 ▼ INTRODUCTION TO INPUT/OUTPUT

The bus-structured organization of the **6800** system discussed in Chapter 7 is an efficient way for the components of the computer to communicate with each other. One of the primary *purposes of a μC, however, is to control an external device* such as a line printer or a drill press. The μC exercises this control by sending commands to the device through the I/O circuits. Usually, these commands are based on comparisons between desired and actual conditions existing in the external system. It may be necessary, for example, to stop the drill press if its motor temperature or speed exceed certain predetermined limits. The system must monitor these crucial conditions and send this information to the μC. *The communications that allow the μC to receive information from an external system* (**Input**) *and present data and commands to it* (**Output**) *is referred to as **Input/Output** (**I/O**).*

8-3.1 ▼ Methods of Digital Input/Output

Two basic methods are used to perform digital I/O functions between the bidirectional internal bus of the μC and the lines associated with the external devices. The fastest and most popular is the *parallel interface,* where many lines can be used to transfer data simultaneously in one step. A second method is to use *serial transmission* of the bits of each byte over one signal path (for each direction). This is done either asynchronously or synchronously (*synchronous* means in step with a clock or timing signal). The need for only two transmission paths makes the serial method attractive where the device being controlled is some distance away. These methods were implemented in the original **6800** systems by several unique parts:

1. The **6821** Peripheral Interface Adapter (PIA) or **68488** General-Purpose Interface Adapter (GPIA) are used for *parallel* transfer.
2. The **6850** Asynchronous Communications Interface Adapter (ACIA), the **6852** Synchronous Serial Data Adapter (SSDA), or the **6854** Advanced Data Link Controller (ADLC) are used for *serial* transfer.

Although the **6821** and **6850** are still available as of this writing, they are rarely used today because their functions are integrated into the many MCU chips now available. As mentioned in Chapter 7, however, they do serve to add functions to systems where additional I/O is needed. They may not be used in all such systems, because they are NMOS parts and require more current than similar CMOS devices. Motorola makes the **68HC24, 68HC26,** and **68HC27** port replacement units, however, which are CMOS and provide parallel I/O expansion for some **6800** family systems. Other choices include those made by third-party vendors. The Rockwell **65C52,** for example, is a CMOS part equivalent to the ACIA in function.

The primary reason to understand their application is that the basic concepts of the PIA and ACIA are used in all the Motorola MCUs that will be described later.

All of these MOS LSI ICs include *control, status,* and *data* registers. In the Motorola memory-mapped methods of system design, the registers within these peripheral ICs are *addressable,* just like memory. This is true whether the registers are internal to the MCU or are included in external components on the μC buses. The mode of operation of each I/O IC is determined by storing one or more control words in the IC's *Control* Registers. The *Status* registers are accessed by the μC to sense the condition of the external device as determined by signals from it. The *data* registers, of course, do the actual work of inputting or outputting information.

8-3.2 ▼ Control Words and Data Words

A **6800, 6802,** or the processor in any **6800** family MCU can communicate with external devices via the PIA, ACIA, SSDA, ADLC, or GPIA. The μP can send out either *data words* or *control words* and receive either *data words* or *status words.* The *control* word selects the mode of operation of the interface component and determines whether the I/O lines are to operate as inputs or outputs. It also selects the polarity sensed by the control lines. Once the interface is properly programmed, the data registers can then be used to transmit commands or data to the external device.

Command words are commands to the external device. They tell it what to do (or control it). If command words are used, the external hardware is often designed so that each bit controls a different function. For example, bit 0 could control a solid-state relay, bit 1 could be connected to a solenoid, and bit 2 could drive an indicator light.

Data words are used to represent either a *code* or a *magnitude.* As a code, for example, one byte could tell a terminal which alphanumeric character to display. As a magnitude, it might tell a drill press how fast to rotate or determine the cutting depth of a lathe.

The CPU can receive either *data* words or *status* words. *Data* words typically represent system parameters such as the position of a tool or the temperature of a motor. *Status* words give the μC the state of the system (e.g., is a relay ON or is a tape rewinding).

8-3.3 ▼ Digital-to-Analog or Analog-to-Digital Converters*

Almost all external mechanical components of a typical industrial control system are controlled by **analog** parameters, such as temperature, pressure, or position. These quantities represent the *status* of the system. They must be converted to electrical voltages by devices called *transducers.* Transducers convert mechanical properties to electrical voltages, but their outputs are analog signal voltages that are usually restricted to the range from 0 to 5 V. They must be converted to digital voltages by using an Analog-to-Digital (A/D) converter before they can be sent to a μP. The μP can then process the status information it receives from the A/D converters to determine what action should be taken.

The μP can then control the system by sending out commands and data, but a μP is restricted to sending out digital information. If, for example, the μP is controlling the speed of a motor, the signals to the motor might have to be analog. Then a Digital-to-Analog (D/A) converter is necessary so that the digital information from the μP can be converted to analog quantities that the system can use.

A block diagram of a typical control system is shown in Fig. 8-1. The D/A half of the system is shown in the upper part of Fig. 8-1. If the μC is to control the cutting depth of a lathe, for example, it is programmed to output a digital word in which the desired information is encoded. This word is sent through the PIA and then converted to an *ana-*

---

*D/A and A/D converters are discussed further in Sections 13-9 and 13-10.

log quantity, typically a voltage, by a D/A converter. The magnitude of this voltage is determined by the binary value of this digital word. Thus to control the lathe's cutting depth, the following steps are necessary:

1. The μC must determine the desired cutting depth (based on input from sensors) and present this as a digital word to the interface IC (the PIA is assumed in this case).
2. The digital output of the PIA must be connected to the input of a D/A converter.
3. The analog voltage output of the D/A converter then drives a mechanical converter that sets the cutting depth of the lathe.

In Fig. 8-1 the wide arrows represent eight or more digital lines to the converters, depending on the resolution required, and the single output line carries the analog output voltage of the D/A converter.

EXAMPLE 8-1

The cutting depth of the lathe can vary from 0 to 16 cm. If the D/A converter has an 8-bit input, how close to the desired value can the cutting depth be set?

SOLUTION

Since an 8-bit input allows for 256 (2^8) different numbers, each digital incre- ment corresponds to 16 cm/256 = **0.0625 cm.** This is the *resolution* of the con- verter. If greater resolution is required, more than eight lines must be used in the converter. This requires a somewhat more sophisticated hardware system.

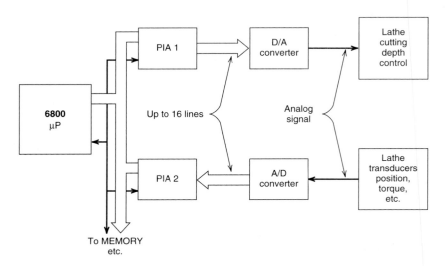

Figure 8-1 Typical μP analog input/output system.

8-3.4 ▼ Analog-to-Digital Conversion

To control an external system, a μC must be able to monitor it. This monitoring is usually accomplished by using *sensors, transducers,* and *Analog-to-Digital* (A/D) *converters.*

Sensors and *transducers* convert physical quantities to analog voltages. *Sensors* are generally used to sense relatively static quantities such as the temperature at a particular point or the weight of the liquid in a fuel tank. *Transducers* generally convert more dynamic physical quantities, such as pressures or velocities, to voltages.

The sensors or transducers are sometimes built into an external module that converts their output voltages to digital form before it is sent to the μC. The A/D converter accepts a DC voltage as its input and produces a corresponding digital output. A/D converters with 8-, 10-, and 12-bit outputs are readily available. The more bits provided, the higher the resolution of the converter, as shown in Example 8-1. A digital word of any size can be accommodated by multiplexing it (dividing it in 8-bit bytes that are brought in sequentially), but if the resolution is adequate, it is simplest to use a byte-sized converter. A block diagram of an A/D input system is shown in the lower part of Fig. 8-1.

Industrial systems are generally controlled by computers as follows:

1. The operation of the system is monitored by sensors and transducers.
2. Their outputs are converted to digital quantities by an A/D converter, if not already in digital form.
3. The outputs are sent to the μC via the PIA.
4. The computer program examines the inputs to determine if the system is operating properly.
5. If the μC determines that adjustments are required, it sends commands out via the PIA.
6. The outputs are converted by a D/A converter to voltages that adjust the system and restore optimal operation.

In recent years, a number of MCUs have been introduced that have an A/D converter function integrated into the chip (see Section 10-12). In this case, the sensor or transducer output voltage is routed directly to the proper pins on the MCU. The MCU then does the conversion internally.

8-4 ▼ PERIPHERAL INTERFACE ADAPTER IN DETAIL

The Peripheral Interface Adapter (PIA) is a 40-pin Large-Scale Integration (LSI) IC designed to control *parallel* data transfers between a **6800** family μC system and external devices. PIAs are used to transfer data or commands when the equipment to be controlled is nearby, and the many lines are easily connected to it. Sections 8-7 through 8-11 describe uses of the serial interfaces, which are more often used for distant control.

A bus interface diagram of the **6821** PIA that is used for parallel data transfer in **6800** family systems is shown in Fig. 8-2. It shows the registers within the PIA, the interface to the μC's data, address, and control buses on the left, and the interface connections to external devices on the right.

8-4.1 ▼ PIA Registers

Figure 8-2 shows that the PIA is a dual I/O port unit (a **port** is defined as an 8-bit parallel interface). The PIA has two similar ports, labeled *A* and *B*. This drawing from Motorola literature shows that each port has three registers associated with it and identifies them as:

1. **Control Register.** This controls the operation of its side of the PIA.
2. **Data Direction Register.** This register determines the direction of data flow (in or out) on each I/O line.
3. **Data Register.** This register holds the I/O data going between the external system and the PIA.

To reduce confusion and to be a bit more accurate for this book, we prefer to refer to the first two registers as follows:

1. **Control/Status Register.** This register has 6 bits used to control the PIA and 2 bits of status.
2. **Direction Register.** This register determines the direction of data flow (in or out) on each I/O line.

The action of these registers is discussed in detail in Sections 8-5 and 8-6.

8-4.2 ▼ PIA/6800 Interface

The PIA registers are treated as a set of *memory locations* by the **6800** family computers. The μP reads and writes these registers as it would any memory location. The user must

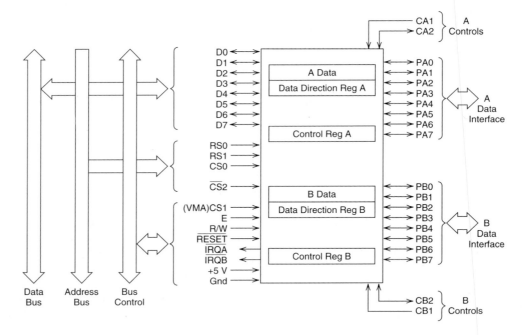

Figure 8-2   6821 PIA bus interface.

assign addresses to the PIA registers as he or she would other memory addresses (see Chapter 7).

The lines connecting the PIA to the μC's buses are shown on the left side of Fig. 8-2. This interface consists of:

1. **Inputs D0–D7.** These comprise the 8-bit μC data bus.
2. **Inputs RS0, RS1 and CS0, CS1, and CS2.** These lines are normally connected to the μC's address bus. The Register Select lines, RS0 and RS1, are usually connected to A0 and A1 and determine, along with a bit in the Control Register, which of the six registers within the PIA is selected. The Chip Select lines CS0, CS1, and CS2 are used to select the particular PIA (see Section 7-14).
3. **Enable (E).** The Enable (E) pin of the **6821** PIA was originally designed to be connected to the E clock on the **6800,** but because the **6821** is now a static part, the E pin can be used as another Chip Select.
4. **PIA READ/WRITE.** This signal is generated by the μP to control the direction of data transfers on the data bus. A LOW state on the READ/WRITE line enables the PIA's input buffers. Data is transferred from the μP to the PIA when the device has been selected. A HIGH on the READ/WRITE line sets up the PIA for a transfer of data to the μP via the bus. The PIA output buffers are enabled when the proper address is present.
5. **RESET.** This active-LOW RESET line is used to reset all register bits in the PIA to a logical 0 (LOW). This pin of the PIA is normally connected to the RESET line of the μC system and is usually activated by a momentary switch or automatic restart circuit during POWER ON.
6. **IRQA and IRQB.** These are the PIA interrupt lines. They are designed for wire-OR operation and are generally tied together and wired to the interrupt input on the μC. A LOW signal on either of these lines causes the μC to be interrupted. Details of this operation are described in Section 9-5.

8-4.3 ▼ Interface between the PIA and External Devices

The connections between the PIA and external devices are shown on the right side of Fig. 8-2. There are two groups of eight direction-switchable data lines (PA0 through PA7 and PB0 through PB7) and two control lines (CA1 and CA2, or CB1 and CB2) for each side. The control lines are used to regulate communication between the PIA and the external devices.

Figure 8-3 shows the output port circuitry for ports A and B of the **6821** PIA. Both sides can send or receive data, but the A side has been designed primarily for input and the B side has been designed primarily for output. The A side is designed to drive CMOS logic to below 30% of V_{CC} for a logic 0 and above 70% of V_{CC} for a logic 1. It incorporates an internal pull-up resistor that remains connected even in the input mode. Because of this, the A side requires more drive current in the input mode than port B. In contrast the B side uses a normal three-state NMOS buffer which cannot pull up to CMOS levels without external resistors. The B side can drive extra loads without difficulty. When the PIA comes out of RESET, the bits of the A port are configured as inputs with pull-up resistors, whereas the B side (also in input mode) will float HIGH or LOW depending on the external load.

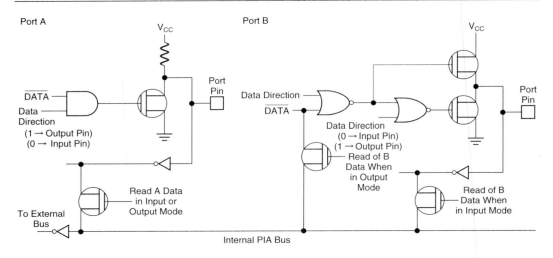

Figure 8-3 Equivalent circuits for ports A and B of the **6821** PIA.

Notice also the difference between a port A and port B read operation for the PIA when in the output mode. When reading port A, the actual pin is read, while the B side read comes from an output latch ahead of the actual pin. These port differences affect primarily the external circuitry and do not otherwise affect functionality.

8-5 ▼ DATA TRANSFERS BETWEEN THE PIA AND EXTERNAL DEVICES

Before any data transfers can take place via the PIA, its Control Registers and Data Direction Registers have to be set up (or *programmed*) to determine the mode of operation and the direction of the data transfer (in or out of the PIA). This is known as *initialization*. Once initialized, these registers generally remain unchanged, although one of the PIA's outstanding capabilities is its programmable nature and ability to change system function during the operation of a program. This permits many unique features to be implemented in special programs with a minimum of external hardware and also permits the same PIA to be used in many applications (see Example 8-8).

8-5.1 ▼ Direction Register

The Direction Register determines the direction of each bit of data being transferred on the PIA's data lines. The Direction Register is 8 bits long, so there is a one-to-one correspondence between the bits of the Direction Register and the PA0–PA7 or PB0–PB7 lines. *A 1 in any bit of the Direction Register causes the corresponding PA or PB line to act as an output, whereas a 0 causes it to become an input.* Typically, direction registers contain 00 or $FF so that an entire byte is transferred in or out, but some bits on either side of a PIA can act as inputs and some as outputs, as shown in Example 8-3.

Page 217

8-5.2 ▼ Data Register

The Data Register contains the data being transferred in or out of the PIA. The Data and Direction Registers have the same address, but whether a word to that address reaches the Data Register or the Direction Register depends on the state of bit 2 of the Control Register.

Table 8-1a shows the addressing scheme for the PIA registers. When RS1 is a 0, the A registers are addressed, and when it is a 1, the B side is accessed. Since RS0 is generally connected to A0 and RS1 to A1, the Control/Status Registers for both sides are located at an odd address, and the Data and Direction Registers are both at the prior even address. Although there are six registers, only four addresses are used, as shown in Table 8-1b. If bit 2 of the Control Register (CRA2 or CRB2) is a 1, the Data Register is accessible, whereas if bit 2 is a 0, only the Direction Register can be accessed. Thus if the PIA receives a write command at the Data/Direction Register address, it will use bit 2 of the control register to determine which register is to be written into. Bit 2 is sometimes called the *steering* bit because it steers reads or writes to either the Direction or the Data Register.

8-5.3 ▼ Initializing the PIA

When the RESET line of the PIA is taken LOW, it clears (or zeros) all registers. This sets up the PA0–PA7, PB0–PB7, CA2, and CB2 lines as inputs and disables all interrupts. Since bit 2 is also 0, the Direction Registers are set to be accessed. The PIA RESET line is normally connected to the μP RESET, so the hardware functions described above will occur, but in addition, a RESTART program routine is accessed automatically (described in Chapter 9) whenever RESET is activated. The desired PIA configuration is *programmed* into the chip during execution of this RESTART program routine.

TABLE 8-1 PIA Addressing

(a) Internal Addressing				
RS1	**RS0**	**CRA2**	**CRB2**	**Registers**
0	0	1	X	Data Register A
0	0	0	X	Direction Register A
0	1	X	X	Control/Status Register A
1	0	X	1	Data Register B
1	0	X	0	Direction Register B
1	1	X	X	Control/Status Register B

(b) Memory Location	
Address	**Registers**
XXX11	B Control/Status (1 register)
XXX10	B Data/Direction (2 registers)
XXX01	A Control/Status (1 register)
XXX00	A Data/Direction (2 registers)

If the PIA needs to be reconfigured without using the RESET line, it must be done in the following sequence:

1. Clear the Control/Status Register (including bit 2).
2. Rewrite the Direction Register.
3. Rewrite the Control Word with bit 2 SET to select the Data Register.
4. Write or read data.

EXAMPLE 8-2

Write a program to send the contents of memory locations $40 and $41 to a peripheral device. Assume that the Control Register is at address $8009, and the Direction Register and Data Register are both at address $8008. Note that because bit 1 of the address is 0, the A side of the PIA is being used.

SOLUTION

The steps of the solution are listed below. The coding has been omitted to save space.

1. Accumulator A is cleared and stored in $8009. This clears all the bits of the Control Registers; in particular, it clears bit 2.
2. Accumulator A is loaded (Immediate) with $FF and stored in $8008. Because bit 2 of the Control/Status Register is now a 0, when $FF is written to address $8008 it enters the Direction Register and causes all the data lines to act as outputs.
3. An appropriate control word is now loaded (using LDAA Immediate) into the accumulator and stored in $8009. This changes bit 2 of the Control Register to a 1, which latches the Direction Register and allows the Data Register to be accessed.
4. The contents of location $40 are loaded into the accumulator and stored at $8008. Because bit 2 of the Control/Status Register is now a 1, these bits go to the Data Register and are output on the I/O lines.
5. After the first word has been read by the peripheral and sensed by reading the status bits (usually signaled by one of the control lines, as described later), the contents of location $41 are loaded in A and stored at $8008. This places that data on the I/O lines.

Note that once the Control and Direction Registers have been set up, data can be sent out repeatedly without reinitializing those registers.

EXAMPLE 8-3

Write a program to read the state of four switches and send the data out to a hexadecimal display.

SOLUTION

One solution is shown in the circuit of Fig. 8-4, where the four switches are connected to lines PA0 through PA3, and the display inputs are connected to peripheral lines PA4 through PA7. The program for the solution proceeds as follows.

1. During initialization, $F0 is written into the Direction Register. This configures the four LSBs as inputs and the four MSBs as outputs.
2. The Control Register is then rewritten to make bit 2 a 1. The instruction LDAA (from) $8008 reads the switch contents into the four LSBs of the accumulator.
3. Four LEFT SHIFT instructions shift the switch settings into the MSBs of the accumulator.
4. Now A STAA at $8008 places the switch settings on the output lines (PA4 through PA7), where they can drive the display.

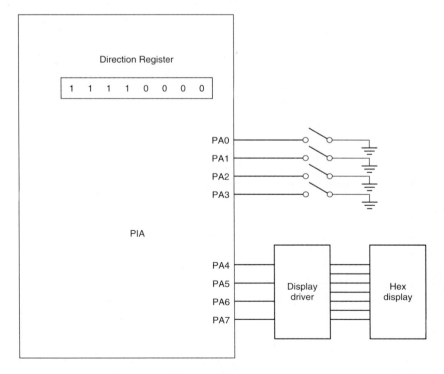

Figure 8-4   PIA connections for Example 8-3.

8-6 ▼ PIA CONTROL LINES

When an external device has information for the μC, it must send the PIA a signal (often called DATA READY). When the byte is read by the PIA, it typically acknowledges receipt of the information by sending an ACK (for acknowledge) signal to the device. A similar situation exists when the PIA is transmitting information to the device. The protocol and signals that control the exchange of information is called *handshaking*.

In Section 8-5 we concentrated on the data lines and ignored the CA1 and CA2 (or CB1 and CB2) lines, which control the interchange of information. The operating mode of these control lines is determined by the bits in the A and B Control/Status Registers. The control lines, in turn, affect the contents of bits 6 and 7 of the Control/Status Registers, as will be explained.

The configuration of the Control/Status Register is shown in Fig. 8-5. The upper register (CRA) is for the A side of the PIA, and the lower one (CRB) is an identical register used to control the B side. The function of bit 2 (Direction Register access) has been described in Section 8-5.2. Bits 0, 1, and 3, 4, 5 of the Control/Status Register are used to select the functions of the control lines. Status bits 6 and 7 are SET when the CA1 and CA2 (CB1 and CB2) lines are taken HIGH or LOW by signals from external hardware. Bits 6 and 7 are *read-only* bits that cannot be changed by writing into the control/status register, but are RESET indirectly by a READ data operation, as explained in Section 8-6.2.

8-6.1 ▼ Control Line Monitoring

The μC system has two ways of responding to any of the control line transitions which indicate that an external device is requesting attention:

1. By *polling* status bits continuously. (Polling means that the system program periodically reads the Control/Status Registers of all I/O devices to determine if the flag bit of one of them has been SET.)
2. By electronically responding to the hardware *interrupt* request lines.

Many systems do not use or need interrupts, and a number of examples of these systems are described in the remainder of this chapter. The use of interrupts is a complex subject and much of Chapter 9 is devoted to it.

8-6.2 ▼ Control Lines CA1 and CB1

Control lines CA1 and CB1 are *input only* lines that function identically. As shown in Table 8-2, they are controlled by bits 0 and 1 of the Control/Status Register, and their action can be determined from Table 8-2, which shows the following:

PIA Control Word Format

	7	6	5	4	3	2	1	0
CR A	IRQA1	IRQA2	CA2 Control			DDRA Access	CA1 Control	

	7	6	5	4	3	2	1	0
CR B	IRQB1	IRQB2	CB2 Control			DDRB Access	CB1 Control	

Figure 8-5   PIA control word format.

TABLE 8-2 Control of Interrupt Inputs CAI and CBI

CRA-1 (CRB-1)	CRA-0 (CRB-0)	Interrupt Input CA1 (CB1)	Interrupt Flag CRA-7 (CRB-7)	MPU Interrupt Request IRQA (IRQB)
0	0	↓ Active	Set high on ↓ of CA1 (CB1)	Disabled — $\overline{IRQ}$ remains high
0	1	↓ Active	Set high on ↓ of CA1 (CB1)	Goes low when the interrupt flag bit CRA-7 (CRB-7) goes high
1	0	↑ Active	Set high on ↑ of CA1 (CB1)	Disabled — $\overline{IRQ}$ remains high
1	1	↑ Active	Set high on ↑ of CA1 (CB1)	Goes low when the interrupt flag bit CRA-7 (CRB-7) goes high

Notes:
1. ↑ indicates positive transition (low to high)
2. ↓ indicates negative transition (high to low)
3. The Interrupt flag bit CRA-7 is cleared by an MPU Read of the A Data Register, and CRB-7 is cleared by an MPU Read of the B Data Register.
4. If CRA-0 (CRB-0) is low when an interrupt occurs (Interrupt disabled) and is later brought high, $\overline{IRQA}$ ($\overline{IRQB}$) occurs after CRA-0 (CRB-0) is written to a "one".

1. If CRA1 (CRB1) is a 0, status bit 7 of the Control/Status Register is set HIGH whenever there is a negative transition (↓) on the CA1 (CB1) line. These lines are typically connected to an external device that causes a transition whenever it requires attention. If CRA1 (CRB1) is a 1, a positive transition (↑) on ÇA1 (CB1) SETs status bit 7 of the corresponding Control/Status Register.

2. Because we are deferring the subject of interrupts until Chapter 9, we will only consider the cases now where CRA0 and CRB0 are set to 0.

Bits CRA7 (CRB7) can be reset only by reading the corresponding *data* register. The reason for this is that a transition on CA1 (CB1) sets CRA-7 (CRB-7) and indicates that the peripheral has data available for the μP. The μP accepts that data by *reading its input port,* the PA or PB data register, which transfers the data to an accumulator. This also resets CRA-7 (CRB-7) because the data has now been taken by the μP.

EXAMPLE 8-4

A PIA is in locations $8004 through $8007. (All addresses are hex.)

(a) How can the user determine if a transition has occurred on CB1?

(b) If bit 7 of control register B is set, how can it be cleared?

SOLUTION

(a) If a transition has occurred on CB1, then CRB-7 will be set. Therefore, reading CRB-7 (at location $8007) will set the N flag in the Condition Code Register. Testing for minus (BMI) is the usual way to test bit 7 of the control register.

(b) If CRB-7 is set, it can only be cleared by reading the corresponding Data Register. Here we need a LDAA $8006 to clear the bit in $8007. The fact that one location ($8006) has to be read in order to clear a bit in another location ($8007) is sometimes confusing. The user must also be sure that the LDAA $8006 is reading the data register and not the Direction Register. Reading the Direction Register will not reset CRB-7.

EXAMPLE 8-5

What happens if 06 is written into Control/Status Register A?

SOLUTION

A control word of 06 results in the conditions specified on line 3 of Table 8-2. Bit 7 is SET by a positive transition of the CA1 line. IRQA is disabled. The Direction Register is unaffected because bit 2 is also SET. If 06 is written to the Control/Status Register and read back before a positive transition on CA1 occurs, the μP reads it back as 06, but if a transition occurs between the writing and reading, the μP reads it back as an 86 because CRA7 is now SET. Once SET, CRA-7 can only be cleared by reading Data Register A, as stated in the footnotes to Table 8-2.

EXAMPLE 8-6

Write a program to monitor the CA1 line constantly and to take action when a transition occurs. Assume that the Control/Status Register's address is $8009.

SOLUTION

First the Control/Status Register must be initialized to select the proper transition (↓ or ↑) and disable interrupts. Then the program can proceed as shown in Fig. 8-6. The instruction at location $1000 loads the contents of the Status Register into the A accumulator and it is tested by the following instruction (at $1003) to see if bit 7 (the interrupt flag bit) is SET. If not, the contents of the register at $8009 are positive and the instruction branches back to $1000 and fetches the status again. It continues to loop in this fashion until bit 7 goes HIGH. Since the resulting byte is then negative, the program falls through to the following instruction. The PIA's Data Register at $8008 is then read to reset CRA7 and get the data. Note that this is a very tight loop; that is, the computer did nothing but monitor the PIA. Interrupts, described in Chapter 9, allow the computer to perform other tasks while waiting for the transition.

ADDR	DATA		MNEMONIC		COMMENTS
1000	B6	8009	LDAA	$8009	Get status
1003	2A	FB	BPL	*-3	If plus, branch back to 1000 and repeat.
1005	B6	8008	LDAA	$8008	Get data.
Etc.					

Figure 8-6 Program for Example 8-6.

EXAMPLE 8-7

A PIA is located at $8004 through $8007. A debounced switch is connected to CA1 and the outputs PA0 through PA6 drive a seven-segment display, as shown in Fig. 8-7. Write a program to increment the number in the seven-segment display every time the switch is thrown. When the number reaches 9 the display must return to 0 after the next switch throw.

SOLUTION

The program is shown in Fig. 8-8. It starts by initializing the A port for outputs. It then monitors Control/Status Register A. A switch throw causes a transition on CA1 and causes CRA7 to go HIGH. When this occurs, the program falls through to location $35 where it:

1. Reads Data Register A to reset CRA7
2. Increments X and resets it to 0 if X has gone beyond 9
3. Jumps to a table to get the proper codes to drive the seven-segment display

    In this program the table starts at location $A0. To show a 0 on the display, the data must cause all segments except g to light. The code in $A0 must therefore be $3F. If $A1 is accessed, a 1 should appear by lighting segments B and C, so that $A1 should contain 06. Fig. 8-7 shows the segments with their PIA interconnections.

    Many µC systems drive their displays directly by using similar tables. Note that this program provides a way for the µP to count and display external events as they occur.

One of the interesting features of the PIA is its programmability. Thus the operation can be changed dynamically during operation as illustrated in Example 8-8.

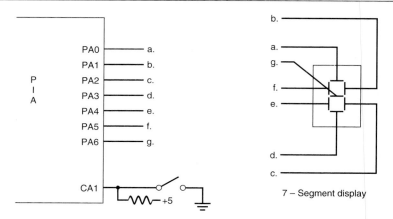

Figure 8-7   Control of a seven-segment display using the PIA.

(a) Program

Addr	Code		Mnemonic			Comments
20	CE	0000		LDX	#0	CLEAR X
23	7F	8005		CLR	$8005	CLR BIT 2 TO SELECT DIR REG
26	86	FF		LDA	A #$FF	SET TO ALL 1S
28	B7	8004		STA	A $8004	SET DIRECTION FOR OUTPUTS
2B	86	04		LDA	A #4	GET WORD FOR NEG GOING CA1 &
2D	B7	8005		STA	A $8005	SET CRA2 TO SELECT DATA REG
30	B6	8005	LOOP	LDA	A $8005	GET STATUS
33	2A	FB		BPL	LOOP	WAIT FOR CRA7 TO BECOME 1
35	B6	8004		LDA	A $8004	CLEAR BIT 7
38	08			INX		INCREMENT X
39	8C	000A		CPX	#$A	IS IT > 9 ?
3C	26	03		BNE	*+5	NO-SKIP NEXT INSTRUCTION
3E	CE	0000		LDX	#0	YES-CLEAR X
41	A6	A0		LDA	A $A0,X	GET THE 7-SEGMENT CODE
43	B7	8004		STA	A $8004	OUTPUT IT TO DISPLAY
46	20	E8		BRA	LOOP	RETURN TO 30 AGAIN

(b) Data Table

Location	Contents	Decimal Number to be Displayed
A0	3F	0
A1	06	1
A2	5B	2
A3	4F	3
A4	66	4
A5	6D	5
A6	7D	6
A7	07	7
A8	7F	8
A9	6F	9

Figure 8-8   Program and data table for Example 8-7.

EXAMPLE 8-8

Write a program that will input characters from a keyboard using a PIA. They will be displayed on the screen and kept in a buffer. This is a program that could be part of a word processor system. In this example the keyboard has a line that goes LOW whenever a key is depressed. It stays low as long as the key is held. Use the CA1 line to set the CRA6 flag when a character is ready. Using the same line, provide a character repeat feature when the key is held down.

SOLUTION

Figure 8-9 shows a program to meet the requirements. This was developed as part of a word processor program that uses a CRT display. It serves to bring in characters from a keyboard whenever keys are pressed and display them on the screen. They also go into a buffer or are acted on if they are control characters. This is all done by the CHOUT routine and will not be shown now.

A *repeat character* feature is included such that if a key is kept down for more than a selected time (a count of $6000), the character will be repeated. The rate of repetition is determined by the smaller count ($A00). This works by first programming the CA1 line so that it looks for a negative-going signal from the keyboard, but once the character is fetched, the CA1 line is reprogrammed to look for a positive-going signal so that the release of the key can be sensed. If the key is held down beyond the timeout period, it is repeated on the screen.

Since the PIA must be reinitialized each time this input character routine is entered, and not by the RESET routine, it has a unique INIT routine. Note that the registers are reset by first clearing the control word and then reprogramming them again. The AECHO flag is used to allow or inhibit the display on the screen. As long as the AECHO flag is zero, the character is "echoed" (displayed). Also, a toggled byte labeled RPT is used to change the duration of the delay. The values of these delays were chosen by cut and try to provide action that was comfortable to the operator. (They will vary if the clock rate is different.)

The PIA's base address is $EB04 for this program but can be changed to any convenient value to match other hardware. The program could be in ROM, but AECHO and RPT must be in RAM since they get changed by the program.

8-6.3 ▼ Control Lines CA2 and CB2

Lines CA2 and CB2 can be used either as input or output control lines and are controlled by bits 3, 4, and 5 of their corresponding Control/Status Register. Table 8-3 reveals that these lines function exactly like CA1 and CB1 except that transitions caused by the external devices set bit 6 instead of bit 7 of the Control/Status Register. Until we study hardware interrupts in Chapter 9, we will only consider the cases where bit 3 of the Control/Status Register is a 0.

Addr Code		Mnemonics		Comments
1000 8E 1FFF	INIT	LDS	#S1FFF	SET STACK POINTER
1003 BD 0400		JSR	INITS	DO OTHER INIT
1006 20 18		BRA	RETURN	SCAN KEYBOARD
	* INITIALIZE KEYBOARD PIA			
1008 4F	CTST1	CLRA		
1009 B7 EB05		STAA	PIA+1	UNLATCH DIRECTION REG
100C B7 EB04		STAA	PIA	SET DIRECTION = INPUT
100F B7 EB07		STAA	PIA+3	UNLATCH DIRECTION REG
1012 B7 EB06		STAA	PIA+2	SET DIRECTION = OUT
1015 86 06		LDAA	#6	GET CW
1017 B7 EB07		STAA	PIA+3	SET "B" SIDE
101A 86 36		LDAA	#$36	SET CA1 FOR NEG GOING
101C B7 EB05		STA A	PIA+1	
101F 39		RTS		
	*			
1020 8D E6	RETURN	BSR	CTST1	RESET PIA EACH TIME
1022 8D 02	CLP	BSR	INCH	GET CHARACTER
1024 20 FC		BRA	CLP	LOOP
	*			
1026 B6 EB05	INCH	LDAA	PIA+1	NEG TRANSITION?
1029 2A FB		BPL	INCH	NO - LOOP
102B B6 EB04		LDAA	PIA	YES - GET CHARACTER
102E 84 7F		ANDA	#S7F	RESET BIT 7
1030 C6 34	IN2	LDAB	#$34	PROG TO DETECT RELSE
1032 F7 EB05		STAB	PIA+1	SET CW
1035 7F 2001		CLR	RPT	CLEAR REPEAT FLAG
1038 7D 2000		TST	AECHO	SET TO ECHO?
103B 27 0E		BEQ	OUTCH	YES
103D B6 EB04	IN1	LDAA	PIA	CLEAR INTR BIT
1040 84 7F		ANDA	#$7F	RESET MSB
1042 C6 36		LDAB	#S36	
1044 F7 EB05		STAB	PIA+1	RESTORE CA1 NEG-GOING
1047 7F 2000		CLR	AECHO	RESET ECHO FLAG
104A 39		RTS		RETURN TO LOOP
	*			
104B 36	OUTCH	PSHA		SAVE A ON STACK
104C BD 3000		JSR	CHOUT	DISPLAY CHAR ON SCRN
104F 32	PULA			RESTORE CHARACTER
1050 CE 6000		LDX	#$6000	SET START DELAY
1053 7D 2001		TST	RPT	WHICH DLY IN EFFECT?
1056 27 03		BEQ	*+5	SKIP IF REPT CLEAR
1058 CE 0A00		LDX	#$A00	SET REPT DELAY
105B F6 EB05	OT1	LDAB	PIA+1	GET STATUS
105E 2B DD		BMI	IN1	RELEASED YET?
1060 09		DEX		NO- DECRMT DLY COUNT
1061 26 F8		BNE	OT1	TIMEOUT?
1063 7C 2001		INC	RPT	SET FOR SHORT DELAY
1066 20 E3		BRA	OUTCH	YES - DISPLAY AGAIN

Figure 8-9   Input character routine with repeat for Example 8-8.

Table 8-3   Control of CA2 and CB2 as Interrupt Inputs; CRA5 (CRB5) Is LOW

CRA-5 (CRB-5)	CRA-4 (CRB-4)	CRA-3 (CRB-3)	Interrupt Input CA2 (CB2)	Interrupt Flag CRA-6 (CRB-6)	MPU Interrupt Request IRQA (IRQB)
0	0	0	↓ Active	Set high on ↓ of CA2 (CB2)	Disabled — IRQ remains high
0	0	1	↓ Active	Set high on ↓ of CA2 (CB2)	Goes low when the interrupt flag bit CRA-6 (CRB-6) goes high
0	1	0	↑ Active	Set high on ↑ of CA2 (CB2)	Disabled — IRQ remains high
0	1	1	↑ Active	Set high on ↑ of CA2 (CB2)	Goes low when the interrupt flag bit CRA-6 (CRB-6) goes high

Notes: 1.   ↑ indicates positive transition (low to high)

2.   ↓ indicates negative transition (high to low)

3.   The Interrupt flag bit CRA-6 is cleared by an MPU Read of the A Data Register and CRB-6 is cleared by an MPU Read of the B Data Register.

4.   If CRA-3 (CRB-3) is low when an interrupt occurs (Interrupt disabled) and is later brought high, IRQA (IRQB) occurs after CRA-3 (CRB-3) is written to a "one".

EXAMPLE 8-9

Assume that a tape drive is connected to a **6800** family system, and it must send the **6800** either data or status information on the same I/O lines. The data would be the words read from the tape, and the status information tells the system what the tape is doing (e.g., running forward, rewinding, at end of tape). How can the system distinguish between data and status information?

SOLUTION

One solution is to connect both CA1 and CA2 to the tape drive. If the tape drive is sending data, it raises CA1 every time it has a byte to send, while if it is sending status information, it raises CA2. The μP system can distinguish between status and data requests by examining bits 6 and 7 of the PIA's Control and Status Register.

8-6.4 ▼ CB2 as an Output in the Handshake Mode

The action of the CB2 line as an output is described in Table 8-4. Note that the CB2 line goes LOW after a WRITE to the Data Register. This simplifies the programming and therefore makes it preferable for the B section of the PIA to be used to send data to external devices (output).

The top line of Table 8-4 illustrates a mode of operation commonly called the handshaking mode. This case is illustrated in Fig. 8-10 and the sequence of events is as follows:

TABLE 8-4 Control of CB2 as an Output; CRB5 Is HIGH

CRB-5	CRB-4	CRB-3	CB2	
			Cleared	Set
1	0	0	Low on the positive transition of the first E pulse following an MPU Write "B" Data Register operation.	High when the interrupt flag bit CRB-7 is set by an active transition of the CB1 signal.
1	0	1	Low on the positive transition of the first E pulse after an MPU Write "B" Data Register operation.	High on the positive edge of the first "E" pulse following an "E" pulse which occurred while the part was deselected.
1	1	0	Low when CRB-3 goes low as a result of an MPU Write in Control Register "B".	Always low as long as CRB-3 is low. Will go high on an MPU Write in Control Register "B" that changes CRB-3 to "one".
1	1	1	Always high as long as CRB-3 is high. Will be cleared when an MPU Write Control Register "B" results in clearing CRB-3 to "zero".	High when CRB-3 goes high as a result of an MPU Write into Control Register "B".

1. The control word to the B side is written as shown. Note that CRB 5, 4, and 3 are 100, respectively.
2. When the system must send data out it writes the data to Data Register B. This causes CB2 to go LOW.
3. The peripheral device acknowledges receipt of the data by placing an acknowledge pulse on CB1. With a $24 in Control Register B, line 1 of TABLE 8-3 shows that the negative transition of CB1 raises the CRB7 flag and, as seen in line 1 of TABLE 8-4, this causes CB2 to return HIGH.

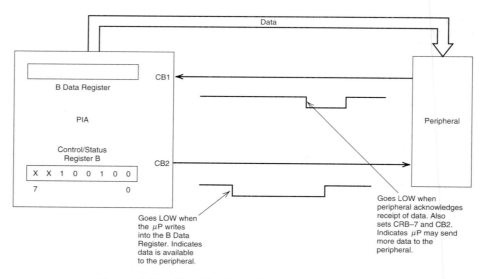

Figure 8-10 Handshaking with the B side of the PIA.

4. The µC system responds to a HIGH on CRB7 as an indication that the data has been accepted by the peripheral, and the next byte can be written to the PIA.

5. Before the next output byte can be written to the PIA, Data Register B must be *read* to reset CRB7.

EXAMPLE 8-10

The data between memory locations $1000 and $104F must be sent to a peripheral using the system of Fig. 8-10. Draw a flowchart to show how this is accomplished.

SOLUTION

The solution is shown in Fig. 8-11 and proceeds as follows:

1. The Control/Status Register is set to 00 (or the PIA is RESET).

2. Direction Register B is initialized to $FF (all bits to be outputs) and then the Control/Status Register is set to $24 to initialize the handshaking procedure described above.

3. The index register is set equal to 1000 and the first memory word to be transmitted is loaded from that location into the accumulator and stored in Data Register B. This causes CB2 to go LOW.

4. The program goes into a loop until the peripheral accepts the data and causes a negative transition (↓) on CB1. This SETS CRB7 and CB2. Before the transition, the result is positive (MSB = 0) and the program continues to loop. After the transition the result is negative and the program exits from the loop.

5. The program reads Data Register B to reset CRB7. It then tests to determine if it has exhausted its data area by comparing the index register with $1050 after each time it has been incremented. If it has, it stops; if it has not, it loads the next data word, causing CB2 to go LOW again and repeats the steps above.

8-6.5 ▼ CB2 in the Pulse Mode

If a peripheral device is connected to a PIA as shown in Fig. 8-12, and bits 5, 4, and 3 of the Control/Status Register are 101 respectively, as also shown, the CB2 line will be pulsed LOW whenever data is written into B Data Register. This line can be used to inform the peripheral that new data is available on the PIA output lines. If the peripheral can accept the data without fail, in the few microseconds it takes before the program can output the next byte, there is no need for an acknowledgment. The pulse mode of the PIA is outstanding for its simplicity of programming. Every WRITE into Data Register B causes CB2 to be pulsed. This mode is capable of very fast operation and is best used for high-speed peripherals such as a floppy disk system.

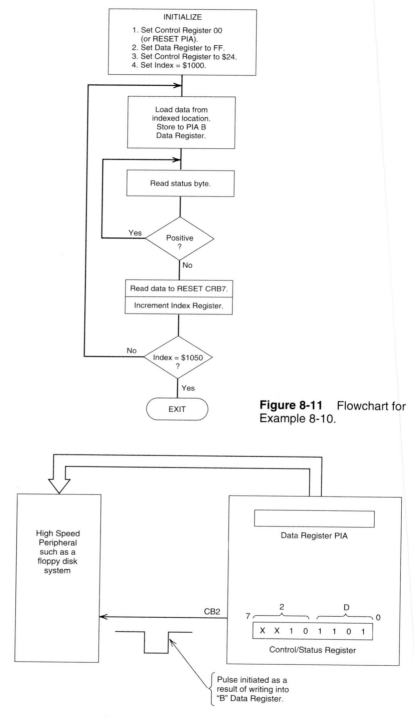

INITIALIZE

1. Set Control Register 00
   (or RESET PIA).
2. Set Data Register to FF.
3. Set Control Register to $24.
4. Set Index = $1000.

Load data from
indexed location.
Store to PIA B
Data Register.

Read status byte.

Positive
?

Yes

No

Read data to RESET CRB7.

Increment Index Register.

Index = $1050
?

No

Yes

EXIT

Figure 8-11 Flowchart for Example 8-10.

High Speed
Peripheral
such as a
floppy disk
system

Data Register PIA

CB2

7   2   D   0

X X 1 0 1 1 0 1

Control/Status Register

Pulse initiated as a
result of writing into
"B" Data Register.

Figure 8-12 Pulse mode of the PIA used with the B side.

EXAMPLE 8-11

Show how the pulse mode can be used on the B side to output data to a high-speed device such as a floppy disk system. Give an example of a program. Assume that the base address of the PIA is $8004 and that the PIA has been initialized with a Control Word of $2D.

SOLUTION

Refer once more to Fig. 8-12 and to the program shown in Fig. 8-13. Again, this pulse mode assumes that data can be accepted as fast as it is put out by the program. The CB2 line can be used to strobe a data latch or to increment an address counter so that the data can be stored in the register of the peripheral, for example. The program shown in Fig. 8-13 is written to reside at $1000 and assumes that the data to be transmitted is in memory at $2000 to $20FF (256 bytes).

The first instruction sets the Index Register (X) to the starting address of the data. The instruction at $1003 loads accumulator A from the location specified by Register X. This byte is then stored to the PIA Data Register (or output), which informs the peripheral by pulsing the CB2 line. The program then increments the X Register to the address of the next byte. The compare X (immediate) instruction is used to determine if all of the data has been sent out. This is done by the instruction at location $1009 to see if the X Register has gone past the end address of the data and, if not, looping back for the next byte.

8-6.6 ▼ ON–OFF Control of CB2

The last two lines of Table 8-4 specify a mode of operation in which the level of CB2 can be directly programmed. If CRB5 and CRB4 are both 1s, the CB2 line assumes the same level as CRB3. This allows the program to control the length of time CB2 is LOW or HIGH. This also enables the system to use CB2 as a ninth output line, if needed.

ADDR	DATA		LABEL	MNEMONICS		COMMENTS
1000	CE	2000		LDX	#$2000	Get pointer to data
1003	A6	00	LOOP	LDAA	0,X	Get data
1005	B7	8006		STAA	$8006	Store to B data register
1008	08			INX		Increment pointer
1009	8C	2100		CPX	#$2100	End of data ?
100C	26	F5		BNE	LOOP	No; get next byte.
100E	. . . . etc.					

Figure 8-13 Program for Example 8-11.

TABLE 8-5 Control of CA2 as an Output: (CRA5 is HIGH)

CRA-5	CRA-4	CRA-3	CA2	
			Cleared	**Set**
1	0	0	Low on negative transition of E after an MPU Read "A" Data operation.	High when the interrupt flag bit CRA-7 is set by an active transition of the CA1 signal.
1	0	1	Low on negative transition of E after an MPU Read "A" Data operation.	High on the negative edge of the first "E" pulse which occurs during a deselect.
1	1	0	Low when CRA-3 goes low as a result of an MPU Write to Control Register "A".	Always low as long as CRA-3 is low. Will go high on an MPU Write to Control Register "A" that changes CRA-3 to "one".
1	1	1	Always high as long as CRA-3 is high. Will be cleared on an MPU Write to Control Register "A" that clears CRA-3 to a "zero".	High when CRA-3 goes high as a result of an MPU Write to Control Register "A".

8-6.7 ▼ CA2 as an Output (Handshaking Mode)

CA2 can be used as an output line to regulate the flow of data from the peripheral to the PIA in the same way that CB2 does (see Example 8-10), except that the CA2 line can be taken LOW after either a READ or WRITE of the A Data Register instead of just a WRITE (see Table 8-5). Use of CA2 is therefore to be preferred when data input is involved.

EXAMPLE 8-12

A **6800** family system must read several words from a disk. To do so, it must first send the disk controller several bytes of information that tell it, for example, the disk address and the number of words to be read. Describe how the transfer can be accomplished.

SOLUTION

1. The Direction Register (B side) is set up for output (FF), and the A-side Direction Register is set for input (00).
2. The μP or MCU sends commands to the disk controller via the data lines PB0 through PB7, using the handshaking procedure discussed in Section 8-6.4. CB2 controls the flow of commands as shown in Fig. 8-10.
3. When the first word is ready, the controller puts it on the A Data Bus lines and causes a transition on CA1, which SETS CRA7 (see Fig. 8-14).
4. The μC now reads the first word from the PIA and places it in memory. This RESETS CRA7 and the μC program then pulses CA2, which requests new data from the disk.
5. This procedure continues until the required number of bytes have been transferred from the disk to the μCs memory.

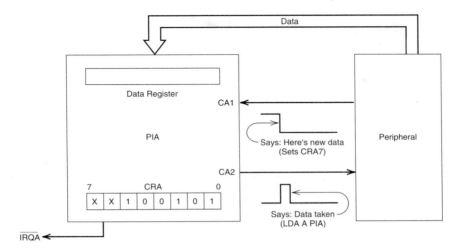

Figure 8-14   Handshaking with a peripheral on the A side.

8-6.8 ▼ Pulse Mode for CA2

If CRA 5, 4, and 3 are 101, respectively, the A side of the PIA operates in a pulse mode identical to that described for the B side, but it is triggered by a READ instead of a WRITE data operation.

8-6.9 ▼ ON–OFF Mode for CA2

When CRA5 and CRA4 are both 1s, the state of CA2 will be the same as that of bit CRA3, and therefore, CA2 can be set HIGH or LOW as desired. This gives the program total control of CA2.

EXAMPLE 8-13

A PIA is to be used to interface a High-Speed Paper Tape Reader to a **6800** family system. The reader has eight TTL output lines (one for each bit) and a sprocket-hole output for a *ready* signal. The tape is advanced a character at a time by a stepper motor that requires a negative-going pulse. What are the Control Words for the ON/OFF mode of the PIA? Give an example of a program. Assume a base address of $8004.

SOLUTION

As shown in Fig 8-15, the eight data lines from the reader's photocell outputs are connected to PA0 through PA7 of the PIA, and the sprocket-hole output is connected to CA1. CA2 is connected to the stepper motor pulse circuit in such a way that a negative-going pulse will step the tape. Reference to Table 8-5 shows that the Control Word should be 3C initially and is changed to a 34 to strobe the stepper motor. The program to control this circuit is shown in Fig. 8-16.

The first instruction is a dummy READ operation to clear CRA7. Accumulator A is loaded with the value in the next (Immediate) byte (34) and it is output to the PIA Control Register. This causes CA2 to go LOW, thus starting the strobe pulse. The next two instructions repeat this action except the Control Word is 3C and bit CRA3 is now brought HIGH, which causes CA2 to return HIGH, terminating the strobe pulse to the stepper motor. The mechanical design is such that one pulse moves the tape one frame (to the next character). The next step is to watch for the sprocket-hole signal to SET the interrupt flag status bit CRA7. This is determined by testing the word loaded into A to see if it is positive (bit 7 is a 0). If it is positive, the program is branched back to input the word again and test it. This loop is repeated until the status goes negative.

Since this program is controlling a mechanical tape reader that reads about 100 characters per second, it takes 10 ms to move the tape to the next character. The μP will loop back about 1250 times before the tape *arrives* at the new position as sensed by the sprocket-hole photocell. In a real system it would be advisable to include a time-out loop at this point to generate an error message if the tape doesn't advance in a reasonable time. Once the tape has reached the sprocket hole, as indicated by the CA1 line going LOW, the program *falls through* the decision point and LOADS the data into accumulator A. The RTS instruction causes the main program to be resumed and it stores or prints the data (in A) before it returns for the next character.

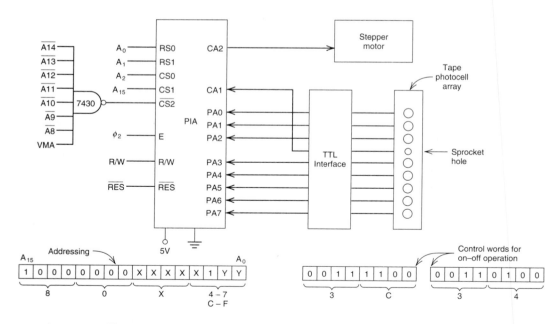

Figure 8-15 PIA circuit for a high-speed Tape Reader (for Example 8-13).

Addr	Data		Mnemonics		Comments
1000 (CRA7)	B6	8004	LDAA	#$8004	Read A Data Reg to clear interrupt
1003	86	34	LDAA	#$34	Load A with $34
1005	B7	8005	STAA	$8005	Store Control Word to turn on pulse
1008	86	3C	LDA	#$3C	Load A with $3C
100A	B7	8005	STAA	$8005	Store Control Word to end pulse
100D	B6	8005	LDAA	$8005	Load A with Status Reg contents
1010	2A	FB	BPL	*-5	If plus, branch back 5 bytes to 100D
1012	B6	8004	LDAA	$8004	Load A from Data Register
1015	39		RTS		Return to the main program

Figure 8-16   Program for Example 8-13.

8-7 ▼ SERIAL DATA TRANSMISSION

When digital data is being transmitted or transferred between components in a **6800** family μC system, it is moved a byte at a time by means of the 8-bit data bus. This is *parallel transmission* and is synchronized by the system clock. When signals are sent to equipment not located in the same cabinet or over cables longer than about 10 feet, the long ground return circuit creates problems of noise or interfering signals (see Chapter 13). Extraneous current pulses and Alternating Currents (AC) are carried by the same ground wires and can induce unwanted pulses or glitches into the digital signals. To alleviate

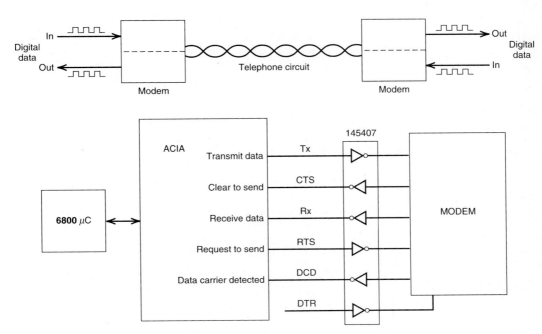

Figure 8-17   Full-duplex data transmission system.

these problems, parallel digital signals are often converted to *serial* form and transmitted on a single line a *bit at a time*. When the distance is more than 50 or 100 feet, as in a system involving a main computer and several satellite terminals, this serial digital signal is frequently changed to audio tones by means of a MODEM (MODulator–DEModulator) and transmitted over telephone circuits. Modems provide for duplex operation (one serial path in each direction) over one telephone circuit. Obviously, serial transmission with only one pair of wires is simpler and cheaper to implement than parallel transmission with eight or more lines and is less likely to cause errors since the grounding problems are eliminated. The operation of a full duplex data transmission system that transmits serial data in both directions simultaneously is shown in Fig. 8-17.

In the transmit part of the Modem, the digital information modulates an audio tone that is then transmitted to the distant device (usually, over telephone circuits). The receive part of the remote Modem demodulates the audio signals and sends them to the local equipment as digital data.

Most serial systems use asynchronous (unclocked) data transmission. The characters are sent in a standard format or code so that equipment made by different manufacturers can be used together in a system. The most common code for asynchronous data transmission is the ASCII (American Standard Code for Information Interchange). As used originally in the Model 33 and 35 Teletypewriters (TTYs), it is a 10- or 11-bit START–STOP code. This code has been adopted by the computer industry and is used in almost all data terminals and μCs that use terminals. The basic pattern for this standard is shown in Fig. 8-18. When the line is quiescent (transmitting no data), it is constantly in the MARK or 1 state. The start of a character is signaled by the START bit that drives the line to the 0 or SPACE state, for one bit time. The 7 bits immediately following the START bit are the data bits of the character. The bits are sent with the least significant bit (LSB) first. The ASCII code (see Appendix D) uses 7 bits to generate 128 unique codes. These include upper- and lowercase let-

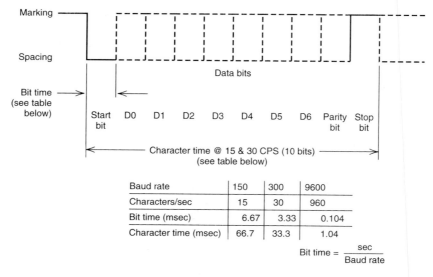

Baud rate	150	300	9600
Characters/sec	15	30	960
Bit time (msec)	6.67	3.33	0.104
Character time (msec)	66.7	33.3	1.04

$$\text{Bit time} = \frac{\text{sec}}{\text{Baud rate}}$$

Figure 8-18 ASCII character bit timing.

ters A to Z, the numbers 0 through 9, plus many punctuation and mathematical symbols. Many nonprintable control characters are also provided. The character consists of 7 data bits and a parity bit. A parity bit is used to detect errors in Transmission. The system designer can choose to use: even, odd, or no parity. Today, 8-bit, no parity is the most popular. Occasionally, *even* parity is used in the incoming direction because most TTY keyboards originally were connected to generate *even* parity characters (the number of 1s in each character are even). The TTY does not check parity on data to be printed, but many high-speed data terminals do.

After the last data bit, the transmission line must go HIGH for either one or two bit times. These are the STOP bits. TTYs use two STOP bits, but terminals operating above 150 baud use only one. If no further data is to be transmitted, the line simply stays HIGH (marking) until the next START bit occurs. This data pattern thus uses 10 or 11 bits as follows:

1. One START bit (always a space or 0)
2. Eight data bits (including parity)
3. One or two STOP bits (always a mark or 1)

EXAMPLE 8-14

    (a) What is the bit pattern of the character shown in Fig 8-19?

    (b) Is the parity odd or even?

SOLUTION

    (a) As shown in Fig. 8-19, the waveform bits are 00001001011. The first 0 is the START bit and the next eight are the character (including the parity bit). Since the LSBs are transmitted first, they must be reversed to correspond to the convention used in most μP literature and in this book. Therefore, the character is 01001000 (48 hex, or ASCII "H"). The two 1s following the last data bit are STOP bits. Any additional 1s following the STOP bit merely indicate that the line is idle.

    (b) Since the character contains an even number of 1s, the parity bit is zero and therefore this is an even-parity character.

A 7-bit ASCII character "H"
even parity – 2 stop bits
$H = 48_{16} = 1001000_2$

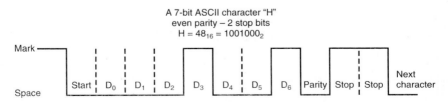

Figure 8-19   Character pattern for Example 8-14.

8-8 ▼ ASYNCHRONOUS COMMUNICATIONS INTERFACE ADAPTER

In the **6800** family systems, serial data transmission is implemented by the **6850** Asynchronous Communications Interface Adapter (ACIA). The ACIA is an interface IC designed to accept parallel data from the μC system data bus, a byte at a time, and to send the bits serially to an asynchronous serial data device such as a CRT terminal, line printer, or Modem. At the same time, other circuits in the ACIA can accept serial data characters from a keyboard, a Modem, or a tape reader, and place them on the μC bus as parallel bytes. Figure 8-20 shows the block diagram of the ACIA. The left side of the diagram shows the lines that connect to the data, address, and control bus lines of the μP. The right side shows the lines used for the serial interface with external hardware.

The ACIA appends START, STOP, and parity bits to the 7 or 8 data bits used for each character. The data could be a standard 7-bit ASCII character or any other 7- or 8-bit code such as EBCDIC, or even binary. The resulting character is either 10 or 11 bits long, depending on whether the character has one or two stop bits. Since the characters can be sent asynchronously, the time between each character can be from zero up. The ACIA is programmed during initialization via the μP data bus for the desired data configuration. It thus provides the following functions:

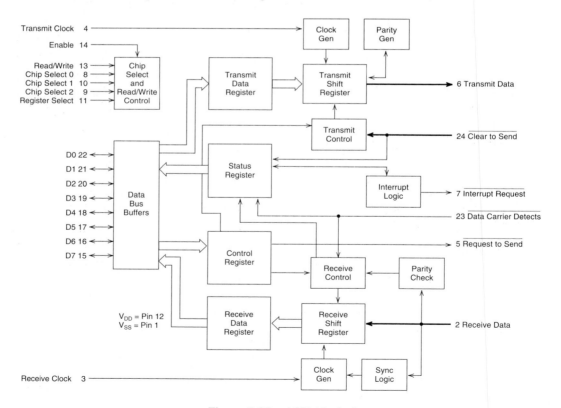

Figure 8-20   ACIA block diagram.

1. Parallel-to-serial and serial-to-parallel conversions of data (simultaneously)
2. Asynchronous transmission by means of START and STOP bits
3. Error control by means of parity, framing, or overrun error detection

8-8.1 ▼ Parallel-to-Serial and Serial-to-Parallel Conversion

The ACIA block diagram shown in Fig. 8-20 includes Transmit Data and Shift registers and Receive Data and Shift registers. It is double buffered. The Transmit Data register and Receive Data registers are interfaced directly to the **6800**'s data bus. As explained below, they provide Parallel-to-Serial and Serial-to-Parallel conversions by shifting the data in and out of 8-bit registers. The wide arrows in Fig. 8-20 indicate the parallel side of the device (eight lines). The externally generated receive and transmit bit-rate clocks are used to shift these registers at the appropriate standard serial data rate [e.g., 110, 300, 2400, etc., bits per second (bps)]. Note that these serial clock inputs for the transmit and receive sides are completely independent and can be used simultaneously at different rates if desired.

8-8.2 ▼ ACIA Registers

Figure 8-21 is a programming model of the ACIA. It shows the μC bus connections and the internal registers. The ACIA's registers are:

1. **Transmit Data Register.** The byte to be transmitted is written in parallel to the Transmit Data Register by the μP. It is transferred to the Transmit Shift Register if it is empty. The byte is then shifted out serially. While one byte is being shifted out, a second byte can be loaded into the Transmit Data Register. It is loaded automatically into the Transmit Shift Register when transmission of the first byte is completed.

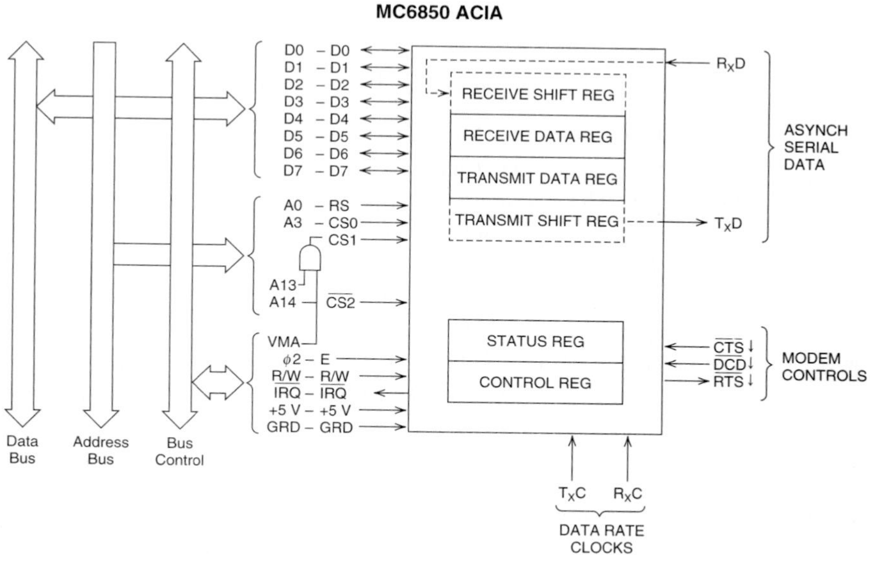

MC6850 ACIA

Figure 8-21   ACIA bus interface and register configuration.

2. **Receive Data Register.** Information from external devices enter the ACIA serially via the Receive Shift Register, which strips off the START and STOP bits and sends the byte in a parallel transfer to the Receive Data Register. The CPU must read the Receive Data Register while the second byte is being received. If it is not read in time, the ACIA loses data and causes the RECEIVE OVERRUN bit in the Status Register to be set (Section 8-8.6).

3. **Control Register.** This register controls the format of both the transmitted and received data. It is discussed in detail in Section 8-8.4.

4. **Status Register.** The Status Register monitors the progress of data transmission and reception and sends it to the μP. It is discussed in detail in Section 8-8.6.

EXAMPLE 8-15

A standard 2400-baud Modem is sending 10-bit characters continuously to the ACIA. How much time does the μP have to read each character?

SOLUTION

Since each character consists of 10 bits, the data rate is 240 characters per second. This allows the μP $1/240 = 4.16$ ms to read each character before the next character is assembled in the Receive Data Register.

8-8.3 ▼ ACIA Signal Lines

The lines connected to the ACIA are shown in Fig. 8-20 and Fig. 8-21. The IC pin number for each line is also shown in Fig. 8-20. The lines and their functions are as follows:

1. **Eight bidirectional data lines.** These are connected to the μC data bus.

2. **Three Chip Select lines.** Like the PIA, the ACIA occupies specific locations in the address map. The RS line is usually connected to A_0, and selects the register to be accessed. The CS lines are connected to the address bus to select the ACIA (see Sections 7-13 and 7-14).

3. **READ/WRITE and Register Select.** The combination of these two inputs selects one of the four major registers. The Transmit Data Register and Control Register are write only; the μP cannot read them. If R/W is HIGH (for read) the Receive Data or Status Register is read (depending on whether the RS pin is HIGH or LOW, respectively). If R/W is LOW, a word is written to either the Transmit Data Register or to the Control Register, depending on whether RS is HIGH or LOW, respectively.

8-8.4 ▼ ACIA Control Register

Table 8-6 shows the contents of the ACIA registers. The Boolean statements at the top of the Table are the signals required to address each register. The Control Register, for

TABLE 8-6 Definition of ACIA Register Contents

Data Bus Line Number	Buffer Address			
	RS • $\overline{\text{R/W}}$ Transmit Data Register	RS • R/W Receive Data Register	$\overline{\text{RS}}$ • $\overline{\text{R/W}}$ Control Register	$\overline{\text{RS}}$ • R/W Status Register
	(Write Only)	(Read Only)	(Write Only)	(Read Only)
0	Data Bit 0*	Data Bit 0	Counter Divide Select 1 (CR0)	Receive Data Register Full (RDRF)
1	Data Bit 1	Data Bit 1	Counter Divide Select 2 (CR1)	Transmit Data Register Empty (TDRE)
2	Data Bit 2	Data Bit 2	Word Select 1 (CR2)	Data Carrier Detect ($\overline{\text{DCD}}$)
3	Data Bit 3	Data Bit 3	Word Select 2 (CR3)	Clear-to-Send ($\overline{\text{CTS}}$)
4	Data Bit 4	Data Bit 4	Word Select 3 (CR4)	Framing Error (FE)
5	Data Bit 5	Data Bit 5	Transmit Control 1 (CR5)	Receiver Overrun (OVRN)
6	Data Bit 6	Data Bit 6	Transmit Control 2 (CR6)	Parity Error (PE)
7	Data Bit 7***	Data Bit 7**	Receive Interrupt Enable (CR7)	Interrupt Request (IRQ)

*Leading bit = LSB = Bit 0
**Data bit will be zero in 7-bit plus parity modes.
***Data bit is "don't care" in 7-bit plus parity modes.

example, has the equation RS * R/W. This means that the control register is addressed only if both the RS and R/W inputs to the ACIA are 0.

The functions of the control register are complex. They are explained in the following paragraphs. The function of counter divide bits (CR0 and CR1) is shown in Table 8-7 and allows three choices; it divides the incoming clock by either 1, 16, or 64. The divide-by-1 mode can be used only if the receive clock is synchronized with the data being received and a bit is available at every positive transition of the receive clock. Most systems using an ACIA are asynchronous, however, and the arrival of the byte is signaled by a START bit that can occur at any time. For these cases the divide-by-16 or divide-by-64 option must be used.

TABLE 8-7 Counter Divide Select Bits

CR1	CR0	Function
0	0	÷ 1
0	1	÷ 16
1	0	÷ 64
1	1	Master Reset

EXAMPLE 8-16

An ACIA operates using the divide-by-16 mode.

(a) If the bit frequency is 100 bits per second (bps), what receive clock frequency is required?

(b) At what point after the START bit begins should the data be sampled?

SOLUTION

(a) Since the clock is divided by 16, the receive clock frequency must be 1600 bps to accept data at a 100-bps rate.

(b) The START bit can be thought of as occupying counts 1 to 16, the first data bit counts 17 to 32, and so on. For maximum accuracy, each bit should be sampled or clocked into the receive shift register in the middle of its time slot or at counts 8, 24, 40, and so on. This is automatically accomplished by the internal logic of the ACIA (see Fig. 8-22).

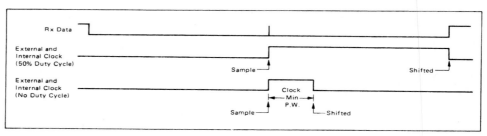

(a) Divide − by − 1

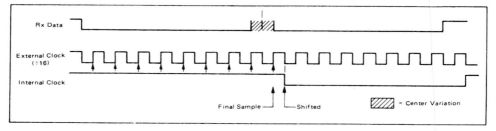

(b) Divide − by 16

Figure 8-22 Relation of the data and sampling clock in an ACIA.

Bit synchronization in the divide-by-16 and divide-by-64 modes is initiated by the leading mark-to-space transition of the START bit. The START bit of the received data is sampled during the positive transitions of the external clock as shown in Fig. 8-22b. If the input remains at a LOW level for a total of eight separate samplings in the divide-by-16 mode, or 32 samplings in the divide-by-64 mode, which is equivalent to 50% of a bit time, the bit is assumed to be a valid START bit. This START bit is shifted into the ACIA circuitry on the negative edge of the internal clock. Once a valid START bit has been detected, the remaining bits are shifted into the Shift Register at their approximate midpoints.

If the receiver input returns to a mark state during the START-bit sampling period, this false START bit is ignored and the receiver resumes looking for the mark-to-space transition or a valid START bit; this technique is called *false bit detection.*

Divide-by-1 mode selection will not provide internal bit synchronization within the receiver. Therefore, the external receive clock must be synchronized to the data under the following considerations. The sampling of the START bit occurs on the positive edge of the external clock, and the START bit is shifted into the shift register on the negative edge of the external clock, as shown in Fig. 8-22a. For higher reliability of sampling the positive transition of the external clock (sampling point) should occur at the approximate midpoint of the bit interval. There is no limitation on the duty cycle of the external receive clock except that the clock must meet the minimum pulse width requirement, as noted on the ACIA data sheet.

Bits CR2, CR3, and CR4 of the control word are written to the ACIA during initialization and determine the configuration of the words being transmitted and received. The user can choose the number of data bits transmitted in each character (7 or 8), the parity (odd, even, or no parity) and the number of stop bits (1 or 2). The options are given in Table 8-8. Note that when transmitting with parity, the user need not be concerned with the parity of the data sent to the ACIA. It calculates the correct parity and inserts the proper bit.

Bits CR5 and CR6 provide Transmit Interrupt Control as well as control of RTS, as shown in Table 8-9. (RTS is the Request-To-Send (RTS) signal used with Modems.) If CR6 and CR5 are 0 and 1, respectively, the ACIA interrupts the μP (if IRQ is connected to the μP) whenever the transmit data buffer is empty. This maximizes the data transmission rate since it causes the system to send the ACIA an output character as soon as it can accept one. If CR5 and CR6 are both 1s, the ACIA transmits a constant 0 level, called a *break.* A break is used as a control signal in some communications systems.

TABLE 8-8 Word Select Bits

CR4	CR3	CR2	Function
0	0	0	7 Bits + Even Parity + 2 Stop Bits
0	0	1	7 Bits + Odd Parity + 2 Stop Bits
0	1	0	7 Bits + Even Parity + 1 Stop Bit
0	1	1	7 Bits + Odd Parity + 1 Stop Bit
1	0	0	8 Bits + 2 Stop Bits
1	0	1	8 Bits + 1 Stop Bit
1	1	0	8 Bits + Even parity + 1 Stop Bit
1	1	1	8 Bits + Odd Parity + 1 Stop Bit

Table 8-9 Transmit Control Bits

CR6	CR5	Function
0	0	$\overline{\text{RTS}}$ = low, Transmitting Interrupt Disabled.
0	1	$\overline{\text{RTS}}$ = low, Transmitting Interrupt Enabled.
1	0	$\overline{\text{RTS}}$ = high, Transmitting Interrupt Disabled.
1	1	$\overline{\text{RTS}}$ = low, Transmits a Break level on the Transmit Data Output. Transmitting Interrupt Disabled.

Bit CR7 is the Receive-Side Interrupt Enable. If CR7 is a 1, the ACIA interrupts whenever the receive data register is full, or the Overrun or Data Carrier Detect (DCD) conditions occur.

EXAMPLE 8-17

What are the characteristics of a transmission system if the control register contains C2?

SOLUTION

CR7 is a 1, so Receive Interrupts are enabled, but Transmit Interrupts are disabled because CR6 and CR5 are 1 and 0, respectively. Bits CR4, 3, and 2 are all 0s, so the data word consists of 7 bits + even parity + 2 stop bits. Finally, because CR1 is a 1 and CR0 is 0, the frequency of the input clock must be 64 times the bit rate of the data.

8-8.5 ▼ ACIA Power-ON Reset

The ACIA does not have a RESET pin but contains an internal Power-ON reset circuit to detect the 5-V turn-on transition and to hold the ACIA in a RESET state until initialization by the μP is complete. This prevents any erroneous output transitions from occurring. In addition to initializing the transmitter and receiver sections, the Power-ON-reset circuit holds the CR5 and CR6 bits of the Control Register at a logic 0 and logic 1, respectively, so that the Request-To-Send (RTS) output is held HIGH and any interrupt from the transmitter is disabled. The Power-ON-reset logic is sensitive to the shape of the V_{DD} power supply turn-on transition. To ensure correct operation of the reset function, the power turn-on transition must have a positive slope throughout its transition. The conditions of the status register and other outputs during power-on reset or software master reset are shown in Table 8-10.

TABLE 8-10 ACIA Initialization Sequence

	POWER-ON RESET	MASTER RESET (Release Power-On Reset)	MASTER RESET (General)
Status Register	b7 b6 b5 b4 b3 b2 b1 b0 0 0 0 0 × × 0 0	b7 b6 b5 b4 b3 b2 b1 b0 0 0 0 0 × × 0 0	b7 b6 b5 b4 b3 b2 b1 b0 0 0 0 0 × × 0 0
$\overline{\text{IRQ}}$ Output	1	1	1
$\overline{\text{RTS}}$ Output	1	1	×
Transmit Break Capability	Inhibit	Inhibit	Optional
Internal: RIE	0	×	×
TIE	0	0	×

Held by Power-On Reset —   Defined by Control Register —

(×- Independent of Reset function)

The internal ACIA Power-ON-reset logic must be released prior to the transmission of data by performing a *software Master Reset,* followed by a second control word. During Master Reset, Control Register bits CR0 and CR1 are set to 1s, which releases the latch condition of bits CR5 and CR6, allowing them to be programmed in the following control word. In recent production the processes have produced faster parts, and this release may occur during master reset. To guard against the possibility of RTS going LOW, it is advisable to use a master reset word of 43 (hex). This retains the preset conditions of CR5 and CR6. The final condition can then be determined in the second control word without any false or momentary shifts in the RTS level. This also applies to Receiver Interrupt Enable (RIE), which is controlled by bit CR7. The $43 will assure that the interrupt is inhibited until its state is specified in the second control word.

After Master Reset of the ACIA, the programmable Control Register must be set to select the desired options, such as the clock divider ratios, word length, one or two stop bits, and parity (even, odd, or none). Bits CR5 and CR6 of the Control Register are no longer inhibited and can now be programmed for the options defined in Table 8-9.

8-8.6 ▼ ACIA Status Register

The status of the ACIA, and what has happened to the data being handled, are determined by examining the Status Register at the proper time in the program. The function of each bit is given in Table 8-6.

- **Bit 0: Receive Data Register Full (RDRF).** This bit is set when a character has been received by the ACIA and should be read by the CPU.
- **Bit 1: Transmit Data Register Empty (TDRE).** This bit indicates that a character to be transmitted can be sent to the ACIA.
- **Bits 2 and 3: Data Carrier Detected (DCD) and Clear To Send (CTS).** These bits will be HIGH only if the pins on the chip are not held LOW by the external circuitry (normally, the RS232C interface—see Section 8-9). This could be the case if a Modem is connected to the port and not ready for transmission or operating improperly, or if the signals are not properly jumpered when a terminal rather than a Modem is being used.

- **Bit 4: Framing Error (FE).** A framing error occurs if there is no STOP bit at the end of a character. It indicates the loss of character synchronization, faulty transmission, or a break condition. If one of the conditions above is present, the internal receiver transfer signal will cause the FE bit to go HIGH. The next internal transfer signal will cause the FE status bit to be updated for the error status of the next character. A HIGH on the DCD input or a Master Reset will disable and reset the FE status bit.

- **Bit 5: Overrun Error (OVRN).** A HIGH state on the OVRN status bit indicates that a character was received but not read from the Receiver Data Register, resulting in the loss of one or more characters. The OVRN status bit is set when the last character prior to the overrun condition has been read. The read data command forces the RDRF and OVRN status bits to go HIGH if an overrun condition exists. The next read data command causes the RDRF and OVRN status bits to return to a LOW level. During an overrun condition, the last character in the Receive Data Register that was not read subsequent to the overrun condition is retained since the internal transfer signal is disabled. A HIGH state on the DCD input or a master reset disables and resets the OVRN status bit.

- **Bit 6: Parity Error (PE).** If the parity check function is enabled, the internal transfer signal causes the PE status bit to go HIGH if a parity error condition exists. The parity error status bit is updated by the next internal transfer signal. A HIGH state on the DCD input or a master reset disables and resets the PE status bit.

- **Bit 7: Interrupt ReQuest (IRQ).** A HIGH level on the IRQ status bit may be generated from three sources:

  (a) **Transmitter.** If the Transmitter Data Register is empty (TDRE = 1), and TIE is SET.

  (b) **Receiver.** If the Receive Data Register is full (RDRF = 1) and RIE is SET.

  (c) **Data Carrier Loss.** A loss of carrier (a HIGH level) on the DCD input generates an interrupt, as indicated by the IRQ bit, if the RIE bit is SET.

EXAMPLE 8-18

The status register of an ACIA reads A3. What is the status of the ACIA?

SOLUTION

The data indicates that bits 0, 1, 5, and 7 are SET. Table 8-6 shows that:

1. The Receive Data Register is full.
2. The Transmit Data Register is empty.

3. A Receive Overrun error has occurred.

4. An Interrupt ReQuest is pending. (Interrupts are explained in Chapter 9.)

The Receive Data Register has overrun, indicating that the µP did not fetch the last character during the time available, and in addition, there is another character in the Receive Data Register waiting to be read and the ACIA is trying to interrupt. The Transmit Data Register is available to accept any data for transmission. Essentially, these conditions mean that the µP is not paying attention to the ACIA. They probably indicate a timing problem (either hardware or software) has caused the system to malfunction.

8-9 ▼ RS232 HARDWARE INTERFACE FOR THE ACIA

For data transmission to remote terminals, Modems and telephone lines are used. Modems use unique logic levels in accordance with EIA (Electronic Industry Association) specification RS232C. The RS232C interface is also universally used to connect to a local terminal. All RS232C signals at the terminal or Modem connector can be described by the following notation:

Data binary state	1	0
Signal condition	Mark	Space
Function	OFF	ON
Voltage	−3 to −15	+3 to +15

The transmit and receive data signals must be between +3 and +15 V for a **0** or *space condition,* or between −3 and −15 V for a **1** or *mark.*

8-9.1 ▼ Level Translators for RS232C

Level translators are required between the TTL levels of the ACIA and the RS232C levels of the Modems. Two popular level translators are the **MC1488** and the **MC1489,** both manufactured by Motorola. The **MC1488** is a quad TTL-to-RS232C level translator for data going *to* the Modem and the **MC1489** is a quad RS232C-to-TTL level translator for data coming *from* the Modem to the ACIA. Unfortunately, these level translators require additional power supplies (typically, −12V and +12V) to generate the required signal voltages. Also, they are NMOS parts.

Fortunately, several other parts are available that eliminate these problems. The **145407** is a silicon-gate CMOS IC that combines three drivers, three receivers, and a voltage doubler/inverter to fulfill the electrical specifications of EIA-232-D and CCITT V.28 while operating from a single +5 V power supply. The on-chip voltage doubler and inverter convert the +5 V to ±10 V. This is accomplished through an on-board 20-kHz oscillator and four inexpensive external electrolytic capacitors. The **145406** is a companion part with three more drivers and three more receivers that are virtually identical to those of the **145407.** For applications requiring more than three drivers and/or three receivers, a **145406** can be added and powered from the **145407**. The **145407** charge pumps have been designed to guarantee ±5 V at the output of up to six drivers. Thus the **145407/145406** ICs provide a high-performance, low-power, 5 V stand-alone solution.

8-9.2 ▼ Connections between the ACIA and a Modem

The connections between the ACIA and a Modem are shown in Fig. 8-23. For asynchronous transmission, the following five signals go between the ACIA and the Modem.

1. **Transmitted Data:** from the digital device to the Modem. This is the data to be transmitted.

2. **Received Data:** from the Modem to the digital device. This is the data received from the remote Modem.

3. **Request To Send (RTS):** from the digital device to the Modem. This signal should be a 0 (ON) whenever data is to be transmitted. In half-duplex communications, it is used to control the direction of transmission. When switched to a 1, the local Modem carrier is turned off, which tells the distant end that it can start sending data. In full-duplex operation RTS remains in the 0 state.

4. **Clear To Send (CTS):** from the Modem to the digital device. This signal is a response to Request To Send and indicates that the Modem can accept data for transmission. In full-duplex operation, it is normally always active and presents a 0 level to the digital device.

5. **Data Carrier Detected (DCD):** from the Modem to the digital device. A 1 on this line indicates that the data carrier is not being received. For half-duplex systems, this would be the signal to turn on the local carrier and begin transmission. In full-duplex systems it indicates an abnormal condition. This line must be in the 0 state for reception of data.

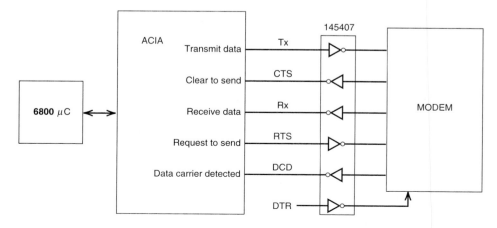

Figure 8-23   RS232C interface between the ACIA and a Modem.

6. **Data Terminal Ready (DTR):** not provided by the ACIA but most Modems need it to indicate the terminal is ready. In some systems it is switched OFF to cause the Modem to disconnect.

8-10 ▼ USES OF THE ACIA

Three typical applications using an ACIA are illustrated in Fig. 8-24. System 1 shows how a terminal is connected to a μC. The interface box between the ACIA and the terminal is the RS232 level translators just described. System 2 shows a remotely located terminal, which can be in the next building or thousands of miles away. Here data transmission takes place via Modems. A number of standard Modems are available for various speeds of operation, up to 19,200 bps. Any Modem that is faster than 2400 bps is slightly more expensive because of built-in error correction circuits and software. System 3 shows one way for computers to exchange data using modems. The degree of automation depends on the ingenuity and capability of the designer.

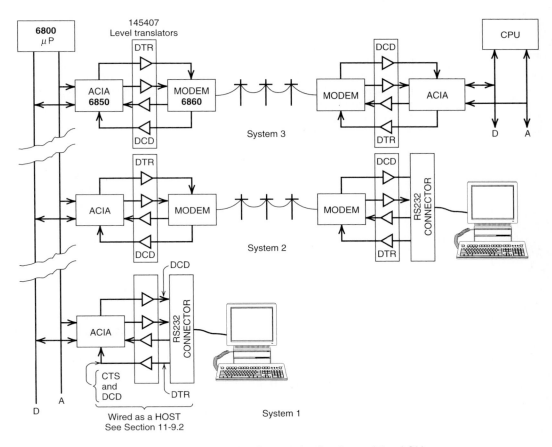

Figure 8-24 System applications of the ACIA.

EXAMPLE 8-19

An ACIA is to transmit and receive data over a Modem from a remote data terminal as described in System 2. The data will be sent in both directions simultaneously, while the μC controls the characters from both channels. The data to transmitted is in memory starting at location $1000, and the received data is to be stored in consecutive locations starting at $2000. Explain how to set up the ACIA and write the program to control the data transfer.

SOLUTION

Figure 8-25 shows subroutines that could be used. The main program is not shown. It would bring the data into a buffer from the input subroutine and send data to the output subroutine. The routines shown consist of an initialization routine to set up the ACIA, an input character routine, an output character routine, an error print routine, and routines to turn RTS ON and OFF. The Request-To-Send (RTS) line and its uses are explained in Section 8-9.2.

First the hardware must be assembled to provide the proper features and then the program must be written. A clock 16 times the baud rate would typically be used with the ACIA in the divide-by-16 mode to produce a baud rate compatible with the Modem and data terminal. Typically, this might be 1200 or 2400 baud to work with an inexpensive Modem.

Since polling is to be used, interrupts are inhibited and the control register must be initialized to $49. This does the following:

1. Bits CR1 and CR0 are 01 selecting the divide-by-16 mode.
2. Bits CR2, CR3, and CR4 are 0, 1, and 0, respectively, selecting a word format of 7 bits + even parity + 1 STOP bit. This is a format formally used by standard terminals working at 300 baud or higher. Today, it is more likely to be 1, 0, 1 to provide 8 bits, no parity, and 1 STOP bit.
3. Bits CR6 and CR5 are 1 and 0, respectively, programming RTS HIGH and disabling transmit interrupts.
4. Bit CR7 is 0, disabling receive interrupts. (Interrupt techniques are explained in Chapter 9.)

As shown in Table 8-10, the initialization is done as follows: A Master Reset control word ($43) is sent to the control register. As explained in Section 8-8.5, this latches the IRQ and RTS internal bits so that neither line can go to their active state (LOW). This is followed by the control word required to set up the system as desired ($49 for 7 bits, even parity, one STOP bit). The ECHO flag is then cleared so that the character received will be *echoed* back to the terminal by the input character routine (see lines 41 and 42).

The input character routine is next and it works as follows:

1. The ACIA status register is read.

2. The status word is shifted right 1 bit. This puts the receive date register full (RDRF) flag into the carry bit.

3. The carry flag is tested. If it is 0, the receive buffer is empty (refer to Table 8-6). To be sure that the Modem is ready, we also test the CTS bit by ANDing it with a 4 to see if it is a "1" (false). If the carry is equal to 1, the program will "fall through" the BEQ instruction and loop back to INPUT for another status word.

4. If the carry is equal to 1, the receive data register is full and the program jumps to IN1. IN1 then shifts the status word until the Framing Bit is in the carry register. It is tested and if the carry is clear, it branches to IN2. The program continues to check the overrun and parity bits. If no error exists, it goes to IN3, where the data character is fetched from the data register. If any of these error bits are set, an appropriate error number is sent to the output routine for transmission back to the terminal. If the character is fetched by line 39, it has the MSB stripped off. The ECHO flag is then tested, and if it is a 0, the data is then "echoed" back to the terminal by the output routine. When the RTS at the end of the output routine is finally reached, the program returns to the main program with the character in accumulator A, where it is stored or printed.

5. The OUTPUT routine tests bit 1 after ignoring bit 0. If it is 0, it loops back until this transmit bit is set, indicating that the Tx register is empty and ready to accept a new character. Note that accumulator B is used to hold the status word so that the character in A is not disturbed.

6. If bit 1 equals 1, the transmit data register is empty. The character in A is then stored to the data register, which then transmits it to the terminal.

7. Return to step 1 of this explanation and repeat.

   This program checks all of the ACIA status bits (except DCD) for errors and echoes an error number back to the remote terminal. Although routines are shown for turning RTS ON and OFF, they are not used in this application.

8-11 ▼ SYNCHRONOUS COMMUNICATIONS

Asynchronous communications via the ACIA are used primarily with slow-speed terminals where information is generated on a keyboard (manually) and where the communication is not necessarily continuous. Synchronous communications are usually encountered where high-speed continuous transmission is required. This information is frequently fed to special Modems at speeds up to 56K baud. Synchronous systems transmit a steady stream of bits even when no characters are available (a *sync* character is substituted). Because there are no START and STOP bits to separate the characters, care must be taken to synchronize the receiving device with the transmitted signal so that the receiver end of the circuit can determine which bit is bit 1 of the character.

```
0001                          NAM    ACIA2
0002              * ACIA2 - PROGRAM FOR USE WITH A MODEM
0003         *
0004    8008      ACIASC  EQU    $8008        ACIA STATUS/CONTROL REG
0005    8009      ACIADA  EQU    $8009        ACIA TX & RX DATA REGS
0006 0200                 ORG    $200
0007 0200 0001   ECHO     RMB    1            ECHO FLAG
0009              *  INITIALIZATION
0010 0201 86  43  INIT    LDAA   #$43
0011 0203 B7 8008          STAA   ACIASC      MASTER RESET - RTS=0
0012 0206 86  49          LDAA   #$49         CONTROL WORD -
0013 0208 B7 8008          STAA   ACIASC
0014 020B 7F 0200          CLR    ECHO        MAKE IT ECHO
0015 020E 39              RTS                 RTN TO OTHER SYSTEM INIT
0017 020F B6 8008 INPUT   LDAA   ACIASC       GET STATUS
0018 0212 47              ASRA                CHAR RCVD?
0019 0213 25  08          BCS    IN1          YES -GO ON
0020 0215 84  04          ANDA   #4           NO - CTS SET?
0021 0217 27  02          BEQ    *+4          NO - SEND MSG
0022 0219 20  F4          BRA    INPUT        YES - TRY AGAIN
0023 021B 20  35          BRA    PRNT         PRNT CTS ERR MSG
0024 021D 47      IN1     ASRA                SKIP TX RDY BIT
0025 021E 47              ASRA                SKIP DCD BIT
0026 021F 47              ASRA                SKIP CTS BIT
0027 0220 47              ASRA                FRAMING ERROR?
0028 0221 24  04          BCC    IN2          NO -
0029 0223 86  33          LDAA   #$33
0030 0225 20  1D          BRA    OUTPUT       YES - RETURN #3 ERROR
0031 0227 47      IN2     ASRA                OVERRUN ERROR?
0032 0228 24  04          BCC    IN4          NO -
0033 022A 86  32          LDAA   #$32
0034 022C 20  16          BRA    OUTPUT       YES - RETURN #2 ERROR
0035 022E 47      IN4     ASRA                PARITY ERROR?
0036 022F 24  04          BCC    IN3          NO -
0037 0231 86  3F          LDAA   #$3F         YES - PRNT "?"
0038 0233 20  0F          BRA    OUTPUT
0039 0235 B6 8009 IN3     LDAA   ACIADA       GET CHARACTER
0040 0238 84  7F          ANDA   #$7F         REMOVE PARITY BIT
0041 023A 7D 0200         TST    ECHO         ECHO INHIBITED?
0042 023D 27  01          BEQ    OUTPUT       NO - DO IT
0043 023F 39              RTS
0044 0240 F6 8008 OUTPUT  LDAB   ACIASC       GET STATUS
0045 0243 57              ASRB
0046 0244 57              ASRB                TRANSMIT BIT SET ?
0047 0245 24  F9          BCC    OUTPUT       NO - LOOP
0048 0247 B7 8009         STAA   ACIADA       YES - SEND IT
0049 024A 7F 0200         CLR    ECHO         CLEAR ECHO FLAG
0050 025D 39              RTS
0051 025E CE XXXX PRNT    LDX    #MSG         GET POINTER TO MSG
0052 0261 BD XXXX         JSR    PRINT        PRINT CTS MSG
0053 0264 39              RTS
0054 0265 86  41  RTSOFF  LDAA   #$41
0055 0267 B7 8008          STAA   ACIASC      TURN OFF RTS
0056 026A 39              RTS
0057 026B 86  09  RTSON   LDAA   #$9
0058 026D B7 8008          STAA   ACIASC      TURN ON RTS
0059 0270 39              RTS
0060                      END
```

Figure 8-25 Program for Example 8-19.

Synchronous systems usually use a preamble (all 1s, for example) to establish synchronization between the receiver and transmitter and will then maintain sync by transmitting a sync pattern until interrupted. Because START and STOP bits are not needed, the efficiency of transmission is 20% better for 8-bit words (8 instead of 10 bits per character).

Synchronous transmission is illustrated in Fig. 8-26. The top line is the clock that is used in most systems to control the data. In this figure, all data changes occur on the positive edge of the clock. For maximum reliability, data should be sampled in the middle of the bit. Note that after the preamble, the data flows continuously.

8-11.1 ▼ 6852 Synchronous Serial Data Adapter

The Synchronous Serial Data Adapter (SSDA) is a 24-pin MOS LSI IC that provides a bidirectional serial interface for synchronous data information interchange with bus-organized systems such as the **6800** family μCs. It is a complex device containing seven registers. Although primarily designed for synchronous data communications using a "Bi-sync" format, several of the **6852**'s features, and in particular, the First-In, First-Out (FIFO) buffers, make it useful in other applications where data is to be transferred between devices that are not being clocked at precisely the same speed, such as tape cassettes, tape cartridges, or floppy disk systems. Because the SSDA is so complex, space does not permit a detailed discussion of it. The reader is referred to the manufacturers' literature (see the references in Section 8-14).

8-11.2 ▼ OTHER 6800 FAMILY DEVICES

Other **6800** family devices, generally known as peripheral controllers, such as the **6854** Advanced Data Link Controller (ADLC) and the **6844** Direct Memory Access Controller (DMAC), are manufactured to perform specific functions in μC systems. They are like the PIA because they are bus compatible and addressable. They also have programmable Control Registers, Data Registers, and Status Registers. These devices are very complex and cannot be explained thoroughly in this book, but if readers have absorbed the principles of PIA and ACIA operation, they should be able to understand these special-purpose ICs after consulting the manufacturers' literature.

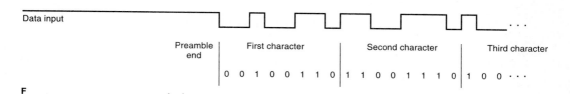

Figure 8-26 Synchronous transmission.

8-12 ▼ SUMMARY

In this chapter we dealt with interfacing and communications between **6800** family μCs and peripheral devices. The two most popular interfacing ICs, the PIA and the ACIA, were discussed in detail. Operation of their internal registers and the programs necessary to make them function properly were explained. The differences between parallel, serial synchronous, and serial asynchronous transmission were explained so that the designer can use the proper interface ICs.

8-13 ▼ GLOSSARY

ACIA (6850) The **6800** family Asynchronous Communications Interface Adapter component.

American Standard Code for Information Interchange (ASCII) The serial data communications code used by the majority of data terminals and computers.

Analog-to-Digital (A/D) converter A device that converts analog signals to digital signals.

Asynchronous Independent of a clock (i.e., random).

Command Words The words sent to a peripheral device to tell it how to act.

Control Register A register where bits are entered to configure or control a peripheral IC device.

Control Word A group of bits written to a peripheral device such as a PIA or ACIA register that controls the mode of operation.

Darlington transistor A pair of transistors in a single package interconnected so as to provide a power transitor output with high enough gain that it can be controlled by a PIA.

Data word A group of bits (usually, 8) that is moved from one device to another in a μC system.

Digital-to-Analog (D/A) converter A device that converts digital information to analog for control of external devices.

Direction Register The register within the PIA that controls the direction of data flow on each of the I/O lines.

EBCDIC Extended Binary-Coded Decimal Interchange Code (IBM).

Handshaking The interchange of signals between devices to acknowledge or authorize communication.

Initialization The process of programming the registers to configure a PIA or ACIA or other device for the required application.

Interrupts A signal that informs the μP that a peripheral device is requesting service. It generally causes the μP to jump to a service routine for the requesting device.

Modem A device that uses digital signals to modulate audio tones in one direction and demodulate similar tones to obtain digital signals for transmission in the other direction.

PIA (Peripheral Interface Adapter) (MC6821) The **6800** family parallel data interface IC component.

Polling Interrogating the status register of each peripheral device in turn to determine if it has data for the μP.

Resolution The voltage represented by the smallest change in the output when one bit is added or deleted.

Sensor A device that senses an analog quantity and typically converts it into a voltage that is proportional to the magnitude of the quantity.

START bit A bit that signals the start of a character in an asynchronous communication system.

Status Register The register that contains status bits.

Status Word The bits in a PIA or ACIA register that indicate what is currently happening in that device.

STOP bit(s) One or two bits (always 1s) that indicate the end of an asynchronous character.

Subroutine nesting The incorporation of subroutines within subroutines.

Synchronous In step with a clock signal.

Transducer A device that converts a dynamic quantity, such as velocity, into a voltage.

Wired-OR circuit Circuits that can be connected together so that any one of them can pull down the interrupt line to activate the μP interrupt function.

8-14 ▼ REFERENCES

ANSI, *USA Standard Character Structure and Character Parity Sense for Serial-by-Bit Data Communication in the USA Standard Code for Information Interchange (ASCII),* USAS X3.4-1968, American National Standards Institute, Washington, D.C., 1968.

IBM, *Binary Synchronous Communications (Bi-sync),* IBM File TP-09, Form GA-27-3004-1, 3rd ed., October 1970.

MOTOROLA, *MC6821 Peripheral Interface Adapter (PIA),* DS9435-R4, Phoenix, Ariz., 1984.

———, *MC6850 Asynchronous Communications Interface Adapter (ACIA),* DS9493-R3, Phoenix, Ariz., 1984.

———, *MC6852 Synchronous Serial Data Adapter (SSDA),* DS9494-R4, Phoenix, Ariz. 1984.

———, *MC6854 Advanced Data-Link Controller (ADLC),* DS9495-R2, Phoenix, Ariz., 1984.

———, *MC68HC24 Port Replacement Unit,* MC68HC24/D, Phoenix, Ariz., 1991.

UNIVERSAL DATA SYSTEMS, *Direct Connect 212A Modem,* Rev. A, Huntsville Ala., May 1980.

8-15 ▼ PROBLEMS

8-1. A D/A converter has 8 input bits. If its output ranges from 0 to 5 V, how much voltage does each digital step require?

8-2. Repeat Problem 8-1 if the output range is from –7 to +7 V.

8-3. An A/D converter is required to have an output range of 0 to +20 V. It must have an input resolution of 0.01 V or more. How many bits are required on the digital input?

8-4. Write a program to configure Direction Register A of a PIA so that lines 6 and 7 are inputs and to configure Direction Register B so that lines 1 and 2 are inputs. All other lines should be outputs.

8-5. Write the coding for Example 8-2.

8-6. Write the instructions for the program of Example 8-10.

8-7. If a PIA Control Register reads $3F, what is the PIA doing?

8-8. A peripheral has two control lines, A and B. If it SETs A, it wants to read the data in location $100. If it SETs B, it wants to read the data in location $200. Write a program to initialize the PIA to allow this to happen. Assume that both control lines are not SET simultaneously.

8-9. Write a program so that a peripheral can write data into memory sequentially, starting at location $100.

8-10. The status register of an ACIA reads $81. What action should the program take?

8-11. Write a program to transmit the contents of locations $100 to $1FF to a peripheral using an ACIA.

8-12. If a peripheral is transmitting serial data to a μP via an ACIA, write a program to store that data in sequential locations, starting at $100.

8-13. A TTY is sending data. The μP must "echo" by transmitting the same data it is receiving so that the TTY operator sees the data he or she is sending. Write an ACIA program to accomplish this.

8-14. Every time a person enters a room a TTY is to type the word "hello." Describe the equipment and the program required to make this happen.

8-15. The following program uses a PIA at location $8020–$8023:

ADDR		MNEMONIC
20		LDX #$100
23		CLR $8021
26		CLR $8020
28		LDA A #$24
2B		STA A $8021
2E	QQ	LDA A $8021
31		BPL *-3
33		LDA A $8020
36		STA A $20,X
38		INX
39		CPX #$200
3B		BNE QQ
3D		BRA *

    (a) Is the data flow in or out of the μP? Which side of the PIA is being used?

    (b) What area of memory is reserved for data? How many bytes?

    (c) Is CA1 or CB1 being used? If so, how?

    (d) Is CA2 or CB2 being used? If so, how?

    (e) What is QQ?

    (f) Explain what the program is doing.

8-16. Modify Example 8-7 by adding a switch connected to the CB1 line to decrement the displayed number.

    After attempting to solve these problems, try to answer the self-evaluation questions in Section 8-2. If any of them still seem difficult, review the appropriate sections of the chapter to find the answers.

INTERRUPTS AND TIMING

9-1 ▼ INSTRUCTIONAL OBJECTIVES

In this chapter we explain how a peripheral device can communicate with a computer using **Interrupts.** Software time-delay loops and counter, timer, and clock ICs are also discussed. After reading the chapter, the student should be able to:

1. Write a *restart routine* to initialize a **6800** μP system.
2. Write an *interrupt service routine* for a device that uses the IRQ or NMI interrupt.
3. Use the SWI and WAI instructions.
4. Design software and hardware timing circuits.
5. Use the **146818T1** Real-Time Clock and the **6840** Programmable Timer Module ICs.

9-2 ▼ SELF-EVALUATION QUESTIONS

Watch for the answers to the following questions as you read the chapter. They should help you to understand the material presented.

1. What is an *interrupt?* What advantages does it give a μP system?
2. How is the interrupt mask *set* and *cleared?*
3. In a system that allows several devices to interrupt on the same line, how is the interrupting device identified?
4. Why is the NMI a higher-priority interrupt than the IRQ?
5. What is the difference between a WAI and an SWI?
6. What does the RTI instruction do? Why is it important?
7. What are the advantages of a hardware timer over software timing routines? What are the disadvantages?

9-3 ▼ INTRODUCTION TO INTERRUPTS

One of the most important features of a μC is the ability to act immediately on requests from peripheral devices such as line printers or machinery controllers and control them accordingly. The μC must be able to sense the operation of the system under its control and respond quickly with corrective commands when necessary.

When conditions that require fast response arise, the system is wired so that an external device, such as a machinery controller, can send an electrical signal called an *interrupt* to the μP. This signal must produce a TTL logic LOW on the NMI or IRQ pin of the μP. *The resulting interrupt causes the μP to stop execution of its main program* and jump to a special program, an **interrupt service routine,** that responds to the needs of the external device. The main program resumes when the interrupt service routine is finished.

Although a computer can perform many useful tasks without using or responding to an interrupt, the ability to do so is necessary in many systems. The **6800** family μCs have a powerful interrupt structure that uses the stack, vectored interrupts, and an interrupt priority scheme provided by the μP logic.

9-3.1 ▼ The Stack Concept

The *stack* was introduced in Section 5-4, where it was used to save return addresses for subroutine calls and to save and retrieve data using PUSH and PULL instructions. The stack is also used during interrupts to save the register contents of the main program so that the main program can later be resumed. Thus any system that uses interrupts must set aside a RAM area for the stack before any interrupts can take place. The use of the stack during interrupts is discussed in this chapter.

9-3.2 ▼ Vectored Interrupts

The **6800** family μCs use four different types of interrupts: *Reset* (RST), *NonMaskable Interrupt* (NMI), *SoftWare Interrupt* (SWI), and *hardware Interrupt ReQuest* (IRQ). Unique *interrupt servicing routines* must be written by the system designer for each type of interrupt used, and these routines can be located anywhere in memory.

When one of the four types of interrupts occurs, the μP logic fetches the contents of two bytes from a specific memory address for each interrupt. Those bytes contain the address of the service routine and they are loaded into the program counter. This causes the program to jump to the proper interrupt routine. The fetched addresses are commonly called **vectors** or **vector addresses** because they *point* to the software routine used to service the interrupt. Three of the interrupts (RST, NMI, and IRQ) are activated by signals on the pins of the μP. The fourth (SWI) is initiated by an instruction.

The eight locations that contain the vector addresses for the four interrupt types must reside at the top of the memory map as follows:

1. Reset (RST) $FFFE–$FFFF
2. NonMaskable Interrupt (NMI) $FFFC–$FFFD
3. SoftWare Interrupt (SWI) $FFFA–$FFFB
4. Interrupt ReQuest (IRQ) $FFF8–$FFF9

These are shown in the memory map of Fig. 9-1. The interrupt vectors must reside in ROM or PROM so that they are present when the system is turned ON. It should be noted (as explained in Sections 7-14, 7-15, and 7-16) that the actual ROM (or PROM) accessed for these vectors may have redundant addressing and contain a program that runs at some lower address. This works as long as the ROM also responds to the vector addresses shown above. The response of the μP to each of these interrupts is described in this chapter.

9-4 ▼ RESET

A *reset* (RST) is used to start the main program in the μP. It should occur whenever power is turned on. It happens when the RESET pin on the **6800** μP is pulled LOW. The RESET line can be pulled LOW by a restart pushbutton or as a result of an auto-restart circuit. The LOW pulse on the RESET pin of the μP causes the starting location of the main program to be fetched from the *reset vector* locations at $FFFE and $FFFF. The vector address is picked up on the data bus by the μP and transferred to the PC.

9-4.1 ▼ Reset Timing

The μP's response to a reset signal is similar to its response to an interrupt. When the RESET line is pulled down and *held*, the following conditions occur:

1. The interrupt mask (the I bit in the condition code register) is SET.
2. VMA is held LOW.
3. The Data Bus is high-impedance.
4. BA is LOW.
5. R/W is HIGH.
6. The address bus contains $FFFE.

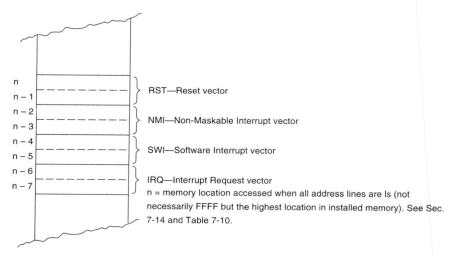

Figure 9-1 Restart and interrupt vector locations in memory.

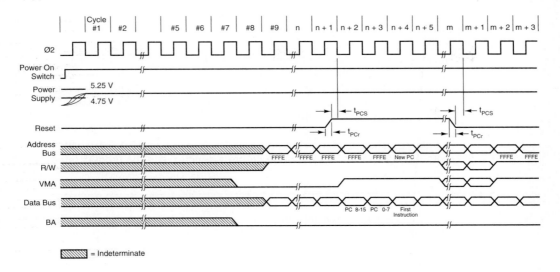

Figure 9-2 Reset timing.

Figure 9-2 illustrates the system responses to the RESET line.

After the power is turned ON and the voltage at the power pin of the μP reaches 4.75 V, the μP must wait at least eight cycles for the clock and internal logic to stabilize. During these eight cycles, RESET should be held LOW since VMA can be indeterminate. Any device, such as a battery-backed RAM, should also be inhibited by RESET because it could experience a false write. RESET can go HIGH asynchronously with the system clock anytime after the eighth cycle. When the RESET line is allowed to go HIGH, it will fetch the *restart vector* and jump to it, as shown in Fig. 9-2.

The RESET line is also connected to any hardware devices that have a hardware reset and need to be initialized, such as the PIA (see Chapter 8). Grounding the RESET line clears all the registers in the PIA, and the restart service routine reprograms the PIA Control and Direction Registers before allowing the main program to start. The ACIA has no RESET pin and depends on software initialization. All software flags and constants in RAM must also be preset. If the system includes power-failure sensors and associated service routines, additional steps will be needed in the restart service routine to provide an automatic restart (see Example 9-1).

EXAMPLE 9-1

A program must start at location $123 (hex). What must be done to assure a proper start?

SOLUTION

Before a program can be started automatically, the RESET vector must be in place. In this case the number 01 must be stored in the location that is accessed when $FFFE is on the address bus and $23 must be in the following location.

When the reset line is grounded (perhaps by a restart timer or by a pushbutton switch), the **6800** family μP fetches the restart vector in two steps by outputting $FFFE and then $FFFF to the address bus. When the contents of each location appear on the data bus (01, followed by $23), they are loaded into the high and low bytes of the program counter, and the program starts in the proper place.

This automatic start is possible only if the vector and the main program are in ROM (or EPROM). If a test system has RAM at the top of memory, a small test program can be loaded, perhaps by hardware switches, and can be started by entering the program address into the restart vector locations and operating the reset switch. Preferably, a μP development system (see Chapter 11) will be used and the program can be loaded and entered directly by routines in the ROM monitor program.

9-5 ▼ IRQ INTERRUPT

The IRQ interrupt is used when peripheral devices must communicate with the μP. It is activated by a LOW signal on the IRQ pin (pin 4) of the **6800** μP. Both the ACIA and PIA have IRQ output pins that can be connected to the μP when the system design requires it.

The IRQ interrupt also depends on the state of the I bit in the Condition Code Register (CCR). Even if the IRQ pin is pulled LOW, the IRQ interrupt cannot occur if the I bit is SET. This is known as *masking the interrupt*.

EXAMPLE 9-2

What conditions must be satisfied for an ACIA or PIA to interrupt the processor?

SOLUTION

All of the following are required.

1. The IRQ output pin of the PIA or ACIA must be connected to the IRQ input pin of the μP.
2. The I flag of the μP must be CLEAR.
3. The control register in the ACIA or PIA must be programmed to enable interrupts.
4. An event must occur at the peripheral to cause it to interrupt. Such an event could be a transition on one of the control lines (CA1 or CB1) of the PIA, the entry of a word into the ACIA shift register, or the TDRE flag going true.

The I bit of the CCR is SET to disable or mask out interrupts in one of three ways:

1. By the hardware logic of the μP as a part of the restart procedure
2. Whenever the μP executes an interrupt sequence
3. By an SEI (set interrupt mask) instruction

Once SET, the I bit can be cleared only by a CLI (clear interrupt mask) instruction. Therefore, if a program is to allow interrupts while it runs, it must have a CLI instruction near its beginning.

9-5.1 ▼ Interrupt Action

As stated in Section 9-3, an interrupt must cause the μP to stop executing its current program and go to an *interrupt service routine* as soon as possible to respond to the interrupt. When an interrupt is initiated, *the instruction in progress is completed before the μP begins its interrupt sequence.* If the interrupt occurs during the last clock cycle of an instruction, one more instruction is executed. The first step in this interrupt sequence is to save the *program status* (the contents of all the registers) by storing the PC, X, A, B, and CC registers on the stack in the order shown in Fig. 9-3.

These 7 bytes are written into memory starting at the current location in the stack pointer (SP) register. It is decremented on each write. When the register stacking is completed, the SP is pointing to the next empty memory location. The I bit is then set by the hardware, the appropriate interrupt vector is fetched, and the interrupt service routine is then executed. The condition of the stack before and after accepting an interrupt is shown in Fig. 9-4.

EXAMPLE 9-3

The instruction LDX #$ABCD is in location $1000. At the start of this instruction the registers in the **6800** contain the following data: A-11 B-22 CC-C1 X-3344 SP-C234. An IRQ interrupt occurs while the instruction is being executed. Where is the stack, and what has been stacked?

SOLUTION

The contents of the stack are shown in Fig. 9-5. Remember that the instruction takes 3 bytes and it was allowed to execute before the interrupt was processed. The stack starts at the location in the SP, $C234, and decrements. The first bytes stacked are the address of the *next* instruction, $1003. Then the contents of X are stacked. Because the instruction wrote new data into X, its contents at the end of the instruction are $ABCD. The contents of A, B, and CC were next written to the stack. At the end of the sequence the SP contains $C22D.

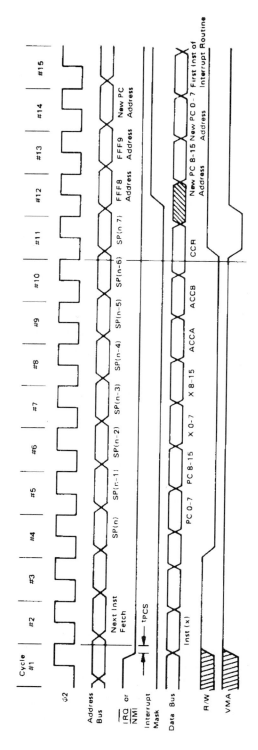

Figure 9-3 Interrupt timing.

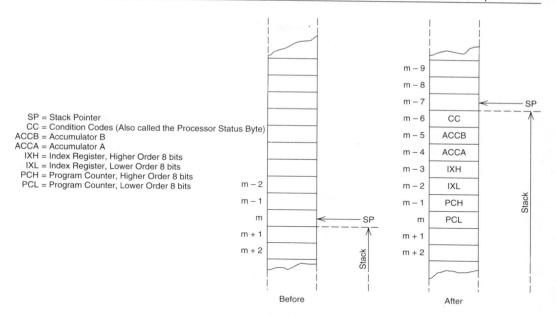

SP = Stack Pointer
CC = Condition Codes (Also called the Processor Status Byte)
ACCB = Accumulator B
ACCA = Accumulator A
IXH = Index Register, Higher Order 8 bits
IXL = Index Register, Lower Order 8 bits
PCH = Program Counter, Higher Order 8 bits
PCL = Program Counter, Lower Order 8 bits

Figure 9-4   Saving the status of the μP on the stack.

	LOCATION	CONTENTS
Original SP —>	C234	03
	C233	10
	C232	CD
	C231	AB
	C230	11
	C22F	22
	C22E	C1
New SP —>	C22D	XX

Figure 9-5   Contents of the stack for Example 9-3

EXAMPLE 9-4

Explain why it is absolutely necessary for a μP to set the I bit before it starts executing an interrupt service routine.

SOLUTION

An IRQ interrupt can occur only if the I bit is CLEAR (0) and the IRQ pin is pulled LOW. When the first instruction of the service routine is executed, the

IRQ pin is still LOW in most cases. Thus if the I bit were still 0, the μP would again be interrupted by the same interrupt that caused it to start the routine. To prevent this, the μP sets the I bit as explained above so that IRQ interrupts are masked out.

After setting the I bit, the μP places $FFF8 and $FFF9 on the address bus and fetches the two bytes from this IRQ vector location. It inserts these bytes into the PC. This is the address of the IRQ service routine. The μP then fetches the first instruction of the service routine from the location now designated by the PC and begins executing the interrupt service routine.

9-5.2 ▼ Return from Interrupt

The interrupt service routine must end with an RTI (ReTurn from Interrupt) instruction. The action of the RTI is shown in Fig. 9-6. It reloads all the μP registers with the values that they had before the interrupt and moves the stack pointer to SP+7, where it was before the interrupt. The RTI uses 10 clock cycles to write the contents of the 7 bytes currently on the stack back into the μP registers. The program resumes at the address restored to the PC, which is the next instruction that would have been executed if the interrupt had not occurred.

EXAMPLE 9-5

What is the state of the I bit after an RTI is executed?

SOLUTION

Because the I bit was set by the hardware just prior to execution of the interrupt routine, it would seem that it should be a 1. This, however, is not necessarily the case. If the interrupt just serviced was due to an IRQ, the I bit had to be 0 when the CCR was stacked or the interrupt routine would not have been executed. However, if it was due to an NMI, the I bit could be either a 1 or a 0 (see Section 9-6). In either case the RTI restores the CCR from the stack to the value it had before the interrupt occurred.

RTI, RETURN FROM INTERRUPT:

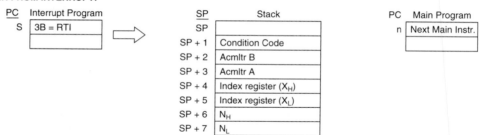

Figure 9-6 Operation of RTI—the return-from-interrupt instruction.

Example 9-5 shows that an interrupt service routine must take some action to cause the IRQ pin to go HIGH before it executes the RTI; *the service routine must remove the source of the interrupt.* If the IRQ pin is still LOW when the RTI is executed, both conditions necessary for an IRQ interrupt will be satisfied and the main program will immediately be interrupted again.

9-5.3 ▼ Selecting and Servicing Interrupts

In Chapter 8, a number of examples were given using the PIA and ACIA without interrupts. Now we will show how some of the same functions can be accomplished using the interrupt capabilities of the **6800** μP. The advantage of using interrupts is that the processor does not have to be dedicated to scanning for an input; instead, it can be executing the main program while waiting for each interrupt to occur.

The **6800** is a μP that only has one IRQ line. If several external devices (PIAs, ACIAs, etc.) are to be allowed to interrupt on the single IRQ line, it is necessary to use either a hardware or software method to identify the interrupting device. A hardware device would have to be built from logic gates and would have to vector the μP to a different *Interrupt Service Routine* for each interrupting device. The software method is a variation of *software polling* but scans only once.

EXAMPLE 9-6

Show how to configure the hardware and how to write a program to handle the interrupts for a system that uses the A side of a PIA for inputs from a keyboard, and the B side for outputs to a printer. Assume that the keyboard interrupts the main program whenever a character is entered by pulsing the Data Ready line LOW. Also assume that the printer operates in accordance with the standard Centronics printer interface. In addition to the data lines, this interface uses a STROBE line and a BUSY line.* When the PIA has a character for the printer, it puts the character on the data lines and pulses the STROBE line. The printer responds by raising BUSY and printing the character. When finished with the character, the printer takes BUSY LOW, and this action is used as an interrupt to request another character.

Use the IRQ lines from the PIA to interrupt the processor and indicate how the proper *interrupt service routine* is selected to input or output a character. This interrupt example should be contrasted with the noninterrupt methods shown in Example 8-12.

SOLUTION

Figure 9-7 shows the interface connections to the PIA for this systems application. The IRQ pins of the interrupting devices are connected together and go to the μP's IRQ pin as shown. The data lines from the keyboard to the PIA

*For the purposes of this example, we ignore the "Out of paper" line normally also provided.

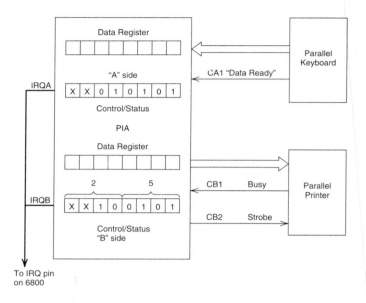

Figure 9-7   Hardware configuration for Example 9-6.

and from the PIA to the printer are connected to port A and port B, respectively. The control lines, CA1, CB1, and CB2, are used to synchronize the data transfer between the PIA and the keyboard and printer.

The program required consists of four basic modules:

1. Initialization
2. Selection
3. Inputting a character from the keyboard
4. Outputting a character to the printer.

ADDRESS	CODE		MNEMONICS		COMMENTS
1000	4F		INIT	CLRA	Set A to zeros
1001	B7	2001		STAA $2001	Clear A Control Register
1004	B7	2003		STAA $2003	Clear B Control Register
1007	B7	2000		STAA $2000	Set A side for inputs
100A	43			COMA	Complement A - Get $FF
100B	B7	2002		STAA $2002	Set B side for outputs
100E	86	15		LDAA #$15	Get keyboard control word
1010	B7	2001		STAA $2001	Store CW in CRA
1013	86	25		LDAA #$25	Set CW for Strobe & RQST
1015	B7	2003		STAA $2003	Store CW in CRB
1018	....			etc.	

Figure 9-8   PIA Initialization Routine for Example 9-6

Assuming that the PIA's RESET pin is connected to the µP's RESET line (as it should be), when a RESET occurs, the PIA's hardware logic will initialize all I/O lines in the PIA as inputs and interrupts will be disabled because all registers are cleared. The restart routine will then fetch the bytes at $FFFE and $FFFF, and *vector* the µP to the start of the *system initialization routines*. The PIA's initialization routine, shown in Fig. 9-8 is normally included with other initialization routines for other parts of the system, and they are all executed whenever the RESET signal line is activated.

The PIA is programmed by this initialization routine by writing into its registers. The instructions at $1001 and $1004 are really not necessary because of the hardware reset. Because bit 2 of both the A and B Control Registers are clear, the writing of 00 into address $2000 by the next instruction and the writing of $FF into $2002 by the next two instructions causes the data to go into the Data Direction Registers (see Section 8-5.3) and sets the A side for inputs and the B side for outputs. The latter occurs because the COMA instruction inverted the 00 it found in accumulator A, making it $FF (all 1s), which is then stored into the B-side Data Direction Register. The next four instructions will effectively *latch* these settings because bit 2 of both control words are *SET* and this switches the PIA so that addresses $2000 and $2002 become Data Registers (see Sections 8-5.2 and 8-5.3).

The $15, entered into Control Register A, programs the CA1 line to interrupt on negative-going transitions (bits 1 and 0 are 0 and 1, respectively) (see Table 8-2). The CA1 line must be connected to external circuitry such that the keyboard produces a negative-going pulse whenever a key is pressed.

The B-side control word ($25) is selected so that the CB2 line will strobe the printer when a character is put into the PIA's Data Register by the output character routine (see Table 8-5, line 1). This will cause the printer to read the data on the output lines. The CB1 line is also programmed by this control word to cause an interrupt whenever the printer pulls it LOW (see Table 8-2, line 2). It will do this as soon as it finishes printing the character.

When the CA1 line is pulled LOW by the keyboard circuits (each time a key is pressed), or the CB1 line is pulled LOW by the printer, they set bit 7 in the appropriate register and the resulting interrupt will *vector* the processor to the selection routine. This is the start of the *interrupt service routine,* which is shown in flowchart form in Fig. 9-9. Its entry address of $0100, pointing to the POLL label, must have been previously stored in $FFF8 and $FFF9, the IRQ vector locations.

When an interrupt occurs, the selection routine must determine which device interrupted. It will then branch to the appropriate character input or printer output routine to service the interrupt. A flowchart of the selection process is shown in the upper right of Fig. 9-9, and the corresponding program for this part is shown in Fig. 9-10. This selection routine loads the contents of the PIA's A-side Control/Status Register into accumulator A and tests it with the BPL (Branch-if-PLus) instruction, to see if status bit 7 of CRA is SET. If it is, a keyboard interrupt has occurred, and because the resulting byte is a negative number, the program falls through to the *input character* handling routine.

The ETC shown in this routine of Fig. 9-9 symbolizes the instructions needed to handle the keyboard data and is part 3 of the program. It serves to get the keyboard characters from the PIA's Data Register and put them in a

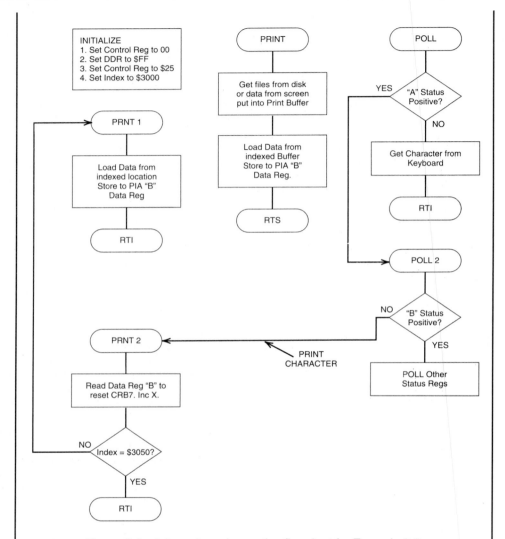

Figure 9-9   Interrupt service routine flowchart for Example 9-6.

buffer somewhere. This is the subject of a programming exercise (see Problem 9-5).

   If bit 7 is not SET, the word is positive and the BPL instruction branches to the POLL2 routine at address $120. If bit 7 of CRB (address $2003) is SET, the *output* interrupt has occurred, the BPL instruction at location $123 does not branch, and the *output character* handling routine is entered.

   This printer interrupt will not occur unless the user has initiated the print routine by jumping into the routine labeled PRINT of Fig. 9-9. This routine does whatever is necessary to get the data into the printer buffer (at $3000) and moves the first character into the PIA's B Data Register. The printer sees

ADDR	DATA	LABEL	MNEMONICS	COMMENTS
100 86	2001	POLL	LDAA $2001	GET "A" STATUS
103 2A	1D		BPL POLL2	BRANCH IF + TO POLL2
		*	INPUT CHARACTER ROUTINE	
... B6	2000		LDAA $2000	GET DATA
... XX	—			
... XX			ETC	REST OF ROUTINE
11F 3B			RTI	RETURN FROM INTERRUPT
120 B6	2003	POLL2	LDAA $2003	GET "B" STATUS
123 2A	1D		BPL POLL3	BRANCH IF + TO OTHERS
		*	OUTPUT CHARACTER ROUTINE (PRINT)	
... B7	2002		STAA $2002	OUTPUT DATA
... XX	—			
... XX			ETC	REST OF ROUTINE
... 3B			RTI	
			END	RETURN FROM INTERRUPT

Figure 9-10 Polling program for Example 9-6.

its STROBE input go LOW, accepts the character, and raises BUSY, the CB1 line. The printer will take a few milliseconds to print the character, and when finished, will clear BUSY. According to Table 8-2, line 2, this action will set bit 7 of Control/Status Register B (at location $2003) and will cause the IRQB pin to go LOW, interrupting the μP.

This time, when the selection routine is entered, bit 7 of the B-side Status Register will be found *set* and the POLL2 routine will branch to PRNT2, clearing bit 7 of CRB and moving a new character to the PIA's Data Register B for a continuation of the printing. When the index register is incremented to $3050, the program exits to execute the RTI instruction and end the printing.

Again, the ETC in the Output Character Routine symbolizes the instructions needed for the fourth part of the program. Its job is to move data from a file or buffer to the PIA's Data Register (see Problem 9-6). Note that this system implementation is almost identical to the system described in Example 8-12 except that the PIA's IRQ pins are connected to the MPU in Fig. 9-7. The flowchart for the required program is also nearly identical except that instead of the program looping until the status bit is set, as shown in the middle of Fig. 8-11, the program must be set up as an **interrupt service routine** and modified to do an RTI instead of just looping.

Because the wiring of the two systems is identical, it is only necessary to change the PIA control word for Control/Status Register B to $25 (instead of $26).

Note that each of these character-handling routines ends with an RTI instruction because they are the termination of the *interrupt service routines*. They serve to return the processor from the interrupt sequence and the main program is resumed at the point where it was interrupted.

9-5.4 ▼ Nested Interrupts

Normally, an interrupt service routine proceeds until it is complete without being interrupted itself because the I flag is SET automatically by the μP when servicing an interrupt. If we have a larger system, however, where several devices may interrupt the μP, a priority problem may arise. Suppose that the system contains a slow device (e.g., a keyboard, which can afford to wait for its interrupt to be serviced) and a fast device (e.g., a disk drive, which requires attention quickly).* If the disk interrupt arrives before the keyboard interrupt, there is no problem. The disk interrupt will set the I bit and lock out the keyboard interrupt until it is completed. Then the keyboard interrupt will be serviced.

The problem arises if the keyboard interrupt arrives slightly before the disk request. This will lock out the disk request until the keyboard service routine finishes, which may be too long. To prevent this situation, we must assign a higher priority to the disk interrupt by allowing it to interrupt the keyboard service routine. This can be done as follows:

1. The first step in the keyboard routine must be to clear the keyboard interrupt (note 3 of Table 8-2 states that the interrupt flag is cleared when the Data Register is read).

2. The second step is to issue a CLI instruction. This will clear the I bit and allow the disk to interrupt. Therefore, the disk will not have to wait for service.

This "interrupt of an interrupt" is called a *nested interrupt.* It is handled in the **6800** by stopping execution of the original service routine and storing another sequence of registers on the stack. This is similar to nested subroutines (see Section 5-5.3). Because of the automatic decrementing of the stack pointer by each interrupt and subsequent incrementing by the RTI instruction, the first interrupt service routine is resumed after the second interrupt is completed, and the interrupts are serviced in the proper order. Interrupts can be nested to any depth, limited only by the amount of memory available for the stack.

9-5.5 ▼ Other Interrupt Service Routines

In response to each type of interrupt, a routine must be written to service that interrupt. The selection process and character-handling routines of Fig. 9-10 are examples of the *interrupt service routines* needed for an IRQ interrupt. The main program must also be written to allow or prevent interrupts at the proper time, as explained in Section 9-9.5.

9-6 ▼ NONMASKABLE INTERRUPT

A NonMaskable Interrupt (NMI) is initiated by placing a *negative-going edge* on the NMI pin of whichever **6800** family μP or μC we are dealing with. When an NMI occurs, the program counter is loaded with the vector accessed from $FFFC and $FFFD. This causes the μP to jump to the start of the NMI *interrupt service routine.*

---

*A disk drive is really not quick in computer terms because it takes milliseconds to respond.

EXAMPLE 9-7

Assume that a system like Fig. 9-11 is being used as a part of a financial terminal where transactions involving customer bank accounts are being handled, and the information must be preserved in the event of a power failure. Describe the interrupt service routines required.

SOLUTION

Since it is necessary in this type of system to save all calculations and status, a nonvolatile RAM is needed with a *Powerfail* detector as shown in Fig. 9-11. The function of the battery is to act as a backup source of energy for the RAM, so the RAM will not lose information when the main power fails.

When a power failure occurs, the NMI line is pulled down by the powerfail logic. The main program is interrupted at the end of the current instruction, and the registers are stored in the stack. (The power supply will take many milliseconds before the voltage is too LOW to operate the system, and this routine only takes microseconds.) The vector for the powerfail routine is fetched and the processor starts its execution. This routine's main function is to save, in battery-backed RAM, all relevant information, such as the contents of PIA and ACIA registers and partial products of any calculations that may be in process. The stack should also be in this memory. The program should then use a PIA to pull down the HALT line to prevent any false operation of the μP while the voltage is marginal.

Figure 9-11 also includes the RESET circuitry necessary to resume operation when the power comes on again. The box labeled "Reset Logic" must decide when the voltage is normal, and it then initiates a RESET pulse. The RESET routine, fetched by the RESET vector, must not only reconfigure the PIAs, and the ACIAs as they were, but must reload all interim products or data into the appropriate registers (the RTI restores the μP registers). The program then resumes from the address restored to the PC register, without loss of vital data.

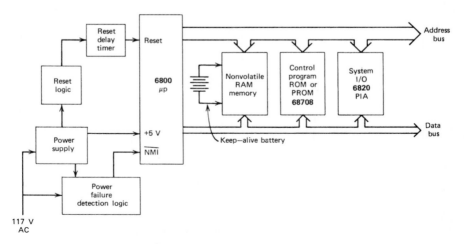

Figure 9-11   A **6800** system for automatic recovery from a power failure.

As its name implies, the NMI is not affected by the I bit of the CCR and an interrupt occurs whenever the NMI pin is pulled LOW. Consequently, NMI functions as a *very high priority interrupt.* It is usually reserved for events such as a power failure in the μP or in a peripheral, which could be catastrophic if the μP did not recognize them and take immediate action. It is also sometimes used for keeping a clock updated.

In contrast to an IRQ, where the interrupt is initiated by the *level* on the IRQ pin, the NMI must be initiated by a *negative-going edge* on the NMI pin. If it were to respond to a LOW level, it would interrupt its own service routine, because an NMI cannot be masked out.

9-7 ▼ SOFTWARE INTERRUPT

The SoftWare Interrupt (SWI) is an instruction that can be placed anywhere within a program. It forces the μP to act as though an interrupt had occurred.* When encountered in a program, it causes the registers to be put away on the stack and a vector to be fetched, just as for other interrupts. The vector for SWI is located at address $FFFA and $FFFB.

The SWI is often used by Monitor Programs such as BUFFALO, found in the EValuation Board (EVB) system (see Section 11-5), to set *breakpoints.* Breakpoints are discussed in Section 11-6.9. They cause the program to stop at a particular location so that the programmer can check the program's progress (the contents of the registers and memory) at that point.

EXAMPLE 9-8

A program that starts at $1000 must stop at $102C so that the contents of its registers can be examined. How can we cause this to happen?

SOLUTION

We can replace the instruction at $102C with an SWI and start the program at $1000. It will run to $102C, where the SWI will interrupt and stack the registers. The contents of the registers can then be read from the stack.

This is essentially what a breakpoint does. Monitor routines allow the user to set breakpoints and simplify the reading of the various registers, but they accomplish this by replacing instructions with SWIs at the breakpoint locations.

---

*The SWI is called a *TRAP* by other manufacturers.

EXAMPLE 9-9

What does the program shown in Fig. 9-12 accomplish?

ADDR	LABEL	MNEMONIC	COMMENTS
0FFE		. . .	
0FFF		. . .	
1000		SWI	Go to SWI service routine
1001		LDAB #3	Resume program by loading
1003		. . .	B with 3, etc.

a) Main Program

ADDR	LABEL	MNEMONICS	COMMENTS
2000	SWISRV	INS	Increment stack pointer
2001		LDAA $40	Load A direct
2003		PSHA	Put A on stack
2004		RTI	Return to main program

b) SWI Service Routine

Figure 9-12 Program for Example 9-9

SOLUTION

The main program encounters an SWI instruction that places the contents of the registers in the stack and then branches to the SWI *interrupt service routine*. The INS instruction increments the stack pointer so that it points to the Condition Code byte rather than the highest vacant stack location. The A accumulator is then loaded and pushed on the stack, causing the contents of memory location $40 to overwrite the contents of the CCR, as stored in the stack. The PSHA instruction also restores the stack pointer to the value it had after the SWI. The RTI now causes the 7 bytes following the stack pointer to be restored to the μP registers. At the end of the program, everything is exactly as it was when the program started, except that the CCR has been replaced by the contents of location $40.

There are easier ways to change the contents of the CCR, such as using the TAP instructions, but this program has been presented to demonstrate the operation of the SWI and RTI instructions.

9-8 ▼ WAIT-FOR-INTERRUPT INSTRUCTION

The **6800** family μPs and μCs also incorporate a WAit-for-Interrupt (WAI) instruction. The WAI causes the μP to stack the registers and suspend operation until an interrupt (IRQ or NMI) occurs.

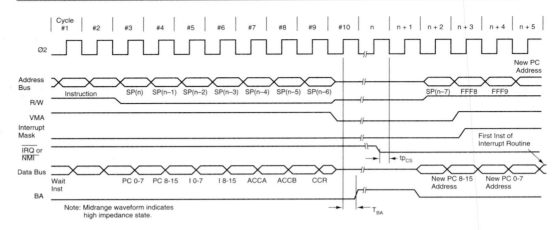

Figure 9-13 WAI (WAIT) instruction timing.

Figure 9-13 is the timing diagram for a WAI. It is similar to an interrupt sequence but provides a way to speed the response to an interrupt. In Fig. 9-13, a WAI instruction has been executed in preparation for an interrupt:

1. The WAI instruction initiates the interrupt sequence one cycle after it is decoded. It stores the 7 bytes of μP register contents in the stack.

2. After cycle 9, the μP goes into a *metamorphic* state by placing the address, data, and R/W lines in their high-impedance mode with VMA held LOW and BA HIGH.

3. It remains this way until an interrupt (IRQ or NMI) occurs.

4. In the fourth cycle following the interrupt line transition, the appropriate vector is fetched and the service routine is started during the sixth cycle.

5. The interrupt mask bit (I) of the CC register must be clear if an IRQ is expected; otherwise, the system will hang up indefinitely.

6. When the interrupt does occur, it is processed more quickly because the registers have already been moved to the stack (six cycles are required until the service routine starts, instead of 14).

9-9 ▼ SOFTWARE TIMING LOOPS

It is often necessary for μPs to control external devices by sending them timing signals at precise intervals. These intervals can vary from a few microseconds to minutes or even hours. Timing sequences and intervals can be controlled by a μP because it, in turn, is controlled by the highly accurate *quartz* crystal clock that generates its φ1 and φ2 signals.

9-9.1 ▼ Construction of a Basic Timing Loop

The basis for μP timing control is the *timing loop,* which is simply a program loop that does nothing, but takes a specific amount of time to do it. Because the number of cycles required by each instruction and the clock frequency can be determined (see Section 4-5), the time to traverse the loop can be calculated. Timing loops are generally constructed by loading the index register, an accumulator, or a memory location with the number of times the loop is to be traversed, decrementing it each time around the loop and leaving the loop when it equals 0. A memory location or the accumulator allows up to 256 counts, but because X is a 16-bit register, it can handle up to 65,536 loops. Still longer times can be generated using a combination of loops.

EXAMPLE 9-10

Set up a program for a 0.1-second delay. Assume that the basic μP clock is 1 MHz.

SOLUTION

The program for a 0.1-second delay is shown in Fig. 9-14.

CODE		MNEMONICS		CYCLES	
CE	2710	LDX	#10000		
09		DEX		4	
01		NOP		2	} Timing
26	FC	BNE	*-2	4	loop
..	..	etc			

Figure 9-14 Program for Example 9-10.

This timing program was constructed by realizing that the DEX and BNE had to be in the loop. Each of these instructions requires four cycles. The NOP (two cycles) was added simply to pad the loop so that it contains a convenient number of cycles. This loop takes 10 cycles or 10^{-5} second if a 1-MHz clock is used. Since the required delay is 10^{-1} second, the loop must be traversed 10,000 times. Therefore, the number $(2710)_{16}$, which is the hex equivalent of the decimal 10,000, is loaded into X at the start of the program. The program branches back to the DEX instruction 10,000 times before reducing X to 0 and falling through. Note that the timing can easily be changed by changing the number loaded into X.

EXAMPLE 9-11

In Example 9-10, can the stack pointer be used instead of X?

SOLUTION

The SP cannot be used instead of X because Table 4-3 shows that decrementing the SP does not set the Z bit. Again, one must determine carefully which instructions set the flags for correct operation.

9-9.2 ▼ Longer Delays

Longer delays can be obtained by combining several loops. This can be done by using one timing loop as a subroutine and having a second timing loop jump to it during its execution. It is very convenient to have the subroutine take exactly 1 second, because this is often used as a timing base.

EXAMPLE 9-12

Write a 1-second timing loop subroutine.

SOLUTION

If the timing loop takes only 10 cycles, as in Example 9-10, a 1-second delay using the X register alone is impossible because the largest number that can be loaded into X is 65,535. If, however, the timing loop is increased to 20 cycles, a 1-second delay is possible and the subroutine can be written as shown in Fig. 9-15.

CODE		MNEMONIC		CYCLES	
DF	F0		STX	$F0	5
CE	C34F		LDX	#49999	3
08		LOOP	INX		4	\
09			DEX		4	|
09			DEX		4	> 20 cycle
01			NOP		2	| timing loop
01			NOP		2	
26	F9		BNE	LOOP	4	/
FE	00F0		LDX	$00F0	5	
01			NOP		2	
39			RTS		5	

Figure 9-15 Program for Example 9-12

The first step in the subroutine is to store X, in case the index register is used by both the main program and the subroutine. Next X is loaded with the proper timing value and the main loop is entered. This loop has been padded so that it takes exactly 20 cycles and effectively decrements X once. When X becomes 0, the subroutine restores the value of X originally saved and exits. For a 1-second delay the 20-cycle loop should be traversed 50,000 times, minus provision for overhead.

The cycles in the subroutine that are not in the main loop are *overhead*. The overhead cycles have also been padded so that they also take exactly 20 cycles. These 20 cycles of overhead are compensated for by reducing the original X value by one, or from $(50,000)_{10}$ to $(49,999)_{10}$ or $(C350)_{16}$ to $(C34F)_{16}$.

Note: In order to keep the overhead to exactly 20 cycles, the direct mode of STX is used, as is the extended mode of LDX. Both use five cycles. The program will have to be changed if the storage for X is at an address above $FF since the direct mode instruction cannot be used.

EXAMPLE 9-13

Set up a circuit to turn a light on for 1 hour and off for $\frac{1}{2}$ hour cyclically.

SOLUTION

One way to do this is to use the CA2 or CB2 line as an output to control the light. The program proceeds as follows.

1. Set CA2 HIGH, turning on the light.
2. Delay for 1 hour.
3. Set CA2 LOW, turning off the light.
4. Delay for $\frac{1}{2}$ hour.
5. Return to step 1.

Figure 9-16 shows the program. It starts at location $10 and the PIA is at $8000.

Location	Code		Label	Mnemonic		Comments
10	86	3C	START	LDAA	#$3C	Store Control Word
12	B7	8001		STAA	$8001	to make CA2 go HIGH
15	CE	0E10		LDX	#3600	Set 1-hour delay
18	BD	XXXX	LOOP1	JSR	DLY1	JSR to 1-second delay
1B	09			DEX		Decrement X
1C	26	FA		BNE	LOOP1	Loop back to addr 18
1E	86	34		LDAA	#$34	Store Control Word
20	B7	8001		STAA	$8001	to make CA2 go LOW
23	CE	0708		LDX	#1800	Set half-hour delay
26	BD	XXXX	LOOP2	JSR	DLY1	JSR to 1-second delay
29	09			DEX		Decrement X
2A	26	FA		BNE	LOOP2	Return to location 26
2C	20	E2		BRA	START	Return to location 10

Figure 9-16 Program for Example 9-13.

The 1-second timing routine (DLY1) can be used as described in Example 9-12. By loading $(3600)_{10}$ into X, we achieve a 1-hour delay and with $(1800)_{10}$ we achieve $\frac{1}{2}$ hour delay. Note that far more complex timing patterns can be generated by this method, and the timing can be changed in response to input signals to the μP by modifying the program.

9-9.3 ▼ Traffic Light Controllers

The program of Example 9-13 can obviously be adjusted to control traffic lights at road intersections where the lights must be alternately red and green. If the traffic lights merely cycle repetitively, electromechanical devices can do as well as μPs. Traffic flow, however, can be optimized using algorithms that consider the volume and speed of the traffic on the intersecting roads, the time of day, and other factors. Traffic control algorithms are becoming more complex and require the computational ability of the μP. Therefore, when traffic control goes beyond just switching the lights on and off and attempts to adjust the lights for optimum control, the intelligence and programmability of the μP are indispensable.

9-9.4 ▼ Real-Time Clocks

In many applications the μC must keep track of the time when certain events occurred, or cause external events to occur at specific times. This timing can be generated internally using software, by an external real-time clock or by a timer IC such as the **6840** (discussed in Section 9-11).

EXAMPLE 9-14

It is necessary to record the time a person passes through a gate, such as at an airport, during the course of an hour. The time of each entry is to be recorded in memory, starting at $A0. Two memory locations are used for each event. The 8 bits of the upper location are divided into two BCD digits that represent the minutes of the hour, and the lower location has two BCD digits that represent the seconds. Describe how to implement this system.

SOLUTION

The following steps are necessary:

1. A photocell and light-beam detector can be used to determine when a person enters the gate. Every time the light beam is interrupted, the photocell puts a pulse on the CA1 or CB1 line of the PIA, which sets bit 7 of the PIA Control/Status Register.
2. The X and SP registers and the PIA Control Register must be initialized before the program can start.
3. Since the time storage is 16 bits long, a pair of memory locations must be reserved for the clock.
4. A 1-second subroutine must be written (see Example 9-12). Each time it expires, it increments the locations that represent the clock. Note that the clock must be set up so that each time the Least Significant Digit (LSD) of the seconds reaches 10, it must return to 0 and increment the MSD of the seconds, when the MSD of the seconds reaches 6, it must increment the LSD of the minutes, and so on.
5. Bit 7 of the PIA Control Register can now be monitored or polled. This can be done within the 1-second timing loop.
6. Each time bit 7 goes HIGH, the contents of the clock can be transferred to a list in memory starting at $A0.
7. At the end of the hour, memory will contain the times people entered the gate.
   The code for this program is too long to be presented here, but the student should be capable of writing it.

To generate a real-time clock using software, a timing loop (see Section 9-9.2) should be written with the time interval set to a value appropriate to the particular problem. One second and 1 minute are typical time values. Whenever the timing loop expires, it increments a memory location or pair of memory locations. The numbers in the memory locations can be used as elapsed time or if the locations are preset to the current time and incremented each second, the numbers will remain current and thus provide a real-time clock.

EXAMPLE 9-15

Each time an event occurs (e.g., a switch being thrown or a person entering a room), the time of this event must be recorded in three consecutive locations in memory in the following format:

HH MM SS

where HH are two decimal digits (in one memory location) that represent the hour of the event, MM represents another byte for minutes, and SS is for seconds. Assume that the event interrupts the μP. Describe the routine required to service this event.

SOLUTION*

An area in memory must be set aside to hold the time data, and a pointer to this area must also be stored at a given location in memory. The starting address of the interrupt service routine is written into $FFF8 and $FFF9, and the program branches to it when the interrupt occurs.

The main program can generate a 1-second timing loop (see Example 9-12). This timing loop must control three locations in memory that each contain two decimal digits (packed BCD) that represent the real-time equivalent of seconds, minutes, and hours. When the timing loop expires, the program must

1. Increment the seconds locations.
2. Execute a Decimal Adjust Accumulator (DAA) instruction (to keep the byte in BCD).
3. If seconds = 60, clear seconds and increment the minutes location.
4. DAA.
5. If minutes = 60, clear minutes and increment hours.
6. DAA.
7. If hours = 24, clear hours.

The main program is shown in the flowchart of Fig. 9-17. When an interrupt occurs, the main program stops and the interrupt routine loads the real time from memory and stores it in the list area. The list pointer is incremented and the interrupt routine terminates with an RTI.

---

*This example was run as a laboratory exercise at the Rochester Institute of Technology. A debounced switch was connected to a PIA, and each switch throw became an event.

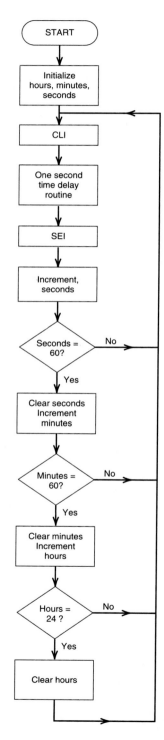

Figure 9-17 Flowchart for the timing routing of Example 9-15.

9-9.5 ▼ Interrupts and Timing

The difficulty with software timing loops is that they use the processor continuously and do not allow the computer to do other useful work. Also, if the main program of Example 9-15 is interrupted while it is incrementing the time, it may be interrupted when it has just finished incrementing the seconds but has not yet incremented the minutes. If the interrupt routine stores the time, the minutes and seconds will not match. Note that numbers like 4A could also be stored in the list if the interrupt occurred between the increment and the DAA instructions.

To prevent these possibilities one can use an SEI to *mask* interrupts before the incrementing part of the routine and then *clear* the interrupt flag (CLI) to permit interrupts, when returning to the timing loop, as shown in Fig. 9-17. This, however, is not a practical solution for software clocks if any other IRQ interrupt (to service a printer, perhaps) is allowed. This would cause the software clock to lose time. Therefore, to implement a reliable clock it is necessary to avoid all interrupts or use a hardware clock as described in Section 9-9.6.

9-9.6 ▼ Hardware Real-Time Clocks

As just mentioned, software timing loops keep the CPU busy full time and nothing else can be done. That is the reason for development of the **146818T1** Real-Time Clock (RTC) described in Section 9-10 and the **6840** Programmable Timer Module (PTM) described in Section 9-11. These ICs and the timing functions integrated into the MCUs described in Chapter 10 provide these delays by counting internally and do not use the CPU. Therefore, the CPU can be executing other programs while waiting. The CPU can be programmed to be interrupted when the time delay expires. If the CPU does not have other work to do, however, it is perfectly reasonable to use a software loop, which is why they have been described here.

Hardware real-time clocks can be fabricated in many ways and interfaced to the μC so that the time information is available as needed. One way is to use an electric clock motor which closes a mechanical contact every minute. This obviously can be connected to CA1 of a PIA. The computer can respond to this interrupt by incrementing a set of memory locations that maintain clock time and then return to its main program. In this way, the main program has real time always available but does not have the task of updating the clock.

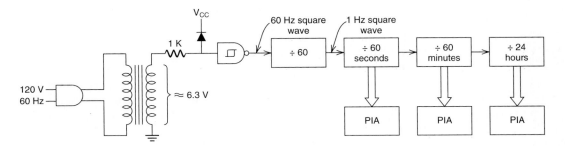

Figure 9-18   Real-time clock (using 60 Hz).

In these days of solid-state electronics, a more reliable method would be to use digital counter ICs that are driven by the 60-Hz power line, such as the **14566B.** A variety of circuits are possible using divide-by-60 counters, one of which is shown in Fig. 9-18. The output of the counter must be brought into the μC system and processed by some type of clock program.

A second solution is to use a Real-Time Clock (RTC) LSI IC as described in the following section. A third solution is to use a special *counter-timer* IC such as the **6840** PTM described in Section 9-11.

9-10 ▼ 146818T1 REAL-TIME CLOCK IC

Timer LSI circuits are proliferating in the industry. They keep track of the real time and do not require complicated hardware assembly and its programming. One such device is the **MC146818T1** Real-Time Clock/RAM (RTC). It is simple to use because it is self-contained and can connect directly to the MCU. Outside of the LSI IC itself, a quartz crystal, two small capacitors, and a resistor are all that is needed. It can also be used with 50/60-Hz line input. The RTC generates seconds, minutes, hours, days, date, month, and year as well as an alarm and a watchdog circuit (which resets the MCU if the SS pin is not toggled periodically by the MCU).

By using the RTC, the μP need not keep track of the time. Whenever the μP needs to know the time, it simply reads the RTC. The time data is sent to the μP in byte form via a serial synchronous, three-wire interface. This interface is available on many of the **6800** family MCUs described in Chapter 10 and is known as the **Serial Peripheral Interface** (SPI). This timer is thus very much like any peripheral chip in the **6800** family and is easily incorporated in a system. (See Application Note ANE425 and the **146818T1** Data Sheet cited in Section 9-15.)

The RTC also has features to allow easy implementation of battery-backup and power up/power down applications. Since it uses low-power CMOS technology, it can be battery powered to keep time in the event of a power failure. A 32-byte RAM is also included to provide nonvolatile storage for users' data.

9-11 ▼ THE 6840 PROGRAMMABLE TIMER MODULE

The **6800** family of components includes the 28-pin **6840** Programmable Timer Module (PTM). This NMOS IC has 3 independent software controllable 16-bit counters along with the registers and logic that make it a very versatile timer module. It can be added to a **6800** family μC system to provide precise delays, count events, or produce timing signals with minimal CPU involvement. The concepts of this IC are the basis for the timers in all of the newer MCUs but they operate somewhat differently, so we will defer detailed descriptions of the MCU timing functions until later chapters (see Sections 10-10, 16-9 and 16-15). The use of the **6840** has been dramatically reduced because timer functions are now available in all of the MCUs, and also because the **6840** is not CMOS. It is available in 1993 as a replacement part, however, as is the **6800.**

9-12 ▼ MULTIPROCESSING

In some computer systems, the amount of work required exceeds the capabilities of a single μP. Since μPs are small and inexpensive, it is often feasible to add a second μP to share the load. The use of two or more processors, working semi-independently but simultaneously, on parts of the same task is called *multiprocessing.*

If the two (or more) μPs can be connected so that they can perform separate tasks at the same time, a real increase in throughput can occur. In such a system, it is necessary to transfer data between subsystems, but this may take only a small percentage of the time.

One of the most time-consuming tasks in μC systems is in the input or output of data. If the data is being printed by a printer, for example, it may take 10 ms for each character. A processor can run 10,000 cycles (3000 to 5000 instructions) during that time. Consequently, if the external printer device requires any degree of intelligence to perform its task, it could be practical to provide a dedicated μP for that purpose.

Some modern automobiles use several μPs, to share the various tasks. The primary use is to provide engine control, where the oxygen content of the exhaust is used to adjust the fuel/air ratio for minimum pollution when cruising or for maximum power when the accelerator is depressed appreciably. Secondarily, however, μCs are used to calculate gas mileage, and in some luxury cars to control shock absorbers. They also control the idle speed of the motor when it is too cold or too hot.

9-12.1 ▼ Master–Slave Systems

In many multiprocessing systems, one μP is designated as the *master.* It controls the operation of the system and apportions tasks between itself and the other μPs, which are called *slaves.* In the system described above, for example, the master μP might sense that there is data for the printer located in a certain area of memory. It can then inform the slave μP that controls the printer, and it becomes the slave's task to send this information to the printer while the master μP does other things. Typically, master and slave μPs share common memory. Because of coordination problems, programming master–slave or other multiprocessor systems is often complex.

One clever method that allows the computers to share memory is shown in Fig. 9-19. The two μPs run on opposite clocks (φ1 of μP1 is φ2 of μP2). Since the μP's only enable memory on their own φ2, they never access memory at the same time. This system requires fast memory. Normal-speed memories require a priority circuit to avoid conflicts when both μPs need to access the same memory location.

9-13 ▼ SUMMARY

In this chapter we described the response of the μP system to an interrupt (storing the registers on the stack, executing the interrupt service routine, restoring the registers, and resuming the main program). Each type of interrupt that occurs in the **6800** family of μCs and the events associated with it were discussed. In addition, timing loops and timer ICs were described. Finally, I/O transfers using multiprocessing were explained.

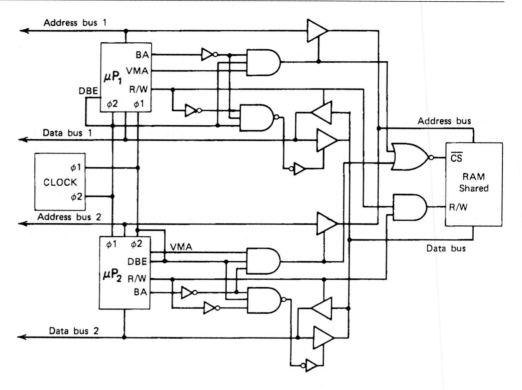

Figure 9-19 Multiprocessing circuit using transposed clock and shared memory.

9-14 ▼ GLOSSARY

Interrupt A signal to the computer that causes it to halt execution of its normal program and branch to a service routine for the interrupting device.

Interrupt service routine A software routine that responds to an interrupt and also directs a peripheral device to take action to remove the need for its interrupting action.

IRQ (Interrupt ReQuest) The name given to the signal line and pin used to interrupt the MC.

Mask bit A bit in the Condition Code Register (bit 4) which, when SET, inhibits the IRQ action.

Masking Setting bits in control registers of the μP or its peripheral ICs, to inhibit them from activating their interrupt lines.

Multiprocessing Using two or more computers to work simultaneously on the same problem.

Nested Interrupts An interrupt of the processing of a previous interrupt service routine.

NMI (NonMaskable Interrupt) A high-priority interrupt that is not affected by the interrupt flag.

Polling The act of querying each peripheral device to determine if it was the device that interrupted.

Reset The action used to start up a computer. Grounding the RESET line will reset the hardware logic of the μP and its peripheral ICs, and the action also fetches the restart vector that jumps the program to an initialization routine prior to entering the main program.

Restart A signal that causes the computer to start its program at the beginning.

RTI (ReTurn from Interrupt) The last instruction in an interrupt subroutine that causes the μP's registers to be restored and the previous program to resume.

Stack An area of memory assigned to hold subroutine return addresses, μP register contents during an interrupt, or data that has been "pushed" onto the stack by the PSH instruction.

SWI (SoftWare Interrupt) An instruction that acts as an interrupt by storing the registers on the stack and jumping to a vector location.

Timing loop A software routine that has the total number of cycles adjusted so that a prescribed amount of time will elapse when it is executed.

Vector An address that "points to" a software routine for servicing interrupts or reset.

WAI Wait for interrupt. An instruction that causes the μP to store its registers and await an interrupt.

9-15 ▼ REFERENCES

GREENFIELD, JOSEPH D., *Practical Digital Design Using ICs,* latest edition, Prentice Hall, Englewood Cliffs, N.J.

MOTOROLA, *Programmable Timer Fundamentals and Applications, MC6840,* 2nd ed., MC6840UM(AD-1), Austin, Texas, 1981.

———, *Real-Time Clock Applications,* MC146818T1, ANE425, Austin, Texas, 1988.

———, *Real-Time Clock Plus RAM CMOS Application,* MC146818T1, Specific Standard ICs DL130 Rev.1, Austin, Texas, 1991.

———, 8-Bit Microprocessor & Peripheral Data, Series C, Austin, Texas, 1983.

9-16 ▼ PROBLEMS

9-1. If a system responds to both high- and low-priority interrupts, why must each low-priority service routine have a CLI instruction near its beginning?

9-2. If a system uses a 1-μs clock, what is the minimum time that reset may be held low?

9-3. The following is a segment of a program for a **6800**:

			SP	X	A	B	CC
20	LDS	#$01E		×	×	×	×
23	LDX	#$155			×	×	×
26	SEC				×	×	C1
27	LDAA	#$AB				×	
29	LDAB	$50					
2B	JSR	$003F					
.							
.							
.							
3F	PSHA						
40	ROLA						
41	ABA						
42	DAA						
43	INX						
44	STAA	$51					

Location $50 contains the number $40.

(a) Fill in the table. Answers that cannot be found have been marked with ×.

(b) During the STAA an interrupt is received. At this time, list all the locations that have been stacked and what is in each location.

9-4. A program consists of a main program and an interrupt routine. In addition, a portion of the main program must not be interrupted. Describe where each SEI and CLI instruction should go in the program.

9-5. In Example 9-6, the keyboard service routine is to store the characters received from the keyboard in a buffer starting at $5000. It must stop if the character $0D is received or if 80 characters have been received. Write the service routine.

9-6. The μP is to use interrupts to send the printer a string of characters starting at location $3000 and ending when the character $0D (return) occurs.

(a) Show the connections between the PIA and the printer.

(b) Write the initialization routine for the main program. Assume that the PIA's addresses start at $2000.

(c) Write the interrupt service routine.

9-7. Modify the service routines of Example 9-6 to allow the printer to interrupt the keyboard service routine, but not vice versa.

9-8. A low-priority device interrupts the program and is then interrupted by a high-priority device. With reference to the original stack pointer, what are the contents of SP-3? Of SP-12?

9-9. A μP system stores an equivalent of real time as a 16-bit number in locations $100 and $101. The μP is interrupted once a second by a 1-second clock and must increment the 16-bit number in those locations. Assume that it is interrupted by a positive transition on a line.

(a) Bring the line in via the PIA and write the initialization routine for the PIA.

(b) Write the interrupt service routine.

(c) Design the hardware to cause the interrupt.

Assume that the 1-second pulse is achieved by counting down the 60 Hz from the AC power lines.

9-10. A μP uses an ACIA. Whenever the Transmit Data Register is empty, it interrupts. If the address of the Transmit Data Register is $8011, write an interrupt routine to transfer the contents of location 40 to the ACIA.

9-11. An ACIA whose data register is at $8011 interrupts each time it receives a character. The first character received should go into location $0100, the second into $0101, and so on. When location $01FF is used, the program should execute an SWI and go to $0500. Write the interrupt routine.

9-12. Explain the following statement: "Whenever the flags are stored by an IRQ interrupt, the I flag is always 0." Is this statement true for NMI and SWI interrupts?

9-13. In response to a switch closure, a signal line should be on for 300 μs, off for 100 μs, on for 500 μs, and then off. Write a program to do this using the PIA.

After attempting to solve these problems, try to answer the self-evaluation questions in Section 9-2. If any of them still seem difficult, review the appropriate sections of the chapter to find the answers.

8-BIT MICROCONTROLLERS

10-1 ▼ INSTRUCTIONAL OBJECTIVES

Since 1974, when the **6800** was first sold, many newer and more sophisticated μPs have been designed and built. The ability to put more circuitry into a chip has permitted these enhanced μPs to be included into a single IC, along with memory, timers, and I/O, to form MicroController Units (MCUs). In this chapter we introduce these 8-bit μPs and MCUs and describe their features. As we have taken most of this book to describe the **6800,** space limitations prevent us from describing all of the other μPs in equal detail. We hope to give the reader a grasp of the functions and capabilities of some of these new μPs, as well as the details of some of their new features, such as the Serial Communications Interface (SCI) and the Serial Peripheral Interface (SPI).

The objective of this chapter, therefore, is to introduce the reader to the MCUs that are derived from the **6800,** so that when a new system is to be designed, the best MCU for that system can be selected. The reader is then advised to consult the manufacturer's literature for more detailed information on the MCU chosen.

10-2 ▼ SELF-EVALUATION QUESTIONS

Watch for the answers to the following questions as you read the chapter. They should help you to understand the material presented.

1. What is the Y register? Which μPs use a Y register?
2. On the **68HC11,** what is the difference between XIRQ and IRQ?
3. What are the differences between the single-chip mode and the multiplexed mode?
4. What **68HC11** registers are associated with the timer and the SCI? Where are they located, and what is their function?
5. What is a "wake-up" feature?
6. What is an LIR? On what MCUs is it used? What is it used for?
7. What are the advantages of CMOS? Of HCMOS? How do you tell if a **6805** is manufactured by using HMOS, CMOS, or HCMOS?
8. How do you tell if a **6805** contains ROM or EPROM?

10-3 ▼ INTRODUCTION

The original **6800** system plan was to provide individual ICs with one computer function in each chip as shown in Fig. 7-1. Thus a custom microcomputer (μC) design was achieved by selecting the appropriate μP, clock, memory, and peripheral ICs, and assembling them together on a Printed Circuit Board (PCB).

With the ability to put more circuitry on each chip, Motorola began providing chips with several of the μC functions in one chip. The growth of these new μCs has expanded into several different families. These are:

1. The **68000** 16- and 32-bit general-purpose family of μPs
2. The **6801** 8-bit MicroController (MCU) family
3. The **68HC11** 8-bit MCU family
4. The **68HC05** 8-bit MCU family
5. The **68HC16** 16-bit MCU family (discussed in later chapters)
6. The **68300** 32-bit MCU family (discussed in later chapters)

The **68000** family of μPs is discussed in Chapters 14 and 15. The 8-bit MCUs are discussed in this and the following chapters. One of the first of the multifunction 8-bit chips was the **6802** μP, which in addition to the **6800** CPU *core,* includes a clock circuit similar to the **6875** and the equivalent of the **6810** RAM IC in one package. Thus the system costs were greatly reduced and this chip became the basis for many high-volume systems. Millions have been used by various industries. Because every μC system uses these basic functions, this chip remains in the general-purpose category.

The **6809** is a newer, high-performance 8-bit μP manufactured by Motorola. It includes an internal clock circuit, and more registers than the **6800** or **6802.** The **6809** is a μP with a more powerful (but different) instruction set than the **6800.**

There are no peripheral functions in the **6809** (except the clock), and because this book concentrates on MCUs, the **6809** will not be discussed further. There are several good books on the **6809** listed in Section 10-19.

10-3.1 ▼ Microcontrollers

The rest of the families in the foregoing list are all MicroControllers (MCUs). They include most, if not all, of the peripheral functions needed to make a complete controller system. The 8-bit versions are all built around a CPU *core* that is very similar to the CPU in the **6800,** which is the reason that we devoted so many chapters to describing the **6800.** The use of the **6800** μP core provides upward compatibility for the software in all the 8-bit families. This has been a very important goal for all of Motorola's new MCU families. Each MCU in these families can be described as **single-chip controllers,** because they have various combinations of ROM, RAM, I/O, Timers, and sometimes other functions, such as an A/D converter, on the same chip with an enhanced CPU core.

These MCUs have branched into several different families, such as the high-performance **68HC11**s, low-cost **68HC05**s, or as discussed in later chapters, the 16-bit **68HC16** and 32-bit **68300** families of MCUs. The **6801, 68HC11,** and **68HC05** families all contain a CPU based on the **6800** *core.* The **6800** instruction set is enhanced in the **6801** and enhanced again for the **68HC11.** An additional register is also provided in the

68HC11. In the **6805** CPU, the index register is made smaller and the B accumulator is removed to lower the costs of manufacturing these ICs.

10-3.2 ▼ μP/MCU Families

Figure 10-1 shows the newer μPs and MCUs in perspective, divided into the various families. There are several members in each family; each member has the same basic family number and additional numbers to differentiate it from the other family members. The chart shows the year of their introduction and the performance of the new μPs compared to the **6800.** Performance generally refers to the speed with which tasks are completed. High-performance μPs often have powerful instructions that accomplish, in one instruction, tasks that require three or four basic **6800** instructions.

On the chart, the letters A and B generally refer to the μPs that are functionally identical to the generic μP but operate at higher speeds. The **68A00,** for example, has a **6800** μP that can use a 1.5-MHz clock, and the **68B00** is for use with 2.0-MHz clocks. If a μP number contains the letters HC, it indicates that the IC uses *high-speed* CMOS (HCMOS) gates rather than NMOS. Like their NMOS predecessors, the HCMOS μPs and MCUs operate up to 2.1 MHz, but HCMOS consumes less power.

The four **6800**-based MCU families shown in Fig. 10-1 are (from bottom to top) the **6805, 6801, 6802,** and **6809.** The **68HC11** is shown as an extension of the **6801** family in the upper right of the figure.

The **6805** family contains a simplified, low-cost version of the **6800** μP core. Figure 10-1 shows that its performance is below the **6800.** Each **6805** version, however, has a variety of peripherals included within the IC. They are used for low-cost, single-chip controller applications. The **6805** family is discussed in Section 10-16.

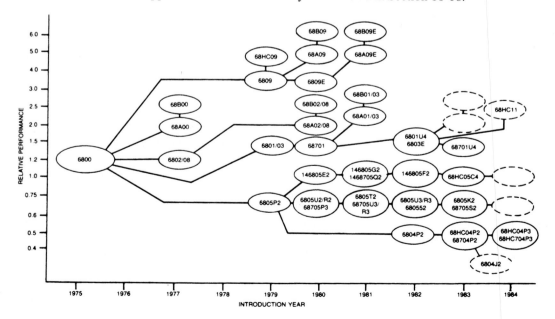

Figure 10-1 Geneology of the **6800** μP/μC family.

All members of the **6801** family contain an enhanced **6800** processor. They also contain RAM, ROM or EPROM, a timer, and serial and parallel I/O similar to an ACIA and PIA. The **6801** family also includes the **6803,** which has no ROM, and the **68701,** which contains an onboard EPROM rather than ROM. The **68HC11,** with its powerful peripheral features, is an outgrowth of the **6801,** but because of its greatly enhanced features, as well as the implementation using the HCMOS process, is really in a new family. The **6801** is discussed in Section 10-4, and the **68HC11** is discussed in Section 10-6.

10-3.3 ▼ 6802/6846 COMBINATION

The **6802** and a companion IC, the **6846,** formed an early, two-chip MCU. The **6846** is now obsolete and no longer manufactured, but it is discussed in the second edition of this book.

10-4 ▼ 6801 MCU FAMILY

The **6801** was introduced in 1979 and is Motorola's first single-chip **MicroController Unit** (MCU). It contains all the elements of a complete controller system and can be operated in a stand-alone mode with very little external circuitry. The following system functions are contained in each **6801** family MCU:

1. An enhanced **6800** μP
2. A RAM
3. A ROM or EPROM
4. A Timer
5. Three 8-bit I/O ports (plus a 5-bit port)
6. A Serial Communications Interface (SCI) (see Section 10-13)
7. A Clock circuit

Since 1979, several variations or enhancements of the basic **6801** have been introduced. The MCUs in the **6801** family as of 1992 are shown in Table 10-1. The differences between the various members of this family depend on the amount of internal RAM and ROM, as shown in Table 10-1. All of the MCUs shown in Table 10-1 include an enhanced **6800** μP with additional instructions (see Section 10-4.1). For added details, readers are referred to the specific Data Sheets listed in Section 10-19.

TABLE 10-1 The 6800 Family of MCUs

μP/μC	Pins	I/O Pins	Ram	Rom	Eprom
6801	40	29	128	2K	—
6803	40	13	128	—	—
68701	40	29	128	—	2K
6801U4	40	29	192	4K	—
6803U4	40	13	192	—	—
68701U4	40	29	192	—	4K

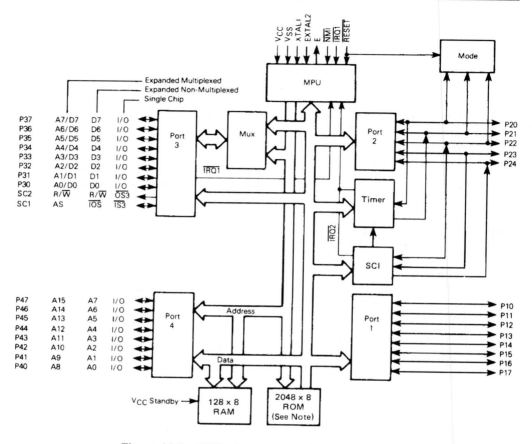

Figure 10-2 **6801** microcomputer family block diagram.

The **6801** has been produced for years and is still listed in Motorola's price sheets, but because it is an NMOS IC, and other advances have been made, it has been superseded by the HCMOS **68HC11** family. We will, therefore, not describe the **6801**s in detail, but for historical purposes and so that its relationship with the **68HC11**s can be seen, the internal configuration is shown in Fig. 10-2. The **6801** is architecturally compatible with the **6800** family, so that it works with any of the **6800** peripheral components.

10-4.1 ▼ 6801 Instruction Improvements

The **6801** contains a more advanced μP. Its instruction set is both source and object code *compatible* with the **6800,** and **6800** programs will run on the **6801** *without* modification. The registers for the **6801** are identical to those of the **6800** and are shown in Chapter 4 (Fig. 4-1). The **6800** instruction set has been augmented in the **6801** by 10 new instruction types (21 Op codes), as shown in Table 10-2.

Additions to the **6801** instruction set include six 16-bit operations on the double accumulator (D). The double accumulator is a 16-bit accumulator made up of accumula-

Table 10-2   Additional Instructions for the **6801**

ADDED INSTRUCTIONS

In addition to the existing M6800 instruction set, the following new instructions are incorporated in the MC6801 microcomputer.

ABX	Adds the 8-bit unsigned accumulator B to the 16-bit X-Register taking into account the possible carry out of the low order byte of the X-Register.	$IX \leftarrow IX + ACCB$
ADDD	Adds the double precision ACCD* to the double precision value M:M+1 and places the results in ACCD.	$ACCD \leftarrow (ACCD) + (M:M+1)$
ASLD	Shifts all bits of ACCD one place to the left. Bit 0 is loaded with zero. The C bit is loaded from the most significant bit of ACCD.	
LDD	Loads the contents of double precision memory location into the double accumulator A:B. The condition codes are set according to the data.	$ACCD \leftarrow (M:M+1)$
LSRD	Shifts all bits of ACCD one place to the right. Bit 15 is loaded with zero. The C bit is loaded from the least significant bit of ACCD.	
MUL	Multiplies the 8 bits in accumulator A with the 8 bits in accumulator B to obtain a 16-bit unsigned number in A:B. ACCA contains MSB of result.	$ACCD \leftarrow ACCA * ACCB$
PSHX	The contents of the index register is pushed onto the stack at the address contained in the stack pointer. The stack pointer is decremented by 2.	$\downarrow (IXL), SP \leftarrow (SP) - 1$ $\downarrow (IXH), SP \leftarrow (SP) - 1$
PULX	The index register is pulled from the stack beginning at the current address contained in the stack pointer +1. The stack pointer is incremented by 2 in total.	$SP \leftarrow (SP) + 1; Msp \rightarrow IXH$ $SP \leftarrow (SP) + 1; Msp \rightarrow IXL$
STD	Stores the contents of double accumulator A:B in memory. The contents of ACCD remain unchanged.	$M:M + 1 \leftarrow (ACCD)$
SUBD	Subtracts the contents of M:M + 1 from the contents of double accumulator AB and places the result in ACCD.	$ACCD \leftarrow (ACCD) - (M:M + 1)$

*ACCD is the 16 bit register (A:B) formed by concatenating the A and B accumulators. The A-accumulator is the most significant byte.

tor A (which forms the 8 most significant bits of D) and accumulator B (the 8 least significant bits). Instructions using the double accumulator are LOAD, STORE, ADD 16 bits, SUBTRACT 16 bits, and SHIFT the double accumulator right or left. Three other new instructions manipulate the index register (X) as follows:

1. Push register X (onto the stack).
2. Pull register X (from the stack).
3. Add accumulator B to register X.

The push and pull of the index register enhances the **6801**'s ability to handle *reentrant* as well as *position-independent* code and allows quick temporary storage of the index register.

The CPX (Compare Index Register) instruction is also modified to set all the condition code bits properly, so that *less than* or *greater than* decisions can be made. The instruction ABX (Add Accumulator B to X) greatly reduces the time to modify addresses in the index register. Perhaps the most interesting new instruction for the **6801** is an 8-bit by 8-bit *unsigned multiply* that multiplies registers A and B and provides a 16-bit result in register D, in only 10 μs. This instruction is 20 times faster than an implementation in **6800** software. The multiply instruction, along with the instruction for adding accumulator B to the index register, makes real-time table lookup and interpolation three to four times faster than before.

10-5 ▼ NEW PROCESSING AND CIRCUIT TECHNOLOGIES

Integrated-circuit technology refers to the way that semiconductor gates are deposited on a silicon substrate during the manufacturing process. The **6800** and **6801** μP and MCU were fabricated using NMOS (*n*-channel Metal Oxide on Silicon) technology. The newer MCUs, discussed in the following sections, are manufactured using HMOS, CMOS, or HCMOS technologies.

10-5.1 ▼ HMOS Features

HMOS (High-density NMOS) is an improved version of NMOS technology. It can produce smaller gates capable of higher speeds. Some of the MCUs produced in the last few years use this process. HMOS gates are faster than CMOS, but like NMOS, they consume more power.

10-5.2 ▼ CMOS Features

CMOS (Complementary MOS) is becoming a very popular technology. CMOS gates use both a *p*-channel and an *n*-channel transistor. The combination of these two transistors give CMOS a unique advantage: CMOS gates use very little power. The unique properties of CMOS are increasingly attractive and CMOS is also widely used in digital electronics. Some applications for MCUs are simply not feasible with PMOS, NMOS, or HMOS, primarily because of heat or excessive current requirements.

Maximum power consumption of CMOS parts ranges from $\frac{1}{15}$ to $\frac{1}{200}$ of that of an equivalent HMOS part. The low-power consumption of CMOS is important in several classes of applications:

1. **In portable equipment.** Hand-held and other portable units are operated from self-contained batteries. Battery drain is frequently important in such applications.

2. **For battery backup.** CMOS is appropriate in ac-powered applications when some or all system functions must continue to operate during a power outage. A small, rechargeable battery keeps a CMOS MCU operable.

3. **With storage batteries.** Automotive and telephone equipment operate from larger batteries. Automobile battery drain must be low when the engine is not running. Telephones must operate independently of ac power.

4. **For low heat dissipation.** Packaging constraints sometimes preclude dissipating electronics-generated heat, or the heat is costly to dissipate. In addition, heat directly affects device reliability.

The CMOS technology inherently operates over a wide range of supply voltages, which is to be expected in battery-powered equipment. If line power is available, CMOS allows a lower-cost, loosely regulated supply to be used.

An additional advantage of CMOS is that circuitry is fully *static* (as opposed to dynamic logic, which must be clocked periodically). CMOS MCUs may be operated at any clock rate less than the guaranteed maximum. This feature may be used to conserve additional power, since power consumption decreases with lower clock frequencies. Static operation may also be advantageous during product developments, where the clock is sometimes stopped for testing.

10-5.3 ▼ HCMOS Features

By shrinking the CMOS circuitry in the same way as HMOS, significant increases in performance are realized. This HCMOS technology emerged in 1984 and 1985. It permits a high level of integration on an extremely small chip. At the same time, the CMOS structure gives it low power and the fully static design. It has features that seem to be the best of both worlds. An increasing number of MCUs are being built using this process.

10-5.4 ▼ Electrically Erasable Programmable ROM

The Electrically Erasable Programmable Read-Only Memory (EEPROM) is a recent development in semiconductor technology. Once it is programmed it acts like any ROM, with similar access times, and will retain the program indefinitely or until reprogrammed. The advantage of an EEPROM is that it can be erased electrically. This allows in-circuit programming to permit storage of semipermanent information such as configuring a program for use with a specific terminal, or to allow operators to select their preferred options when running a machine. The disadvantage of the EEPROM is that the programming or erasing is relatively slow in terms of normal IC access times because it takes 10 ms to program each byte. See the manuals listed in Section 10-19 for details of the programming and erasure processes. The EEPROM is being included in a growing number of MCUs. It is used in the **68HC11E9** (Section 10-7.4) and in the **68HC805C8** (Section 10-16.7).

10-5.5 ▼ Added Circuit Features

Because the newer technologies can put more circuitry on an IC chip, the complexity of the μPs themselves has increased and many additional circuit functions have been added. Memory, I/O, and other system components have been placed inside the MCU. These include analog circuits, such as A/D converters and Phase-Locked Loops (PLLs), and many digital devices, such as Timers.

Another area of expansion has been to provide additional digital communications circuits to allow processors to exchange data with external peripheral devices or other processors. This allows engineers to design multiprocessor systems with a variety of specialized MCUs communicating with each other. This communication is provided by the SCI as described in Section 10-13 and by another important addition, the SPI, which is explained in Section 10-14.

10-6 ▼ 68HC11 FAMILY

The **68HC11** ICs make up a family of single-chip MCUs that use HCMOS technology. It is an advanced branch of the **6801** family. The first member of the family, the **68HC11A8,** was introduced in 1985 and reflects the advances in technology that occurred between 1979 (when the **6801** was introduced) and 1985. Over seven years later, new **68HC11** versions continue to provide added features and increased performance.

The **68HC11** CPU core can execute all **6800** and **6801** instructions (using the same machine language op codes) plus more than 90 new instructions. Because there are more than 256 instructions in the **68HC11,** some new instructions are specified by 2-byte op codes.

The **68HC11** CPU offers several new capabilities compared to the earlier **6801** and **6800** CPU. The biggest change is the addition of a second 16-bit index register (Y). Powerful new bit-manipulation instructions are now included, allowing modification of any bit or combination of bits in any memory location in the 64K-byte address space. These are discussed in Section 10-9.3. Exchange instructions allow the contents of either index register to be exchanged with the contents of the 16-bit double accumulator. As in the **6801,** the **68HC11** can use the 16-bit Accumulator D (the concatenation of the 8-bit Accumulators A and B) and several instructions have been upgraded to make full 16-bit arithmetic operations even easier than before.

These instructions are described further in Section 10-9.2 and described in detail in Appendix E. The appendix also includes detailed cycle-by-cycle bus activity and Boolean expressions for condition code bits.

10-6.1 ▼ 68HC11 Family Features

The first member of the **68HC11** family was the **68HC11A8.** The family was built around this IC and it is still being sold. It includes the following features:

Hardware Features

- 8K bytes of ROM
- 512 bytes of EEPROM
- 256 bytes of RAM (all saved during standby)

- An enhanced 16-bit Timer system including:
  - A four-stage programmable prescaler
  - Three Input Capture functions
  - Five Output Compare functions
- An 8-bit Pulse Accumulator circuit
- An enhanced NRZ Serial Communications Interface (SCI)
- A Serial Peripheral Interface (SPI)
- An eight-channel, 8-bit Analog-to-Digital Converter/(ADC)
- A real-time interrupt circuit
- A Computer Operating Properly (COP) watchdog system
- The IC is available in dual in-line or Leaded Chip Carrier Packages (DIP or LCCP)

Software Features

- An enhanced **6800/6801** instruction set
- Eight-bit multiplication and 16-bit division instructions
- Bit manipulation instructions
- A WAIT mode
- A STOP mode

Some of these features, such as the SCI, were used in the **6801,** but others, such as the SPI (see Section 10-14) and COP (Section 10-8.5), are new.

The **68HC11** family of MCUs is composed of many members (see Table 10-3) and is still one of the fastest-growing lines in the world for embedded control applications. The performance is being improved constantly, and as a result, many of today's versions offer 3- and 4-MHz bus speed with added peripheral features.

10-6.2 ▼ 68HC11E9 MCU

One of the most popular general-purpose units currently in use is the **68HC11E9.** The block diagram for the **68HC11E9** is shown in Fig. 10-3. It is basically the same as the **68HC11A8** but more circuitry has been placed on the same-size chip. This provides increased speed and memory size as well as added features. The ROM in the **68HC11E9** is 12K bytes and the RAM is 512 bytes.

10-6.3 ▼ 68HC11 Hardware Configurations

In addition to the advances being made in the circuitry to put more features into a single chip, big strides have been made in the packaging of these chips. With more functions, such as I/O interfaces inside the IC, more pins are needed. Advances in soldering techniques have allowed closer spacing between pins and units designed for through-holes in the Printed Circuit Boards (PCBA) have been replaced with surface-mounting packages. The standard packages used today for all Motorola μC families are shown in Fig. 10-4. The PLCC (Plastic Leadless Chip Carrier) and QFP (Quad Flat Pack) packages are *big*

Table 10-3 **68HC11** Family Members

PART NUMBER	ROM	EEPROM	RAM	EPROM Ve	BUS	COMMENTS
68HC11A7	8K	0	256	HC711E9	3 MHz-Mux	Family Model-No EEPROM
68HC11A8	8K	512	256	HC711E9	3 MHz-Mux	Family Model-3 MHz for 40 to 85 C
68HC11A1	0	512	256		3 MHz-Mux	'A8 with ROM Disabled
68HC11A0		---	256		3 MHz-Mux	'A8 ROM and EEPROM Disabled
68HC11E8	12K	0	512	HC711E9	3 MHz-Mux	4 INPUT CAP-512 RAM-12K ROM
68HC11E9	12K	512	512	HC711E9	3 MHz-Mux	4 INPUT CAP-512 RAM-12K ROM
68HC11E1	0	512	512	N/A	3 MHz-Mux	'E9 with ROM Disabled
68HC11E0	0	---	512		3 MHz-Mux	'E9 with ROM and EEPROMDisabled
68HC11E2	0	2K	256		2 MHz-Mux	'No ROM Part for Expanded Systems
68HC11D0	0	0	192		3 Mhz-Mux	Low-Cost 40-Pin Version, No A/D
68HC11D3	4K		192	HC711D3	3 Mhz-Mux	Low-Cost 40-Pin Version, No A/D
68HC11F1	0	512	1K		4 MHz-Non	High-Performance Non-Mux 68-Pin
68HC11G5			512		2 MHz-Non	10-bit A/D. 4 PWMs, 66I/O
68HC11G7			512		2 MHz-Non	10-bit A/D, 4 PWMs, 66 I/O,
68HC11K0	0	0	768		4 MHz-Mux	
68HC11K1	0	640	768		4 MHz-Mux	
68HC11K3	24K	0	768	HC711K4	4 MHz-Mux	
68HC11K4	24K	640	768	HC711K4	4 MHz-Mux	> 1 Meg mem space PWM, CS, 84-pin
68HC11L0	0	0	512		3 MHz-Mux	
68HC11L5	16K	0	512	HC711L6	3 MHz-Mux	
68HC11L6	16K	512	512	HC711L6	3 MHz-Mux	Like 'E9 with more ROM & I/O, 64/68
68HC11M2			1.25K		4 MHZ Non	A/D, 4-DMA, Math Coprocessor
68HC11N4		640	768		4 MHz Non	PWM, Math, 62-pin
68HC11P2		640	1.0K		4-MHz Non	2 Additional SCI
68HC11						
68HC11						
68HC11						
68HC11						

steps in *miniaturization* of the computer. They take up much less room on the Printed Circuit Board. These packages were not available for the **6800** or **6801** MCUs.

The **68HC11A8** comes in a 48-pin DIP or a 52-lead PLCC (designated FN in Fig. 10-4), and the **68HC11E9** is packaged in a 52-pin PLCC or 64-pin QFP (designated FU). The 64-pin QFP pinout of the 68HC11E9 is shown in Fig. 10-5.

We cannot hope to describe any of these new MCUs in detail. We will, however, try to point out some of the unique features of the **68HC11** family and suggest that students obtain from Motorola the latest **68HC11** Reference Manual (MC68HC11RM/D) for general **68HC11** family information and the Technical Data manual for the specific version selected (MC68HC11E9/D, for example) (see Section 10-19).

10-6.4 ▼ Operating Modes

The **68HC11** has four ways of operating. These are called *operating modes*. Depending on the mode, the **68HC11** can operate as a stand-alone, one-chip controller, or it can serve as a central processor and control external memory and peripheral devices. It also has a bootstrap and a test mode.

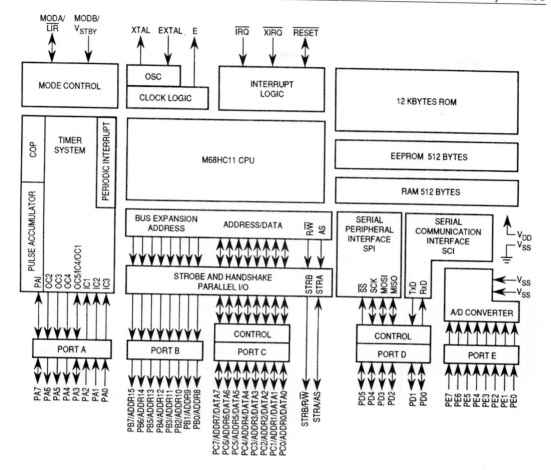

Figure 10-3 68HC11E9 block diagram.

When operating in the stand-alone mode, it can run only limited-size programs that can be contained in the RAM and ROM inside the IC. In this mode most of the external lines or pins are devoted to I/O. For large programs, however, external address and data lines are needed to address added memory or peripheral devices. To keep the package size small, a technique of using the pins in a dual role has been developed. It is called **multiplexing.** When switching to the modes where external devices must be addressed, some of the pins that were used for I/O in the single-chip mode are switched to become *multiplexed* address/data lines.

During RESET, the logic levels on the MODA and MODB pins determine which mode is selected. These are shown in Table 10-4. The modes are described as follows:

1. **Single-Chip Mode.** In single-chip mode the **68HC11** functions as a monolithic MCU without external Address or Data buses. It uses only the internal memory of the MCU. The **68HC11E9,** for example, uses its internal 12K bytes of ROM and 512 bytes of RAM.

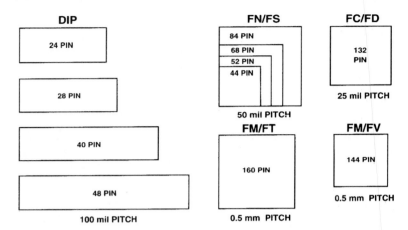

Figure 10-4   Packaging options.

2. **Expanded Multiplexed Mode.** In this mode the **68HC11** has the capability of accessing a full 64K-byte address range by using Port B for the MS byte and the multiplexed lines on Port C as the LS byte of the external address bus (see Section 10-6.6). Some of the newer **68HC11** versions, such as the **68HC11F1** and **68HC11K4,** are in a larger package with more pins and do not need to multiplex the lines. In all **68HC11**s, the on-chip memory and registers and the external peripheral and memory devices share the total 64K range.

3. **Bootstrap Mode.** This a special single-chip mode, as distinguished from the normal single-chip mode. In bootstrap mode, a separate 192 bytes of ROM are enabled as internal memory space at $BF40 through $BFFF. This ROM contains a small boot loader program which, in the case of the **68HC11A8,** reads a user's 256-byte program into on-chip RAM ($0000 through $00FF) via the SCI. After the character for address $00FF is received, control is passed to that program automatically at memory address $0000. In the **68HC11E9** and other newer versions, a variable-length program of up to 512 bytes can be loaded.

   The program that is loaded can do anything that a factory test or user application program can do because protected control bits are accessible in Bootstrap Mode. The Mode Control bits can also be changed while in the Bootstrap Mode, so expanded mode resources are available. For complete information refer to the Motorola Application Note AN1060 listed in Section 10-19.

4. **Test Mode.** This mode is used only for factory testing.

10-6.5 ▼ MCU Configuration Registers

All **68HC11**s include a block of *configuration control registers.* The **68HC11E9** has 64 internal registers in this block, which are used to control the operation of the MCU. They are shown in Fig. 10-6. Some of the registers in the configuration control block control the timer, other peripherals, or the configuration of the **68HC11** itself, but many control the operations of the **68HC11**'s input/output (I/O) ports. These port registers can be divided primarily into three groups:

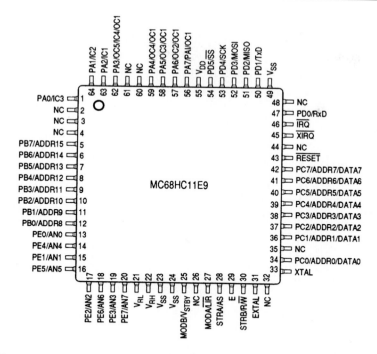

Figure 10-5   Pinouts for the **68HC11E9** in the 64-pin Quad Flat Pack.

1. Data Registers for the I/O ports
2. Data Direction Registers for the ports
3. Control Registers, which determine how the port will operate

10-6.6 ▼ Ports

As seen in Fig. 10-3, there are four 8-bit and one 6-bit port in the **68HC11A8** and **68HC11E9** MCUs. The **68HC11F1** has one more 8-bit port. At least two of these ports serve more than one purpose, depending on the mode configuration of the MCU. A summary of the pins versus function and mode for the **68HC11E9** is shown in Table 10-5. Many pins serve two or more functions. The ports are discussed in the following paragraphs.*

Table 10-4   Operating Mode selection using MODA and MODB

MODB	MODA	Mode Selected
1	0	Single Chip
1	1	Expanded Multiplexed
0	0	Special Bootstrap
0	1	Special Test

*Details of the configuration of these ports can be found in the *M68HC11 Reference Manual* listed in the Section 10-19.

The register block can be remapped to any 4K boundary

Addr	Bit 7	6	5	4	3	2	1	Bit 0	Register
$1000	PA7	PA6	PA5	PA4	PA3	PA2	PA1	PA0	PORTA
$1001									Reserved
$1002	STAF	STAI	CWOM	HNDS	OIN	PLS	EGA	INVB	PIOC
$1003	PC7	PC6	PC5	PC4	PC3	PC2	PC1	PC0	PORTC
$1004	PB7	PB6	PB5	PB4	PB3	PB2	PB1	PB0	PORTB
$1005	PCL7	PCL6	PCL5	PCL4	PCL3	PCL2	PCL1	PCL0	PORTCL
$1006									Reserved
$1007	DDC7	DDC6	DDC5	DDC4	DDC3	DDC2	DDC1	DDC0	DDRC
$1008	0	0	PD5	PD4	PD3	PD2	PD1	PD0	PORTD
$1009	0	0	DDD5	DDD4	DDD3	DDD2	DDD1	DDD0	DDRD
$100A	PE7	PE6	PE5	PE4	PE3	PE2	PE1	PE0	PORTE
$100B	FOC1	FOC2	FOC3	FOC4	FOC5	0	0	0	CFORC
$100C	OC1M7	OC1M6	OC1M5	OC1M4	OC1M3	0	0	0	OC1M
$100D	OC1D7	OC1D6	OC1D5	OC1D4	OC1D3	0	0	0	OC1D
$100E	Bit 15	14	13	12	11	10	9	Bit 8	TCNT (High)
$100F	Bit 7	6	5	4	3	2	1	Bit 0	TCNT (Low)
$1010	Bit 15	14	13	12	11	10	9	Bit 8	TIC1 (High)
$1011	Bit 7	6	5	4	3	2	1	Bit 0	TIC1 (Low)
$1012	Bit 15	14	13	12	11	10	9	Bit 8	TIC2 (High)
$1013	Bit 7	6	5	4	3	2	1	Bit 0	TIC2 (Low)
$1014	Bit 15	14	13	12	11	10	9	Bit 8	TIC3 (High)
$1015	Bit 7	6	5	4	3	2	1	Bit 0	TIC3 (Low)
$1016	Bit 15	14	13	12	11	10	9	Bit 8	TOC1 (High)
$1017	Bit 7	6	5	4	3	2	1	Bit 0	TOC1 (Low)
$1018	Bit 15	14	13	12	11	10	9	Bit 8	TOC2 (High)
$1019	Bit 7	6	5	4	3	2	1	Bit 0	TOC2 (Low)
$101A	Bit 15	14	13	12	11	10	9	Bit 8	TOC3 (High)
$101B	Bit 7	6	5	4	3	2	1	Bit 0	TOC3 (Low)
$101C	Bit 15	14	13	12	11	10	9	Bit 8	TOC4 (High)
$101D	Bit 7	6	5	4	3	2	1	Bit 0	TOC4 (Low)
$101E	Bit 15	14	13	12	11	10	9	Bit 8	TI4/O5 (High)
$101F	Bit 7	6	5	4	3	2	1	Bit 0	TI4/O5 (Low)
$1020	OM2	OL2	OM3	OL3	OM4	OL4	OM5	OL5	TCTL1
$1021	EDG4B	EDG4A	EDG1B	EDG1A	EDG2B	EDG2A	EDG3B	EDG3A	TCTL2

Addr	Bit 7	6	5	4	3	2	1	Bit 0	Register
$1022	OC1I	OC2I	OC3I	OC4I	I4/O5I	IC1I	IC2I	IC3I	TMSK1
$1023	OC1F	OC2F	OC3F	OC4F	I4/O5F	IC1F	IC2F	IC3F	TFLG1
$1024	TOI	RTII	PAOVI	PAII	0	0	PR1	PR0	TMSK2
$1025	TOF	RTIF	PAOVF	PAIF	0	0	0	0	TFLG2
$1026	DDRA7	PAEN	PAMOD	PEDGE	DDRA3	I4/O5	RTR1	RTR0	PACTL
$1027	Bit 7	6	5	4	3	2	1	Bit 0	PACNT
$1028	SPIE	SPE	DWOM	MSTR	CPOL	CPHA	SPR1	SPR0	SPCR
$1029	SPIF	WCOL	0	MODF	0	0	0	0	SPSR
$102A	Bit 7	6	5	4	3	2	1	Bit 0	SPDR
$102B	TCLR	0	SCP1	SCP0	RCKB	SCR2	SCR1	SCR0	BAUD
$102C	R8	T8	0	M	WAKE	0	0	0	SCCR1
$102D	TIE	TCIE	RIE	ILIE	TE	RE	RWU	SBK	SCCR2
$102E	TDRE	TC	RDRF	IDLE	OR	NF	FE	0	SCSR
$102F	R7/T7	R6/T6	R5/T5	R4/T4	R3/T3	R2/T2	R1/T1	R0/T0	SCDR
$1030	CCF	0	SCAN	MULT	CD	CC	CB	CA	ADCTL
$1031	Bit 7	6	5	4	3	2	1	Bit 0	ADR1
$1032	Bit 7	6	5	4	3	2	1	Bit 0	ADR2
$1033	Bit 7	6	5	4	3	2	1	Bit 0	ADR3
$1034	Bit 7	6	5	4	3	2	1	Bit 0	ADR4
$1035	0	0	0	PTCON	BPRT3	BPRT2	BPRT1	BPRT0	BPROT
$1036–8									Reserved
$1039	ADPU	CSEL	IRQE	DLY	CME	0	CR1	CR0	OPTION
$103A	Bit 7	6	5	4	3	2	1	Bit 0	COPRST
$103B	ODD	EVEN	ELAT	BYTE	ROW	ERASE	EELAT	EEPGM	PPROG
$103C	RBOOT	SMOD	MDA	IRVNE	PSEL3	PSEL2	PSEL1	PSEL0	HPRIO
$103D	RAM3	RAM2	RAM1	RAM0	REG3	REG2	REG1	REG0	INIT
$103E	TILOP	0	OCCR	CBYP	DISR	FCM	FCOP	TCON	TEST1
$103F	0	0	0	0	NOSEC	NOCOP	ROMON	EEON	CONFIG

Hardware priority is built into RAM and I/O remapping. Registers have priority over RAM and RAM has priority over ROM. When the 64-byte register block is mapped at the same location as the RAM, a read of the dual-mapped location results in a read of the register. If RAM is relocated on ROM, RAM has priority.

Figure 10-6 Register and control bit assignments.

TABLE 10-5   Port Signal Functions

Port/Bit	Single-Chip and Bootstrap Mode	Expanded Multiplexed and Special Test Mode
PA0	PA0/IC3	
PA1	PA1/IC2	
PA2	PA2/IC1	
PA3	PA3/OC5/IC4/and-or OC1	
PA4	PA4/OC4/and-or OC1	
PA5	PA5/OC3/and-or OC1	
PA6	PA6/OC2/and-or OC1	
PA7	PA7/PAI/and-or OC1	
PB0	PB0	ADDR8
PB1	PB1	ADDR9
PB2	PB2	ADDR10
PB3	PB3	ADDR11
PB4	PB4	ADDR12
PB5	PB5	ADDR13
PB6	PB6	ADDR14
PB7	PB7	ADDR15
PC0	PC0	ADDR0/DATA0
PC1	PC1	ADDR1/DATA1
PC2	PC2	ADDR2/DATA2
PC3	PC3	ADDR3/DATA3
PC4	PC4	ADDR4/DATA4
PC5	PC5	ADDR5/DATA5
PC6	PC6	ADDR6/DATA6
PC7	PC7	ADDR7/DATA7
PD0	PD0/RxD	
PD1	PD1/TxD	
PD2	PD2/MISO	
PD3	PD3/MOSI	
PD4	PD4/SCK	
PD5	PD5/$\overline{SS}$	
—	STRA	AS
—	STRB	R/$\overline{W}$
PE0	PE0/AN0	
PE1	PE1/AN1	
PE2	PE3/AN2	
PE3	PE3/AN3	
PE4	PE4/AN4	
PE5	PE5/AN5	
PE6	PE6/AN6	
PE7	PE7/AN7	

Port A.   The PA0 through PA7 lines for port A are shared with the timer. When RESET has just occurred (see Section 10-8.1), and all the bits in the *port and timer control registers* are 0s, port A is configured as I/O, with three input data lines (PA0, PA1, and PA2), three output data lines (PA4, PA5, and PA6), and two direction switchable lines (PA3 and PA7). All of these lines can be individually reconfigured during initialization by setting bits in PACTL (Port A ConTroL), the timer control register at $1026, to become signal lines for the **Input Capture** or **Output Compare** functions of the timer subsystem (see Sections 10-10.4 and 10-10.5). PA3 and PA7 each have three possible functions, depending on bits in the PACTL register. When acting as I/O they each have a Data Direction bit to control them. The PA3 line can be switched from Output Compare to Input Capture by setting the I4/O5 bit in the PACTL register.

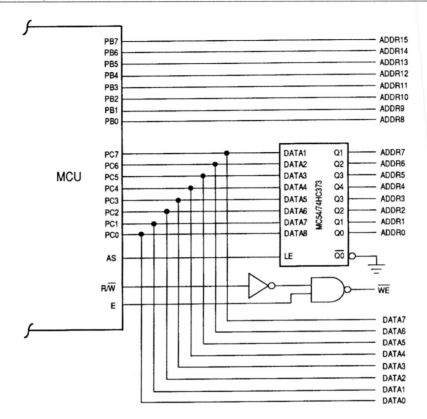

Figure 10-7 Demultiplexing latch.

The Pulse Accumulator uses Port A bit 7 as the PA1 input, but the pin can also be used for a general-purpose I/O line or as an Output Compare signal. The *Pulse Accumulator* is an 8-bit register that can be used to count external events and is incremented by a transition on the PA7 line. The actions of Input Capture, Output Compare, and the Pulse Accumulator are discussed further in Section 10-10.

Port B. This port is strictly for outputs. In *Single-Chip Mode* it functions as an output data port and can be used as a strobed output where the STRB output pin pulses each time port B is written. In Expanded *Multiplexed Mode,* Port B provides the high-order 8 bits of the 16-bit memory address.

Port C. In Single-Chip Mode, port C is an 8-bit I/O port whose direction is controlled by the Port C Data Direction Register. It also has handshake modes where the STRA and STRB lines act as control lines for a simple *strobe* mode (similar to the PIA) or can be enabled in either an input or output handshake mode where data is latched into the PORTCL register.

In Multiplexed Mode, port C carries the lower 8 bits of the address and the memory data. STRA is the address strobe (AS) and STRB is the read/write (R/W) line. These lines are used to *demultiplex* the address and data signals at port C as shown in Fig. 10-7. When AS is HIGH, port C presents the lower 8 bits of the address on its lines, and because the address bits must be preserved for the full memory access cycle, they are latched by the 74HC373 shown in Fig. 10-7. When AS is LOW, port C is the bidirectional data bus.

STRB, when acting as the R/W line, is used to control the external data bus. A low-level (write) on the R/W pin indicates that the data bus output drivers are connected to the external data bus. A high level (read) on this pin indicates that the output drivers are in a high-impedance state and data can be read from the external bus. R/W will stay low during consecutive data bus write cycles, such as in a double-byte store.

EXAMPLE 10-1

What are the functions of pin 42 on the **68HC11E9?**

SOLUTION

Figure 10-5 shows that pin 42 is labeled as PC7/ADDR7/DATA7. This means that it has three uses. In Single-Chip Mode, it functions as I/O bit 7 for Port C. In Expanded Multiplexed Mode, it provides bit 7 of the memory address when AS is high, and contains bit 7 of the data when it is low during the last half of the bus cycle and data is being transferred.

Port D.　This port is independent of the operation mode. Bits 0 through 5 may be used for general-purpose I/O or with the Serial Communications Interface (SCI; see Section 10-13) and the Serial Peripheral Interface (SPI; see Section 10-14). For the SCI, bit 0 of Port D is the receive data input (RxD) and bit 1 is the transmit data output (TxD). Bits 2 through 5 are used by the SPI.

Port E.　This is an input port. Its pins can be used as general-purpose input or as input to the internal A/D converter.

10-6.7 ▼ Memory Maps and Types

The memory maps for each mode for the **68HC11E9** are shown in Fig. 10-8. Memory locations are shown in the shaded areas and the contents are described on the right of the figure. In the Expanded Multiplexed or Special Test operating modes, the memory locations are the same as the Single-Chip operating modes; however, the locations between the shaded areas (designated EXT) are for externally addressed memory and I/O. The map is also controlled by the INIT and CONFIG registers (see Sections 10-6.8 and 10-6.5). Figure 10-8 is the map for the **68HC11E9,** but the specific map for each **68HC11** version is frequently different because of different size and types of memories.

The Special Bootstrap operating mode memory locations are similar to the Single-Chip operating mode memory locations except that a bootstrap program at memory locations $BF00 through $BFFF is enabled. The reset and interrupt vectors are addressed at $BFC0 through $BFFF while in the Special Bootstrap operating mode. These vector addresses are within the 192-byte ROM memory used for the bootstrap program. The memory map for the Special Test operating mode is the same as for the Expanded

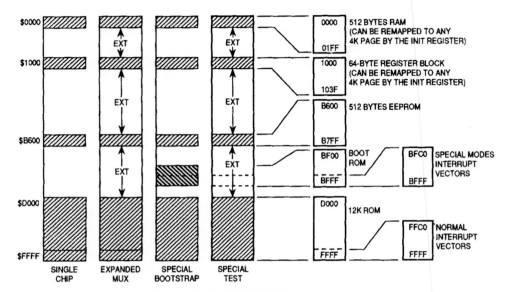

Figure 10-8   68HC11E9 memory map.

Multiplexed operating mode except that the reset and interrupt vectors are located at external memory locations $BFC0 through $BFFF.

10-6.8 ▼ INIT Register

The INIT register (initially located at address $103D) determines the position of the on-chip RAM and of the configuration control register block in the memory map. The most significant 4 bits of the INIT register specifies the upper hexadecimal digit of the RAM address, and controls the position of the RAM in the memory map accordingly. By changing these bits, the RAM can be repositioned to the beginning of any 4K-byte page in the memory map. When the MCU is reset, the INIT register is set to $01. Because the most significant hex digit is then zero ($0), the RAM is initially positioned from $0000 through $01FF.

EXAMPLE 10-2

The 512-byte internal RAM in a **68HC11E9** is to occupy locations $F000 through $F1FF. How can the user make this happen?

SOLUTION

The user can write a byte starting with $F into the INIT register. The four 1s in the highest positions of the INIT register will cause RAM to start at $F000.

The initial position is preferred because it positions the on-chip RAM to include the direct addressing range ($0000 through $00FF). This RAM is normally used to store the user program variables, which frequently require changing. Direct addressing instructions use only 2 bytes to address a location because they assume the upper 8 bits of the address are $00; thus they take up less program memory space and operate faster than the equivalent extended addressing mode instructions.

After reset the 4 least significant bits of the INIT register (REG3 through REG0) are 0001 (or 1 hex), which positions the register block to start at $1000. These 4 bits determine the position of the register block in the map. If these bits are written to 1s ($F), the registers move to $F000 through $F03F. One reason for remapping the RAM and registers would be to make maximum use of an external 32K-byte RAM in the lower half of the memory map.

Users not needing this capability can leave the RAM and I/O registers in their default locations ($0000–$01FF for RAM and $1000–$103F for registers). If the INIT register is to be written, it must be done very early in the program. This is because the INIT register becomes write protected 64 bus cycles after reset and can no longer be written into.

10-7 ▼ MEMORY IN THE 68HC11

All members of the **68HC11** family contain one or more of the following types of memory: RAM, ROM, EPROM, and EEPROM. The amount and memory types depends on the particular family member chosen. In the discussion in this section, the **68HC11E9** will be used as an example, but the user should consult the manual on any particular **68HC11** for more specific details on the memory.

10-7.1 ▼ RAM

The **68HC11E9** has 512 bytes of internal RAM. It is normally located from $0000 to $01FF. The RAM is implemented with static cells and retains its contents during WAIT and STOP modes. The contents can also be retained by supplying a low current backup power source to the MODB/V_{STBY} pin. Then, when using a standby power source, V_{DD} can be removed; however, reset must go low before V_{DD} is removed and remain low until V_{DD} has been restored.

10-7.2 ▼ ROM

In the **68HC11E9** the internal 12K ROM occupies the highest 12K of the memory map ($D000–$FFFF). This ROM is disabled when the ROMON bit in the CONFIG register is clear (see Section 10-7.4). In the Single-Chip operating mode, internal ROM is enabled regardless of the state of the ROMON bit.

As mentioned previously, there is also a 192-byte mask-programmed boot ROM in the **68HC11E9.** This bootstrap program ROM controls the operation of the Special Bootstrap operating mode and is only enabled following reset in the Special Bootstrap operating mode. For more information, refer to Bootstrap Mode in Section 10-6.4 and to Section 10-6.7.

10-7.3 ▼ EPROM

The **68HC711E9** is similar to the **68HC11E9** except that it has 12K bytes of EPROM in place of the ROM. It is available in a *windowed* version for development purposes or in a *One-Time-Programmable* (OTP) package for small production runs. The windowed version can be erased by ultraviolet light and reprogrammed. The EPROM of the **68HC711E9** is located at $D000 through $FFFF, in all modes, if the ROMON bit in the CONFIG register is set to a 1. In the Single-Chip mode the EPROM is enabled regardless of the state of the ROMON bit.

10-7.4 ▼ EEPROM

EEPROM is Electrically Erasable Programmable Read-Only Memory. It can be written to while the μC is in the circuit, but each write cycle takes 10 ms, so this is done at a time when the delay does not interfere with normal program operation. Most versions of the **68HC11** include some EEPROM.

In the **68HC711E9,** the 512 bytes of EEPROM are located at $B600 through $B7FF and have the same read cycle time as that of the internal ROM. The write (or programming) mechanism for the EEPROM is controlled by bits in the PPROG and BPROT registers. The CONFIG register is also implemented with EEPROM cells and is programmed using the same procedures as those used for programming the on-chip EEPROM. It contains the ROMON and EEON bits, which enable or disable these memories. For programming information, refer to the M68HC11E9/D Technical Data Manual listed in Section 10-19.

10-8 ▼ RESETS AND INTERRUPTS IN THE 68HC11

Resets and interrupts are often discussed together because they are similar functions. The **6800** has four possible sources of interrupts, but the **68HC11** has 21 and requires the same number of interrupt vectors. The interrupt vectors go from $FFD6 to $FFFF. Most of the sources of interrupts can be disabled by either the I bit in the CCR or by changing a bit that applies specifically to the source of the interrupts. Six interrupt sources are not maskable, however, and are listed in the order that they are acted on (priority) by the hardware:

1. Power-On Reset (POR) or the RESET pin
2. Clock Monitor reset
3. Computer-Operating-Properly (COP) Watchdog reset
4. XIRQ interrupt
5. Illegal Op code interrupt
6. SoftWare Interrupt (SWI)

Although not maskable, the Clock Monitor and COP resets can be disabled by bits in the configuration registers. This list shows that there are four possible sources of reset: POR, RESET, Clock Monitor, and COP. The first two share the normal reset vector. The reset vectors are shown in Table 10-6 along with three interrupts that also have their own vectors.

TABLE 10-6   Reset and Nonmaskable Interrupt Vectors

	NORMAL MODE VECTOR	SPECIAL TEST OR BOOTSTRAP
	Reset Vectors	
POR or RESET pin	$FFFE, FFFF	$BFFE, BFFF
Clock Monitor Failure	$FFFC, FFFD	$BFFC, BFFD
COP Watchdog Timeout	$FFFA, FFFB	$BFFA, BFFB
	Nonmaskable Interrupt Vectors	
XIRQ Interrupt	$FFF4, FFF5	
Ilegal op code Interrupt	$FFF8, FFF9	
Software Interrupt	$FFF6, FFF7	

10-8.1 ▼ Power-On Reset

When a reset occurs, it causes the **68HC11** to clear most of its registers and start executing its ROM-based initialization program. The **68HC11**s reset and interrupt operations follow the same rules as those described for the **6800.**

A positive transition of the power supply voltage, V_{DD}, generates a power-on reset (POR), which is different than other resets because it invokes a 4064 internal clock cycle delay (t_{cyc}), after the oscillator becomes active, to allow the clock generator to stabilize.

It is important to protect the MCU during power transitions. Most **68HC11** systems need an external circuit that holds the RESET pin low whenever V_{DD} is below the minimum operating level. Such an external RESET circuit is shown in Fig. 10-9. The mini-

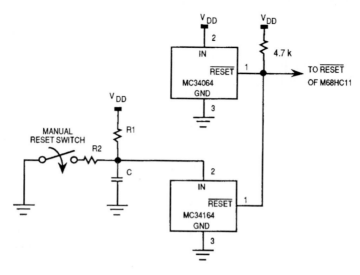

Figure 10-9   External reset circuit.

mum circuit consisting of the **MC34064** and the 4.7K pull-up resistor shown in the upper part of Fig. 10-9 is suggested. The **MC34064** is an undervoltage-sensing IC, which is manufactured by Motorola and others for this purpose. It holds RESET low until the power supply voltage returns to normal. The manual reset circuit shown in the lower part of Fig. 10-9 is optional. The **MC34164** is also an undervoltage sensor but with slightly different specifications.

As explained in Section 10-6.4, levels on the MODA and MODB pins at RESET determine the operating mode of the **68HC11.** After RESET these pins take on a different function. The MODA pin becomes an output signal called the *Load Instruction Register* (LIR). It goes LOW during the first E clock of each instruction and remains LOW for the duration of that cycle to indicate an op code fetch. During software debugging it is sometimes necessary to know when the op code fetches are occurring. The MODB pin becomes a source of standby power (V_{stby}) for the on-board RAM. If a small battery is connected to MODB, it will preserve the contents of the internal RAM when power to the **68HC11** is removed.

The sources of interrupts are:

1. **Instruction interrupts.** These include both SWI and Illegal op code interrupt. The SWI is identical to the SWI in the **6800.** It cannot be masked off.

2. **Externally generated interrupts.** See Section 10-8.2.

3. **Internally generated interrupts.** See Section 10-8.3.

10-8.2 ▼ External Interrupts

An external interrupt is caused when a system's peripheral device places a low level on either the IRQ or XIRQ pin. The IRQ pin on the **68HC11** is similar to the **6801** and is set for level sensitive triggering during reset. It can be programmed after reset to be either level sensitive or negative edge sensitive by a bit in the OPTION register. The IRQ pin is designed for use in a *wired-OR* circuit, so several external devices can activate it and it therefore requires an external resistor to V_{DD}.

The XIRQ pin is for requesting asynchronous nonmaskable interrupts. It is an improved version of the NMI available on the **6800.** During reset, the X bit of the Condition Code Register (CCR) is set and the XIRQ interrupt is masked to preclude interrupts on this line until μP operation is stabilized. The XIRQ is a level-sensitive pin and requires an external resistor to V_{DD}.

The X interrupt mask bit of the CCR is set only by hardware (RESET or XIRQ acknowledge). After minimum system initialization, the X bit may be cleared by a TAP instruction, thus enabling XIRQ interrupts. Thereafter, software cannot set the X bit and XIRQ functions as an NMI. The X bit is also set when an interrupt appears on the XIRQ line, so the interrupt service routine will not be interrupted, but the RTI (return from interrupt) instruction restores the X and I bits to their preinterrupt request status.

The STOP instruction effectively stops the **68HC11** from executing instructions. It puts the **68HC11** in a comatose state, where it cannot function and consumes little power. The STOP DISABLE bit (S) in the CCR is set to disable the STOP instruction. An interrupt will cause the μP to resume normal operation. The S bit is program controlled. The STOP instruction is treated as a NOP (no operation) if the S bit is set.

10-8.3 ▼ Internal Interrupts

There are also many internal interrupts that occur in the **68HC11.** These can be caused by the Pulse Accumulator register overflowing, or by timer Input Capture or Output Compare functions as well as communication interrupts. The **68HC11** has 15 additional vectors which point to its various service routines.

10-8.4 ▼ Clock Monitor Reset

The Clock Monitor is used as a backup for the COP system because the COP needs a clock to function. The Clock Monitor system can detect clock failures not detected by the COP system. If no MPU clock edges are detected during a period of time, the clock monitor can cause an interrupt. This function is enabled or disabled by the CME control bit in the OPTION register. A reset will restore the MCU system to normal operation.

10-8.5 ▼ Computer-Operating-Properly Function

The *Computer-Operating-Properly* (COP) function has been developed to ascertain that a computer is functioning properly. Its purpose is to reset the system automatically if the computer stops executing its normal program for any reason.

The COP usually is implemented by requiring that the program reset a "Watchdog" counter before it reaches a limit or before the allotted time expires. This counter is not decremented by processor action but by direct clock pulses. If the program does not reset this counter periodically, the COP counter will expire and cause an interrupt that begins execution of a service routine (which restarts the regular program).

10-9 ▼ PROGRAMMING CONSIDERATIONS FOR THE 68HC11

The instruction set for the **68HC11** is a superset of the **6800.** It contains all the **6800** instructions and many additional instructions that enhance the operation of the **68HC11.** Operation of these additional instructions is discussed in this section.

10-9.1 ▼ CPU Registers

The Programming Model of the **68HC11** CPU registers, shown in Fig. 10-10, is identical to that of the **6801** except for the additional Y register and the top 2 bits of the Condition Code Register. The stack operation (pointer writes and then decrements) and the interrupt stacking order are the same, except for the additional 2 bytes needed for the Y register. These differences do not affect execution of either **6800** or **6801** programs.

The 16-bit Y index register is used with indexed mode instructions almost the same as the X register. However, all instructions using the Y register require an extra byte of machine code and an extra cycle of execution time since they are 2-byte op codes.

10-9.2 ▼ 68HC11 Instruction Set

A complete list of **68HC11** instructions is given in Appendix E. It shows that the **68HC11** instructions associated with the Y register have a prebyte of 18 and a second op code byte that is the same as the one used for the X register. For example, the op code for

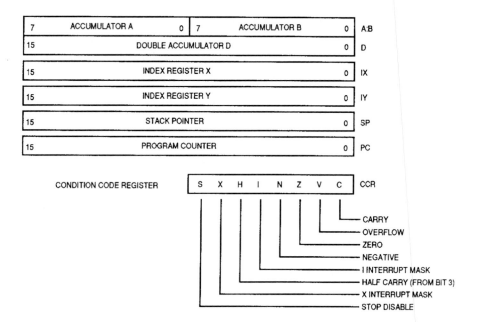

Figure 10-10 68HC11 programming model.

ABX is 3A, and the code for ABY is 18 3A. It should also be noted that almost every instruction type has an additional *indexed with Y* instruction that has the same op code (as indexed with X) except that it also takes a prebyte. For example, the instruction ANDA 0,X codes as A4 00, while the instruction ANDA 0,Y codes as 18 A4 00. This alone accounts for 52 of the new instructions.

10-9.3 ▼ Bit Manipulation Instructions

Another new group of instructions that have been added to the basic **68HC11** core are identified as *Bit-Manipulation* instructions. The implementation for the **68HC11** family is described briefly here.

Bit Manipulation is an important and often used function in MCUs. Because many of the I/O lines are frequently connected to indicators or electrically activating devices, such as solenoids or transistor switching circuits, a large percentage of the program is devoted to sensing or turning these individual devices ON or OFF. These instructions provide this ability with considerably fewer bytes of machine code. Bit-manipulation instructions permit the program to:

1. Set a bit
2. Clear a bit
3. Branch on BIT SET
4. Branch on BIT CLEAR

The **BIT SET/CLEAR** mode allows individual memory and I/O bits to be set or cleared under program control (ROM, obviously, can not be changed). The **BIT TEST AND BRANCH** mode allows any bit in memory to be tested and, depending on the instruction, to execute a branch conditionally as a result. For these instructions, the memory address location (containing the bit to be modified) is specified either as a direct address in the location following the op code, or as an indexed address. With the direct addressing mode, only the first 256 memory locations can be addressed, but the indexed instructions (see Example 10-4) permit access to any location in memory.

The BIT SET and BIT CLEAR instructions operate on any individual bit in the word accessed, whether the memory is RAM or I/O. Because the **6800** family uses memory-mapped I/O, the bit instructions can operate directly on the I/O registers, thus directly controlling the I/O pins. The BSET and BCLR instructions read the operand, manipulate the selected bits within the operand, and write the result back to the operand address. Some care is required when read–modify–write instructions such as these are used on I/O and control register locations because the physical location read is not always the same as the location written.

The actual bit or bits to be modified within the byte is (are) specified by a *mask* byte. The bits to be modified in the memory location correspond to the 1s in the mask byte. The BIT SET and CLEAR instructions are 3-byte instructions (except for those using the Y register); 1 (or 2) bytes for the op code, another to address the byte that contains the bit(s) of interest, and one to specify which bit(s) are to be modified.

EXAMPLE 10-3

Compare the **68HC11** instructions necessary to clear bits 2 and 3 of a flag that is located at an offset of 3 from $C300 with the **6800** or **6801** instructions required. Assume that $C303 contains $CF.

SOLUTION

The programs are shown in Fig. 10-11. Note that the programs are the same except that one instruction of Fig. 10-11a (at $103) replaces the three instructions needed in Fig. 10-11b. The **68HC11** Instruction Set in Appendix E shows the BCLR Boolean instruction operation. This is interpreted as *ANDing* the value in memory at $C303 ($CF), with the complement of the *mask* byte (06 = $F9) to get a new memory value of $C9.

In the **68HC11** instructions of Fig. 10-11a, the $1D is the op code, and 03 is the offset to be added to the index register that locates the byte to be modified. The 06 defines the bits (2 and 3) to be cleared. Although not shown, the value in location $C303 would then be $C9.

Figure 10-11a shows that the BCLR instruction takes only 3 bytes, compared to 6 bytes for the same function using conventional instructions (Fig. 10-11b). (The index register must be initialized properly in both cases.) A similar savings will result for the BRSET, BRCLR, and BSET instructions. This shows the byte-efficiency comparison that is important in MCUs with their limited-size ROMs.

```
0100  CE  C3  00        LDX    #$C300      Set index register
0103  1D  03  06        BCLR   3,X 6       Clear bits 2 & 3

C300                    FCB    ...
C301                    FCB    ...
C302                    FCB    ...
C303                    FCB    $CF
```

           C300= X-register contents (added to offset)

(a)

```
0103  A6  03            LDAA   3,X         Get present status
0105  84  FB            ANDA   #$F9        Clear bits 2 & 3
0107  A7  03            STAA   3,X         Send to OUT
```

(b)

FIGURE 10-11 Programs for Example 10-3: (a) **68HC11** instructions;
(b) **6800** or **6801** instructions.

EXAMPLE 10-4

Illustrate the preferred **68HC11** instruction needed to turn ON lines 2 and 3 of the B side of a PIA located at $4000.

SOLUTION

Because the address of the PIA is not in the direct addressing range, an indexed BIT-SET instruction is used, as shown in Fig. 10-12. The example uses a BSET indexed Y instruction at $104 to illustrate a 4-byte example. Bytes 1 and 2 are the op code, and byte 3 is the offset (pointing to $4002). Byte 4 is the mask byte, which according to the *operation* formula from Appendix E is *ORed* with the existing data at this location, to set bits 2 and 3 high (to a "1"). If the value at $4002 were $C9, for example, it would become $CF after this instruction was executed.

```
       4000         PIAB   EQU    $4000
...                        ...    .....
100  18  CE  40  00        LDY    #PIAB
104  18  1C  02  06        BSET   02,Y 06         SET bits 2 & 3
```

Figure 10-12 Indexed BIT-SET Instruction for Example 10-4

10-9.4 ▼ Bit Test and Branch Addressing Mode Instructions

The BRSET (BRanch if bit SET) and BRCLR (BRanch if bit CLeaR) instructions test a bit in a location and cause the program to branch depending on whether the bit is set or clear. They use the same addressing and masking as described for the Bit Set or Clear instructions. BRSET or BRCLR instruction consists of 4 bytes as follows:

1. The op code
2. The offset from the index register
3. The mask to indicate which bit is being tested
4. The branch offset, which determines where the instruction will branch to

---

EXAMPLE 10-5

Write a routine to add one value or another to a number, depending on whether an external signal occurs.

SOLUTION

Figure 10-13 is part of a listing of a Timer example in the MC68HC11RM/D Reference Manual for a **68HC11** system. You will note that the X register is initialized to $1000, which is the start address of the Register Block, and then the BRCLR instruction that uses the X is executed. TCTL1 is a register at an offset of $20 in the register block for this system. The binary number %01000000 is used so that it is easy to see which bit in the mask is selected. ADDLO ($C2CE) is the address that the program goes to if the ANDing of the bits results in 0.

10-10 ▼ TIMING SYSTEM ON THE 68HC11

All **68HC11**s have a timing subsystem, which allows them to determine the time taken by an external event, such as when a switch is operated or the duration of a digital pulse. It also allows the **68HC11** to cause events, such as the change of level on an output line, to occur at a specific time.

The timing system inside a **68HC11** has five clock divider chains. The main clock divider chain includes a 16-bit free-running counter, which is incremented by every cycle of the system clock. The counter can be operated at a slower rate by using a *prescaler* that divides the system clock by 1, 4, 8, or 16.* Taps off this main clocking chain drive circuitry that generates the slower clocks used by the Pulse Accumulator, the real-time interrupt (RTI), and the Computer Operating Properly (COP) watchdog subsystems.

---

*The prescale factor is normally 1. It can be changed by changing 2 bits in the TMSK2 register at $1024, but these bits must be changed during the first 64 cycles after reset.

```
                    * SV70C2 - Output Compare 2 service routine
c2c2 ce 10 00    [3] SV70C2 LDX   #REGBAS      Point to register block
c2C5 1f 20 40 05 [7]         BRCLR TCTL1,X %01000000 ADDLO  Which half of cyc?
c2c9 fc dO 21    [5]         LDD   OFFHI        High part so add OFFHI to OC2
c2cc 20 03       [3]         BRA   UPOC2
c2ce fc dO 23    [5] ADDLO   LDD   OFFLO        Low part so add OFFLO to OC2
c2d1 e3 18       [6] UPOC2   ADDD  TOC2,X       Add to last compare value
c2d3 ed 18       [5]         STD   TOC2,X       Update OC2 (Schedule next
  edge)
c2dS a6 20       [4]         LDAA  TCTL1, X     Change OL2 to qetup next edge
c2d7 88 40       [2]         EORA  #%01000000   Inverts OL2 bit
c2d9 a7 20       [4]         STAA  TCTL1,X      Update control register
c2db 1d 23 bf    [7]         BCLR  TFLG1,X $BF  Clear OC2F
c2de 3b          [12]        RTI * * Return from OC2 service **
                    *
```

Figure 10-13 Interrupt service routine showing use of BRCLR instruction.

EXAMPLE 10-6

How often is the timer counter incremented if the system clock for the **68HC11** is 2 MHz and the prescale factor is:

(a) 1

(b) 8

SOLUTION

(a) If the prescale factor is 1, the clock increments the counter directly. It will be incremented at a 2-MHz rate or once every 0.5 μs.

(b) If the prescale factor is 8, the clock will be slowed down by this factor and will increment the clock once every 4 μs.

10-10.1 ▼ TCNT Register

The count in the free-running counter can be accessed at locations $100E and $100F. This is the 16-bit TCNT Register that is in the register control block. It is *read only*. It cannot be changed by writing into it, but it is incremented by each cycle of the clock. All main timer system activities are referenced to this free-running counter. The counter begins incrementing from $0000 as the MCU comes out of reset, and continues to the maximum count, $FFFF. Then the counter rolls over to $0000, sets an overflow flag, and continues to increment. As long as the MCU is running in a normal operating mode, there is no way to reset, change, or interrupt the counting.

10-10.2 ▼ Timer Implementation

The main timer block diagram is shown in Fig. 10-14. The capture/compare subsystem is a major feature of the timer implementation. It has three Input Capture channels (see Section 10-8.4, four Output Compare channels (see Section 10-8.5), and one channel that can be selected to perform either Input Capture or Output Compare. Each of the three Input Capture functions has its own 16-bit input capture register (time capture latch), and each of the Output Compare functions has its own 16-bit compare register. All timer functions, including the timer overflow and Real-Time Interrupt (RTI), have their own interrupt controls and separate interrupt vectors.

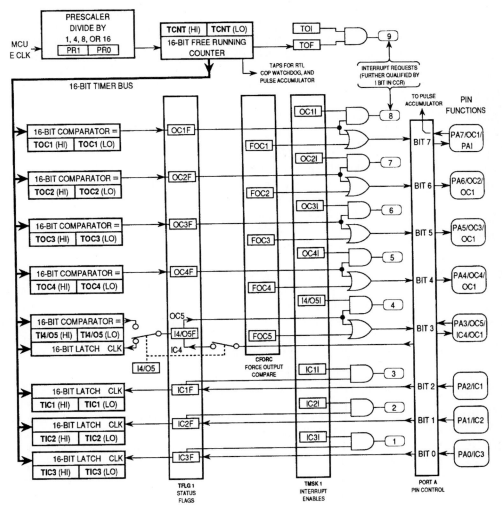

Figure 10-14 Capture/Compare block diagram.

10-10.3 ▼ Pulse Accumulator

Each **68HC11** timing subsystem includes a Pulse Accumulator, which has an 8-bit counter and edge select logic. The Pulse Accumulator can operate in either the event counting or gated time accumulation modes. In the event counting mode, the Pulse Accumulator's 8-bit counter increments when a specified edge is detected on an input signal connected to pin PA7. During the gated time accumulation mode, an internal clock source increments the 8-bit counter while this input signal has a predetermined logic level. Flags can be set whenever the Pulse Accumulator is incremented or when it rolls over. The **68HC11** can also be configured to interrupt whenever these flags are set.

10-10.4 ▼ Input Capture

The Input-Capture (IC) function records the time an external event occurs by latching the value of the free-running counter when a selected edge is detected at the associated timer input pin. Software can store latched values and use them to compute the periodicity and duration of events. For example, by storing the times of successive edges of an incoming signal, software can determine the period and pulse width of a signal. To measure period, two successive edges of the same polarity are captured. To measure pulse width, two alternate polarity edges are captured.

10-10.5 ▼ Output Compare

The Output-Compare (OC) function is used to raise or lower the voltage on an output pin at a specific time when the 16-bit counter reaches a specified value. For each of the five Output Compare functions, there is a separate 16-bit compare register and a dedicated 16-bit comparator. The value in the compare register is compared to the value of the free-running counter on every bus cycle. When they match, an output-compare status flag is set, and automatic pin actions for that output compare function are triggered.

To produce a pulse of a specific duration, a value is written to the output-compare register that represents the time the leading edge of the pulse is to occur. The output-compare circuit is configured to set the appropriate output either high or low, depending on the polarity of the pulse being produced. After a match occurs, the output-compare register is reprogrammed to change the output pin back to its inactive level at the next match. A value representing the width of the pulse is added to the original value and then written to the output-compare register. Because the pin state changes occur at specific values of the free-running counter, the pulse width can be controlled accurately at the resolution of the free-running counter, independent of software latencies. To generate an output signal of a specific frequency and duty cycle, this pulse-generating procedure is repeated.

There are four 16-bit read/write output-compare registers: TOC1, TOC2, TOC3, and TOC4, and the TI4/O5 register, which functions under software control as either IC4 or OC5. Each of the OC registers is set to $FFFF on reset. A value written to an OC register is compared to the free-running counter value during each E-clock cycle. If a match is found, the particular output-compare flag is set in timer interrupt flag 1 register (TFLG1). If that particular interrupt is enabled in the timer interrupt mask 1 register

(TMSK1), an interrupt is generated. In addition to an interrupt, a specified action can be initiated at one or more timer output pins. For complete details on the use of these functions, the student should refer to the technical manual listed in Section 10-19.

EXAMPLE 10-7

One of a system's requirements is that PB0 go high 10 ms after a program is entered. Describe how the program and hardware can do this. Assume that the E clock is running at 1 µs.

SOLUTION

This example requires a very simple program that uses an Output Compare to control a software time delay. For simplicity, this example uses polled mode and does not cause any automatic pin changes as the result of the Output Compare. The program generates a 10 ms delay such as the user might utilize to time an EEPROM program or erase operation; however, instead of actually programming EEPROM, it will just produce a pulse on an output port pin so the results can be studied on an oscilloscope. Output-compare functions can also cause automatic pin changes and generate interrupt requests. A partial listing of the program for this example is shown in Fig. 10-15.

    This example is only intended to show the most basic use of an output-compare function. It is not intended to be an especially efficient way to delay a fixed period of time. The following three instructions are a simple way to delay if no other tasks are to be performed during the delay:

```
cld9 18 ce 16 4e  [4]       LDY  #5710   5710*(7~/loop) =
                                         about 20 ms
cldd 18 09        [4] DLP1 DEY           Top of software
                                         delay loop
cldf 26 fc        [3]       BNE  DLP1    Loop until Y
                                         is zero
```

By contrast, an output compare in interrupt-driven mode has the advantage of allowing the user to perform other tasks while waiting for the delay.*

EXAMPLE 10-8

The time between a pulse on line 1 and a pulse on line 2 is critical. Show how to measure it using the **68HC11** Input Capture function.

---

*Examples of this type can be found in *The 68HC11 Microcontroller,* by J. D. Greenfield, published by Saunders College Publishing, Philadelphia, 1992.

SOLUTION

Line 1 can be connected to PA0, which uses Input Capture register 1. It will then capture the time of the pulse edge on line 1. Similarly, line 2 can be connected to a second Input Capture pin with its register. After the two times have been captured, a software routine can be used by the **68HC11** μP to compute the pulse width. If the appropriate bit is set in the TMSK1 register, it will generate an interrupt to the μP to inform it that new data is available.

10-10.6 ▼ Real-Time Interrupt

The **68HC11** can be set to interrupt at specific time intervals. This is called a *Real-Time Interrupt* (RTI). If invoked, RTI will interrupt the μP once every 4 to 32 ms. The exact time interval is determined by 2 bits in the PACTL register at $1026 and the frequency of the E clock.

10-11 ▼ OTHER PERIPHERAL FUNCTIONS

Table 10-3 shows the hardware configuration of each of the various versions of the **68HC11** family. They all have the same basic μP, but they differ in the peripherals they include. Some of the peripherals inside a **68HC11** MCU include:

```
clbc ce 10 00    [3] INZA  LDX #REGBAS        Point to register block
clbf 86 80       [2]       LDAA #$80
clc1 a7 23       [4]       STAA TFLG1,X        Clear any pending OC1F flag
clc3 6f 04       [6]       CLR PORTB,X         Initialize port B to zero
clc5 86 01       [2] TOP4A LDAA #1            Top of Ex10-4a
clc7 a7 04       [4]       STAA PORTB,X        Set LSB of port B
                 *
           * This is where the 10 ms delay part actually start
clc9 ec 0e       [5]       LDD TCNT,X          Get current timer count
clcb c3 4e 20    [4]       ADDD #20000         What will count be in 10
ms?
clce ed 16       [5]       STD TOC1,X          Set OC1 to trigger then
cld0 1f 23 80fc  [7] LP1   BRCLR TFLG1,X       $80 LP1 Loop here till
OC1F=
                 *
           * Delay is actually done here; rest is just support
cld4 1d 23 7f    [7]       BCLR TFLG1,X $7F Clear OC1F
cld7 6f 04       [6]       CLR PORTB,X         Clear PB0 pin
cld9 18 ce 164e  [4]       LDY #5710          5710*(7/loop)= about 20 ms
cldd 18 09       [4] DLP1  DEY                 Top of software delay loop
cldf 26 fc       [3]       BNE DLP1            Loop 'till Y is zero
cle1 20 e2       [3]       BRA TOP4A           Repeat for O-scope
```

- Analog-to-Digital Converters (ADC)
- An asynchronous (NRZ) Serial Communications Interface (SCI)
- A synchronous Serial Peripheral Interface (SPI)
- Programmable Chip Selects
- Timers
- A Computer-Operating-Properly (COP) watchdog system
- Direct Memory Access channels (DMA)
- Pulse-Width Modulation outputs (PWM)
- An 8-bit Pulse Accumulator
- A 16-bit on-chip Math Coprocessor

The most important of these are discussed in the following paragraphs.

10-12 ▼ ANALOG-TO-DIGITAL CONVERSION

Many versions of the **68HC11** MCU family, including the **68HC11A8** and **68HC11E9**, have A/D converters. These allow the user to send analog signals into the **68HC11** and have them digitized so that they can be acted upon by the μP.

As seen in the block diagram (Fig. 10-3), the A/D system is a separate subsystem that uses port E. A separate low-noise reference voltage is provided on the V_{RH} and V_{RL} pins. These pins establish the range of analog voltages to be converted to digital.

This subsystem uses an all-capacitive charge redistribution technique to convert analog signals to digital values. Each of the eight input lines can be connected to separate and distinct sources of signals, such as pressure or temperature sensors. The A/D system is an eight-channel, 8-bit, multiplexed-input converter. It does not require external sample and hold circuits because of the charge redistribution technique used.

The routing of the signal lines to the chip (see Section 13-8.2) and the software calculations require different methods than those used for digital signals. The internal details of this subsystem is the subject of a separate section in the Motorola manuals and will not be covered here. See the MC68HC11E9/D Technical Data or MC68HC11RM/D Reference Manuals described in Section 10-19.

10-13 ▼ SERIAL COMMUNICATIONS INTERFACE

The **68HC11** contains a Serial Communications Interface (SCI), which provides a full-duplex communications capability. It uses the industry standard asynchronous NRZ data format, which is also used by the ACIA (see Section 8-6) and other Universal Asynchronous Receive/Transmit (UART) peripheral chips. The NRZ interface is used to communicate with standard data terminals or Personal Computers.

The SCI in the **68HC11** is compatible with other SCI implementations on other Motorola MCUs as well as with standard data terminals. With the introduction of the **68HC11**s, however, a second communications function, the SPI interface, was incorporated with the capability for high-speed synchronous serial communications to peripherals or other MCUs (located on the same printed circuit board).

10-13.1 ▼ SCI Wake-up Feature

One of the features of the SCI receiver circuits is the ability to enter a temporary standby or *sleep* mode used to ignore messages intended for other receivers. This allows several MCUs to be connected together using the SCI ports. These serial I/O connections can be routed through modems if desired.

If one processor sends a message, all the other processors can receive it. The message may be addressed to only one or two of the processors, however, and the other processors will ignore it.

The software protocol must identify the desired addressee(s) at the beginning of a message, to permit other MCUs to ignore the messages not directed to them. For those μPs that are not addressed, all further SCI signal processing is inhibited until the *wake-up feature* is invoked either by the data line returning to the idle state, or if selected by the WAKE control bit in SCCR1, by the MSB signal (address mark).

An SCI message starts after a string of at least 11 consecutive 1s. This string of 1s causes all processors to wake up and pay attention to the characters on the line. The first character after the string of 1s is an address. Those MCUs that are addressed will receive the message. The other MCUs will "remain asleep" by ignoring the message until another string of 1s wakes them up. Software for the transmitter must provide for the required idle string between consecutive messages and prevent it from occurring within messages.

EXAMPLE 10-9

Describe a software routine to insert a string of 1s between messages.

SOLUTION

Perhaps the simplest way is to have the μP jump to a time delay routine (see Section 9-9) after each message is transmitted. This will cause the line to be idle, or transmitting 1s, while the μP is waiting for the time delay to expire. Of course, the delay of the loop should be at least as long as the time required to transmit 11 bits.

10-13.2 ▼ SCI Programmable Options

The following features of the SCI are programmable:

- Baud rate
- Wake-up feature, enabled or disabled
- Interrupt requests, enabled individually for transmitter and receiver
- 8- or 9-bit format
- WAKE bit selects one of two wake-up methods

EXAMPLE 10-10

Show how to connect the SCI to an RS232C interface to a data terminal (or a PC emulating one).

SOLUTION

The example discussed here uses the two SCI I/O lines from port D as the serial input and output lines. This is shown in Fig. 10-16a, which is a portion of the schematic diagram of the RS232 interface of the 68HC11EVBU Evaluation Board (see Section 11-5.3). This interface uses an **MC145407** RS232 Receiver/Driver chip whose internal gates are shown in Fig. 10-16 b. This is a commonly used part for this purpose because it is CMOS and eliminates the need for a −12 V power supply. (It has built-in voltage-doubler circuitry that requires only +5 V.)

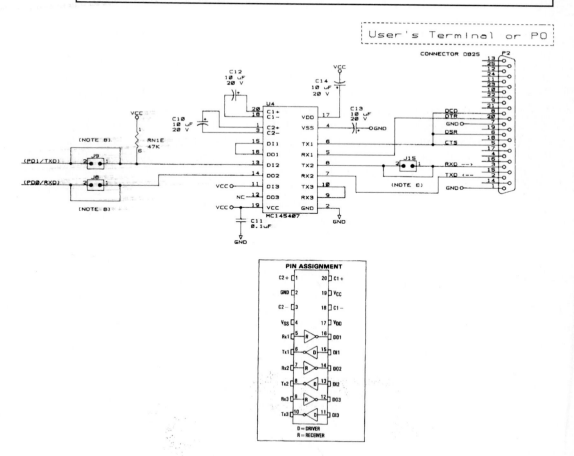

Figure 10-16 SCI/RS232 interface.

Table 10-7 Baud Rate Prescale Selects

SCP[1:0]	Divide Internal Clock By	Crystal Frequency in MHz			
		4.0 MHz (Baud)	8.0 MHz (Baud)	10.0 MHz (Baud)	12.0 MHz (Baud)
0 0	1	62.50 K	125.0 K	156.25 K	187.50 K
0 1	3	20.83 K	41.67 K	52.08 K	62.50 K
1 0	4	15.625 K	31.25 K	38.4 K	46.88 K
1 1	13	4800	9600	12.02 K	14.42 K

10-13.3 ▼ SCI Registers

The SCI system in the **68HC11**s is configured and controlled by five registers (BAUD, SCCR1, SCCR2, SCSR, and SCDR). These registers are located in the register block at addresses \$102B through \$102F, as shown in Figure 10-6. The user is referred to the Motorola Reference Manual (M68HC11RM/AD) for details.

10-13.4 ▼ Baud Rate Register

The Baud Rate Register at \$102B controls the SCI bit rate. Normally, this register is written once during initialization to set the baud rate for the SCI system. The receiver and transmitter use the same rate, which is derived from the MCU bus rate clock. A two-stage divider is used to develop customary baud rates from normal MCU crystal frequencies. Bits SCP1 and SCP0 determine the Prescaler division ratio, and bits SCR0, SCR1, and SCR2 select one of the standard baud rates. Bit 6 is not used. The other 2 active bits are used for factory testing.

The implementation shown in Example 10-10 requires software selection of the proper baud rate by programming the **68HC11**'s Baud Register as shown in Tables 10-7 and 10-8 (see the register at \$102B in Fig. 10-6). Table 10-7 shows the prescale bit selection required to adjust for the crystal frequency used, and Table 10-8 shows the required register bit values to obtain the standard baud rates of 300, 1200, 2400, 4800, and 9600. The baud rates are determined by the divide-down internal logic in the MCU, and therefore the crystal frequency (f_{osc}) must be within 5% of the designated frequencies. This is the maximum tolerance for a typical RS232 serial data link. The SCI is used in a number of other MCUs, such as in the **68HC05** family.

Table 10-8 Baud Rate Selects

SCR[2:0]	Divide Prescaler By	Highest Baud Rate (Prescaler Output from Previous Table)		
		4800	9600	38.4 K
0 0 0	1	4800	9600	38.4 K
0 0 1	2	2400	4800	19.2 K
0 1 0	4	1200	2400	9600
0 1 1	8	600	1200	4800
1 0 0	16	300	600	2400
1 0 1	32	150	300	1200
1 1 0	64	—	150	600
1 1 1	128	—	—	300

10-14 ▼ SERIAL PERIPHERAL INTERFACE

The Serial Peripheral Interface (SPI) is a second serial interface built into the **68HC11** family MCUs as well as in a number of other MCUs. This interface allows several MCUs or an entire family of CMOS interface chips to be interconnected within a single module or on the same Printed Circuit Board. These TTL signals are very high speed and therefore cannot be transmitted very far because of grounding and coupling problems and the subsequent electrical noise (see Section 13-4). The CMOS interface chips make it possible to connect other peripherals to an MCU system. One important advantage of SPI over SCI is the 2.1-MHz data bit rate. Table 10-9 shows some of the devices that have the SPI interface.

10-14.1 SPI System Considerations

In an SPI, separate wires (signals) are required for data and clock. The clock is not included in the data stream and must be furnished as a separate signal. In an SPI system some MCUs are designated as masters and some as slaves.

Figure 10-17 illustrates two different system configurations. These are identified as **6805** MCUs in this figure, but the functions can be implemented with any of the MCUs that have the SPI interface. Figure 10-17 shows that the SPI bus contains four lines. They are:

1. **Slave Select (SS).** A low on this input designates the device as a slave. It also allows the slave to transmit on the MISO lines. If SS is HIGH, the slave's MISO lines must be held in the high-impedance state.

TABLE 10-9 μP, MCU, and Peripheral Chips with SCI and SPI

PART TYPE	SCI	SPI	COMMENTS
μPs and MCUs			
6801	x		Introduce SCI
6801U4	x		
68701/U4	x		
68HC11A8	x	x	
68HC805C4	x	x	EEPROM
68HC05C4	x	x	Introduce SPI
68HC05C8	x	x	8K ROM
6805S2/S3		x	
6805K2/K3		x	UV erasable EPROM
Peripherals			
68HC68A1		x	ADC; 8-bit accuracy; 10-bit
68HC68R1/R2		x	SRAM; 128/256 bytes
68HC68T1		x	RTC; RAM; with PS + control
MC145000/01		x	LDC drivers, master/slave
MC145040/41		x	ADC; 11 channels, 8-bit SAT
MC145157/58		x	PLL;
MC144110/11		x	DAC; 6-bit, four-channel

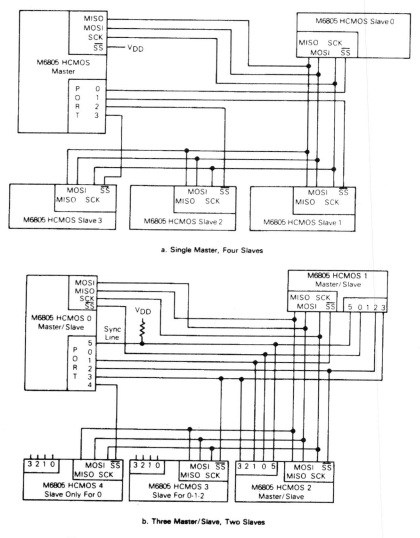

Figure 10-17 Master–slave system configuration.

2. **Master-Out, Slave-In (MOSI).** This is a serial data line for transmission from a master to a slave MCU.

3. **Master-In, Slave-Out (MISO).** This is a serial data line for transmission from a slave to a master MCU.

4. **SCK.** This is the clock that synchronizes the data bite on the line. The clock rate can be as high as 2.1 MHz.

Figure 10-17a also shows a system where there is one master MCU and four slaves. The master MCU generates the SCK clock and the slaves all receive it. The master also controls the MOSI and MISO lines, writing data to the slave devices on the MOSI lines and reading data from the slave devices on the MISO lines. The SS pins to the slaves are connected to an output port on the master. Thus the master can enable the slaves selectively, by pulling down the SS inputs only to the proper slaves. To ensure proper data transmission, the master MCU may have the slave respond with a previously received data byte. (This data byte could be inverted, or differ in some other prescribed way from the last one sent by the master.) Other transmission security methods might be defined using ports for handshake lines or data bytes with command fields.

A multimaster system may also be configured by the user. A system of this type is shown in Fig. 10-17b. An exchange of master control could be implemented using a handshake method through the I/O ports or by an exchange of code messages through the serial peripheral interface system. The major device control bits in this system are the MSTR bit in the serial peripheral control register and the MODF bit in the serial peripheral status register.

More detailed information on the SPI is available in the **68HC11** and **6805** technical data manuals (see Section 10-19).

10-14.2 ▼ SPI Features

The major features of the SPI subsystem are:

- Full-duplex, three-wire synchronous transfers
- Master or slave operation
- 1.05-MHz (maximum) master bit frequency
- 2.1-MHz (maximum) slave bit frequency
- Four programmable master bit rates
- Programmable clock polarity and phase
- End-of-transmission interrupt flag
- Write collision flag protection
- Master–master mode fault protection capability

10-15 ▼ 68HC11 FAMILY UPDATES

New versions of the **68HC11** are being developed continually. For example, since this third edition was started, a number of more advanced units have been released. We have attempted to keep Table 10-2 as current as possible but we have been unable to describe all the new features now listed.

To give the reader a feeling for the changes that are occurring, we describe briefly the **68HC711K4** MPU. In addition to, or in place of, the features included in the **68HC11E9,** we find the following:

- A bus cycle time of 4 MHz
- A nonmultiplexed Address and Data Bus
- 24K bytes of EPROM
- 640 bytes of EEPROM
- 768 bytes of on-chip RAM

- Four programmable Chip Selects
- Four 8-bit Pulse-Width Modulation (PWM) outputs
- An enhanced SCI
- An enhanced SPI
- Register block increased from 64 to 128 registers
- Available in 84-pin PLCC (OTP) or windowed Ceramic Leaded Chip Carrier (CLCC) (EPROM) packages

As you can see, many of these advances are significant. A preview description follows.

The *Nonmultiplexed Bus* running at 4 MHz results in simplification of the chip logic and thus makes it smaller. This is possible by using a new 84-pin package. Other improvements result in more memory of all three types.

The *Programmable Chip Selects* is another important step because it allows the use of very popular third-party EPROM, ROM, and RAM memories without the need for external interface components, and thus reduces the size and cost of the systems manufactured.

Pulse-Width Modulation (PWM) is an important method for motor control and other variable functions, and its inclusion on-chip further simplifies many designs.

The SCI has been enhanced in the **68HC711K4** and many other new family devices by providing a full range of standard baud rates from 150 up to 38.4K baud. Some registers and control bits have been rearranged.

As suggested, there are many more updates appearing almost daily. When making a decision about starting a new design, it is recommended that this book be augmented with the latest reference material from Motorola.

10-16 ▼ 6805 FAMILY OF MCUs

There is a large and still growing demand for industrial control machines that use *microcontrollers* (MCUs). The high-speed processing or expandable memory of the **68HC11** is not, however, necessary in many small control systems such as the MCU in a microwave oven, for example. These systems often consist of a minimal μP, a small RAM, some ROM to hold the user's program, a timer, and perhaps an A/D converter or a Phase-Locked Loop (PLL) subsystem.

Motorola has provided an alternative to the **68HC11** family called the **6805** family. It also is a descendant of Motorola's original **6800** NMOS line. This family of MCUs has slightly lower performance but costs less. It eliminates some of the lesser-used **6800** instructions, but includes new bit-modify-and-test instructions and is optimized for Single-Chip control applications.

The **6805** family of MCUs includes most of the same integrated subsystems used in the **68HC11** family, and modern members of the **6805** family are also implemented using HCMOS technology, like the **68HC11**. Because of a simplified design of the basic μP, these MPUs are smaller and easier to manufacture. This accounts for the lower cost and is the principal reason for using a **6805** in place of **6801**s or **68HC11**s. The declining costs make it possible to automate simpler and lower-cost industrial controllers and thus realize increases in the number of applications for these MCUs. Figure 10-18 shows a thermostat system that can be controlled by a **6805** MCU.

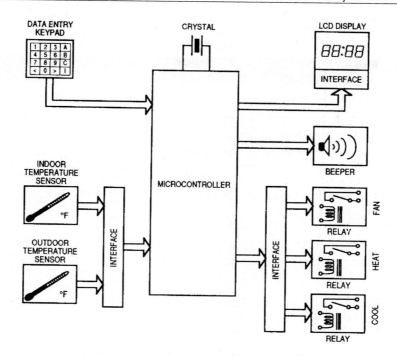

Figure 10-18 Thermostat project block diagram.

10-16.1 ▼ 68HC05 MCUs

Today, nearly a hundred different types of **68HC05** MCUs exist and more are constantly being developed. They include a variety of peripheral subsystems integrated into the same chip as the CPU.

Table 10-10 gives the features of 49 **68HC05** and 18 **6805** HMOS MCUs. All versions of these MCUs contain a simplified **68HC05** CPU core that is based on the **6800** μP. The MCUs in Table 10-10 have between 64 and 480 bytes of RAM and from 504 to 16K bytes of ROM or EPROM. They also have between 16 and 40 I/O lines. All these MCUs contain a timer. Many contain an A/D converter, a Phase-Locked Loop (PLL), Pulse-Width Modulation (PWM) capability, or another subsystem. Thus the user can select the MCU that best satisfies the particular requirements of the system being designed from a wide variety of available **68HC05**s without incurring unnecessary costs for unused features. In some high-volume applications, such as intelligent toys, the low price is crucial.

10-16.2 ▼ 68HC705K1 MCU

The **68HC705K1** is an interesting example of current low-cost **68HC05** products. This MCU is available in a **Small Outline Integrated Circuit** (SOIC) package that is approximately 0.4 by 0.3 by 0.1 inch. This is about the smallest MCU that Motorola has made. It has only 16 pins, but it has all the features of a powerful controller. This particular ver-

Table 10-10   6805 Family

MICROCONTROLLERS

Motorola Part Number	ROM	RAM	EEPROM	Timer	Serial	A/D	I/O	Bus Speed, MHz	Package†	EPROM or EEPROM Version	Comments
M68HC05 (HCMOS)											
MC68HC05B4	4K	176	0	16-Bit–2 IC, 2 OC, WDOG	SCI	Yes	32	0-2.1	56-B 52-FN	705B5 805B6	2 PWMs
MC68HC05B6	6K	176	256	16-Bit–2 IC, 2 OC, WDOG	SCI	Yes	32	0-2.1	56-B 52-FN	705B5 805B6	2 PWMs
MC68HC05B8	8K	176	256	16-Bit–2 IC, 2 OC, WDOG	SCI	Yes	32	0-2.1	56-B 52-FN	N/A	2 PWMs
MC68HC05C4	4K	176	0	16-Bit–1 IC, 1 OC	SPI, SCI	No	31	0-2.1	40-P 44-FN 44-FB	705C8 805C4	Low Voltage & High Speed Versions Available
MC68HC05C5	5K	176	128	16-Bit–1 IC, 1 OC, WDOG	SIOP	No	32	0-2.1	40-P 44-FN	705C5	10 mA Sink Port, LVPI
MC68HC05C8	8K	176	0	16-Bit–1 IC, 1 OC	SPI, SCI	No	31	0-4.0	40-P 44-FN 44-FB	705C8	Low Voltage & High Speed Versions Available
MC68HC05C9	16K	352	0	16-Bit–1 IC, 1 OC, WDOG	SPI, SCI	No	31	0-2.1	40-P 44-FB 44-FN	705C9	Expanded Port D
MC68HC05D9	16K	352	0	16-Bit–1 IC, 1 OC	SCI	No	31	0-2.1	40-P 44-FN	705D9	5 PWMs, 25 mA Sink Port
MC68HC05D24	24K	352	0	16-Bit–1 IC, 1 OC, WDOG	SCI	No	31	0-2.1	40-P 44-FN	N/A	5 PWMs, 24 mA Sink Port
MC68HC05E0	0	480	0	2 Periodic Timers, WDOG	SPI or I²C	No	36	0-4.0	68-FN	N/A	External Address
MC68HC05E1	4K	368	0	15 stage multi-function, RTC, RTI, WDOG	—	No	20	0-4.0	28-P 28-DW	705E1	Internal PLL Clock Synthesizer
XC68HC05F6	4K	320	0	16-Bit–1 IC, 1 OC	SPI	No	28	0-2.1	42-B	N/A	DTMF
XC68HC05G8	8K	172	0	15 stage multi-functional, RTC, WDOG	Dual SCI	Yes	40	0-2.1	160-FT	N/A	Power Management, PLL, Keyboard Control
MC68HC05J1	1K	64	0	15 stage multi-function, RTI, WDOG	—	No	14	0-2.1	20-P 20-DW	705J2	Low Cost
XC68HC05L5	8K	256	0	16-Bit–1 IC, 1 OC 8-Bit–1 IC, 1 OC	SIOP	No	39	0-2.1	80-FU	N/A	156-Segment LCD, External Address
XC68HC05L6	6K	176	0	16-Bit–1 IC, 1 OC	SPI	No	24	0-2.1	68-FN	N/A	96-Segment LCD
MC68HC05L7	6K	176	0	16-Bit–1 IC, 1 OC, RTC	SCI	No	27	0-2.1	128-FT Die	N/A	960 Segment LCD, External Address
MC68HC05L9	6K	176	0	16-Bit–1 IC, 1 OC, RTC	SCI	No	27	0-2.1	128-FT Die	N/A	640 Segment LCD, External Address
MC68HC05L10	13K	352	0	16-Bit–1 IC, 1 OC	SPI, SCI	No	28	0-3.6	128-FT Die	N/A	LCD Driver, MMU, External Address
XC68HC05M4	4K	128	0	8-Bit; 16-Bit–1 IC, 1 OC, WDOG	—	Yes	32	0-2.1	52-FN	N/A	24 Lines (3 Ports) VFD on Chip
MC68HC05P1	2K	128	0	16-Bit–1 IC, 1 OC	—	No	21	0-2.1	28-P 28-DW	705P9	
XC68HC05P3	3K	96	128	16-Bit–1 IC, 1 OC WDOG	—	No	22	0-2.1	28-P 28-DW	N/A	Keyboard Interrupt
MC68HC05P4	4K	176	—	16-Bit–1 IC, 1 OC, WDOG	SIOP	—	21	0-2.1	28-P 28-DW	705P6	
MC68HC05P7	2K	128	0	16-Bit–1 IC, 1 OC, WDOG	SIOP	No	21	0-2.1	28-P 28-DW	705P9	
XC68HC05P8	2K	112	32	15 stage multi-function, RTI, WDOG	—	Yes	20	0-2.1	28-P 28-DW	505P8	LVPI Option on EEPROM
XC68HC05P9	2K	128	—	16-Bit–1 IC, 1 OC, WDOG	SIOP	Yes	21	0-2.1	28-P 28-DW	705P9	Low cost
MC68HC05SC11	6K	128	0	—	—	No	5	0-2.1	Die	N/A	8K EPROM, Security
MC68HC05SC21	6K	128	3K	—	—	No	5	0-2.1	Die	N/A	Security
MC68HC05SC24	3K	128	1K	—	—	No	5	0-2.1	Die	N/A	Security
MC68HC05T1	8K	320	—	16-Bit–1 IC, 1 OC, WDOG	SIOP	Yes	30	0-2.1	40-P	705T3	On-Screen Display, 9 PWMs
XC68HC05T2	15K	320	0	16-Bit–1 IC, 1 OC, WDOG	SIOP	Yes	30	0-2.1	40-P	705T3	On-Screen Display, 9 PWMs
XC68HC05T4	5K	96	0	16-Bit–1 IC, 1 OC, WDOG	—	Yes	16	0-2.1	42-B	705T4	On-Screen Display, 6 PWMs
XC68HC05T7	8K	320	0	16-Bit–1 IC, 1 OC, RTC	I²C	Yes	28	0-2.1	56-B	705T7	On-Screen Display, 9 PWMs

Table 10-10 (Continued)

MICROCONTROLLERS (Continued)

Motorola Part Number	ROM	RAM	EEPROM	Timer	Serial	A/D	I/O	Bus Speed, MHz	Package†	EPROM or EEPROM Version	Comments
M6804 (HMOS)											
MC6804J1	504	32	0	8-Bit	—	No	12	83-229 kHz	20-P	N/A	
MC6804J2	1000	32	0	8-Bit	—	No	12	83-229 kHz	20-P	N/A	
MC6804P2	1024	32	0	8-Bit	—	No	20	83-229 kHz	28-P	704P2	
M6805 (HMOS)											
MC6805P2	1K	64	0	8-Bit	—	No	20	0.1-1.0	28-P 28-FN	705P3	LVI Option
MC6805P6	2K	64	0	8-Bit	—	No	20	0.1-1.0	28-P	705P3	LVI Option
MC6805R2	2K	64	0	8-Bit	—	Yes	32	0.1-1.0	40-P 44-FN	705R3	LVI Option, Prog. Prescaler Option
MC6805R3	4K	112	0	8-Bit	—	Yes	32	0.1-1.0	40-P 44-FN	705R3	7-Bit Prescaler, LVI Option
MC6805R6	4K	112	0	8-Bit	—	Yes	32	0.1-1.0	40-P 44-FN	705R3	
MC6805S2	1K	64	0	16-Bit; 8-Bit	SPI	Yes	16	0.1-1.0	28-P	705S3	15-Bit Prescaler, LVI
MC6805S3	4K	104	0	2 8-Bit; 16-Bit	SPI	Yes	21	0.1-1.0	28-P	705S3	1 Extra 8-Bit Timer
MC6805U2	2K	64	0	8-Bit	—	No	32	0.1-1.0	40-P 44-FN	705U3	LVI Option
MC6805U3	4K	112	0	8-Bit	—	No	32	0.1-1.0	40-P 44-FN	705U3	7-Bit Prescaler LVI Option

sion has 504 bytes of EPROM and is available in either a windowed or a One-Time-Programmable (OTP) package.

The features of the **68HC705K1** include the following:

- A **68HC05** Central Processor Unit (CPU)
- Memory-mapped Input/Output (I/O) Registers
- 504 Bytes of EPROM, including eight user vector locations
- 32 Bytes of user RAM
- An on-chip oscillator with crystal or resonator connections
- A Computer-Operating-Properly (COP) watchdog circuit
- A 15-bit multifunction timer with real-time interrupt circuit
- External interrupt capability on four I/O pins
- 8-mA sink capability on four I/O pins
- 10 bidirectional I/O pins

As small as this unit is, it has all the components needed for a small control system. The Block Diagram for the **68HC705K1** is shown in Fig. 10-19. The memory map, which includes EPROM, RAM, and all the I/O registers, is shown in Fig. 10-20. The EPROM occupies the map from $200 to $3FF and includes the eight interrupt vectors. The I/O control registers are located between 00 and $1F and are memory-mapped as in any **6800** family system. The I/O data is transferred primarily through port A, an 8-bit port, and the direction of each line is controlled by a Data Direction Register.

Addresses $00E0 through $00FF serve as both stack RAM and user RAM. This seems like a small RAM area, but even with the limited number of I/O pins, many important small systems can be built. (The CPU uses 5 bytes to save all the register contents before processing an interrupt. During a subroutine call, the CPU uses 2 bytes to save the return address.)

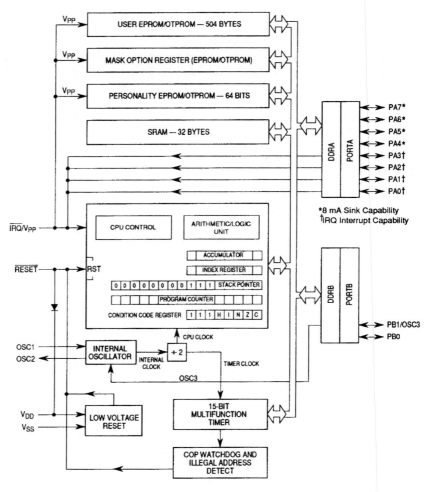

Figure 10-19   MC68HC705K1 block diagram.

10-16.3 ▼ Key Entry System Using the 6805

A 16-bit key entry system can easily be built using a **68HC705K1,** as shown in Fig. 10-21. Here, the program would be written to drive all four rows (PA4–PA7) high and wait for a key closure. The key closure generates an interrupt by pulling one of the PA0–PA3 lines high. The program then drives each line high singularly and searches (PA0–PA3) for the column with the closed switch.

10-16.4 ▼ 68HC05 CPU

The same **68HC05** CPU core is used in all members of the **68HC05** family and is a simplified version of the **6800** CPU. Figure 10-22 is the Programmer's Model, showing the registers. The CPU differences between the **68HC05** and the **6800** are:

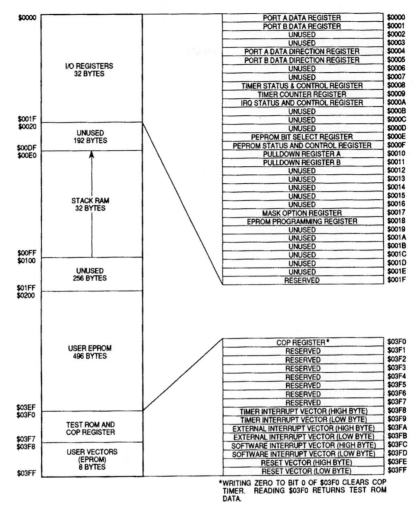

Figure 10-20   68HC705K1 memory map.

1. The PC and stack pointer (SP) are 5 to 14 bits long, depending on the size of the usable memory (both RAM and ROM), instead of 16 bits.

2. Accumulator B has been eliminated (this also eliminates all instructions that referenced accumulator B).

3. The index register is only 8 bits long.

4. The V bit has been deleted from the Condition Code Register.

The Stack Pointer register is a 16-bit register that contains the address of the next location on the stack. During a reset or after the Reset Stack Pointer (RSP) instruction is executed, the SP is set to $00FF. In the **68HC705K1** version, the 11 most significant bits of the stack pointer are permanently fixed at 00000000111, so the stack pointer produces

68HC705K1

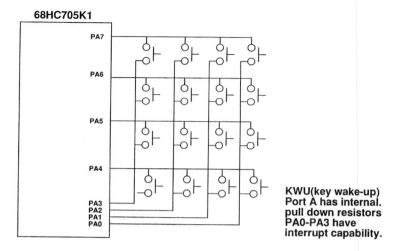

KWU(key wake-up)
Port A has internal.
pull down resistors
PA0-PA3 have
interrupt capability.

Figure 10-21 Keypad interface.

addresses from $00E0 to $00FF. If subroutines and interrupts use more than 32 stack locations, the stack pointer wraps around to address $00FF and begins writing over the previously stored data. A subroutine uses two stack locations and an interrupt uses five.

The Program Counter is a 16-bit register that contains the address of the next instruction or operand to be fetched. In the **68HC705K1,** the 6 most significant bits of the program counter are ignored and appear as 000000. The 3 most significant bits of the Condition Code Register are fixed at 111.

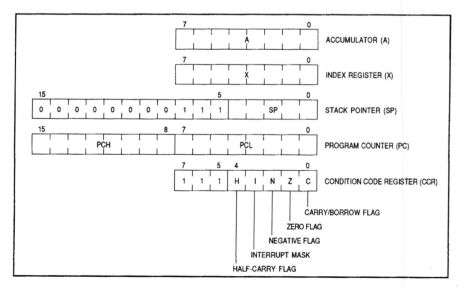

Figure 10-22 Programming Model for the **68HC05K1** showing the CPU registers.

The **68HC05** instruction set is similar to the **6800** set but has some instructions deleted or changed because there is no B register and the X register is only 8 bits long. At the same time, a number of instructions have been added that are specifically designed for byte-efficient program storage. Table 10-11 is an op code map of the **6805** instructions.

Except for the indexed mode, and the added **bit set/clear** mode, all addressing modes for the **68HC05** are identical to the **6800** modes. The indexed mode consists of three submodes:

1. **No-offset (or 0 offset) mode.** In this mode there is no offset byte and the index register contains the Effective Address (EA) of the operand. Therefore, the addresses are restricted to the range $0000 through $00FF.
2. **8-bit offset mode.** In this mode the EA is the sum of the offset (the second byte of the instruction) and the contents of X.
3. **16-bit offset mode.** In this mode the EA is the sum of the second and third bytes (read as a 16-bit number) of the instruction and the contents of X. This is the only indexed mode that allows access to the entire memory space.

Each indexed instruction (LDA 0,X, for example) has three different op codes to tell the μP which submode to use. The no-offset instructions, listed as IX in Table 10-11, are single byte instructions (only the op code is needed). The 8-bit offset instructions, listed as IX1, require 2 bytes, and 16-bit offset instructions, listed as IX2, require 3 bytes.

EXAMPLE 10-11

Write a program to move a block of data, $20 bytes long, from $1500 to $1700. Use indexed instructions.

SOLUTION

A possible program is shown in Fig. 10-23. The program is smaller if we start at the last byte and decrement X each time through the loop because it simply tests for a minus number to see when it is done. A compare instruction is unnecessary. Therefore, each time through the loop the accumulator is loaded with the contents of memory, starting at $1520, and then it is stored at the top of the block in the new location.

Now, if X is $20 the first time through the loop, $1F the second time, and so on, the contents of $1520 will be loaded and stored at $1720, then the contents of $151F at $171F, and so on, until X goes negative.

```
100  AE  20              LDX #$20        Preset the X register
102  D6  15 00    LOOP   LDA $1500,X     Fetch the data
105  D7  17 00           STA $1700,X     Store it
108  5A                  DEX             Decrement the X register
109  26  F7              BPL LOOP        Loop until X is minus
```

Figure 10-23 Block Move using indexed instruction for Example 10-11.

TABLE 10-11 6805 Op Code Map

Legend for each cell: MNEMONIC · (cycles) · addressing mode · (bytes)

LO\HI	0 0000 (Bit-Manip DIR)	1 0001 (Bit-Manip DIR)	2 0010 (Branch REL)	3 0011 (RMW DIR)	4 0100 (RMW INH)	5 0101 (RMW INH)	6 0110 (RMW IX1)	7 0111 (RMW IX)	8 1000 (Control INH)	9 1001 (Control INH)	A 1010 (Reg/Mem IMM)	B 1011 (DIR)	C 1100 (EXT)	D 1101 (IX2)	E 1110 (IX1)	F 1111 (IX)
0 0000	BRSET0 5·DIR·3	BSET0 5·DIR·2	BRA 3·REL·2	NEG 5·DIR·2	NEGA 3·INH·1		NEG 6·IX1·2	NEG 5·IX·1	RTI 9·INH·1		SUB 2·IMM·2	SUB 3·DIR·2	SUB 4·EXT·3	SUB 5·IX2·3	SUB 4·IX1·2	SUB 3·IX·1
1 0001	BRCLR0 5·DIR·3	BCLR0 5·DIR·2	BRN 3·REL·2						RTS 6·INH·1		CMP 2·IMM·2	CMP 3·DIR·2	CMP 4·EXT·3	CMP 5·IX2·3	CMP 4·IX1·2	CMP 3·IX·1
2 0010	BRSET1 5·DIR·3	BSET1 5·DIR·2	BHI 3·REL·2		MUL 11·INH·1						SBC 2·IMM·2	SBC 3·DIR·2	SBC 4·EXT·3	SBC 5·IX2·3	SBC 4·IX1·2	SBC 3·IX·1
3 0011	BRCLR1 5·DIR·3	BCLR1 5·DIR·2	BLS 3·REL·2	COM 5·DIR·2	COMA 3·INH·1	COMX 3·INH·1	COM 6·IX1·2	COM 5·IX·1	SWI 10·INH·1		CPX 2·IMM·2	CPX 3·DIR·2	CPX 4·EXT·3	CPX 5·IX2·3	CPX 4·IX1·2	CPX 3·IX·1
4 0100	BRSET2 5·DIR·3	BSET2 5·DIR·2	BCC 3·REL·2	LSR 5·DIR·2	LSRA 3·INH·1	LSRX 3·INH·1	LSR 6·IX1·2	LSR 5·IX·1			AND 2·IMM·2	AND 3·DIR·2	AND 4·EXT·3	AND 5·IX2·3	AND 4·IX1·2	AND 3·IX·1
5 0101	BRCLR2 5·DIR·3	BCLR2 5·DIR·2	BCS 3·REL·2								BIT 2·IMM·2	BIT 3·DIR·2	BIT 4·EXT·3	BIT 5·IX2·3	BIT 4·IX1·2	BIT 3·IX·1
6 0110	BRSET3 5·DIR·3	BSET3 5·DIR·2	BNE 3·REL·2	ROR 5·DIR·2	RORA 3·INH·1	RORX 3·INH·1	ROR 6·IX1·2	ROR 5·IX·1			LDA 2·IMM·2	LDA 3·DIR·2	LDA 4·EXT·3	LDA 5·IX2·3	LDA 4·IX1·2	LDA 3·IX·1
7 0111	BRCLR3 5·DIR·3	BCLR3 5·DIR·2	BEQ 3·REL·2	ASR 5·DIR·2	ASRA 3·INH·1	ASRX 3·INH·1	ASR 6·IX1·2	ASR 5·IX·1		TAX 2·INH·1		STA 4·DIR·2	STA 5·EXT·3	STA 6·IX2·3	STA 5·IX1·2	STA 4·IX·1
8 1000	BRSET4 5·DIR·3	BSET4 5·DIR·2	BHCC 3·REL·2	LSL 5·DIR·2	LSLA 3·INH·1	LSLX 3·INH·1	LSL 6·IX1·2	LSL 5·IX·1		CLC 2·INH·1	EOR 2·IMM·2	EOR 3·DIR·2	EOR 4·EXT·3	EOR 5·IX2·3	EOR 4·IX1·2	EOR 3·IX·1
9 1001	BRCLR4 5·DIR·3	BCLR4 5·DIR·2	BHCS 3·REL·2	ROL 5·DIR·2	ROLA 3·INH·1	ROLX 3·INH·1	ROL 6·IX1·2	ROL 5·IX·1		SEC 2·INH·1	ADC 2·IMM·2	ADC 3·DIR·2	ADC 4·EXT·3	ADC 5·IX2·3	ADC 4·IX1·2	ADC 3·IX·1
A 1010	BRSET5 5·DIR·3	BSET5 5·DIR·2	BPL 3·REL·2	DEC 5·DIR·2	DECA 3·INH·1	DECX 3·INH·1	DEC 6·IX1·2	DEC 5·IX·1		CLI 2·INH·1	ORA 2·IMM·2	ORA 3·DIR·2	ORA 4·EXT·3	ORA 5·IX2·3	ORA 4·IX1·2	ORA 3·IX·1
B 1011	BRCLR5 5·DIR·3	BCLR5 5·DIR·2	BMI 3·REL·2							SEI 2·INH·1	ADD 2·IMM·2	ADD 3·DIR·2	ADD 4·EXT·3	ADD 5·IX2·3	ADD 4·IX1·2	ADD 3·IX·1
C 1100	BRSET6 5·DIR·3	BSET6 5·DIR·2	BMC 3·REL·2	INC 5·DIR·2	INCA 3·INH·1	INCX 3·INH·1	INC 6·IX1·2	INC 5·IX·1		RSP 2·INH·1		JMP 2·DIR·2	JMP 3·EXT·3	JMP 4·IX2·3	JMP 3·IX1·2	JMP 2·IX·1
D 1101	BRCLR6 5·DIR·3	BCLR6 5·DIR·2	BMS 3·REL·2	TST 4·DIR·2	TSTA 3·INH·1	TSTX 3·INH·1	TST 6·IX1·2	TST 4·IX·1		NOP 2·INH·1	BSR 6·REL·2	JSR 5·DIR·2	JSR 6·EXT·3	JSR 7·IX2·3	JSR 6·IX1·2	JSR 5·IX·1
E 1110	BRSET7 5·DIR·3	BSET7 5·DIR·2	BIL 3·REL·2						STOP 2·INH·1		LDX 2·IMM·2	LDX 3·DIR·2	LDX 4·EXT·3	LDX 5·IX2·3	LDX 4·IX1·2	LDX 3·IX·1
F 1111	BRCLR7 5·DIR·3	BCLR7 5·DIR·2	BIH 3·REL·2	CLR 5·DIR·2	CLRA 3·INH·1	CLRX 3·INH·1	CLR 6·IX1·2	CLR 5·IX·1	WAIT 2·INH·1	TXA 2·INH·1		STX 4·DIR·2	STX 5·EXT·3	STX 6·IX2·3	STX 5·IX1·2	STX 4·IX·1

ABBREVIATIONS FOR ADDRESSING MODES

INH	Inherent	REL	Relative
IMM	Immediate	IX	Indexed, No Offset
DIR	Direct	IX1	Indexed, 8-Bit Offset
EXT	Extended	IX2	Indexed, 16-Bit Offset

LEGEND

F 1111	High Byte of Opcode in Hexadecimal High Byte of Opcode in Binary
0 0000	Low Byte of Opcode in Hexadecimal Low Byte of Opcode in Binary

SUB 3 — Number of Cycles / Opcode Mnemonic
1 IX — Opcode Addressing Mode / Number of Bytes/Addressing Mode

10-16.5 ▼ Bit Manipulation

New instructions created for the **68HC05** family include *bit test and branch* and *bit set and clear*. They allow the user to *set* or *clear* a bit and to branch on a *set* or *clear* bit. These instructions are often used in control applications. Only direct addressing is supported, however, so these instructions operate only on any individual bit in the first 256 bytes of the address range. As in the **68HC11A8,** the instructions can work directly on I/O registers (because they are memory mapped), and thus directly control the I/O pins.

In the **6805** or **68HC05,** the bit *set* and *clear* instructions are 2-byte instructions; one for the op code that includes the bit number, and the other to address the byte that contains the bit of interest. An analysis of those instructions in Table 10-11 will show that the actual bit to be modified is specified within the low nibble of the op code. Bits 1 to 3 of this nibble contain the bit number, and the LSB (bit 0) determines whether the bit involved is *set* or *cleared*. If it is a 0, it is *set,* and a 1 indicates that it is to be *cleared.* This is the complement of what actually happens to the bit.

EXAMPLE 10-12

Explain the following instructions:

                    PORTB EQU $01

            XXXX 15 01 BCLR 2, PORTB

SOLUTION

BCLR is the op code for the BIT CLEAR instruction. The bit to be cleared is bit 2 of port B, which is at location $01, as the EQU directive specifies. This instruction translates to machine language as 15 01. In the first nibble of the op code, the 1 designates this instruction as a BCLR. The next 3 bits (010 in binary) indicate that bit 2 is affected. The 1 in the LSB indicates that the bit is to be cleared rather than set. The second byte, 01, is the memory location that contains the bit that is to be cleared.

EXAMPLE 10-13

Use a **6805** bit-manipulation instruction to turn OFF an LED (using bit 2 of port B) and conventional instructions to turn the LED ON.

SOLUTION

The example program polls the *Timer Control Register* (TCR) interrupt request bit (TCR, bit 7) to determine when the LED should turn ON. This program is shown in the assembly listing of Fig. 10-24. The bit-manipulation routine shown in Fig. 10-24 uses a bit test and branch instruction to poll the timer:

```
REPT  BRCLR 7,TIMER,REPT
```

The first REPT is a label and is followed by the op code mnemonic of the instruction. The BRCLR op code causes the program to branch if the bit being tested (bit 7) is clear. TIMER is a symbol for the address of the byte being tested. The last REPT is the object of the branch, which means that this statement loops on itself and causes TIMER bit 7 to be tested repeatedly until it is *set,* at which time the program falls through to turn on a LED. Figure 10-25 illustrates this loop by showing both the *branch* and *no branch* status. Note that if TIMER bit 7 is *clear* (timer not timed out), a backward branch is taken (the negative offset byte $FD is added to $0594 to get $0591). When the timer times out, TIMER bit 7 is *set* (the C bit is also *set*) and the program falls through to $0594. The condition codes are unaffected by the BSET instruction except for the C bit, which is *set* to the state of the bit being tested.

The *bit test and branch mode* instructions, BRCLR and BRSET, are a combination of direct, relative, and bit set/clear addressing. The data byte to be tested is located via a direct address in the location following the opcode. The actual bit to be tested in the byte is specified within the low-order nibble of the op code (bits 1 through 3). The relative offset address for branching is in the byte following the direct address (second byte following the op code). Thus the bit test and branch instructions are 3-byte instructions (op code byte, direct byte, and relative byte). A bit test and branch has a relative addressing range of PC –125 to PC +130 from the beginning of the instruction.

In Fig. 10-24, reference to the bit set/clear instruction at address $58F and to its equivalent in conventional code (starting at $59C) shows that 2 bytes do the work of 6 bytes in this case.

```
0001                   PORTB  EQU  $01    Define Port B Address
0009                   TIMER  EQU  $09    Define TCR Address

                 *   BIT MANIPULATION INSTRUCTIONS

058F 15 01             BCLR  2,PORTB            Turn Off LED
0591 0F 09 FD REPT     BRCLR 7,TIMER,REPT       Check Timer status
                 *                        Repeat if not timed out
0594 14 01             BSET  2,PORTB  Turn ON LED if Timer times out

                 *   CONVENTIONAL INSTRUCTIONS

0596 B6 09    AGAIN LDA   TIMER  Get Timer status
0598 A5 80          BIT   #$80   Mask out proper bit
059A 26 FA          BNE   AGAIN  Test-turn On if timer times out
059C B6 01          LDA   PORTB  Get port B data
059E A4 FB          AND   #$FB   Clear proper bit
05A0 B7 01          STA   PORTB  Save modified data to turn OFF LED
05A2 .. ..          Continue
```

Figure 10-24 Program to illustrate the efficiency of **6805** instructions.

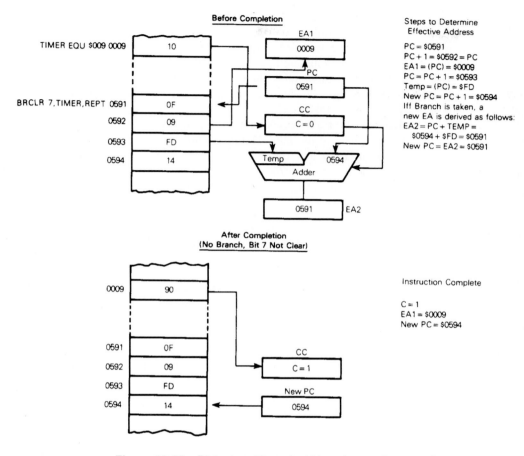

Figure 10-25 Bit test and branch addressing mode example.

10-16.6 ▼ Advanced 6805 MCUs

The **68HC05** family of MCUs are implemented using a single address map with internal memory-mapped I/O. Unlike the **6801** and **68HC11,** they do not have more than one mode of operation, so with one exception (**68HC05E0**) the external component addressing is not used. Instead, external components are added to a system by means of the SCI or SPI serial interfaces. Motorola manufactures a family of CMOS external peripherals with serial interfaces for this purpose. (The **68HC05E0** is described in Section 10-16.8.)

10-16.7 ▼ 68HC05C8 MCU

The **68HC05** family also includes complex and powerful MCUs. Some of these are in the so-called C-series, which means that they have a C (**68HC05C4** or **68HC05C8,** for example) in their designation. These general-purpose devices offer a wide variety of memory options. An on-chip SCI provides asynchronous communications with software-selectable baud rates from 75 Hz to 131 kHz. The SPI is ideal for driving off-chip displays and peripherals that reside on the same PC board, at rates up to 2.1 MHz.

The C-series devices include a 16-bit free-running programmable counter to be used in conjunction with Input Capture and Output Compare functions for simultaneous-input waveform measurement and output waveform generation. A watchdog timer is available to guard against software runaway in noisy environments.

These HCMOS versions all include a timer similar to the one in the **6801.** This more capable timer has a 16-bit architecture. Pulse widths can vary from several microseconds to many seconds.

The **68HC05C8** MCU is an example of one of the most popular HCMOS (High-density CMOS) versions of the **6805** family. Figure 10-26 is the block diagram for the **68HC05C8,** and it shows that this 8-bit MCU contains all the same blocks as the **68HC05K1** plus more ports and the SCI and SPI serial interface systems. It also has larger memories, and a much larger 40-pin DIP or 44-pin PLCC package.

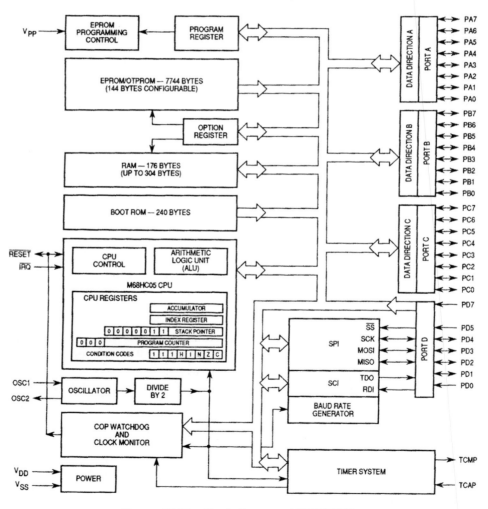

Figure 10-26   Block diagram of **68HC05C8.**

Like all CMOS or HCMOS implementations, the fully static design allows operation at clock frequencies down to zero, thus further reducing its already low power consumption. The small size of the HCMOS die allows the use of larger memories as well as the addition of functions such as the SPI and a timer.

The **68HC05C8** MCU is a *middle-of-the road* version. It is similar to the **68HC05C4** version except that the user ROM is 7744 bytes instead of 4096 bytes. The memory map is actually the same, but the area from $4362 to $7935 is also used.

The **68HC705C8** EPROM version is very useful for *emulating* the **68HC05C8** or **68HC05C4** in early stages of testing. Since the EPROM version has a quartz window to permit ultraviolet light erasing, it is more expensive than the ROM version but can be used when first assembling a system to *prove out* the design. When no more program changes are expected and the designers are satisfied that the program is working properly, the **68HC705C8** can be replaced with an OTP version for production runs.

10-16.8 ▼ 68HC05E0 MPU

The **68HC05E0** is a one-of-a-kind implementation in that it has no ROM (or EPROM) and has external 16-bit address and 8-bit data bus interfaces similar to the **68HC11.** Otherwise, it follows all the **68HC05** family standards. It has the following additional features:

- A 4-MHz bus frequency
- 480 Bytes of RAM
- LED drive capability on 8 I/O pins (port A)
- A 6-bit Timer with 8-bit prescaler
- A 14-bit Timer with 8-bit scaler
- Control signals for emulation purposes
- An internal address decoder
- An SPI/I^{2}C Serial Bus Interface (I^{2}C is a Phillips serial communications standard)

This MCU is *not* typical of the many other **68HC05** MCUs, but it can substitute for the **68HC11** in some systems. It, of course, uses the **68HC05** CPU and instruction set.

10-17 ▼ SUMMARY

The **6801, 6802, 6805, 68HC05,** and **68HC11** μPs and MCUs were described and it was shown that the previous chapters on the **6800** are applicable to these upwardly compatible components. The instruction sets and hardware features are similar and were discussed for each μP. The new and unique features of each μP, such as the SCI, SPI, and the Timer, were explained in some detail.

10-18 ▼ GLOSSARY

Arguments Mathematical variables associated with one routine that must be transferred to another.

Bit manipulation The process of changing one or more bits in a byte, usually associated with flags or I/O registers.

Byte efficiency Achieving more tasks or functions with fewer bytes of machine code.

Computer Operating Properly (COP) A special function of the MCU to check for possible program failure. Also called *watchdog*.

Handshaking The process in which devices test signals from each other to determine readiness.

Input Capture Register One of the registers in the timer of a MCU used to latch the value of a counter when a signal line transition is sensed by an edge detector.

Latching The technique of retaining a signal condition after the state has changed. Usually done with a flip-flop for each bit.

Mask byte A byte that is effectively ANDed with another byte to assure that only the desired bits are kept in the HIGH state.

MicroController Unit (MCU) A simple low-cost μC that includes peripheral functions in the same chip.

Multiplex Using one signal line for two purposes; usually at different times.

Offset Byte following a branch op code that determines the relative address that will be accessed next; usually, a 2s-complement 8-bit number.

Output Compare Register One of the registers in a MCU timer.

Position-independent code Software that uses relative (BRA or BSR) instructions instead of JMP or JSR, so that it will operate properly when located at any address in memory.

Reentrant code A technique for writing a subroutine so that the status can be saved while it is used by a higher-priority program and then the original program can be continued.

Static The condition whereby a flip-flop or latch will retain its information indefinitely as long as power is applied; applied to logic circuitry. This is opposed to *dynamic* circuits, which must be clocked or refreshed constantly to retain their information.

Strobe A pulse on a signal line, usually to start a process or latch data.

Throughput The speed of processing data.

Wake-up feature An SCI feature to decode and alert a specific MCU when several are connected on the same serial data line.

Watchdog circuit A circuit that must be reset periodically or it will interrupt and restart the program; the COP circuit.

10-19 ▼ REFERENCES

J. D. GREENFIELD, *The 68HC11 Microcontroller,* Saunders, Philadelphia, 1992.

MOTOROLA, CONFIG *Register Issues Concerning the MC68HC11 Family, AN997/D,* Phoenix, Ariz., 1988.

———, *8-Bit Microprocessor and Peripheral Data,* Phoenix, Ariz., 1983.

———, *HCMOS Single-Chip Microcomputer,* Phoenix, Ariz., 1985.

———, *MC6801/6803 Data Sheet,* DS 9841-R1, Austin, Texas, 1982.

———, *MC6801U4 Advance Information,* ADI 896, Austin Texas, 1982.

———, *M6805UM(AD2), M6805 HMOS, M146805 CMOS Family Users Manual,* Prentice Hall, Englewood Cliffs, N.J., 1983.

———, MC68HC05C4, MC68HC05C8, MC68HC805C4, 8-Bit Microcomputers, ADI 991R1, Phoenix, Ariz., 1989.

———, *MC68HC11 Bootstrap Mode, AN1060/D,* Phoenix, Ariz., 1990.

———, *MC68HC11 EEPROM Programming from a Personal Computer,* AN1010/D, Phoenix, Ariz., 1988.

———, *MC68HC11 Floating-Point Package, AN974/D,* Phoenix, Ariz., 1987.

———, *MC68HC11 Reference Manual,* MC68HC11RM/D Rev. 3, Phoenix, Ariz.,1991.

———, *MC68HC11A8 HCMOS Single-Chip Microcomputer,* ADI 1207, Phoenix, Ariz., 1985.

———, *MC68HC11E9 Technical Data,* MC68HC11E9/D Rev. 1, Phoenix, Ariz., 1991.

———, *MC68HC11F1 Technical Data,* MC68HC11F1/D Rev. 2, Phoenix, Ariz., 1990.

———, *MC68HC24 Port Replacement Unit,* MC68HC24/D Rev. 2, Phoenix, Ariz., 1987.

———, *Motorola's New High Technology Seminar, Microprocessors, Arrays, Systems,* Austin, Texas, 1983.

———, *Single-Chip Microcomputer Data,* Phoenix, Ariz., 1987.

———, *Systems on Silicon,* Mesa, Ariz., 1982.

10-20 ▼ PROBLEMS

10-1. The register contents of a **68HC11** are

```
P-C007 Y-7982 X-FF00 A-44 B-70 C-C0 S-0054
```

What are the results of the following instructions?
(a) ABX
(b) ABY
(c) XGDX (exchange D and X)

10-2. Location $23 contains $0F. What does it contain after the following instructions?
(a) BSET $23 $11
(b) BCLR $23 $11

10-3. Again location $23 contains $0F. Which of the following instructions will cause the μP to branch?
(a) BRSET $23 $10

     (b) BRCLR $23 $10

     (c) BRCLR $23 $11

10-4. The following **68HC11** instructions are found in $C100.

```
$C100       LDX #$C200          CE C2 00

C103        BRSET 05 40 CC      1E 05 40 CC
```

     (a) Which bit of which location is tested?

     (b) Where does the program go if the bit is set? If it is clear?

10-5. The circuit of Fig. 10-27 uses one-shots and three-state gates to set the operating mode of a **68HC11.** Explain how it works. What is the purpose of the one-shot and three-state gates?

10-6. A switch is connected to pin PA7. Explain how to cause the **68HC11** to interrupt after 20 throws of the switch.

10-7. The INIT register on a **68HC11E9** contains $23.

     (a) What is the lowest address of the internal RAM? What is the highest address?

     (b) What is the lowest address of the configuration control block? What is the highest address?

10-8. If the clock in a **68HC11** runs at 2 MHz, how often does the TCNT register overflow (and set the timer overflow flag)?

10-9. An instruction in a **68HC11** is executed when TCNT reads FFF0. The clock is 2MHZ. What will it read 3 ms later?

10-10. The **68HC11** is to interrupt 3 ms after the program reaches location $C200. What instructions should be placed at $C200 to cause this to happen?

10-11. Show how to measure the pulse width of a pulse on a single line using two input capture registers.

10-12. Write a routine to move a block of data using the ABX instruction. Write the same thing in **6800** language and compare the number of bytes as well as the cycle times.

10-13. In the **68HC11** there are a set of numbers in memory from $C300 to $C3FF. Some of them are the number AA. Write a program to count the number of AAs in the buffer. Store this number in $C400. Make a list of the addresses of these locations starting at $C410. (*Hint:* Use the two index registers.)

10-14. List the hardware features of the **68HC705C9.**

10-15. Write a **6805** program to add the numbers in locations 1700 through 1708. Assume that the sum does not overflow an 8-bit register.

10-16. What does the **6805** instruction 12 34 do?

10-17. For a **68HC05C4,** write the code to set bit 3 of port A if port A is at address $EE.

10-18. In a system that uses a **1468052,** write instructions that will branch to a new routine when the tested bit (3) is a bit-manipulation instruction.

     After attempting to solve these problems, try to answer the self-evaluation questions in Section 10-2. If any of them still seem difficult, review the appropriate sections of the chapter to find the answers.

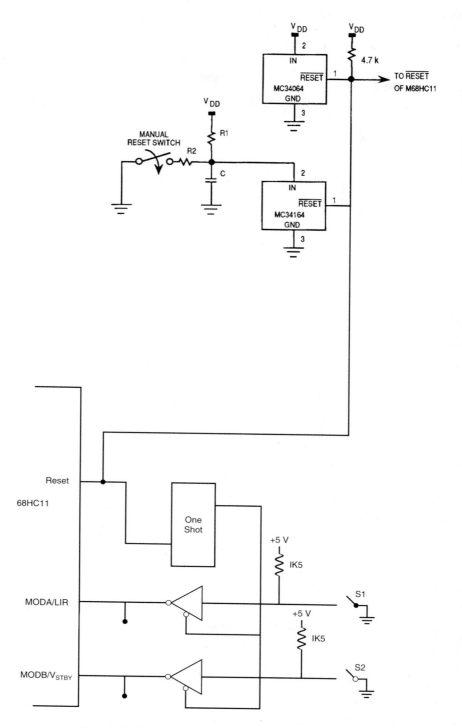

Figure 10-27   68HC11 MODE Setting Reset circuit.

11 SYSTEM DEBUGGING

11-1 ▼ INSTRUCTIONAL OBJECTIVES

The preceding chapters have covered the design of μC and MCU systems using the **6800** family of components. This chapter covers the development of testing procedures as they have evolved since μPs and μCs were introduced. Many methods necessary to perfect the design are discussed. After reading this chapter, the student should be able to:

1. Assemble the hardware and software needed for a specific design and test to see if they work together properly.
2. Make the hardware/software trade-offs by evaluating performance.
3. Use the BUFFALO Monitor Program and the EValuation Board (EVB).
4. Select the best methods to perfect the system under development.
5. List the features of the various debugging systems.
6. Explain how firmware debug programs (Monitor ROMs) can be used.
7. Use breakpoints in a program.
8. Save programs and load them during development.
9. Determine trade-offs of time saved and ease of use to the cost of a Microcomputer Development System (MDS).

11-2 ▼ SELF-EVALUATION QUESTIONS

Watch for the answers to the following questions as you read the chapter. They should help you to understand the material presented.

1. What is the lowest-cost method of analyzing the operation of a μC?
2. Why does low initial cost not necessarily provide the most economical method to develop a μC system?

3. Why is it necessary to know the register contents in debugging a μC?
4. How do Breakpoints speed the location of faults in μC systems?
5. What are the features of ROM Monitor systems?
6. What are pseudoregisters? What is their function?

11-3 ▼ INTRODUCTION TO SYSTEM DEBUGGING

When a computer program is written, it is necessary to choose the proper instructions and to format each instruction statement properly. Spacing and punctuation are important. Assemblers and compilers will flag these and other *syntax errors* when processing source program statements that are written improperly. However, even when these programs are edited to eliminate all syntax errors, there is no guarantee that the program will run successfully or function properly. The program's logic can only be tested by executing the instructions. A newly written program is likely to have mistakes and therefore must be tested carefully before attempting to let it run by itself.

This chapter and some of the chapters to follow describe various debugging methods. They progress from very simple debugging tools such as *Monitor ROMs,* to Evaluation Boards such as the EVB described in Section 11-5, to Hardware/Software Development stations (HDSs), and currently to the Motorola Modular Development Systems (MDS05 and MDS16). The latter units are powerful testing stations built specifically for system development and debugging of the **68HC05** and **68HC16** family of MCUs.

With these tools, the program or hardware can be analyzed and corrected when a fault occurs. *System debugging* is the name given this process. A good development system not only verifies that the software does calculations and handles data correctly but that the external hardware is properly connected and controlled by the software.

11-3.1 ▼ Rudimentary Debugging Systems

Any method of testing and debugging a μC system must include at least the ability to:

1. Read or write into memory at any location.
2. Run and HALT the program.

To be really useful, a development system should also have the ability to:

3. Display or change the registers.
4. Set **breakpoints.***
5. Single-step a program (run the program one instruction at a time) and observe its effect.

When it comes to debugging a system, engineers will differ as to the best approach. Hardware engineers tend to want to look at the signals, while software engineers want to run debug programs. Undoubtedly, to do both as done by a Microcomputer Development

---

*The term *Breakpoints* refers to a software technique whereby an address can be entered to stop the user's program and return to the debugger program. This allows the designer to progress through a program to find problems. The methods are described in Section 11-6.9.

System is best, but if an MDS is not available, the software approach is next best because it will locate both types of problems.

Some primitive debugging systems used digital hardware to single-step the μP. Lights and switches were used to enter data and monitor the results. These systems are now obsolete but were discussed in the second edition of this book.

11-4 ▼ ROM MONITOR SYSTEMS

As we have been suggesting in the last nine chapters, it is possible to use a μC for many tasks. Two of those tasks can be the *development* and *testing* of software.

Since the introduction of the **6800** in 1974, many methods to debug and monitor μC operations have been used. The most common has been to develop debugging programs and place them in ROM or EPROM. These **Monitor** ROMs were then plugged into the system under test and executed as the primary program. They provided a prompt on the terminal and accepted commands from the keyboard. These systems provided RAM to allow loading the user's application program. Routines were provided in the debugger program to allow the user to examine the contents of the registers and memory, and to step through the program to find and fix any problems.

Many versions of these ROM-based debug programs have been developed, starting with one called MINIBUG that was only 256 bytes long. Most of these are now obsolete; they were discussed in the second edition of this book.

11-4.1 ▼ Terminals and Personal Computers

A data or video terminal is a combination of a keyboard, used for entering commands, and a CRT display for showing the results and the progress of the program. The combination of a Monitor ROM and a terminal is one of the earliest debugging systems and is still used in some laboratories. The use of a terminal and a Monitor ROM running in some kind of test system allows testing of concepts but requires entering programs manually. For a while this was expanded to using a system that had disk drives and its own printers to develop and test programs in the same system. These specialized systems were expensive, so alternative methods were sought. It was soon realized that inexpensive Personal Computers could be used as a terminal for a debugger ROM (by using a terminal emulation program) and to develop large programs as well. Most PCs already have an editor program that can be used for MCU program development. Simply by adding an Assembler program, such as AS11 (see Section 6-6.4), a complete facility is provided. The PCs are excellent for program development because they are equipped with disk drives for preserving programs, and a printer. Thus the MDS can be greatly simplified and made less expensive. Substituting a PC for a specialized development system takes care of software development, but the task of debugging remains. Motorola has therefore developed a number of simple *evaluation* systems to work with most of their MCUs.

11-5 ▼ 68HC11 EVB

One of the most common Motorola evaluation systems for 8-bit MCUs is the **68HC11** EValuation Board (EVB) shown in Fig. 11-1. It is a printed circuit board that contains a **68HC11** MCU and other ICs that enhance its operation. This EVB has been specifically

Figure 11-1   M68HC11EVB evaluation board.

designed to test the **68HC11,** but it is also **6800** compatible. The **6800** instruction set is a subset of the **68HC11** instruction set and **6800** programs will execute without difficulty on this EVB. The Y register in the **68HC11** can be ignored while running **6800** programs or instructions. The other registers are the same as in the **6800.**

    This EVB includes the latest Monitor debug program called BUFFALO. It is a complete inexpensive μC system that will run or debug the user's **6800** or **68HC11** programs.

    The EVB's RS232C terminal/host I/O port interface circuitry provides communication and data transfer operations between the EVB and the external terminal/host computer (as described in Section 11-9). When the EVB is used with a PC, the PC must have a communications channel available and be under the control of a communications program such as PROCOMM or KERMIT.

    The BUFFALO Debugger/Monitor program contains many features for program development and analysis. One of its best features is a one-line Assembler/Disassembler (see Section 11-6.5). This is an EVB *command* (or routine) that can be used manually to assemble instructions from mnemonics or disassemble them (to mnemonics) from previously loaded machine code. Other commands can then execute the instructions *one at a time* or in segments and observe their effects on memory, I/O ports, and the registers. This system therefore makes an excellent tool to study any of the **6800** example programs or instructions described in previous chapters. Many other features of the enhanced **68HC11** MCU, such as the Timer, can also be evaluated using this EVB.

11-5.1 ▼ Block Diagram of the EVB

The Block Diagram of the **68HC11EVB** system is shown in Fig. 11-2 and includes:

1. A **68HC11A1** MCU that incorporates within it:
   (a) An enhanced **6800** family processor
   (b) An oscillator circuit, requiring only an external inexpensive crystal, and two small capacitors
   (c) A 256-byte RAM
   (d) A 512-byte EEPROM
   (e) Other built-in peripheral features based on the PIA, ACIA, and the **6840** Timer (see Chapter 10 for details)
2. A separate **6850** ACIA to provide a second RS232C terminal interface
3. An **HC4040** baud rate generator to supply clocks for the ACIA
4. Sockets for an optional 8K RAM or EPROM
5. An 8K-byte EPROM with the BUFFALO program
6. An **MC68HC24** Port Replacement Unit (PRU) that allows the EVB to *emulate* accurately a **68HC11** with true I/O characteristics (see the EVB manual or the **68HC24** data sheet for details)

The EVB can be purchased by universities or individuals from Motorola sales offices or from the Training Department of the Semiconductor Products Sector of Motorola in Phoenix, Arizona. It requires a user-supplied +5, +12, and -12 V dc power supply.

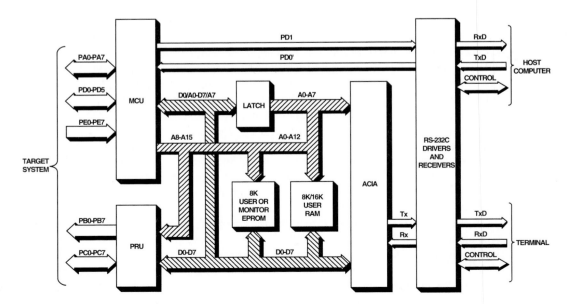

Figure 11-2 EVB block diagram.

The EVBs are not intended to take the place of more powerful and flexible tools such as the Motorola **M68HC11EVM** EValuation Module or the development systems described in Chapter 12.

11-5.2 ▼ EVB Memory Map

The memory map for the **68HC11** EVB is very similar to a typical **6800** system map, but certain differences should be noted. The EVB is normally equipped with a **68HC11A1** which has 256 bytes of internal RAM at locations 0 through $FF.

As stated in Chapter 10, the **68HC11** contains control registers for its peripherals that normally reside between $1000 and $103F (see Section 10-6.5). As explained in the earlier section, these default locations can be changed.

The **68HC11A1** normally includes a ROM from $E000 to $FFFF. In the EVB, the internal ROM is disabled and that map space is used by an external EPROM. The BUFFALO program resides in that EPROM. When the EVB's BUFFALO program is executed, it uses part of the MCU's internal RAM from $36 to $FF. Thus the remaining RAM from $00 to $35 is available for the user.

In the EVB, a separate socket for a RAM chip for user programs is provided and resides at $C000 to $DFFF. An additional optional RAM or EPROM can be installed in still another socket which puts that memory at $6000 to $7FFF. The space from $B600 to $B7FF (512 bytes) is occupied by an internal Electrically Erasable Programmable Read-Only Memory (EEPROM), which is another feature of the **68HC11** MCU (see Section 10-7.4).

11-5.3 ▼ EVBU

Motorola has introduced an even-lower-cost evaluation board called the EVBU. It has reduced capability, however, that makes it less useful as delivered. It has only two ICs: the **68HC11E9** MCU and a level-converter chip, the **MC145407,** which is used to provide the RS232 interface. This part also generates +10 and –10 V dc, so that only a 5-V power supply is needed for the EVBU. A socket is provided for an optional **68HC68T1** Real-Time Clock (RTC) (see Section 9-10). The EVBU has a slightly newer version of the BUFFALO monitor (version 3.2) but this system provides only 325 bytes of RAM for use by the developer. A wire-wrap area is provided, however, that permits building a system approximately equal to the EVB. The EVB is fully assembled with sockets for extra RAM or EPROMs. Both EVBs use the BUFFALO Monitor program and will allow the same debugging capabilities. The EVBU is a newer product and uses a newer MCU with some expanded features (512 bytes of RAM, 12K bytes of EPROM, and a slightly different version of BUFFALO). Unfortunately, the EVBU has no room for programs larger than 325 bytes in RAM unless sockets are added and wire-wrapping modifications are made.

Machine language can be entered manually (see Section 11-6.3) or assembled on the EVB or EVBU using the one-line assembler (Section 11-6.5). Other routines in the BUFFALO monitor are then used to debug the user's program.

11-6 ▼ BUFFALO MONITOR PROGRAM

The complete listing of the BUFFALO program is included in the user's manual that is shipped with the **68HC11EVBs.** Details regarding the manual are given in Section 11-12. The entire BUFFALO monitor program is included in the manual and studying the program is an excellent way to learn programming and to learn how the hardware and software work together. The various commands are described in succeeding paragraphs.

11-6.1 ▼ Restart

RESTART is an action required to start up the EVB. When the power is turned on or the RESET button is pressed, the RESET vector is fetched and the initialization routine at $E000 in the BUFFALO monitor is entered. The **68HC11**'s internal configuration is set up by the INIT routine as it writes predetermined values to the *options* and *Timer Mask* registers. This process is described in the **68HC11A1** Advanced Information manual (ADI 1207), listed in Section 11-12. These INIT routines are followed by setting the stack pointer, programming the ACIA, and then initializing the other internal serial port. As far as a user is concerned, when RESET occurs, the BUFFALO program displays its name, waits for a <cr> (or ENTER), displays a prompt, and then waits for an input command.

11-6.2 ▼ Memory display

The BUFFALO monitor commands are shown in Table 11-1. When the keyboard displays its prompt (>), a command can be given by typing the appropriate letters, as shown in the figure, followed by the parameters required by the command.

One of the most useful commands in BUFFALO is the MD (Memory Dump) command. It causes the terminal or PC to display a portion of RAM or ROM memory. MD must be followed by at least one address. If it is followed by a single address, nine lines of data will be displayed. Each line will start on a 16-byte boundary and consists of 16 bytes. If two addresses are specified after the MD, the contents of memory between those addresses will be displayed. Figure 11-3 shows such a display.

Table 11-1 BUFFALO Monitor Program Commands

COMMAND	DESCRIPTION
ASM [(address)]	Assembler/disassembler
BF (address1) (address2) (data)	Block fill memory with data
BR [–] [(address)]. . .	Breakpoint set
BULK	Bulk erase EEPROM
BULKALL	Bulk erase EEPROM + CONFIG register
CALL [(address)]	Execute subroutine
G [(address)]	Execute program
HELP	Display monitor commands
LOAD	Download (S-records) via host port
LOAD (T)	Download (S-records) via terminal port
MD [(address1) [(address2)]]	Dump memory to terminal
MM [(address)]	Memory modify
MOVE (address1) (address2) [(destination)]	Move memory to new location
P	Proceed/continue from breakpoint
RM [p,y,x,a,b,c,s]	Register modify
T [(n)]	Trace $1–$FF instructions
TM	Enter transparent mode
VERIFY	Compare memory to download data via host port
VERIFY (T)	Compare memory to download data via terminal port

EXAMPLE 11-1

In Fig. 11-3, what are the contents of memory location $F81C?

SOLUTION

Location $F81C is the twelfth entry on the line beginning at $F810 (remember to start counting at 0). It is circled on the figure and contains the number $CD.

11-6.3 ▼ Memory Modify

The Memory Modify (MM) command can be used to change the contents of a RAM memory location. If the user types an "MM" (upper or lower case), followed by an address and a carriage return <cr>, BUFFALO will display the contents of that location, as shown in Fig. 11-4.

If the data in that location must be changed, the new data is entered from the keyboard (one or two hex characters) followed by a carriage return <cr>, a line feed <lf>, or a space. (If the keyboard does not have an <lf> key, a control-J can be used.) If an lf is used, the system stores the byte and displays the next address and its contents on the next line. It then waits for the next operator response. New data can now be entered at the new location. If a space is used, it displays the byte in the next location but without an address. This is acceptable for a few bytes, but the user tends to lose track unless the address is displayed. Another line feed or space will display the next location and an up arrow (^) will back up to the previous location. A carriage return (or ENTER) terminates the Memory Modify (MM) routine, and returns to the prompt, ready for the next command. The last line of the display in Fig. 11-4 shows the display of the data when spaces

```
>MD F7D0

F7D0    AA  AA  AA  AA  AA  AA  AA  AA  AA  AA  AA  AA  AA  AA  AA  AA
F7E0    AA  AA  AA  AA  AA  AA  AA  AA  AA  AA  AA  AA  AA  AA  AA  AA
F7F0    AA  AA  AA  AA  AA  AA  AA  AA  AA  AA  AA  AA  AA  AA  AA  AA
F800    AA  AA  AA  AA  AA  AA  AA  AA  AA  AA  AA  AA  AA  AA  AA  AA
F810    AA  AA  AA  AA  AA  AA  AA  AA  AA  AA  AA  12 (CD) 34  56  EE
F820    AA  AA  AA  AA  AA  AA  AA  AA  AA  AA  AA  AA  AA  AA  AA  AA
F830    AA  AA  AA  AA  AA  AA  AA  AA  AA  AA  AA  AA  AA  AA  AA  AA
F840    AA  AA  AA  AA  AA  AA  AA  AA  AA  AA  AA  AA  AA  AA  AA  AA
F850    AA  AA  AA  AA  AA  AA  AA  AA  AA  AA  AA  AA  AA  AA  AA  AA
A   >

>MD C000 C020

C000    FF  FF  FF  FF  FF  FF  FF  FF  FF  FF  FF  FF  FF  FF  FF  FF
C010    FF  FF  FF  FF  FF  FF  FF  FF  FF  FF  FF  FF  FF  FF  FF  FF
C020    FF  FF  FF  FF  FF  FF  FF  FF  FF  FF  FF  FF  FF  FF  FF  FF
B   >
```

Figure 11-3 Memory Display (MD) command.

```
mm     c100   cr

c100   F7    44   1f
c101   55    33   1f
c102   A5    1a   1f
c103   BA    ↑
c102   1A    1b   1f
c103   BA    1f
c104   41    cr

mm    c100   cr
>
C100   44   33   1B   BA   41  cr
>
```

All operator entries are underlined

Figure 11-4   Memory Display/Change using the MM command.

are used instead of line feeds. Any number of spaces can be entered to space across the page. The MM command can be used to view or change bytes after a program is downloaded from the host, as described in the following section.

EXAMPLE 11-2

Explain what happened in Fig. 11-4.

SOLUTION

First the MM command was entered to change location $C100. Then the following occurred:

Line 1:	The contents of $C100 were changed to $44.
Line 2:	$C101 was changed to $33.
Line 3:	$C102 was changed to $1A.
Line 4:	The user decided that $C102 should really contain 1B, so he typed an ^ to back up.
Line 5:	$C102 is changed to 1B.
Line 6:	The contents of $C103 are correct, so the user only typed an lf, which left them unchanged.
Line 7:	The contents of $C104, $41, were now displayed. The user decided to exit MM and typed ENTER.

The contents of all the locations were reviewed by using the MM command again, but with spaces this time.

Note that the program displays all hex numbers in upper case but entries can be either upper or lower case.

11-6.4 ▼ Register Modify

In analyzing programs, the CPU registers must be displayed and changed as well as memory. The Register Modify command (RM) is provided for this purpose. When RM is entered, followed by a <cr>, it displays all of the registers as shown in Fig. 11-5a.

On the next line it repeats the contents of the P (program counter) register. If the user wishes to change the contents of the PC, he simply types in a new value followed by ENTER. In Fig. 11-5a, the contents of the PC were changed from $C007 to $C020.

The user can change the contents of any other register by typing RM followed by a register designation. In Fig. 11-5b, the user typed in RM X. The X register was now displayed on the second line and was changed from $FF00 to $C020.

After typing RM, the user can access all registers by typing spaces as shown in Fig. 11-5c. If a *space* is entered, the next register is displayed below the first, on the next line. Another space displays the next register, and so on, as shown. If any register must be changed, the new data is entered prior to entering the space as shown (the X register is again changed to $1234). If a <cr> is entered at any time, even after the first display, it

```
>RM<cr>
P-C007   Y-7982    X-FF00    A-44    B-70    C-C0    S-0054
P-C007   C020<cr>
```

a. Changing the PC register

```
>RM X<cr>
P-C020   Y-7982    X-FF00    A-44    B-70    C-C0    S-0054
X-FF00   C020<cr>
```

b. Changing a selected register

```
>RM<cr>
P-C020   Y-7982    X-C020    A-44    B-70    C-C0    S-0054
P-C020   Space Bar
Y-7982   Space Bar
X-C020   1234SPace Bar
A-44     SPace Bar
B-70     SPace Bar
C-C0     SPace Bar
S-0054   SPace Bar
>
```

c. Using Spaces to display registers

Figure 11-5   Register Modify (RM) command. All operator entries are underlined.

terminates the Register Modify (RM) command and returns to the command loop. This is indicated by the prompt in column 1.

The contents of the CPU registers associated with the user's program are kept in locations in the monitor program RAM, called *Pseudoregisters*. In the case of the EVB, those locations are $9E through $A6 (9 bytes). They are updated each time the EVB processes a command.

11-6.5 ▼ ASM Command

One of the most useful features of the EVB is the one-line Assembler/Disassembler. This command allows the user to enter the assembly mnemonics which are translated by the program and written as machine language directly into memory. Figure 11-6 shows how the ASM command is used. The operator first types ASM followed by an address. The monitor program responds with the instruction at that address and presents the operator with an indented carat (>). The user can now type in an assembly language statement. ASM translates the statement into machine code, modifies the locations, and presents the next location (in the figure LDAA #55 is translated into 86 55). The $, which is required in Assemblers, is not permitted in BUFFALO. It assumes that all numbers are hex. As also shown in Fig. 11-6, the user can continue to enter assembly language instructions into the following locations. No symbols are allowed and the destinations of branches or jumps must be entered as absolute addresses.

The user exits ASM by typing control-A. This is an excellent way to generate a small program segment for evaluation of a concept. Once the concepts have been entered and evaluated, the program can be written on the host and downloaded as described in the next section.

```
>ASM C000
C000 STX $FFFF              Immediate mode addressing, requires #
     >LDAA #55              before operand.
      86 55
C002 STX $FFFF              Object mode addressing.
     >STAA C0
      97 C0
C004 STX $FFFF              Index mode, if offset = 0 (,X) will not
     >LDS 0.X               be accepted.
      AE 00
C006 STX $FFFF              Branch out of range message.
     >BRA C500

Branch out of range
C006 STX $FFFF              Branch offsets calculated automatically,
     >BRA C030              address required as conditional branch
      20 28                 operand.
C00B STX $FFFF
     >(CTRL)A               Assembler operation terminated.
     >
```

Figure 11-6 ASM Command. (All entries by the operatorare underlined).

11-6.6 ▼ LOAD

The BUFFALO monitor includes a LOAD function that will download an object program in S-record format (see Section 6-7 or 11-9.3) from a Host computer such as an IBM-PC. In method 1, the serial port (usually COM1) of the PC must be connected to the terminal port of the EVB using an RS232 cable. In this case the Host also acts as a terminal by using terminal emulation communications software such as PROCOMM, Kermit, or perhaps MacTerminal or White Knight (if a Macintosh is being used) (see the references in Section 11-12).

The downloaded program must have been assembled properly on the Host, with the ORG statement set to an address that matches the RAM locations. The bytes received from the port are stored in those locations specified by the addresses in each S-record.

To begin to download, the command LOAD T <cr> is sent to the EVB. The user then exits from the communications link back to the HOST system and sends the file using a file transfer feature of the terminal program.

If the S-record file being loaded attempts to write to a location in ROM or to a location where there is no RAM, the "error addr XXXX" message will be sent to the terminal. If the LOAD completes successfully, the "done" message will be displayed.

If, after a time, the EVB appears to do nothing, the user can enter a control-A or depress the RESET button to regain control of the EVB. Then he (or she) could check memory to ascertain if any of the program was written to the EVB's RAM, but that is not likely if the "done" message was not displayed. The download may never have started because the path or filename was wrong or misspelled, or possibly it was aborted when an address error was encountered.

Method 2 is better able to cope with these problems because the correct filename and path can be verified. In this method, files are downloaded by connecting the Host to the Host port of the EVB and a terminal (or another PC using Terminal Emulation software) to the terminal port with the proper RS232C cables (see Section 11-9). This method cannot be used with the EVBU to download programs because it does not have a Host port. The Host path, using method 2, can also be through *modems*. If the Host is another MS-DOS computer, a *CTTY COM1* command is entered on that MS-DOS machine, which switches DOS control to the COM1 serial port. We then go to the terminal and enter BUFFALO's *Transparent Mode command* (TM). This will cause the DOS prompt from the Host to be displayed on the terminal as shown in Fig. 11-7. This allows us to communicate with the host to prepare it for the download of a file: for example, to change to the directory that has the desired file. This file would contain the S-record object program that has previously been assembled on the host. We can verify that the file is present and that our syntax is correct by entering a command such as "type hc11.lx." This will use the host's *type* command to display the S-records on the EVB's terminal, as shown in Fig. 11-7. Once the communications are possible (assuring that the cables, baud rates, other port parameters, and the filename are correct), the TM mode is exited (using control-A). After getting the EVB's prompt, the *load* command is then entered on the EVB's terminal, as shown in Fig. 11-7. A typical entry would be "load type hc11.lx." The "load" part of the command sets up the BUFFALO program, to receive S-records, ready to put them in memory, and sends the rest of this command to the host. The DOS *type* command causes the host to start listing the *hc11.lx* object file as it did

```
>tm <cr>                     (EVB's Transparent Mode command)

A>  C:<cr>                   (Host's prompt, assuming it is ON and
ready)

C>  type  hcll.lx            (Host's command to list the S-record
file)

S10B0020860FB700307EC160B9
S109C1608EDFFFBDC200EA
S106C2004C5C3956
S9030000FC

C>     ^A                    (TM's exit command)

>load  type  hcll.lx  <cr>   (Download command)
done
>md  20  27  <cr>

0020 86 0F B7 00 30 FF FF FF FF FF FF FF FF FF FF FF
>md  c160  c166  <cr>

C160 8E DF FF BD C2 00 FF FF FF FF FF FF FF FF FF FF
>md  c200  c202  <cr>

C200 4C 5C 39 FF FF FF FF FF FF FF FF FF FF FF FF FF
```

Figure 11-7 Typical download procedure.

before, but this time it goes into the EVB's memory. When the S9 record is received, the EVB exits from the LOAD routine and sends the word *done* to the EVB's terminal. The EVB's prompt is then displayed, ready for another command. If an error occurs during the load, the "error addr xxxx" message is displayed. Once the "done" message appears, the user can check to see if the program is actually in the proper memory locations. The last three commands shown in Fig. 11-7 show the use of the MD command to display portions of the memory where it will be seen that the bytes are actually in place.

11-6.7 ▼ GO to User's Program

The G command is used to start program execution. It will pick up the address entered with the G command and run the program starting at that point. Of course, once the program has been started with the G command, it runs at full speed, but this must never be done if the program has not been tested for errors. (It could crash and there would be no way to tell where the error was.) Most commonly, a means to stop the program must be installed before attempting to run uninhibited. BUFFALO has two methods of doing this: TRACE and BREAKPOINTS. These commands (described in Sections 11-6.8 and 11-6.9) effectively stop the program at the appropriate time (to be explained) and return control to BUFFALO (displays the prompt) and waits for a new command.

11-6.8 ▼ TRACE

The TRACE (T) command runs a single user instruction and then displays the op code just executed and the CPU registers. **TRACE** is also known as the *run-one-instruction* command. It is a convenient way to step through a program instruction by instruction. The correctness of the user's program instructions can be observed by studying the display of the registers, particularly the Condition Code (or status) register, before and after each instruction is executed.*

To use TRACE to examine a program's operation, the Program Counter is first set to the address of the instruction to be tested by using the RM command. A T command is then entered to execute that instruction. A portion of a user's test program is shown in Fig. 11-8a and the results of the trace are shown in Fig. 11-8b. The μC will run the instruction pointed to by the Program Counter at normal clock speed. It gets the register

```
0020  86 0F     LDAA   #$F
0022  B7 0030   STAA   $30
0025  7E C160   JMP    $C160

C160  8E DFFF   LDS    $DFFF
C163  BD C200   JSR    $C200
C166  .. ....

C200  4C        INCA
C201  5C        INCB
C202  39        RTS
```

a) User's program partial listing

```
>rm
P-FFFF Y-FFFF X-FFFF A-0F B-FF C-FF S-FFFF
P-FFFF C160<cr>
>t<cr>

OP- 8E
P-C160 Y-FFFF X-FFFF A-0F B-FF C-C8 S-DFFF
>t<cr>

OP- BD
P-C163 Y-FFFF X-FFFF A-0F B-FF C-C8 S-DFFD
>t<cr>

OP- 4C
P-C200 Y-FFFF X-FFFF A-10 B-FF C-C8 S-DFFD
>t<cr>

OP- 5C
P-C201 Y-FFFF X-FFFF A-10 B-00 C-C4 S-DFFD
>t<cr>

OP- 39
P-C166 Y-FFFF X-FFFF A-10 B-00 C-C4 S-DFFF
>
```

b) EVB responses

Figure 11-8 Use of the TRACE command.

*Recall that the branch instructions either branch or go to the next instruction, depending on the state of these codes. These are the decision makers.

contents from the stack, stores them in the pseudoregisters, and displays them. It then reenters the BUFFALO command loop, displays the prompt (>), and awaits the next command. Figure 11-8b shows the T command repeated for five instructions. It is possible to see the effect on the registers for each instruction traced.

The T command is probably the most useful of all to find errors since the program can be stepped through a program segment one instruction at a time while observing the register changes and the effect on the program branching due to the Condition Codes. The T command uses an EVB hardware interrupt and thus will also trace through instructions in ROM. The method is slow but it allows the user to check the program's progress very thoroughly.

11-6.9 ▼ Breakpoints

A computer must often run through several thousand instructions before it reaches a segment that has an error and must be debugged. Trying to trace through these instructions is much too burdensome, so **breakpoints** are used. A breakpoint command is entered, along with the address of a particular instruction. The user's program then runs until it reaches that instruction, where it halts and returns to the debugger. The registers or memory contents can then be examined. This is known as *running to a breakpoint,* or simply *using a breakpoint.*

The breakpoint is placed into the program at some point between sections or segments of instructions, such as after an initialization routine or after the RAM is cleared. These segments of the user's program are run at normal clock speed, and the breakpoint is used to stop it at any desired instruction. The user can continue to trace the next instructions or may decide to resume running the program at full speed. If so, the P (proceed) command is entered and the program will *proceed* to the next breakpoint. Thus it is possible to execute portions of the user's program, using breakpoints, until the program does something improper or crashes. The bad program segment can then be examined in detail by using the trace routine. Breakpoints are the fastest way to find problems in a program and are therefore frequently used to troubleshoot μC systems.

In BUFFALO, up to four breakpoints can be stored at one time. They are kept in a *breakpoint table.* To *insert a breakpoint,* it is only necessary to enter the BR command, followed by an address. This places the address in the breakpoint table. To *remove a breakpoint,* the operator enters BR followed by a – (minus) and the address. A BR followed by a – and no address will remove all breakpoints. The BR command alone will display the addresses of all breakpoints in the table.

The breakpoint routines temporarily insert a SoftWare Interrupt (SWI) instruction in place of a user's program instruction, and provides an *interrupt service routine* that displays the contents of the pseudoregisters. Note also that the use of SWI in this way requires that the user's program be in RAM. This is necessary, however, because it is then easily possible to correct the instructions where required. This is known as *patching* the program (see Section 11-6.11). Since RAM is used, this also means that the user's program must be loaded (see Section 11-6.6) either from the Host's disk (using S-records) or manually from the keyboard as described in Sections 11-6.3 and 11-6.5.

EXAMPLE 11-3

A segment of a user program is shown in Fig. 11-8a. It starts at location $20 but jumps to other areas of memory. Describe the methods used with the BUFFALO program to perform breakpoint testing of this user's program and system. Location $C160 was chosen for the first breakpoint, with location $C200 as the second and $C166 as the third.

SOLUTION

The user's program, shown in Fig. 11-8a, can be put into memory using the MM or ASM commands as described in Sections 11-6.3 and 11-6.5, or assembled on a Host and downloaded as described in Section 11-6.6. Figure 11-9 shows the BUFFALO commands required to enter the breakpoints and their responses. The steps are:

1. The first breakpoint is entered using the BR command. This displays the breakpoints on the next line, and $C160 is shown. The second breakpoint is then entered, and both breakpoints are then displayed along with the zeros for the two unused breakpoints.

2. The third BR is then entered and all three are displayed.

3. The Go command is used to start the program (G 20).

4. When the breakpoint is encountered, the register contents are displayed with no perceptible delay, since the execution up to the SWI is at full clock speed. Note that accumulator A has changed to 0F as a result of the first instructions of the user program, and the SP is $004A, which is the default value used by the EVB.

5. The P command is entered to *proceed* to the next breakpoint, and this causes the next register display. Note that the PC is at $C200, as it should be, and the SP is $DFFD because the SP was set to $DFFF by the fourth instruction. The return address has been put on the stack before stopping at the breakpoint, which is at the beginning of the subroutine.

6. Another P command will cause the program to *proceed* to the last breakpoint.

   Note that accumulators A and B have been changed by the subroutine routine at $C200.

As stated above, a breakpoint automatically inserts an SWI (op code 3F) in place of the op code for the instruction. After executing the breakpoint, BUFFALO will replace the SWI with the original instruction. It sometimes happens, however, that the program does not reach the breakpoint because it goes into a loop or encounters an error and branches improperly. In that case the EVB may have to be reset, but the 3F op codes will remain in the program.

```
>br c160 <cr>

C160 0000 0000 0000
>br c200 <cr>

C160 C200 0000 0000
>br c166 <cr>

C160 C200 C166 0000
>g 20 <cr>

P=C160 Y=FFFF X-FFFF A-0F B-FF C-D0 S-004A
>p <cr>

P-C200 Y-FFFF X-FFFF A-0F B-FF C-C8 S-DFFD
>p <cr>

P-C166 Y-FFFF X-FFFF A-10 B-00 C-C4 S-DFFF
>
```

Figure 11-9   Breakpoint operation for Example 11-3.

The appearance of 3F in a program instead of the original instructions often puzzles students. After the EVB is reset, the user may have to restore the original op codes before the debugging can be resumed. The program can also be restored by having the operator reload it. This may be necessary because if the program ran away, it may have altered some of the instructions. A breakpoint can then be entered at the address that was reached successfully and the program can then be traced from there until the incorrect or omitted instruction is found.

A common programming problem is the failure to set the stack before beginning the program. In a typical program, if the stack pointer isn't set to the planned area, the program will attempt to "stack" things wherever it is and will frequently, but not always, cause the program to *bomb out* since some of the code or variables get overwritten. The EVB's use of a *default* stack (at 004A) avoids trouble when debugging if the user forgets to set up a stack, but the stack must be set to an unused area of RAM when an attempt is made to run the program in the system under development.

When a Breakpoint is reached or a Trace completed, the registers are first stored in the stack area by the interrupt, moved to the pseudoregisters, and then displayed on the terminal by the EVB's *interrupt service routine*. All this can be seen in Fig. 11-10. The MD command was used as shown in the lower part of Fig. 11-10 to display the area of Buffalo's RAM from $40 to $AF. There is both a monitor and a default user's stack area. Note that prior to the user setting up his or her own stack, the register values are stored here ($42 through $4A) in reverse order. The pseudoregister locations at $9E through $A8 contain the current information. The monitor stack (at $68) is never displayed by BUFFALO, but reference to the BUFFALO program listing in the EVB's User's manual will show that the addresses of $E4E7, $E7FB, and $E18C in that stack are legitimate return addresses for the MD function of the BUFFALO program.

```
>rm

P-C160 Y-1234 X-5678 A-0F B-08 C-C0 S-004A
 P-C160

>g 20

P-C160.Y-1234 X-5678 A-0F B-08 C-C0 S-004A
>p

P-C200 Y-1234 X-5678 A-0F B-08 C-C8 S-DFFD
>p

P-C166 Y-1234 X-5678 A-10 B-09 C-C0 S-DFFF
>md 40 af

0040 C0  06  C0  08  0F  56  78  12  34  C1  60  FF  E4  E4  E4  E4        Vx  4  `
0050 95  E3  C6  00  E4  E4  E4  95  E3  C6  00  E4  95  E3  C6  00
0060 B4  00  20  E4  E7  E7  FB  E1  8C  6D  64  20  34  30  20  61  p  a      md 40  a
0070 66  0D  FF  FF  FF  FF  FF  FF  FF  FF  FF  FF  FF  FF  FF  FF  f
0080 FF  FF  FF  FF  FF  FF  FF  FF  FF  FF  FF  FF  4D  44  20  30            MD  0
0090 2F  FF  FF  FF  00  AF  C1  60  C2  00  C1  66  00  00  C1  66  /   `      f  f
00A0 12  34  56  78  10  09  C0  DF  FF  01  01  01  00  02  00  40  4Vx       @
```

Figure 11-10 Use of EVB commands.

11-6.10 ▼ Servicing a User's Interrupts

The BUFFALO EPROM in the EVB occupies the memory area from $E000 through $FFFF. This includes the normal vector area from $FFD6 to $FFFF. Many systems under development, however, need the ability to test response to interrupts. Some way must be provided to change the vectors to accommodate different users' programs. This is done in the BUFFALO monitor by setting up a vector table in RAM that is accessed indirectly by the normal vectors in EPROM. The vector locations in EPROM *point* to locations in RAM (at $C4 through $FD).

Each group of three bytes in this area consists of the op code for a JUMP instruction (7E), followed by the address of the service routine for the particular interrupt. For example, the three locations starting at $EE are used to store the user's IRQ vector. When the user's *interrupt service routines* address is entered in these locations and an IRQ interrupt occurs, the μP will jump to the service routine *indirectly* through these vectors. If the IRQ interrupt is involved, the IRQ mask bit must not be set for it to respond.

EXAMPLE 11-4

The IRQ service routine is to start at $C123. What must be done to the vectors to cause this to happen?

SOLUTION

First the IRQ vector, at $FFF8 and $FFF9, must point to the RAM vectors at $00EE. This means that $FFF8 must contain 00 and $FFF9 must contain $EE. These vectors are already in the BUFFALO monitor's ROM, so no action is required.

The RAM at $00EE must be programmed as follows:

```
00EE        7E        Op code for JUMP
00EF        C1        Address of the
00F0        23        service routine
```

When an IRQ occurs, the contents of $FFF8 and $FFF9 will vector the interrupt to $00EE, where it will be instructed to jump to $C123, the start of the service routine.

Each time the EVB is RESET, BUFFALO fills all RAM vector locations with a jump to a routine called STOPIT, which executes a **68HC11** STOP instruction (STOP is one of the **68HC11**'s added instructions). If an interrupt should occur at this point, it would HALT the μP and require a RESET to recover. Therefore, before allowing an interrupt, the user must set up the expected interrupt's vector location (in the RAM table) to contain a jump instruction which points to the user's service routine. BUFFALO also installs interrupt vectors for SWI, as well as some for the **68HC11A8** internal peripherals, such as the timer and I/O ports that are used by BUFFALO. If the user wants to use those features in a system, he or she can install vectors but then cannot use the Trace or Breakpoint features of BUFFALO.

11-6.11 ▼ Program Patching

There are two ways of correcting bugs (or programming errors). The first way is to reassemble and reload the program. If the bug is relatively minor, however, such as loading the wrong register or accessing the wrong address, it may easily be *patched*—that is, corrected in memory by changing a few bytes. With this type of patch, a written record should be made of the patch so that the source program may be corrected later. It is also a good idea to save the patched program on disk so that the program, with its corrections, can be restored in memory in the event of a runaway or program crash while pursuing the next bug.*

Debugging a machine language program usually results in correcting inverted logic (BNE where BEQ is needed), replacing the value of an offset to branch to a different place, or inserting omitted statements. In the first two cases, a single byte of code is simply replaced with another. In the last case, however, no room exists for the addition. This requires another form of *program patching* where additional instructions are needed. The patch to add the instructions consists of a jump from the main program to a vacant area of memory. The additional instructions are written in this area, plus those instructions in the main program that were written over by the jump. The patch is completed by jumping back to the main program.

*The EVB or EVBU do not have a SAVE command for this purpose, but some of the more advanced Microcomputer Development Systems do (see Chapter 12).

EXAMPLE 11-5

Assume that the following multiplication routine (similar to Table 5-3) is installed in memory at $C000 using the ASM command of the EVB. The listing will be as shown in Fig. 11-11. Now assume that the stack pointer had to be initialized at the start of the program. How can this be done?

(a) Assume that the addresses before location $C000 are available.

(b) Assume that there is no memory just before location $C000, as is the case with the EVB.

SOLUTION

(a) If the locations before $C000 are available, we can write the 3-byte LDS IMMEDIATE instruction into location $BFFD, $BFFE, and $BFFF. Then the starting address of the program can be changed to $BFFD and the program will operate correctly.

(b) If memory before $C000 is unavailable, a patch must be made. The contents of locations $C000, $C001, and $C002 are replaced by a JMP to $C020 (i.e., 7E C0 20). This assumes that $C020 is a vacant memory area.

The patched listing, which includes the main program instructions that were overwritten by the jump to the patch plus the necessary additional instruction, is shown in Fig. 11-11.

The example shows that it is unwise to start a test program at the beginning of a block of memory. If a program is started at $C100 instead, and the need arises to add instructions at the beginning of the program, locations $C000 through $C0FF can be used instead of having to patch by jumping.

If, after a program is written, an instruction is found to be unnecessary, it can be replaced by a NOP (or several NOPs). This removes the instruction without causing the entire program to be rewritten. If a group of instructions are found to be unnecessary, they can be skipped by inserting a jump following the last useful instruction to the point where the program must resume.

All of the foregoing changes are made only during program development. After several patches have been collected, the source program should be edited and the bugs corrected. Then the program can be recompiled or reassembled, and testing can continue with the new version of the object program. If the program bug is major, such as an error in program organization, it may be necessary to go directly to the reedit, recompile, or reassemble procedure. Eventually, the program should be "cleaned up," eliminating useless NOPs and awkward jumps, before it is finalized and written to a ROM.

11-6.12 ▼ Debug Summary

The BUFFALO program and the EVB are used to debug and patch programs until they work. This **68HC11** EVB system is about the simplest possible development tool that can be used effectively. The features of BUFFALO allow software and hardware debugging, although they are not as easily done as with the development systems to be described later.

C000	C6	08	LDAB	#8	Put 8 in B register
C002	D7	31	STAB	$31	Save shift count in $31
C004	D6	30	LDAB	$30	Load multiplicand into B
C006	4F		CLRA		Clear A
C007	74	0034	LSR	$34	Shift multiplier right
C00A	24	01	BCC	$C00D	Skip to $C00D if carry clear
C00C	1B		ABA		Add accumulators
C00D	46		RORA		Shift product MS byte Rt.
C00E	76	0033	ROR	$33	Shift product reg LS byte
C011	7A	0031	DEC	$31	Decrement count
C014	25	F1	BNE	$C007	Branch back to C007 if not 0
C016	97	32	STAA	$32	Is 0. Done. Store MS byte
C018	20	FE	BRA	*	HALT program by looping

a. Original Program

C000	7E	C020	JMP	$C020	Jump to patch
C020	8E	xxxx	LDS	#$xxxx	Set the stack pointer to xxxx
C023	C6	08	LDAB	#8	Replace overwritten instructions
C025	D7	31	STAB	$31	
C028	7E	C004	JMP	$C004	Return to main program

b. Added Patch

```
30  Multiplicand
31  Count
32  Product Register (MS byte)
33  Product Register (LS byte)
34  Multiplier
```

Figure 11-11 Program for Example 11-5.

The EVBU, if modified by adding additional circuitry in the wire-wrap area, works almost the same as the EVB. Minor differences exist in the commands.

11-7 ▼ ALTERNATE DEBUGGING METHODS

Another approach to program development is to use the third-party software products that are available. For example, P & E Microcomputer Systems Inc. of Woburn, Massachusetts, has a number of programs designed specifically to work with the Motorola Evaluation Boards. They have one product called the IASM11, for example, that is an MS-DOS based Editor/Cross-Assembler/Communications package. Figure 11-12 shows one of the displays provided by this program. This is a window-oriented program that features the ability to switch quickly from one function to the other. Thus it

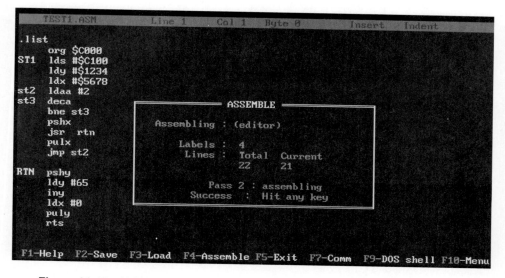

Figure 11-12   IASM11 Display screen showing EDIT and ASSEMBLE windows.

is possible to write a source program using the IASM11 editor, as shown on the left of Fig. 11-12, and with one keystroke (F4), to assemble it. The assembly window opens briefly as shown. Errors are highlighted in the source for instant correction. Once assembled, the communications window is opened (by another keystroke), as shown in Fig. 11-13, and the object is downloaded to the EVB or EVBU with a few more keystrokes. You then communicate with BUFFALO in the EVB, just as with any communications program, and the object can be debugged in the EVB using BUFFALO as described previously. If program corrections are necessary, a few more keystrokes put you back into the

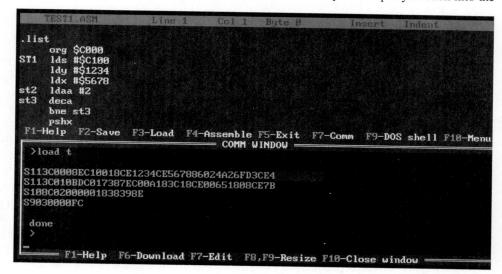

Figure 11-13   IASM11 display screen showing COMM window on top of Edit window.

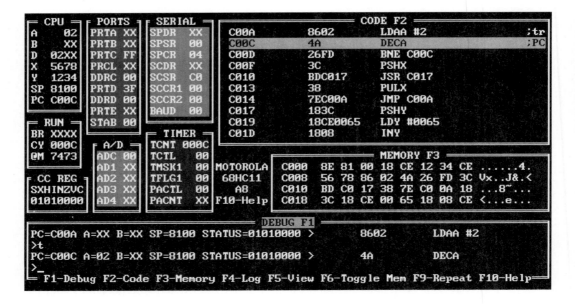

Figure 11-14 SIM11 display screen showing conditions after the four instructions have been executed.

editor. IASM11 has a HELP function that lists the standard Motorola instruction set mnemonics and directives as well as the required IASM commands. Debugging in the EVB is no different than when using a communications program in any IBM-PC host, but the ease of switching back to the editor and assembler is very efficient. P & E has similar user interface programs for **68HC05** and **68HC16** systems.

Still another method for development is the use of a **simulator** program. The window displayed by P & E's SIM11 program for the **68HC11** is shown in Fig. 11-14. This program runs in the MS-DOS system and will load **68HC11** object code and allow it to be debugged without the need for any evaluation hardware. The Trace and Breakpoint features work the same as if the program were being executed in an evaluation board. The program *simulates* the **68HC11** CPU. It has multiple windows open at the same time showing the registers, disassembled code, memory, timer registers, and so on. This makes it easy to see what is happening and speeds development. Figure 11-14 shows the SIM11 display after the object file of the same TEST1 program, shown in Fig. 11-13, has been loaded. The PC was set to $C000 and the first four instructions have been executed (using the Trace command). The diassembled code is shown in the CODE F2 window at the upper right, with the current PC location highlighted. The hex code in memory is shown just below that in the MEMORY F3 window, and the register window in the upper left shows the register values as set by the first four instructions. If several more instructions were traced, the CC REG window at the lower left would undoubtedly be of interest to watch the zero bit of the CCR. This all shows how a program can be tested and fixed without requiring any hardware (other than an IBM-compatible Personal Computer) and this SIM11 program.

This simulator program is useful to debug the software routines but the EVBs, on the other hand, provide this same software testing ability and also allow interactive testing with the external hardware by reading or writing to the I/O registers.

P & E has similar programs for the **68HC05**s and **68HC16**s (which we discuss in Chapter 16). The simulator program does not include an editor or assembler. The Motorola EVMs (or EVSs) come with P & E IASM software. Unfortunately, the SIMxx programs (and IASM for the EVBs) have to be purchased (in lieu of an emulator). They are all very easy to use and will save the engineer's time. These trade-offs must frequently be made in the business of developing μC systems.

Many similar products are provided by the many other third-party vendors. Avocet Systems of Rockport, Maine, is another company that makes assemblers and simulators for Motorola μPs. The *MCU Toolbox* catalog cited in Section 11-12 lists several other companies.

11-8 ▼ μC DEVELOPMENT SYSTEMS

The Monitor ROM systems, including the EVBs described previously, all have limitations that make some tasks difficult. Microprocessor Development Systems (MDSs) provide added capability due to larger debug programs and added hardware features. These greatly enhance the capability to debug both software and hardware and to further simplify the development process.

Several more capable MDSs have been created to overcome the limitations of evaluation kits and modules. In addition, most of them will program EPROM or EEPROMs. They also have enough memory that any of the MCUs can be emulated.

Since most development systems are a complete operational system to which the user's system can be attached, the problems of getting the user's system running are greatly reduced. Each of the major manufacturers of μPs has introduced such an instrument for their products, and we describe several Motorola systems in Chapter 12. Most MDSs will support several different μP types. Although all μP development systems provide the ability to develop and debug software, not all of them provide a full hardware emulation capability or the ability to evaluate prototype or production hardware.

11-9 ▼ HOST COMPUTER COMMUNICATIONS

The advent of MCU development systems such as the EVBs have placed new emphasis on communications between computers. The EVB can be operated in a stand-alone mode (without a host) to execute instructions and exercise the target hardware, but all test programs must then be either written in machine language or generated by the one-line assembler. Some short user programs may be written in this way, but anything over 20 lines or so is usually produced on a *Host* computer and *downloaded* to the EVB. Motorola provides software to do this with MS-DOS or Macintosh Hosts. Therefore, there is a need to communicate with a local PC, or in some cases, remotely with PCs or mainframes via Modems.

To be useful as a host, a computer must be able to generate the μC's object code and have a communications program available to transmit it to the development system.

This program must be more than a terminal emulator because the object program to be transmitted is usually in a disk file. The communications program must be able to read the disk and send the object file to the test system via its serial port.

Motorola and a number of third-party suppliers are now making Assemblers or Compilers that run on PCs or mainframe computers. These programs will produce object code for many Motorola processors. Fortunately, The Motorola S-record concept can be used to download the object codes to the MDSs. Also since S-records are implemented in ASCII–Hex characters, most computers have a communications program that will transmit them.

The EVB and several EValuation Modules (EVMs) that are described in Chapter 12 have two RS232C ports for communicating with a terminal and a Host computer. They also have a Transparent Mode (TM) command similar to that of other Motorola Monitor ROMs for use with the two-port configuration. This is shown for the EVB in Fig. 11-15 as Configuration 2. It is also possible to communicate and download through the Terminal port with one cable as shown in configuration 1, but the feedback on the screen is not as helpful (see Section 11-6.6).

A number of items are involved in this communication process:

1. The ASCII standard
2. The RS232 standard
3. The Motorola S-record standard
4. Methods of "flow control"
5. Baud rate conventions
6. The Host's communication port requirements
7. Terminal communications programs

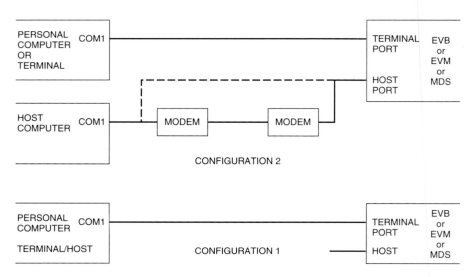

Figure 11-15 Communications configurations.

11-9.1 ▼ ASCII Standard

The American Standard Code for Information Interchange (ASCII) has been adopted by nearly all computer and terminal manufacturers. The ASCII standard is described in Section 8-7.1 and the character codes are shown in Appendix D.

11-9.2 ▼ RS232 Standard

The RS232C standard describes the hardware interface that has been adopted as the standard for use between terminals and computers (see Section 8-9.2). It is also used for computer-to-computer communications. RS232C defines names of signal lines and signal levels. A de facto standard connector with the appropriate pin numbers has also been adopted. Originally, this standard was designed to work with Modems and thus several **handshaking** signals are involved. These signals can be a source of confusion, particularly when Modems are not needed.

Figure 11-16 shows the full implementation (for asynchronous systems) of the RS232 interface. The standard specifies two interfaces: Data Terminal Equipment (DTE), typically a terminal or the serial port of a computer, and Data Communications Equipment (DCE), typically a Modem. The use of DTE to describe a terminal should be easily understood, but it should be noted that any device that is intended to talk to a terminal must be connected as a DCE (i.e., a Modem or a Host computer). Also, when one computer talks to another directly (without Modems), one must be connected as a Terminal (DTE) and the other as a Modem (DCE).

In addition to the data lines, terminals normally send control signals on the Request To Send (RTS) and Data Terminal Ready (DTR) lines and receive signals on Clear To Send (CTS), Data Carrier Detect (DCD), and sometimes on the Data Set Ready (DSR) line. Both configurations have a transmit data (TxD) line and a Receive Data line (RxD). A signal ground between the devices is also necessary, but a chassis ground through the cable is not, because all equipment of this type require grounds through the power cord. Thus the RS232C cable for asynchronous communications needs wires only on pins 2, 3, 4, 5, 6, 7, 8, and 20. Not all signals are implemented in many systems, and in fact, the only ones really necessary are TxD, RxD, and a ground. However, many systems use some or all of the other lines to provide helpful error messages or to control the system. This is known as *handshaking*. CTS, for example, is intended to inhibit transmission of data when false and DCD inhibits reception, in proper RS232C implementations. DTR is sometimes used to "disconnect" calls in autodialing systems. DSR is seldom used.

DTE (Terminal)			DCE HOST or MODEM
2	**TXD**	⟶	2
3	**RXD**	⟵	3
4	**RTS**	⟶	4
5	**CTS**	⟵	5
8	**DCD**	⟵	8
7	**GROUND**		7
6	**DSR**	⟵	6
20	**DTR**	⟶	20

Figure 11-16   RS232 standard connections.

Therefore, with such a variety of ways to connect equipment, most systems either use all signals or provide a way with jumpers to force them to be *true* so that the system will work. CTS, DSR, and DCD can be jumpered to DTR (usually, in one of the cable plugs) to be *true* if the signal is not implemented from the other end. A ring indicator is used only in automatic answering systems.

Lines other than 2, 3, 4, 5, 6, 7, 8, and 20 should not be connected, because in some equipment they are used for nonstandard purposes. Many of these other lines do have RS232C standard uses in synchronous and auto-answering systems.

11-9.3 ▼ S-Record Standard

The S-record concept has been used by Motorola since 1974 to move data between systems and is described in Section 6-7. The binary 8-bit data is converted into printable ASCII-hex characters because these can be transmitted through any serial link even if it is only capable of handling 7-bit transmissions. Also, both *byte counts* and *checksums* are used to ensure integrity. The S-record concept has been used in almost all Motorola Monitor ROMs, Assemblers, Compilers, and Linkers.

Unfortunately, some differences exist in the various implementations of S-records. The standard is shown in the appendixes of many of the Motorola manuals. All of the versions are consistent in the use of the 1s-complement checksum on each S-record and the use of the address to load the data in the proper place. The differences exist in the treatment of the S9 record and whether carriage returns and line feeds are included on each line. The proper implementation as done in EXbug, and all of the MDOS 8-bit software uses byte count and checksum in the S9 record also (i.e., l/f S9030000FC c/r). Some assemblers replaced the four 0s in the S9 record with the program entry address, in which case the checksum is calculated appropriately.

Note that the S-record concept uses two ASCII characters to generate each 8-bit byte of (binary) data, so 7-bit transmission (with or without parity) will work. Eight-bit transmission (with bit 8 = 0) is also usable.

Because of the lack of standardization in some S-record programs, it may be necessary to edit them or write a conversion program to add or delete carriage returns or line feeds on each line. Generally, a <cr> is required after each checksum. Line feeds are not required but help to make the records readable on the screen or printer. The loader programs will generally ignore all characters after a <cr> until the next capital S, but characters can be edited out if they are not included in the byte count or checksum.

11-9.4 ▼ Methods of Flow Control

Data can be read or written to a disk much more rapidly than it can be transferred to a remote computer or EVB via Modems. Writing to a screen display is also slower. Flow control is the term used for the handshaking required so that no data will be lost during the transfer; it is the name given to methods to stop and restart transmissions.

If a file that contains S-records is to be transmitted, it is generally read from the disk into a memory buffer and then sent to the Modem or screen. Flow Control ensures that the buffer does not overflow. In some cases, if the data rate is slowed below 2400 baud, the download may be successful without Flow Control. This slower rate is automatic when using most Modems since most operate at 1200 or 2400 baud.

Some ASCII control characters are of special interest for communications use. They are ACK, NAK, DC1, and DC3. They are specifically for use in data transmission and flow control.

The method of flow control known as X-ON/X-OFF uses the ASCII control characters DC1 and DC3. The loader program receiving the data senses when the buffers are nearly full and sends a DC3 (same as control-S) to the sending program. This stops the transmission until the buffer empties and then the control-Q or DC1 is sent to start the data again (which solves the buffer overflow problem). Many communications programs can provide this feature.

Another method of flow control uses the ASCII characters ACK and NAK. They are used by the XMODEM program described in Section 11-9.7.

11-9.5 ▼ Baud Rate Conventions*

The standard baud rates for most data transmission go from 50 to 115,200 Bits Per Second (BPS), but not all systems are equipped with all those rates. The most common baud rates are 1200, 2400, 4800, 9600 and 19,200 bps. The lower rates are normally used only when Modems are involved. The most common for local (in the same room) systems is 9600 baud. These serial ports also use asynchronous transmission. When Modems are used at rates above about 19,200 baud, synchronous operation is usually required. This requires special software and Modems not commonly used in any Motorola products.

11-9.6 ▼ Host's Communications Port Requirements

When setting up a link for downloading it is necessary to make sure that the host can satisfy all the requirements. Typically, all computers have RS232C ports and can be configured for the proper baud rates, parity, bits/character, and stop bits. (The obsolete TTY is the only terminal that uses 2 stop bits.) Parity is seldom used but could be as added insurance against errors. Seven-bit even parity used to be quite common. UNIX used it by default, but today most systems use 8-bit characters with no parity. The Macintosh has RS422 ports but they can be connected to work with RS232 systems. Typically, all IBM or DEC computers, as well as those with CPM or UNIX, can handle X-ON/X-OFF, so it is the preferred flow control method.

Whether the host uses CTS, DCD, DSR, or combinations of them varies with the driver program in use. Some programs, for example, will communicate without DSR being true, but others require it.

11-9.7 ▼ Terminal Communications Programs

Most computer systems are equipped with *terminal emulation* software so they can be used as a terminal to talk to a remote system through the serial port. When two computers talk, they must speak the same language. This can be just straight ASCII, but a number of programs use special *protocols*** to ensure error-free transmission. For example, in one protocol, the data is sent as a block of 128 bytes with a checksum. Also, each block is numbered. The receiving system will verify the checksum and the block number and if

---

*The term *baud* is used here as being synonymous with BPS (Bits Per Second).

** A protocol is a set of rules governing the interchange of information.

they are not correct, will ask for a retransmission. Some protocols use 1024-byte blocks, and some use Cyclical Redundancy Checks (CRCs) instead of a checksum. It is understandable that both systems must use the same protocol. Two of the most popular protocols are XMODEM and KERMIT. XMODEM is one of the oldest and has several variations. One is known as YMODEM.

KERMIT is a Terminal Emulation and file transfer program provided by Columbia University Center for Computing Activities. It is placed in the public domain for free use (it cannot be sold). It has been adapted to many different computers. A copy for use with the IBM-PC is available.

XMODEM is a universal standard program used by thousands of CPM and MS-DOS systems since 1977. It uses a specific protocol, known as "Ward Christensen's Protocol," for actual data transfer. It also includes straight ASCII terminal emulation to allow it to control file transfers. It uses the standard ACK/NAK characters but also does block numbering and checksum or CRC on each 128-byte block. It retransmits blocks in the event of error, so it is extremely reliable. Perfect results are easily achieved. Many other systems also use this protocol and it is available in several programs for the IBM-PC or Macintosh.

The better known programs usually provide one or the other or both of these two standards and frequently include several more lesser known protocols. One of the most commonly used data transfer programs is PROCOMM, sold by Datastorm Technologies, Columbus, Missouri.

It is usually necessary for the communications programs to be able to do two things in order to *download* object code. The first is to be able to *emulate* a terminal to talk to the MDS for the purpose of setting up and testing the communications path and to set up the remote system to send the object files. The second requirement is to read the file from the disk and transmit S-records, preferably, with some method of flow control. Most terminal communications software does both; however, few S-record loader programs use flow control.

UNIX-based systems and some of the Motorola Assemblers need to use the BUILDS program for generating S-records from COFF files. COFF is a standard output format for many mainframe computers. The UNIX commands of CU and CAT are useful in file transferring. CU provides communications and Terminal Emulation. CAT can be used by redirecting it to the files (i.e., CAT < filename) for downloading.

11-10 ▼ SUMMARY

The problems involved in testing **6800** family MCUs were described in this chapter. The use of hardware debuggers was explained and the evolution of the ROM monitor program concept for MCU debugging was shown. Two Motorola EValuation Boards which include the latest Monitor ROM, called BUFFALO, were described. Program patching methods were described, and the factors involved in communicating between computers were discussed.

11-11 ▼ GLOSSARY

68HC11A1 An enhanced **6800**-type MCU that includes a clock and 256 bytes of RAM, 512 bytes of EEPROM, and 8K bytes of ROM.

Bipolar PROM A TTL-type device that is programmed by blowing out fuse-type links.

Breakpoint A software technique for halting a program at a specified address; used for debugging.

Carriage Return <cr> The data terminal character used to shift the cursor to the left end of a line.

CRT terminal A data terminal that uses a CRT (cathode ray tube or TV tube).

Debugging Troubleshooting or analyzing programs or hardware.

Firmware ROM or PROM.

Glitch A momentary impulse on a signal line usually causing false operation. It is usually due to unwanted coupling between lines or from external sources.

Interrupt Vector An address pointing to the interrupt service routine.

Line Feed <lf> The data terminal character that moves a cursor down one line. It is the same as the ASCII control-J.

Memory map A diagram of the full addressable range of memory locations.

Microprocessor Development System (MDS) An instrument designed to aid in the design and testing of µC systems.

Module A Printed Circuit Board (PCB) of standard size with specific functions implemented in TTL or MOS ICs.

Monitor program A program in ROM used to display registers or memory contents. It is also used to load, dump, change, or debug a user's program.

Real Time Executing at the normal clock rate of 1 or 2 MHz (not slowed down).

Run-one-instruction A software technique whereby a single instruction is executed in real time and the registers are then displayed; also called TRACE or single-step.

S-records Motorola's standard method of formatting a machine language object program by converting bytes that are in binary form to their two-character hexadecimal equivalent. These ASCII characters plus addresses, byte count, and checksum are included on each S1 line. An S9 record terminates each program.

System debugging Verifying that the software does calculations and handles data properly and that the external hardware is controlled properly by the software.

Transparent Mode (TM) A command to allow the terminal to communicate directly with the host (transparently through the evaluation system).

TTY Western Electric Model 33 teletypewriter.

Valid Memory Address (VMA) Signal line on the **6800** µP that tells devices when to accept the address on the bus.

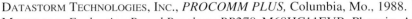

11-12 ▼ REFERENCES

DATASTORM TECHNOLOGIES, INC., *PROCOMM PLUS,* Columbia, Mo., 1988.

MOTOROLA, *Evaluation Board Brochure BR278,* M68HC11EVB, Phoenix, Ariz., 1986.

———, *Evaluation Board User's Manual,* M68HC11EVB/D1, Phoenix, Ariz., 1986.

———, *Evaluation Board User's Manual,* M68HC11EVBU/D1, Phoenix, Ariz., November 1990.

———, *HCMOS Single-Chip Microcomputer,* MC68HC11A8, ADI 1207, Phoenix Ariz., 1986.

P&E MICROCOMPUTER SYSTEMS, INC., IASM11 Integrated Assembler and Editor, Woburn, Mass., 1989.

MOTOROLA, The MCU Toolbox, Phoenix, Ariz., 1991.

11-13 ▼ PROBLEMS

11-1. Rewrite Example 10-11 using the stack instead of the index register.

11-2. A program is halted at location $50 by the instruction

```
$50    20   FE          BRA  *
```

Add instructions prior to $50 so that before the program halts, it stores the contents of A at $3E, B at $3F, and X at $3A and $3B.

11-3 In Figure 11-2, list the components associated with:
   (a) The Host RS232 interface
   (b) The terminal RS232 interface

11-4. Explain how to examine the contents of $C100 through $C122, and how to change the contents of $C101, $C102 and $C103 to $11, $22, and $33, respectively.

11-5. There is a read character subroutine in the BUFFALO monitor starting in location $E47A. How can it be listed? How can we determine where it ends?

11-6. A program starts at $C020 and does not use the stack. A breakpoint must be put in at $C040 to save all the registers in locations $20 through $28. You may add an LDS at $C01D and start the program there. What address would you use for the stack?

After attempting to solve these problems, try to answer the self-evaluation questions in Section 11-2. If any of them still seem difficult, review the appropriate sections of the chapter to find the answers.

MICROCOMPUTER DEVELOPMENT SYSTEMS

12-1 ▼ INSTRUCTIONAL OBJECTIVES

In this chapter we consider the design, development, and testing of μC-controlled systems such as exist in automobiles, production plants, and in VCRs and microwave ovens used in the home. Testing of these systems using logic analyzers and Microcomputer Development Systems (MDSs) is emphasized. After reading this chapter, the student should be able to:

1. Understand the procedures for MCU system design.
2. Analyze the hardware performance of a μC-controlled system.
3. Use Logic Analyzers.
4. Understand how a hardware/software development station works.
5. Set up address and data breakpoints in an MMDS05.
6. Analyze signals on an MCU bus using real-time Bus Analysis.

12-2 ▼ SELF-EVALUATION QUESTIONS

Watch for the answers to the following questions as you read the chapter. They should help you to understand the material presented.

1. In a logic analyzer, what is the difference between a timing display and a state table?
2. How can Personal Computers be used to develop μC systems?
3. What additional features does a Microcomputer Development System (MDS) have as compared to an EValuation Board (EVB)?
4. What additional features does a Logic Analyzer have?
5. What is meant by emulation? Why is it useful?
6. What is a personality pod? A station module?

377

12-3 ▼ MICROCOMPUTER SYSTEM DESIGN AND DEVELOPMENT

In Chapter 11 we discussed system development using EVBs; they worked well for testing of simple control systems. Many hardware-related design problems were not covered, however. MCU-controlled hardware systems have many applications. In the home, MCUs control microwave ovens, washing machines, and VideoCassette Recorders (VCRs). The use of MCUs in the electronic control modules of automobiles* and to control manufacturing processes in a factory are more complex examples.

12-3.1 ▼ Design Process

The first step in system design is to define the requirements of the system, as in Example 12-1.

EXAMPLE 12-1

Conceptually design a VCR.

SOLUTION

The following requirements must be satisfied in the design of a typical VCR:

1. There must be a sensor to determine if there is a tape in the VCR.
2. The user must be allowed to set the mode of the VCR (play or record).
3. The speed and direction of the motor driving the tape must be selected (forward, fast forward, or rewind).
4. The MCU must keep track of the real time, and there must be a way to reset this clock.
5. The user must be able to enter the start and stop times of any programs that he or she wishes to record.

   Many VCRs have additional functions, and the MCU system must be able to control all of them.

The initial stages of development for a μC-based controller system requires that the designer determine what devices need to be to controlled and how they can be interfaced to a computer system. The designer must also decide how to monitor the external actions of the controlled system and what sensors are needed. Both tasks usually involve developing electronic or electromechanical interfaces that are TTL compatible so that they can be connected directly to an MCU. These interface devices are beyond the scope of this book, but with the help of competent engineers, such as power transistor designers, they can be built and used to interface external hardware with an MCU system.

---

*The **68HC11** or equivalent has been used by Chrysler and GM in the electronic control modules of many of its automobiles.

The development of a μC or MCU system requires at least four stages:

1. The conceptual design of the system must be developed. This means determining what the system must do and what external devices it must control. The conceptual design of a VCR was illustrated in Example 12-1.

2. The hardware must be selected and assembled. External components are often required, such as additional memory, I/O ICs, or power transistor interface circuits. In a VCR, for example, the interface between the MCU system and the motor driving the tape must be designed.

3. The software must be written.

4. The MCU system must be integrated or interfaced with the system it is to control. All the components of the VCR, for example, must be assembled to determine if they function together properly.

12-4 ▼ DESIGN PROCEDURE

The development of a μC-based system normally involves two parallel efforts: *hardware design* and *software design*. They are often done by two different teams. Before long, however, the software has to be integrated with the new hardware being designed.

12-4.1 ▼ Hardware Design

The first step in this design process is to select an MCU that has all or most of the features needed to accomplish the conceptual design goals. To demonstrate the capabilities of the MCU selected, and to permit analysis of its operation, Motorola has designed several types of testing systems. The simplest is the EVB. It is an operating MCU system that cannot only execute and debug the software but is provided with a 60-pin I/O interface connector to which the external system components can be connected. This allows evaluation of the capability of the MCU to control external devices. The connector is a double-row, 60-pin header type, Amptronics 929715-01-30, and can be seen at the left edge of the EVB in Fig. 11-1. The connections to the external hardware can be done with individual wires or if the interface circuits for the target system are assembled on another board, that board can then be connected to the EVB by means of a cable. When attaching wires to MCU pins, as in any digital circuit, it is necessary to avoid excessive capacitive or resistive loading. Therefore, the wires or cables must be kept short. This capacitance between the wires causes interference, which can cause a malfunction (see Sections 12-6.11 and 13-4.2).

At least two types of cable assembly construction techniques are available to the user. The first type is low cost and simplest to construct, and is illustrated in Fig. 12-1. This type of assembly provides an indirect connection of the EVB MCU I/O ports to the target system devices. Indirect connection is accomplished via another 60-pin connector, installed on the target system board along with the interface components. The second type of cable assembly is shown in Fig. 12-2. This type of assembly provides a direct connection of the EVB MCU I/O ports to the target system MCU device socket. Direct connection is accomplished via a specialized plug platform constructed by the user. This type of plug platform mates directly with the target system MCU device socket. This type

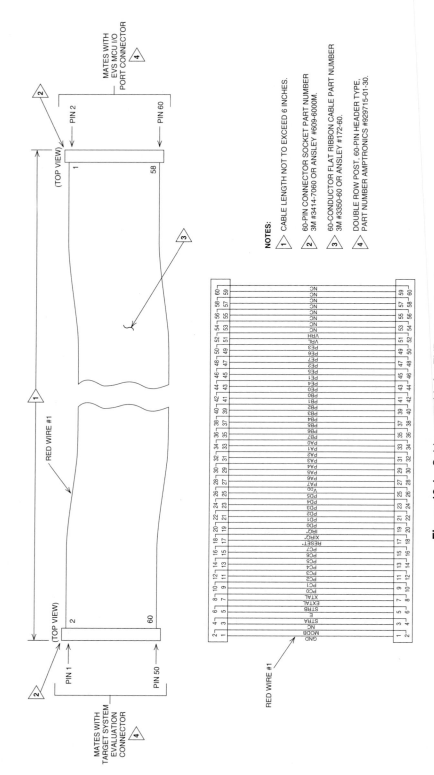

Figure 12-1 Cable assembly for EVB to target system.

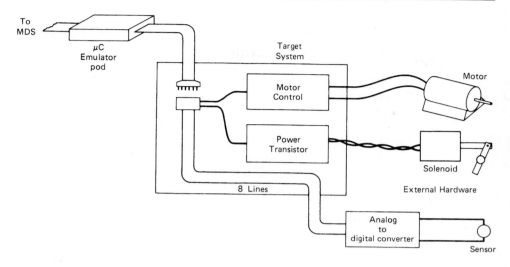

Note: Some µC's include the A/D converter.

Figure 12-2 User's target system.

of cable assembly makes it easier to transition from the prototype to the production stages of the developed MCU-based product. Also, it should be noted that this type of cable assembly is used by the higher-performance Motorola Modular Development Systems (MMDSs) described later in this chapter (see Section 12-8 and in Section 16-16).

12-4.2 ▼ Software Design

Once external devices are connected properly, they can be controlled by the MCU's internal I/O circuits in the same way as described for the PIA (see Section 8-6). The user can test the hardware interfaces by using the *Memory Display* (MD) and/or *Memory Modify* (MM) commands of the debug program to read or write the I/O registers. If a parallel output port in the MCU is involved, one of its lines may be used to cause a motor to run, a solenoid valve to open, or a relay to close. Interface circuitry would have to be constructed to recognize the digital TTL signal on that line and to activate the device. A byte with the appropriate bits *set* must then be sent to the Direction Register to set its associated I/O pins for output. A data word is then sent to the output Data Register to raise or lower the correct pin. If the desired action should fail to occur, a scope, meter, or Bus Analyzer can then be used to observe the signals on the output lines and/or peripheral devices, so that the wires can be moved or the control word changed to correct the problem.

Inputs from sensors monitoring the system to be controlled must also be tested. After setting the Direction Register for inputs, a data byte can be read from the input Data Register. The bits of this byte should match the data levels on the lines from the sensor hardware.

When both the control and status words are correct, a routine to exercise the external hardware can be entered into memory. This can be done by entering machine language, using the *Memory Modify* (MM) command or with the *one-line assembler* (ASM) using mnemonics. The routine should be tried and modified until a complete I/O driver routine for this particular peripheral is developed. The same techniques can be repeated for any other subsystems and their peripheral units, and finally for the main system software, until the entire system is assembled.

This entire design process is shown in Fig. 12-3. We have just described the functions shown at the top and on the left in Fig. 12-3. The software development depicted in the boxes on the right of Fig. 12-3 was discussed in Chapter 6.

Each step in the figure has feedback paths so that the designer can go around the loop to modify the hardware or software any number of times until the desired performance is achieved. Once the interfaces are designed and a prototype built, it should be connected to an MCU system for further testing, as shown in the lower middle of Fig. 12-3.

12-4.3 ▼ Testing Prototype or Production Systems

The process of using a test system such as the EVB or MMDS, plugged into a *wirewrap prototype board* in place of the MCU, is known as *emulating* the user's system. It performs like, or *emulates,* the real MCU. This technique is used because the emulation can be started and stopped and the registers monitored to indicate where the problems are. Once the system is operating properly, construction of a Printed Circuit Board (PCB) prototype is the next step. By emulation, the user now knows exactly how many output ports or lines are required, what interface circuitry is needed, what the clock circuit should be, and if any external memory or I/O device is needed, what decoding scheme must be used. This information allows the user to design a hardware prototype that is reasonably close to the final production units. The need for a prototype has not been eliminated altogether, but probably several iterations have been bypassed. When construction is completed, the user must test the new prototype in the same way and determine whether it performs as well as the wirewrap system did.

It is still possible to operate and test the prototype system using the emulation RAM of the MDS in place of the μC's RAM, ROM, or PROM. This is known as *emulating the RAM or ROM.* The program can be tested with the MDS debugging routines until the user is satisfied that the system is firm enough for the program to be put into PROM or EPROM. The user must be certain that the proper restart vector is in the EPROM.

12-5 ▼ SYSTEM TESTING AND DEBUGGING

We have discussed the testing of software in Chapter 11. Simple software programs can be debugged using EVBs with Monitor ROMs or even with a simulator program as discussed in Section 11-7. These types of debuggers have many features that help to find software problems but have no *real-time* or hardware debug capabilities. *Real-time debugging* refers primarily to the problems of timing. A typical situation is where a peripheral sends a signal to an MCU and requires a response within a fixed time. If a disk is being read, for example, the data goes from the disk to the disk controller and then to the MCU. The data is moved into a block of memory called a *buffer.* The MCU must read the data from the buffer promptly or else the next disk read will overwrite it and data will be lost.

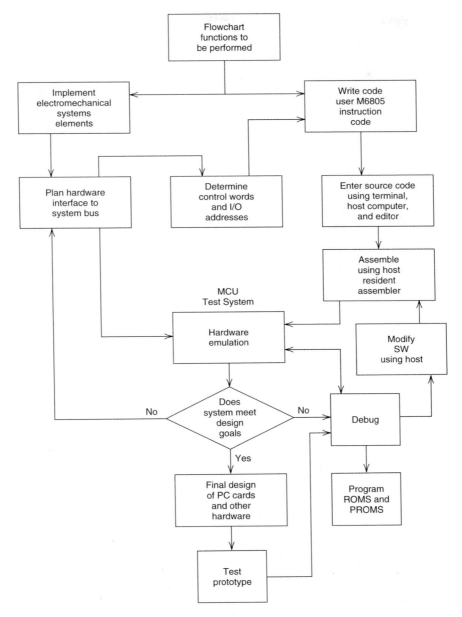

Figure 12-3 System designing and verifying procedure.

Real-time testing must verify the performance of the external I/O devices operating in conjunction with the MCU. This can be done by observing the command signals and the responses of sensors. Sometimes this testing will reveal that the software must be reworked to speed up the response, but it may also reveal that there must be built-in delays to prevent conflicts between the peripheral devices connected to the system.

12-5.1 ▼ Testing Methods

The design process to develop an MCU system involves not only writing the program and designing the electrical interface so that the external hardware is properly controlled, but in monitoring the results to verify that the system performs as it should. A development system therefore should not only provide proper stimulus of all controls but must allow analysis facilities to monitor the results.

Testing must be involved at each stage of a system's development to determine if that portion of the system is working properly. There are two main aspects of system testing:

1. Rudimentary hardware testing.
2. Rudimentary software testing.

When signals are sent to external circuitry, such as electromechanical devices, they usually have finite time requirements to accomplish their functions. For example, in the VCR design, the signal to start the rewind or fast-forward motors should not be applied until the playback motor has been turned off and the tape has come to a stop.

12-5.2 ▼ Rudimentary Testing of Digital Systems

The external hardware circuits and devices in an MCU-controlled system must be tested to ascertain that they are functioning properly. This involves monitoring the signals on the various pins or lines of the IC packages or electrical components. The simplest instruments for this digital testing are devices that can differentiate between a 1 and a 0, such as a voltmeter or a *logic probe*. One type of a logic probe is a fountain-pen-shaped device that has Light Emitting Diodes (LEDs) which indicate whether the line is at a logic 1 or 0 level. The LEDs also blink when the tip probe is touched to a line that is changing between those levels.

A more powerful test instrument for this type of testing is the Cathode Ray Oscilloscope (CRO) because it can be used to observe rapidly changing signals on a line or MCU pin. The CRO has a Cathode Ray Tube (CRT) similar to the one in a data terminal. Most oscilloscopes, however, can display only one or two signals at a time. In many cases the CRT is a very valuable tool, but it is not adequate for complete debugging of modern digital systems. Logic Analyzers (see Section 12-6) are a more sophisticated digital test instrument for this purpose.

12-6 ▼ LOGIC STATE ANALYZERS

The CRO is probably the best tool for examining waveforms and determining voltage levels and rise times of the MCU signals. It has two limitations, however:

1. High-speed random pulses are not easily observed.
2. CROs can monitor only a few lines simultaneously. Four is about the largest number of inputs on a commonly available CRO.

For these reasons, a new device, a Logic Analyzer, has been developed. It operates on a slightly different principle.

Because there are many signal lines on an operating μP, and the data is changing rapidly on each line, a Logic Analyzer must take a *snapshot* of the activities on the lines and store the *state* of each signal in memory for each cycle of the system clock. The conditions under which the snapshot is taken are determined by *triggering* circuits, which can respond to various combinations of events, such as when an interrupt occurs.

The information can then be displayed in a number of ways. The data or addresses can be shown as binary, octal, decimal, or hexadecimal numbers, with which we are already familiar, or can be displayed as a timing diagram (see Section 12-6.6), where each signal forms a line across the screen. The line makes a jog up or down to represent a 1 or 0. The analyzer's formatter inserts a vertical line to connect the transitions of HIGH to LOW, or vice versa. Thus each signal appears as a series of rectangular pulses where the timing of transitions can easily be seen.

To debug an MCU system, it is usually necessary to monitor or observe *many constantly changing signal lines.* Even in a simple 8-bit μP, signal changes occur on 8 data lines, 16 address lines and several control lines at the same time. The **Logic Analyzer** is a test instument that has been created specifically for digital circuit testing. It can monitor the signals on many lines simultaneously.

Figure 12-4 shows the 1230, a Logic Analyzer manufactured by Tektronix, Inc., which is a relatively inexpensive analyzer and is used in many college laboratories. It comes in a console that consists of three parts:

1. **Keypad.** On a 1230 the keypad is on the right side of the console. It is used to enter commands and set up the parameters, such as the pattern recognizer or memory timing, that the logic analyzer will use.

Figure 12-4 Tektronix 1230 logic analyzer.

2. **CRT display.** The CRT displays the command menu for the operator. It also displays the output data.

3. **Pod Slots.** These are the connections for the pods that carry data from the MCU or digital circuit to the logic analyzer.

12-6.1 ▼ Data Sampling

Standard oscilloscopes display the signals in *analog* form, where the actual signal waveform is shown. Logic Analyzers, on the other hand, obtain information by taking samples of the data throughout the system at *discrete time intervals*. These are called *sample times* or *sample clocks*. The voltage is read at each input on each sample clock. The voltage at each sample, however, is recorded only as a logic 0 or logic 1, depending whether on it is above or below a threshold voltage. In many logic analyzers, the threshold is set to 1.4 V, so the logic 0s and 1s correspond to standard TTL logic levels. The concept is shown in Fig. 12-5, where a channel on a logic analyzer is sampling a sine wave. Observe that the sample points occur at discrete time intervals. Because the logic analyzer can resolve its inputs only to 0 or 1, the output is the square wave shown on the lower trace.

We must concede that the logic analyzer trace of Fig. 12-5 is only a crude approximation to the input sine wave—an oscilloscope would show it far more accurately. No matter how fast you sampled a sine wave, it would still look like a square wave on a logic analyzer. But *a logic analyzer is not meant to analyze sine waves.* They may be the most commonly used waveforms in transistors and audio circuits, but they rarely occur in the digital world, and a logic analyzer can do what an oscilloscope cannot; it can monitor the digital outputs at many points simultaneously.

12-6.2 ▼ Input Pods

When testing an MCU or any digital system, the connections to the pins or signals must not interfere with the normal operation. For this reason special input pods are used. These devices present a very small load on the circuits. A simple 10-input pod is shown in Fig. 12-6. It is connected by means of 10 *grabbers,* which are probes with clips on the end of them to grab onto various points in a circuit. The pod is connected to the logic analyzer

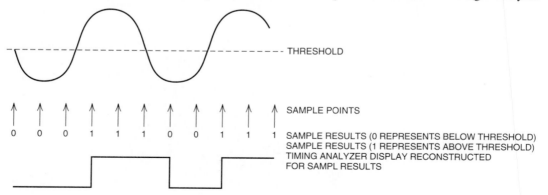

Figure 12-5 Sampling a sine wave.

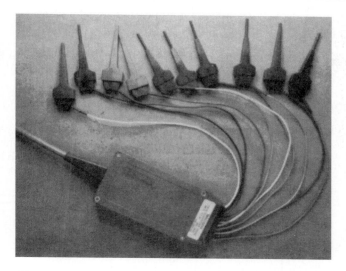

Figure 12-6 Logic analyzer pod. (Courtesy of Ed Pickett.)

via a cable. Actually, the pod of Fig. 12-6 consists of only eight data inputs, a ground input, and an input used for other functions, such as the *system clock.* It is considered to be an eight-channel pod, where each channel is a data point. An important requirement is that the test instrument must present no more than a very small capacitive or resistive load on the signal's lines. Otherwise, it will change the timing and increase the interference between signals. A modern logic analyzer such as the Tektronix **1230** uses 16-input general-purpose pods and can accommodate up to four of them. Figure 12-7 shows how a pod is connected between the circuit under test and the Logic Analyzer.

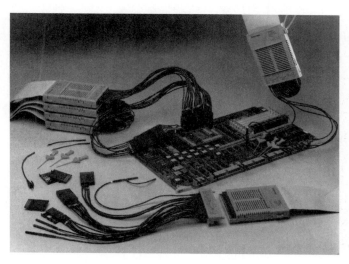

Figure 12-7 Various Tektronix logic analyzer input pod configurations.

EXAMPLE 12-2

A 32-channel logic analyzer is to monitor the buses on a **6800** microprocessor. Where would the inputs be connected?

SOLUTION

Sixteen of the channels should monitor the address bus, and eight channels should monitor the data bus. The remaining eight channels could monitor other points. Typically, the control lines on the **6800,** such as R/W, VMA, and the clock, would be monitored. The other five channels can monitor other points in the system.

In addition to these general-purpose pods, Personality Pods for specific μPs are also available. They are described in Section 12-6.7.

12-6.3 ▼ Memory in a Logic Analyzer

The memory is the core of any logic analyzer. The signals to be monitored are connected to the pods and then become the data inputs to the memory. This data is written into the memory at the sample clock rate shown in Fig. 12-8. In the figure the sample clock is assumed to be a square wave, and a WRITE pulse is generated on every negative transistion. The WRITE pulses must be as long as the cycle time of the memory.

EXAMPLE 12-3

The memory in a logic analyzer has a 150-ns cycle time and needs 50 ns to recover. What is the maximum sample rate for this analyzer?

SOLUTION

A logic analyzer monitors data only at discrete time intervals, rather than constantly, as with a CRO. This can be realized by noting that this memory requires 200 ns for each write. This is its maximum sample rate. For many applications this is too slow. Most logic analyzers have faster memories that allow them to handle higher clock rates.

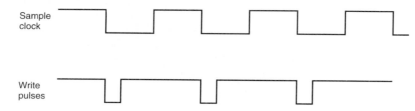

Figure 12-8   Write pulses to a logic analyzer's memory.

Logic analyzers offer the user a choice of many clock rates. The **1230,** for example, has clock rates from 10 ns to 40 ms. The sampling rate can be selected from the menu on the console. The slower clock rates allow for a larger time range but have less resolution.

In addition to selecting specific sampling rates, such as 1 μs, the user can select EXTERNAL. This allows the clock from the system under test to determine the sample rate. This is very important because many systems, including MCUs, are *synchronous* and change their states only on a clock edge. In an MCU system, using the system clock allows the logic analyzer to record the state of the system at every clock cycle.

12-6.4 ▼ Data Acquisition

A logic analyzer operates in one of two modes, data acquisition and data display. During data acquisition, the memory is constantly being written. The Tektronix **1230** has a 2K word memory. If the sample rate is 1 μs, for example, the memory will be filled in 2.048 ms. Acquisition *does not stop* when the memory is filled, however. Instead it continues, with the *new data overwriting the old data.* Thus at any time during acquisition, the memory will contain the most recent 2K data samples from the external system.

12-6.5 ▼ Trigger

The trigger is an *event that causes the logic analyzer to stop writing data into memory* and leave the acquisition mode. After the trigger, the most recently acquired data remains in memory, where it can be examined. The trigger can be an edge on a line in the external system, or a response to an event such as an input capture or an output compare, or to a combination of events, such as the fifth time the computer executes the instruction at $C100 after a pulse accumulator has overflowed. A trigger is, however, usually caused by a *pattern match.** Before entering the acquisition mode, a pattern of 1s, 0s, and Xs is entered on the console. The Xs are don't cares. When the data on the input lines has 1s that match all the 1s in the pattern, and 0s that match all the 0s in the pattern, the trigger occurs.

EXAMPLE 12-4

The logic analyzer is connected to a **68HC11** μP. It should trigger whenever the μP reaches address $200C. How can we make this happen?

SOLUTION

With 32 channels available, there would be a 32-bit pattern that could be set into the logic analyzer. The bits corresponding to the 16 address inputs could be set to 200C, and the other bits could be set as X's (don't cares). The analyzer would trigger whenever it found 200C on the address bus.

---

*A pattern match is sometimes called a *word recognizer.*

When the trigger occurs, the logic analyzer does not stop acquiring data immediately. In most cases it continues to acquire data until it fills half the memory. Thus a logic analyzer with a 2K word memory will acquire 1024 words after the trigger and then stop. Consequently, the memory will hold 1024 data points that occurred after the trigger and 1024 data points that occurred before the trigger. The ability to examine events that occurred *before* the trigger, sometimes called *negative time,* is one of the logic analyzer's most important features. It helps the user debug, because he or she can examine the cause of the trigger.

12-6.6 ▼ Display Mode

After the trigger, the logic analyzer goes from the acquisition mode to the display mode. The information in the memory is no longer changing and can be displayed on the console.

There are two ways to display the information in the memory: a *timing diagram* and a *state diagram.* A typical timing diagram, taken from the Tektronix **1230** manual, is shown in Fig. 12-9. It looks like the output of a multitrace oscilloscope except that none of the waveforms have any slope; they are all square. This is because each waveform is sampled at one time slot and converted to a 1 or 0. It retains that value until the next sample. Waveform changes between samples cannot be shown on a logic analyzer.

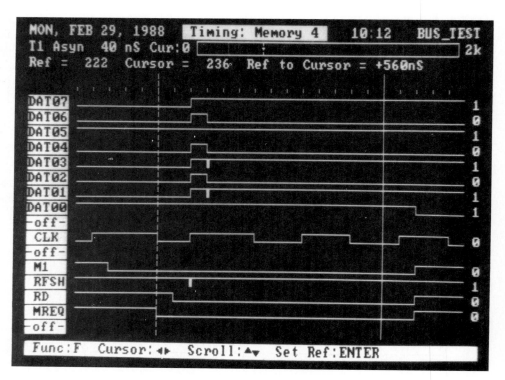

Figure 12-9 Logic analyzer timing display.

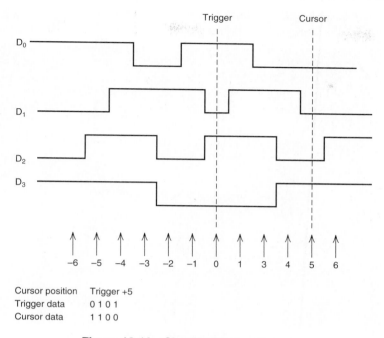

Figure 12-10 Simplified timing diagram.

A simplified, four-channel timing diagram is shown in Fig. 12-10. While in display mode, the memory data and the trigger are fixed. The *cursor,* however, is a marker that represents time and can be moved ahead or back to allow the user to examine any part of the captured event. Figure 12-10 shows three points of particular interest:

1. The cursor position relative to the trigger position. In Fig. 12-10 the cursor is at TRIGGER+5, or five positions after the trigger.
2. The data at the trigger. This should be the same data as entered into the trigger pattern. Here it is shown as 0101.
3. The data at the cursor position. Here it is 1000.

EXAMPLE 12-5

In Fig. 12-10, what would the cursor data be if the cursor position were TRIGGER-3?

SOLUTION

The cursor would be at three positions or locations before the trigger. The data in Fig. 12-10 at this position is 1110.

THU, FEB 25, 1988			State: Memory 4		10:24	MICROCHK
Loc	DAT	ADR	STB	CTL	I/O	COM
	hex	hex	bin	bin	hex	hex
1983	C2	24CA	00000	000	FC6C	FCE3
1984	C7	24CB	01101	111	FC6C	FCE3
1985	20	24CC	01101	111	FE48	FEEE
1986	1B	24C7	01001	111	FE48	FEEE
1987	7A	24C8	01001	111	FE48	FEEE
1988	B3	24C9	01001	111	FE48	FEEE
1989	C2	24CA	01001	111	FFC0	FF95
1990	C7	24CB	01101	111	FFC0	FF95
1991	20	24CC	01101	111	FFC0	FF95
1992	1B	24C7	01001	111	FFC0	FF95
1993	7A	24C8	01001	111	7FC0	7F95
1994	B3	24C9	01001	111	7FC0	7F95
1995	C2	24CA	01001	111	7FC0	7F95
1996	C7	24CB	01101	111	3FC0	3FD5
1997	20	24CC	01101	111	3FC0	3FD5
1998	1B	24C7	01001	111	3FC0	3FD5
1999	7A	24C8	01001	111	3FC0	3FD5
2000	B3	24C9	01001	111	1FC0	1FDE
2001	C2	24CA	01001	111	1FC0	1FDE
2002	C7	24CB	01101	111	1FC0	1FDE
Func:F	Scroll:▲▼		Cursor:◄►		Jump:ENTER	Radix:E

Figure 12-11   State table.

Referring back to Fig. 12-9, the timing diagram for the **1230** shows first that the clock rate is 40 ns. The *reference,* the point where the trigger occurred, is at memory location 222, and the cursor is at 236. The cursor is at REF + 14 and shows what occurred 560 ns after the trigger. The 1s and 0s at the right side of the timing diagram show the data at the cursor position. Note that when the data changes at the cursor position, it is the data after the cursor that is reported.

A state table display is shown in Fig. 12-11. It lists the memory data, usually in hexadecimal form, rather than displaying it as a timing chart. Many engineers prefer a state table display, especially when debugging a μP.

EXAMPLE 12-6

Due to a fault, a μP is jumping to a location around $2100. How can a logic analyzer help solve this problem?

SOLUTION

Even though the erroneous address is not fully known, the logic analyzer can help. The inputs can be put on the μP's address bus. The trigger pattern can be set to $(21XX)_{16}$, where XX means that 8 least significant bits are set to don't cares, and sampling started using the μP's clock. When the μP reaches the first address starting with 21, wherever it is, the logic analyzer will trigger and display not only the first address, but the addresses that preceded the jump to the $2100 area. This should allow the user to examine these locations to discover what caused the erroneous jump.

12-6.7 ▼ Personality Modules

Personality modules are used to tailor a logic analyzer to a specific μP. They are connected between the inputs to a logic analyzer and the buses of a μC in place of the Logic Clip Pod. Figure 12-12 shows a personality module in use. There is a different personality module for each popular μC. The module consists of a small PC board that includes a μC socket that accepts a specific μC and a plug that fits into a similar socket on the user's target system. To install, the user's μC is removed from the target system, the module is plugged in, and the μC is plugged into the module. A cable connects this PC board to the pod so that the channels are connected directly to the appropriate address, data, and control bus signals. Logic clips are needed only to observe signals on the target system that are not included in the standard buses. Software is supplied with each module that displays the data as that particular μC's instructions. This software is called a *disassembler.*

Figure 12-12 1230 with Personality Pod connecting to the target system.

Figure 12-13 shows the display of such an output. It shows a code segment for the Motorola **68000** μP. This μP is discussed in Chapter 14. In the figure the **Loc** column is the address in the analyzer's memory. The **Addr** column is the 24-bit memory address of the **68000** instruction, expressed as six hex digits. The **Data** column is the 16-bit data found at that location, expressed as four hex digits. In the last columns the disassembled code is displayed.

12-6.8 ▼ Newer Tektronix Logic Analyzers

The PRISM 3000 is a new series of high-performance logic analyzers built by Tektronix. In addition to the other logic analyzer capabilities, the PRISM 3000 series can perform limited emulation.

The memory in the PRISM 3000 series can be used to emulate the target system's ROM, and several options are available to allow the Analyzer to control some of the functions of a number of popular μCs. Although the software testing capabilities are limited, debugging of interrupt routines and other program segments is possible. The PRISM 3000 line is three times as expensive as the Model 1230, but it has much better performance. It can be used to analyze 32-bit μC and MCU systems that the 1230 cannot, and will work with the much faster clock rates of those new systems.

The PRISM 3000 line of logic analyzers has four basic configurations, as shown in Fig. 12-14: the 3001 portable, 3002C and 3002P benchtop units, and the 3002E expan-

```
TUE, FEB 16, 1988    Disasm  Memory 1    10:31   -DEFAULT
 Loc   Addr   Data  68000 Disassembly   Md Operation

 1071  0F1FC2 1028 ?MOVE.B 0010(A0),D0   S
 1072  0F1FB0 1210  MOVE.B (A0),D1       S    FFFF03=00C5
 1073  0F1FB2 0201  ANDI.B #10,D1        S
 1076  0F1FB6 6600  BNE      0F1E88      S
-1078--0F1FBA-1210--MOVE.B (A0),D1-------S--FFFF03=00C5-
 1079  0F1FBC 0201  ANDI.B #02,D1        S
 1082  0F1FC0 67EE  BEQ      0F1FB0      S
 1083  0F1FC2 1028 ?MOVE.B 0010(A0),D0   S
 1084  0F1FB0 1210  MOVE.B (A0),D1       S    FFFF03=00C5
 1085  0F1FB2 0201  ANDI.B #10,D1        S
 1088  0F1FB6 6600  BNE      0F1E88      S
 1090  0F1FBA 1210  MOVE.B (A0),D1       S    FFFF03=00C5
 1091  0F1FBC 0201  ANDI.B #02,D1        S
 1094  0F1FC0 67EE  BEQ      0F1FB0      S
 1095  0F1FC2 1028 ?MOVE.B 0010(A0),D0   S
 1096  0F1FB0 1210  MOVE.B (A0),D1       S    FFFF03=00C5
 1097  0F1FB2 0201  ANDI.B #10,D1        S
 1100  0F1FB6 6600  BNE      0F1E88      S
 1102  0F1FBA 1210  MOVE.B (A0),D1       S    FFFF03=00C5
 1103  0F1FBC 0201  ANDI.B #02,D1        S

 Func: F    Scroll: ▼▲    Cursor: ◀▶    Jump: ENTER
```

Figure 12-13   Disassembly of 68000 μP instructions.

Figure 12-14   Tektronix PRISM 3000 family of logic analyzers.

sion cabinet (not shown). The 3002C has a large high-resolution color display terminal, while the 3001 has a built-in 9-inch CRT. The chassis for these different models are about the size of a Personal Computer. They also include a keyboard, a $3\frac{1}{2}$-inch DOS format floppy drive, and a 40- or 80-MB hard disk to save the captured data for later analysis.

Hardware modules can be added to the basic logic analyzer to enhance its capabilities. The modules currently available include the following:

30MPX   Microprocessor Analysis Module
30HSM   High-Speed Timing Analysis Module
30DSM   Digital Storage Oscilloscope Module
32GPX   General-Purpose Timing, State, and μP Analyzer Module

Each chassis has room for two modules. If more than two are needed, the extension chassis is used. Provisions are made for a cross trigger between modules and time correlation acquisitions.

The modules connect to the μC socket of the system under test via a cable that plugs into connectors on the side of the 3002 chassis. This cable connects to a P6480 probe, which in turn connects to a probe adapter that is like a personality module; it is unique for each μC or μP. The probe adapter has either test clips or a plug compatible with the socket for the μC involved.

To add the *emulator functions* to the PRISM 3000, a **Prototype Debug Tool (PDT)** is provided as an option. The 30RP2 EPROM probe is a General-Purpose PDT. It emulates the system EPROMs by loading the user's object program into RAM in the Logic Analyzer. The program can then be executed and/or halted as desired. Although the debugging ability is limited, the GP version is very useful for software/hardware integration. The 30RP2 connects to the 3002 chassis with a second cable. Cables and plugs to mate with appropriate EPROM sockets are supplied with each probe adapter.

The new 32GPX module has a probing system that can acquire synchronous and asynchronous signals simultaneously and view data in both State and Timing displays.

12-6.9 ▼ Hewlett-Packard Logic Analyzers

The Hewlett-Packard company is also a leading manufacturer of Logic Analyzers. They have several series of instruments that are designed specifically to analyze and debug μC systems. One of these is the HP 16500 series shown in Fig. 12-15.

The basic model, the HP 16500A, is a Logic Analyzer System Mainframe that includes the color display tube, two 3.5-inch floppy disk drives, and five card slots for optional HP 165xx measurement modules. An expansion box can accommodate an additional four modules. These two cabinets can be used to configure a system to meet a variety of needs. At least 12 different types of modules are available for State or Timing analysis at up to 1 ns sampling rate [1 gigahertz (GHz)]. For example, the HP 16550A will provide State analysis at up to 100-MHz rates or Timing analysis at up to 500 MHz. Each HP 16550A card has 102 channels (to monitor the address and data buses or other

Figure 12-15 Hewlett-Packard 16500 Series of Logic Analyzer Modules. (Courtesy of Hewlett-Packard.)

signals) with a memory depth of 4K. Two cards can be connected together to provide 204 4K-deep channels, or 102 8K-deep channels. The 4K or 8K denotes the number of cycles of system activity that can be captured at one time. Another module that can be used at the same time provides a 1 GHz/second Digitizing Oscilloscope function to show an analog view of signals or glitches (see Section 12-6.11).

Connections can be made to the user's system using Logic Probes, but it's much easier and faster to use one of the preprocessor assemblies offered by HP. These are like a personality module. Most of the popular μPs are supported. The preprocessor provides all of the connections needed and provides some interface logic in the form of latches to demultiplex the signals, if required. The HP 10315G/H is the Preprocessor module for the **68HC11** MCU.

A disk is also provided to load the appropriate mnemonics as well as other predefined configuration information so that the user's program can be disassembled and displayed. Some symbols are provided in the disassembly display, but no control of the μC is possible. The signals are simply monitored in a very unobtrusive way without noticeably loading or slowing the target system. Triggering is possible on a variety of signals and conditions, however, so that events such as interrupt service routines can be analyzed. Cross-triggering of up to nine modules is possible so that correlation between State and Timing displays can be accomplished.

12-6.10 ▼ Advantages and Limitations of Logic Analyzers

A Logic Analyzer's primary role is timing analysis of a number of signals simultaneously. It can also be used to do performance analysis, such as determining the time required to accomplish a task. Many logic analyzers provide μC code disassembly (they can show mnemonics) and can therefore help in software analysis. They can also be used to find intermittent hardware problems due, perhaps, to a glitch* or crosstalk between signal lines.

Unfortunately, basic Logic Analyzers are not the best instrument for software analysis. They do not include the ability to change memory or registers or download code. Some of them, however, include options to add a limited set of these features.

12-6.11 ▼ Glitch Detection

The inputs and outputs of the MCU and the other ICs on the wirewrap board are *electrical signals* that are rapidly switched between HIGH and LOW voltage levels as the computer executes the program. All through the evolution period, from the days of discrete components to the highly integrated designs of today's ICs, hardware circuit assemblies have frequently been plagued with electrical problems where false or unwanted *glitches* or extra pulses are sometimes created because of coupling between the signal lines (see Chapter 13). These signals can cause 1s to appear as 0s or can set flip flops erroneously, which could completely destroy proper functioning of the system.

The integration of more and more of the circuitry into the MPU has minimized the effects of glitches and crosstalk, but whenever external components are involved, they can still be a problem. Successful execution of a computer program depends not only on the software being correctly written, but also on the ability of the hardware engineers to

---

*A glitch is an unwanted pulse in the address, data, or control lines usually due to the close coupling to other lines on the printed circuit board. See Chapter 13 for details.

avoid glitch signals in the electrical design of the system. Consequently, the debugging process of a μC system also involves monitoring its hardware performance.

Logic analyzers are especially useful in detecting glitches. Many have a circuit called a *glitch latch* that will detect glitches even if they occur between clock pulses. After the glitch is detected, it may be possible to find a way to suppress it.

12-7 ▼ MCU TEST SYSTEMS

Because the testing of MCU systems is so important, Motorola has developed three classes of low-cost testing systems:

1. The EValuation Board (EVB)
2. The EValuation Module or System (EVM or EVS)
3. The Motorola Modular Development Systems (MMDSx)

12-7.1 ▼ Evaluation Modules or Systems

The 68HC11EVB has already been discussed (see Section 11-5). However, a number of more capable evaluation systems are available for the **68HC05, 68HC11, 68HC16,** and **68300** families. (The **68HC16** and **68300** families of MCUs are discussed in Chapter 16.) These new boards are called EValuation Modules (EVMs) or EValuation Systems (EVSs) or even Kits (EVKs). They are complete μC systems on a single Printed Circuit Board (PCB), like the EVBs, but with many more features. They are also sold without a case or power supply. They have RAM or EEPROM memory that can substitute for all of the memory in the MCU devices.

By providing all the essential timing and I/O circuitry, the EVM (or EVS) simplifies user evaluation of prototype hardware or software. Monitor ROMs (or EPROMs) are supplied for debugging as well. As expected, these evaluation units are more expensive than the EVBs, but they are also more affordable than more complex systems. RS232 ports are provided so that they can work in conjunction with a terminal or host PC to develop the software (see Sections 11-9 and 12-4.2).

12-7.2 ▼ Microcomputer Development Systems

Simple evaluation boards such as the EVBs or EVMs do not have facilities to fully monitor the hardware signals. Motorola and other third-party suppliers also manufacture *Microcomputer Development Systems* (MDSs) that are even more helpful to engineers and programmers in designing and debugging MCU systems. These are much more sophisticated tools than an EVB, EVM, or even a logic analyzer, and they are more complex and more expensive. An MDS is, however, less expensive than the combination of a logic analyzer and an EVM.

12-8 ▼ MOTOROLA MODULAR DEVELOPMENT SYSTEM

The Motorola's Modular Development System (MMDS05) for the **68HC05** family of MCUs is shown in Fig. 12-16. It consists of three parts:

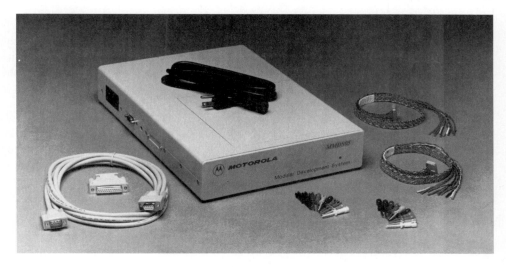

Figure 12-16 Motorola Modular Development System for the 68HC05 MCUs.

1. **Host system.** This is a computer that controls the MDS system. It often uses an IBM, or compatible, computer.
2. **Station module.** This is the main chassis of the development system and contains the emulation and Bus Analyzer circuitry.
3. **Plug-in cable assembly.**

As described in Section 12-4.3, the MMDS05 *emulates* the selected MCU, but in addition, adds a new dimension to the development process by also implementing *bus analysis.* As discussed in Section 12-6, a Bus Analysis feature provides a means of capturing the state of the real-time data on the buses, including signals from the external hardware, during the execution of a program in the target system. This function is performed in the MMDS by logic on the platform board, under control of the bus analyzer software. The debugging and Bus Analysis software starts and stops tracing, displays data captured during the tracing operation, and controls buffer triggering. Bus analyzer operation using the MMDS05 is discussed in Section 12-11.

12-8.1 ▼ Emulation and Bus Analysis

We discussed System Testing in Section 12-5 and Logic Analyzers in Section 12-6, and now we show how these subjects are combined in the MMDS to perform the same design procedures as those described in Section 12-4. We discussed emulation of the selected MCU in Section 12-4.3.

Figure 12-16 shows that the target system MCU is removed and replaced by a cable and plug that connects the MMDS to the target system just as done in Section 12-4.1. The MDS acts as the MCU that will be incorporated into the target system after it is fully tested. This combination of Emulator and Bus Analyzer reduces the total cost for development tools, and the dual capability of analyzing hardware and software allows the designer to integrate them more easily into a working system, as explained in the following sections.

12-8.2 ▼ Adapting the MMDS to the Task

A **68HC11** high-performance MCU is employed in the MDS and is used in conjunction with a processor on a personality board to emulate the instructions and functions of the MCU selected (a **68HC05C4,** for example). The memory map associated with the MCU selected is also emulated. There are 16 external logic clips available, to permit connections to the external hardware, if desired.

As explained in Chapter 10, there are many versions of the **6805.** The MMDS05 is adapted to emulate each version by this *Emulator Module* (EM) acting as a *personality* board. The EM is a small module that plugs into the platform board, inside the top cover of the MMDS05. A personality file is also provided and it is loaded into the host computer along with the operating software. It allows the host to assume the software characteristics of the particular **6805** used in the system. A Monitor (Debugger) program is provided to allow the designer to download the **68HC05** code or generate it with the Assembler/Disassembler function, and to debug it by emulating the **68HC05** system under development.

12-8.3 ▼ Hardware Features of the MMDS05

The MMDS05 is a full-featured MDS. Some of the features are:

- Built-in emulation memory
- Transparent, real-time, in-circuit emulation
- Bus Analysis using an 8192 by 64-bit Trace buffer
- 16 logic clips for individual signal analysis
- MS-DOS 3.0 (or later) host operation
- Serial RS232 connection to the host
- Baud rates from 2400 to 57,600 bps

12-8.4 ▼ Software Features of the MMDS05

P & E Microsystems of Woburn, Massachusetts, supplies the software to Motorola for the MMDS05 system. This software resides in an IBM or clone host computer and communicates with the MMDS05 via an RS232C interface. It provides communication with the user by a set of commands. Debug operations with this software uses windows on the PC's display screen in much the same way as the simulator software described in Section 11-7. Two programs are included: MMDS05.EXE and IASM05.EXE. The Integrated ASseMbler (IASM05) program includes an Editor to help write and format a source file properly, and by pressing F4 can be instantly switched to assemble it. It generates the object code in S-record format, a Program Listing, if requested, and a MAP file. The MAP file contains the Symbols. Pressing F6 causes the MMDS05 program to be entered and downloads both the S-record and MAP files. In the event that another Assembler is used, a Utility file is provided that will generate a MAP file from the Program Listing. This software provides target system emulation, source-level debugging of assembly language source code, bus analysis, and log and script file support (see Sections 12-10.3 and 12-10.4).

12-9 ▼ WINDOWS IN THE MDS

One of the trends in modern MDS operation is the concept of using **windows** to provide a screen display of registers and other items that *stands still* instead of continuously scrolling off the screen as each command is executed, as done by the EVB and all earlier debuggers. In the MMDS05 system, when a user program is loaded, the initial Debug Screen opens with five smaller windows, as shown in Fig. 12-17. Later, when commands are entered, it will be seen that the registers and disassembled code remain stationary (but are updated) during most operations. The commands provide control of target system emulation and other MMDS05 functions. Bus analyzer operations (described in Section 12-11) use special windows in addition to those of the debug screen.

12-9.1 ▼ Debug Screen

The Debug Screen, shown in Fig. 12-17, consists of five small windows:

1. **CPU Window:** shows the registers, including an ASCII display of the CCR. This window is always active.
2. **Debug Window:** shows commands, results, and status; selected by pressing the F10 function key.
3. **Code or Source Window:** shows Object or Source code.
4. **Memory Window:** shows memory contents; selected by pressing F3.
5. **Variables Window:** selected by pressing F8.

In subsequent paragraphs we describe these windows, ordered from left to right, top to bottom.

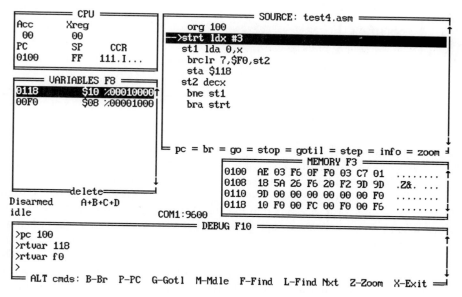

Figure 12-17 Debug Window with Test4.asm Source Program.

12-9.2 ▼ CPU Window

The CPU window, located in the upper left corner of Fig. 12-17, shows the contents of the CPU registers dynamically (they change whenever the contents of the registers changes). The CPU window displays the contents of

- The Accumulator (A register)
- The index register (X register)
- The Program Counter (PC)
- The Stack Pointer (SP)
- The Condition Code Register (CCR)

A properly designed program will initialize the registers as it is executed, but the user can change those values for testing by entering a new value on the command line in the DEBUG window (Section 12-9.7). The user enters the register mnemonic followed by a space and the value desired (PC 20C4, for example). The new value is displayed instantly in the CPU window. The values remain current as long as the Debug Screen is displayed. The condition code register (CCR) is displayed as ASCII characters, at the lower right of the CPU window (e.g., 111HINZC, where H is half-carry, I is the interrupt mask, N is negative, Z is zero, and C is carry). The bits of the CCR are each represented by a corresponding letter, if set, or by a period (.), if clear, and although the registers stand still on the screen, their values change as the MDS executes the instructions.

EXAMPLE 12-7

In the CPU window of Fig. 12-17, which flags are set?

SOLUTION

The line under CCR reads 111.I.Z. and means that the I and Z bits are set and the H, N and C bits are clear.

12-9.3 ▼ SOURCE/CODE Window

The SOURCE/CODE window is shown in the upper right of Fig. 12-17. When the user's S-record and MAP files are first downloaded from the host and the starting address (PC 100, for example) is entered, the window is designated as the **SOURCE** window and displays the Source code of the test 4 program (assuming that the source file is present in the current directory). As shown in Fig. 12-18, entering the SOURCE command toggles the display between Source and disassembled code and changes the window's name to **CODE F2**. When viewing the Object code display, the disassembled instructions change when the corresponding byte or bytes of memory change. When in the **CODE F2** mode, the instruction at the PC is highlighted, and as each instruction is traced, the window scrolls up. When switched to the **CODE F2** display and F2 is pressed, the keys that can be used to move the lines are displayed at the bottom of the window. In this mode, the display can be scrolled up or down to scan other parts of the program.

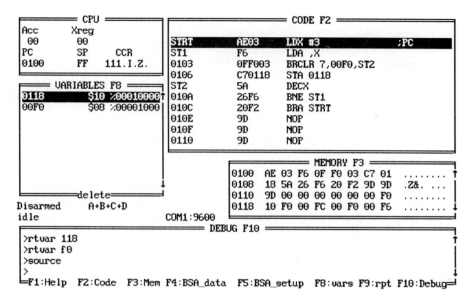

Figure 12-18 Debug Window with Disassembled Test4 Program.

EXAMPLE 12-8

Assuming that the instructions in the CODE F2 window of Fig. 12-18 have been executed down to $103, what will happen when that instruction is executed by entering a T (for "trace")?

SOLUTION

The instruction at $103 is BRCLR 7,00F0,ST2. If the bit tested by this instruction, (bit 7 of location $F0) is set, the PC value in the CPU window will change to $106 and the disassembled code in the window will move up one line, leaving the line highlighted on the next instruction at $106. Thus the program did not branch. If, however, bit 7 is clear, the PC will branch, changing the PC to $109, which is the value of the symbol st2 and displaying the new section of code starting at that address. That line will be highlighted.

12-9.4 ▼ VARIABLES Window

The variables window is on the left side of Fig. 12-17. As we know from our studies of programs in earlier chapters, many programs or routines need a place in memory to store values that may change during program execution. These variables are defined initially by a properly written initialization routine. The window is blank when debugging is started, but up to 32 variables can be selected for viewing by entering the VAR (variables) or RTVAR (real-time variables) command, followed by the associated address. For this simple test program, two real-time variables were entered. Only 11 variables can be displayed at one time, but the window can be scrolled to view each of them. The values, when enabled, are shown in hexadecimal, binary, decimal, or ASCII format. These variables can be deleted from the window by first pressing the F8 function key to select the window and then using the keyboard arrow keys to move the highlight up or down to the variable desired. It can then be deleted by the delete key or by clicking on the delete button at the bottom of the window. The window can be scrolled to view each of the defined variables. When a variable is specified with the RTVAR command, it becomes a *real-time variable,* which means that the display of the values of *these* variables *changes* as the instructions are executed during tracing or even when the user's program is running (emulation is occurring at full clock speed). Also, the real-time values can be changed *during* emulation, using the Memory Modify (MM) command from the DEBUG window. This is an extremely powerful new feature for testing machinery controllers or the MCUs of process controllers that cannot be stopped arbitrarily. When an MCU is being used to control a system and is in the final stages of debugging, the program cannot just be stopped to make adjustments without stopping the machinery, or process. This could be very expensive in spoiled product, or even catastrophic damage might occur. The ability to change variables while in operation is very valuable. As many as 32 real-time variables can be specified.

12-9.5 ▼ MEMORY Window

The memory window, in the middle on the right side of Figs. 12-17 and 12-18, displays the contents of 32 locations in memory and it will be seen that they contain the machine language of the test program. As the contents of these locations are modified by the user, the new values are displayed. Similarly, as the program alters the contents of memory, the display is updated. Note that the variables locations of $118 and $F0 are shown. Pressing the F3 function key selects the MEMORY window. The scroll bar is displayed and the arrow keys can then be used to display lower or higher addresses.

The user will note that many of the windows have little arrows along their right-hand edge which can be used with a mouse to scroll the display to show other areas of memory. This is a technique taken from Apple's Macintosh graphics interface.

12-9.6 ▼ Real-Time Memory Window

The MMDS05 has 32 bytes of dual-ported memory. Dual-ported memory ICs are used in multiprocessor systems to allow two independent, essentially simultaneous accesses to a block of memory. In the MMDS05 that block is assigned to any valid memory address by the RTMEM command. When enabled by the F3 key, real-time memory is displayed in a window that replaces the memory window during emulation. The display shows current contents of those bytes as they are altered during execution of the code. Dual-ported memory also allows new values to be placed in these variables during emulation (see Section 12-9.4) from the DEBUG window using Memory Modify commands.

12-9.7 ▼ DEBUG Window

The DEBUG window, along the lower part of the screen, is the window selected initially, or whenever F10 is pressed. This window contains the command line, identified by a greater-than (>) symbol as a command prompt, and the blinking cursor. Commands such as PC 200, to set the program counter or MD 100 to set up the memory window to display from $100 to $11F (32 bytes), can be entered. As a command is entered, it is displayed at the prompt. When the command is completed and the user presses ENTER, the software displays any additional prompts for the command, and any messages or data. If the command is not entered correctly, or is not valid, the software displays an appropriate error message. Many commands ignore invalid arguments.

EXAMPLE 12-9

The instruction at $0103 in the memory window of Fig. 12-17 is to be changed to a BCLR 4,PORTC (clear bit 4 of location $F0). How can this be done?

SOLUTION

The ASM command assembles **6805** instruction mnemonics and places the resulting object code into memory at the address specified. ASM requires that operands be entered as absolute addresses unless the MAP file has been downloaded, in which case Symbols can be entered as operands also. Let's assume that PORTC is at $F0 for this example. Because we want to overwrite the existing instruction at $103, we enter ASM 103 and a return. When we see the new prompt, we then type in the new instruction mnemonic. For example, if BCLR 4,F0 were entered, this would replace the BRCLR 3-byte instruction with the 2-byte BCLR, so to keep the processor from interpreting the left over third byte as a new op code, it would be necessary to follow the previous entry with a NOP. To end the entries, a period (.) is entered.

When the DEBUG window is active, after executing a command, the software again displays the command prompt. As a new line is displayed in the DEBUG window, the preceding lines scroll upward; the window displays the line that contains the command prompt and the three previously displayed lines. When any other window is selected, the cursor is removed from the DEBUG window. The F10 function key can be pressed to restore the cursor to the DEBUG window. Any command can be repeated by pressing the F9 function key. The software displays that command along with any data or messages.

12-9.8 ▼ STACK Window

The STACK window is displayed when the STACK command is entered. It appears over the top of the existing window. Figure 12-19 shows the contents of the SP register and the contents of the stack. It also shows the contents as if an interrupt has just occurred. (i.e., the current values of CCR, A, X, and ret. are identified). Pressing the Esc key removes the window and allows the user to continue.

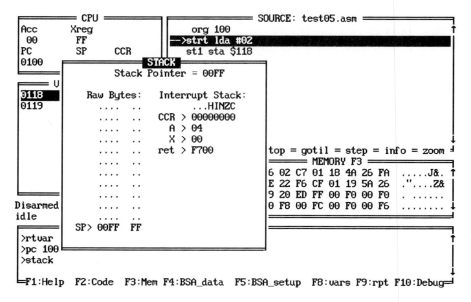

Figure 12-19 Stack Window.

12-10 ▼ SYSTEM DEVELOPMENT USING THE MMDS05

The steps involved in the development of an MCU system were described in Section 12-4. It involves attaching external hardware to the test system and then writing and testing the software to control it. This includes testing the target system's external functions using the input and output port lines as described in Section 12-4.1.

12-10.1 ▼ Software Development

Application program development has at least three distinct phases:

1. Determining the original system algorithms and I/O parameters needed
2. Writing, assembling, and linking of software on the host computer
3. Debugging

Again, as described in Section 12-4.2, the MMDS05 is used at the outset, for testing original algorithms and I/O requirements. For this, the Assembler/Disassembler feature of the MMDS05's CODE F2 window is very helpful. A small routine to exercise the I/O can be written quickly and tested.

12-10.2 ▼ MMDS05 Operation

In addition to the MMDS05 providing an emulating MCU, it must have emulation memory that can be substituted for the target system memory. The MMDS05 automatically loads memory-mapping information from the personality file that matches the MCU used in the Emulator Module. If a different map is anticipated, the Set Memory map (SET-

Figure 12-20 SETMEM Command Window.

MEM) command configures as many as four blocks of RAM and four blocks of ROM for a possible custom configuration. The address and memory type of each block can be specified. Write protection is implied if ROM is the memory type. The Command window for the SETMEM command is shown in Fig. 12-20.

EXAMPLE 12-10

In Fig. 12-20, what locations are covered by ROM1 and ROM2?

SOLUTION

The figure shows that ROM1 contains locations from $0100 to $08FF, whereas ROM2 contains locations from 1FF0 to 1FFF.

12-10.3 ▼ Logging File

The MMDS05 includes the ability to save commands and responses on the host in a *Log file*. Entries in the Log file include:

- Commands entered on the command line
- Commands read from a script file (see the next section)
- Responses to commands

- Error messages
- Notification of events such as Breakpoints

A log file can be opened with the open Log File command (LF) to receive information. When the specified file already exists, the software prompts the user to choose to overwrite or append to the current log file. While the log file remains open, the log information is written to the file or device. Another LF command is entered to terminate logging.

12-10.4 ▼ Script Files

The MMDS05 has another feature whereby any frequently used sequence of commands can be written to a *script file*. This type of file is identified by a .SCR extension. It would normally be kept in the directory with other MMDS files, such as the personality file. The script file can be generated with an editor (in nonformat mode) just like a source file would be made. It could also be a renamed and modified LOG file. Use of a script file saves time and promotes accuracy. The MMDS05 system has three commands that can be entered on the command line or that work in conjunction with a *script* file:

1. **SCRIPT** This command, when entered followed by a filename, reads commands from a script file and passes them to the command interpreter for execution.
2. **WAIT** This is a command normally included in a SCRIPT file. It will cause the Command Interpreter to pause for a specified number of seconds.
3. **WAIT4RESET** This command causes the emulator to wait for a RESET signal.

12-10.5 ▼ Source-Level Debugging

In some test systems, when an S-record file is loaded, the program will appear in disassembled form. The disassembler converts the op codes to mnemonics, but unfortunately, the operands remain in numeric form. With the MMDS05, the LOAD command also downloads a MAP file which includes a *Symbol Table,* if available, which is then used to convert the operands to mnemonics. This produces a display in the CODE F2 window that is very similar to the assembler listing and is more easily understood by the programmer. This is the concept of *Source Level Debugging* (SLD), which has been introduced in recent years and variations of it are used in the MMDS05.

In Chapter 6 we discussed the use of mnemonics to help people understand the computer's language when writing a program. SLD has the same purpose in debugging. For it to work, a Symbol Table has to be provided to reference the labels to their addresses (Section 12-8.4).

SLD debugging allows a user to view and manipulate the target system via source language. The context of the execution is always on display within the source window. This allows the user to maintain a perspective of the program execution that is unattainable with a debugger that shows only the next line to be executed. Variables may be displayed at any time to check on the state of the program being debugged.

In the MMDS05, the DASM command (followed by an address) dissassembles and displays three instructions in the debug window, beginning at the address specified. This allows programmers to see a small bit of their programs other than the part that is being displayed in the CODE F2 window. It is displayed in mnemonics as well as in machine language.

12-10.6 ▼ Breakpoints

The MMDS05 has two types of breakpoints: *Instruction* and *Data*. *Instruction* breakpoints are similar to those used in Monitor ROM debuggers and are implemented by the BR command. The program halts and displays the debug prompt when the MCU accesses an instruction at one of the specified addresses or an address within a specified address range.

Entering BR <address> or BR <address> <address> sets a breakpoint, specifying the address or range of addresses. When a specific breakpoint has already been set using BR, entering the command again clears that breakpoint. When the BR command is entered with no arguments, all active breakpoints are displayed. All breakpoints can be cleared by executing a NOBR command. Addresses of breakpoints must not be set in the middle of an instruction. They must be at the instruction fetch addresses (first byte). The total number of breakpoints of this type that can be set is 64.

EXAMPLE 12-11

To prevent a program crash, it must be stopped at any address between $00B0 and $00FF. How can we cause this to happen?

SOLUTION

The BR command will set a breakpoint at an address or range of addresses. Therefore, the command would be

```
BR B0 FF
```

When an instruction breakpoint address is reached, emulation stops and the software displays the following message:

```
idle    Inst brkpt
```

A properly defined breakpoint is very helpful in debugging, because the contents of registers and memory locations and the states of various signals can be analyzed at designated addresses in the program. It is usually necessary to use breakpoints of this type as well as the run-one-instruction (trace) mode initially, to debug the program so that it will run without crashing (as described in Section 11-6.9). Then noninvasive bus analyzer testing (see Section 12-11) can be performed.

12-10.7 ▼ Data Breakpoints

Up to four *Data* Breakpoints can be set using the Bus Analyzer Events/Breakpoint Setup screen shown in Fig. 12-21. This screen is displayed by pressing F5 while in the DEBUG window and has the dual role of defining Data Breakpoints or Bus Analyzer Events. Bus Analyzer Events are described in Section 12-11. The choices depend on the entries made in the various columns. To do this, a user must understand the meaning of the column headings.

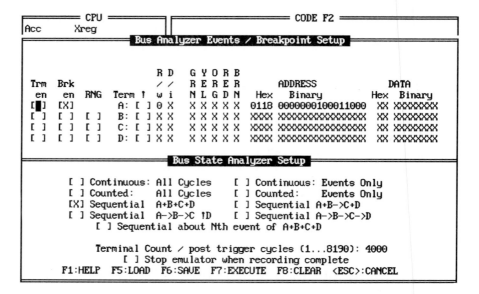

Figure 12-21 Bus Analyzer Events/Breakpoint Setup Window Showing Breakpoint Setup.

1. **Trm en** This stands for *term enable*. Four possible terms can be defined. They are listed as A, B, C, and D in the Term column. The set of values listed on one of the lines in the display is a *term*. An X between the brackets in the *Trm en* column indicates that this is a term to be used for a breakpoint or by the bus analyzer (see Section 12-11.3)

2. **Brk en** An X in the *Brk en* box indicates that this term will be used as a breakpoint. A break will then occur only if all the conditions in the term are matched by the signals.

3. **RNG** This stands for *range*. An entry is made when a starting and stopping address must be entered. Two term lines are used.

4. **!** This is the logic NOT indicator. A term can be the negation of a defined pattern. This field is set to invert the logic of the term signals.

5. **R/w** Setting this Read/write bit searches for read bus cycles; if the number in this column is 0, only write cycles are searched for.

6. **D/i** This Data/instruction bit, if clear, looks for instruction fetch bus cycles; if set, it searches for any data byte.

7. **Five color designations** There are five external clips in pod A that can be used to define a term. They are color coded. The signals on these clips can be used to activate the term, or they can be ignored by typing an X in the column.

8. The address can be entered in hex or binary.

9. The data can be entered in hex or binary.

To use the Bus Analyzer Events/Breakpoint Setup screen to set a data breakpoint, proceed as follows:

1. Using the arrow keys or the Tab key, position the cursor between the brackets for the term being defined (A, B, C, or D) in the *Trm en* column and press the space bar, which places an X between the brackets. Because we are setting a data breakpoint, we also place an X in the *Brk en* column on the same line. With the arrow keys or the Tab key, position the cursor for defining each of the other values on that line, and type a 0, 1, or X. For hexadecimal fields, type a hexadecimal digit or an X for don't care.

2. When all the data breakpoints have been defined, pressing F7 activates them and returns to the DEBUG screen so that the program can be started. To save the definitions to a file, F6 should be pressed before pressing F7. When one of these breakpoints is taken, the program halts and returns to the Debug prompt and the following is displayed in the status area of the DEBUG screen:

```
Data brkpt
```

To illustrate this feature, a breakpoint can be set up as shown in Fig. 12-21 to determine whether the instruction at $106 in the Test4 program is working properly. Note that Brk en is selected, the R/w bit is set to 0 (write), and the address is set to $118. When the program is executed by setting the PC to 100 and entering G, the screen blinks and the words "Data brkpt" are displayed. Also the PC is then at $106, which indicates that the breakpoint was reached. The bottom of the screen is used to define the Bus Analyzer modes explained in Section 12-11.1.

12-11 ▼ REAL-TIME BUS ANALYSIS

The *Bus State Analyzer* is one of the MMDS05's most important features. This function captures the state of the bus signals cycle by cycle in a trace buffer as the user's program is executed. The buffer contents can then be displayed to permit program analysis. The screen displayed is similar to the *State* display of a separate *Logic Analyzer*. This can be done without halting the emulation. To appreciate the usefulness of this feature, we first show the results to be expected and then describe how to implement the bus analysis.

A sample Bus Analyzer display is shown in Fig. 12-22. It shows the Raw Mode data collected for 20 frames (or cycles) of program execution and consists of the following columns:

- **Frame number:** a sample is taken at each system clock. Each sample is assigned a frame number.
- **Address:** the contents of the address bus on each frame.
- **Data:** the contents of the data bus on each frame.
- **R/w and D/i:** as explained in Section 12-10.7.
- **Pod B and Pod A:** there are two 8-bit pods that can bring external signals into the bus analyzer. The states of these signals is recorded at each frame. In Fig. 12-21 the pods were not connected to anything and always read 0. Five of these 16 signals can be used to define a term as described in Section 12-10.7.
- **Time of occurrence for each frame** (see Sections 12-11.6 and 12-11.9).

```
┌─────────────────────────── Bus State Analyzer ───────────────────────────┐
│Frame  Address   Data    RD    Term     POD B      POD A     Time tag      ↑
│                         wi             gpbgyorb   gpbgyorb   abs:nSec
│     1 0100       AE      10    ....    00000000   00000000  5.00000000E+02
│     2 0101       03      11    ....    00000000   00000000  1.00000000E+03
│     3 0102       F6      10    ....    00000000   00000000  1.50000000E+03
│     4 0103       0F      11    ....    00000000   00000000  2.00000000E+03
│     5 0003       00      11    ....    00000000   00000000  2.50000000E+03
│     6 0103       0F      10    ....    00000000   00000000  3.00000000E+03
│     7 0104       F0      11    ....    00000000   00000000  3.50000000E+03
│     8 00F0       80      11    ....    00000000   00000000  4.00000000E+03
│     9 0105       03      11    ....    00000000   00000000  4.50000000E+03
│    10 0105       03      11    ....    00000000   00000000  5.00000000E+03
│    11 0106       C7      10    ....    00000000   00000000  5.50000000E+03
│    12 0107       01      11    ....    00000000   00000000  6.00000000E+03
│    13 0108       18      11    ....    00000000   00000000  6.50000000E+03
│    14 0118       10      11    ....    00000000   00000000  7.00000000E+03
│    15 0118       00      01    ....    00000000   00000000  7.50000000E+03
│    16 0109       5A      10    ....    00000000   00000000  8.00000000E+03
│    17 010A       26      11    ....    00000000   00000000  8.50000000E+03
│    18 010A       26      11    ....    00000000   00000000  9.00000000E+03
│    19 010A       26      10    ....    00000000   00000000  9.50000000E+03
│    20 010B       F6      11    ....    00000000   00000000  1.00000000E+04
└───────────────────────────────────────────────────────────────────────────┘
F1:"1" F2:"2" F3:Find F4:Disp F7:data F8:tt <ESC>:exit   ⌐c:
 ALT-A,B,C,D,E,F1,F2,T:goto ALT-P:log c1<>c2 ALT-S:log scrn ALT-N:filename
```

Figure 12-22   Bus Analyzer Data Display (Raw Mode).

EXAMPLE 12-12

What are the conditions on the lines of Fig. 12-22 during frame 11?

SOLUTION

Figure 12-22 shows that the address on the bus is 0106 and the data is C7. This data is being read (R/W = 1) and it is an op code fetch (D/i = 0). Therefore, C7 must be the op code for the instruction that is going to be executed.

Figure 12-22 shows only one way the data can be displayed. There are several other ways, as explained in Section 12-11.7.

12-11.1 ▼ Setting up the Bus Analyzer

The Bus Analyzer Events/Breakpoint Setup screen shown in Fig. 12-21 is also used for setting up the Bus Analyzer. The terms are set up as described for Data Breakpoints except that no entry is made in the Brk en brackets. When the terms have been defined, the cursor is moved to the bottom of the screen to define the mode.

The various modes of the Bus Analyzer make it possible to analyze the actions of the MCU prior to a trigger point (see Section 12-11.3). The trigger can be set to occur when a certain pattern (term) or sequence of terms appears on the bus. With the cursor between the brackets for a mode, the space bar is used to set or clear a selection. The modes are described in Section 12-11.4. A post-trigger count can be typed in if required. The state of the terms and modes can be saved in a file using the F6 key (from the BSA setup window).

Any bus analyzer setup information saved previously can be restored by entering the LOADTRIGGERS command. The terms are set up to capture the information on the MCU busses to determine the source of a problem. When the entries are complete, an F7 returns the user to the DEBUG screen so that the ARM command can be entered. Emulation begins when a go (G, GO, or GOTIL) command is executed. The Bus Analyzer then starts collecting the state of the address, data, and control signal lines, as well as the state of up to 16 user-selected signals (using the *Logic Clips*) for each bus cycle. These *states* are stored in a *trace buffer,* along with the time tags (time of occurrence). When the end of the buffer is reached, the bus analyzer counter wraps around to the first frame in the buffer and continues recording. This continues until some *term* or sequence of terms, called an *event* or *trigger,* halts the recording and thus holds or *captures* the contents of the trace buffer.

When setting up the Bus Analyzer setup screen, it is necessary to understand the use of **Terms** or **Events.** *Term* has already been defined in Section 12-10.7. An *Event* is a sequence of terms and is defined further in Section 12-11.2. A single term can be used to cause the Bus Analyzer to trigger, in which case that term is also an event.

12-11.2 ▼ Defining Events

As many as four terms can be enabled. The F8 key on the bus analyzer setup screen can be used to clear terms defined previously. Whenever a range of values is defined, an additional term is defined for the upper limit of the range. For example, if Term A were the start of a range, Term B would be used to contain the upper limit of the range and could not be defined as a separate term. Thus no more than two ranges can be defined: range Term A and B, and range Term C and D. If a single range is required, it can consist of either Terms A and B, Terms B and C, or Terms C and D.

EXAMPLE 12-13

In a **6805** system, any address between $C100 and $C1FF is to be an event. Show how to set or define this event using Terms A and B.

SOLUTION

Press F5 to bring up the Bus Analyzer setup screen. On the first line (for the A term) select *Trm en* and then enter the C100 address in the Hex column. On Term B's line select *Trm en,* and *RNG* and enter C1FF in the Hex column. Then press F7 to activate these conditions.

The sequencer modes require one or more terms to define the trigger events. Pressing the F7 key stores or initializes the definitions in the BSA setup window.

12-11.3 ▼ Bus Analyzer Triggers

Many different conditions can be specified to trigger the Bus Analyzer, including:

1. A trigger event as defined in the preceding subsection
2. The specified number of frames have been recorded
3. The specified number of post-trigger cycles have been recorded

The BSA will capture up to 8191 cycles (or frames) of this information when the trigger conditions (or events) are met. This allows the conditions on the bus to be displayed and lets the user determine what is occurring in a system without actually disturbing it. The various modes of the bus analyzer make it possible to analyze the MCU's actions when a certain pattern *(term)* or *sequence of terms* appears on the bus.

When the bus analyzer is armed and the emulator is running, a frame is strobed into the trace buffer at each clock. When a term or terms have occurred in the sequence specified to trigger the analyzer, the defined number of additional frames are stored and tracing stops. At this point the trace buffer contains as many as 8191 of the most recently stored frames.

When the desired frames of bus states have been collected, the bus analyzer software provides a variety of methods to view those cycles. The bus analyzer can display raw data, disassembled instructions, a combination of these, or source code. The bus analyzer also supports single-key commands for moving around the display buffer, including horizontal scrolling commands.

12-11.4 ▼ Sequencer Trace Modes

The sequential trace mode stores all bus cycles, beginning when both the ARM and the GO commands have been executed. Tracing stops when the specified term or sequence of terms triggers the analyzer and the specified number of post-trigger frames have been stored. This does not stop emulation, however. This is an important feature of a Bus Analyzer because the external system being controlled is often a process or machine that cannot be stopped instantly. This allows transitions or mode switchovers in the operation to be studied without damage or extra costs being incurred.

To facilitate the gathering of pertinent bus data, the bus analyzer can be operated in several modes, as follows:

1. Continuous Trace Mode. This mode provides a real-time, noninvasive trace of MCU bus activity. (It does not interfere with normal computer operation.) The bus analyzer can trace all cycles, or only those cycles that are defined as events. In this mode the bus analyzer continuously records bus data in the trace buffer whenever the user target system is being emulated. No qualifications for triggering or halting data collection are defined. This mode could be used with an instruction breakpoint, or the DARM command to stop collection, or the STOP command to stop emulation. Then the host trace buffer contents can be examined.

2. Counted Mode. This mode configures the bus analyzer to record a specified number of cycles. The user can trace a specified number of cycles of any type.

3. Sequential Event Mode. This mode provides for triggering the sequencer with as many as four terms, in one of five sequences. The five sequences are:

a. *term A or term B or term C or term D:* triggers the sequencer on any one of as many as four terms. In this case the words term and event are synonomous. When fewer than four terms are required, only the required terms are enabled.

b. *term A or term B, then term C or term D:* triggers the sequencer on either of two terms followed by either of two other terms.

c. *term A then term B, then term C if not term D:* triggers the sequencer on three terms in sequence, provided that the fourth term remains false. When the fourth term occurs before the trigger, the sequence starts again with the first term. This sequence can be used as a three-term sequence by enabling only terms A, B, and C.

d. *term A, then term B, then term C, then term D:* triggers the sequencer on cycles of four terms in sequence.

e. *term(s) A or term(s) B or term(s) C or term(s) D:* triggers the sequencer on the specified count of all terms. The analyzer strobes the specified terms into the trace buffer; when the specified total number of terms has been stored, the bus analyzer stores 4096 post-trigger frames. When fewer than four terms are required, only the required terms are enabled.

12-11.5 ▼ Collecting Bus Data

To illustrate how the Bus Analyzer function is used, we set up the Bus Analyzer Event/Data Breakpoint Setup window to work with the Test4 program used earlier. Figure 12-23 shows a trigger point set at address $10C to capture the results of running through the Test4 program once. After the entries were made, the F7 key was used to return the MMDS to the Debug window. The Bus Analyzer was armed (by entering ARM) and

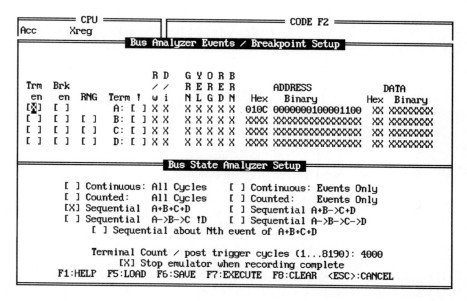

Figure 12-23 Bus Analyzer Events Window with Term A defined.

the program started (by entering G). When emulation begins, the MCU status, as shown on the Debug screen changes from IDLE to RUNNING. As each term specified in the sequencer mode occurs, the highlighting of the term is removed, indicating that the term has occurred. In many cases, the changes in the background occur too quickly to be observed.

The DARM command disarms the bus analyzer so that it can no longer acquire data. To halt data collection manually, the user must enter the DARM or STOP command (which stops emulation as well). When data collection has ceased, the bus analyzer state changes to DISARMED. Manually halting the bus analyzer with the DARM command does not cause emulation to cease. When a trigger is detected, the term cycle is latched into the buffer and the bus analyzer continues recording data until the specified number of post-trigger cycles have been collected. The bus analyzer then stops collecting data, and the status changes to DISARMED. The bus analyzer automatically begins searching for the next term with the first post-trigger cycle. If other terms occur while collecting the post-trigger cycles for the first term, the bus analyzer marks those term cycles while continuing to collect the post-trigger cycles.

12-11.6 ▼ Viewing Collected Bus Data

When the bus analyzer has finished collecting data in response to a term, the software loads the trace buffer contents into the host's memory. The Debug window will continue to be displayed until the F4 key is pressed. Initially this displays the contents in the *raw bus cycles* mode as shown in Fig. 12-22, or in the most recently viewed mode. While the loading operation is in progress, the word *LOADING* flashes in the upper right corner of the screen. The newest data in the trace buffer may not be correct until the loading operation has been completed. Pressing the Home key will display the first 20 bus cycles. The F1 and F2 keys mark bus cycles to be used in time-tag difference calculations. The F3 key is a means of searching the buffer for a pattern of data (see Section 12-11.11). The F4 key selects the display mode desired. If the key is pressed repeatedly, the display cycles through the four modes. The F7 key can be used to alternate between hexadecimal and binary display of data. The F8 key can be used to select the absolute time-tag format, the relative time-tag format, or time-tag in clock periods (see Section 12-11.9). In the lower right corner of the screen, the software displays the time tag difference, Δc, in seconds (0.00000400, for example, which is 4 μs).

12-11.7 ▼ Trace Buffer Display Format

As indicated earlier, the trace buffer can store 8191 64-bit frames of data. In addition to displaying the raw data as captured, the BSA can also display the data as disassembled instructions, as a mixture of raw and disassembled code, or as source code. In the disassembled instruction mode, only the lines that contain instructions are displayed. To display the source code the source file must be accessed by the analyzer. The source file must be in the same directory as the object file. The Source Code Display shows information similar to the disassembled instructions display, but it also displays the comments from the source code file.

12-11.8 ▼ Bus Analyzer Example

Figure 12-24 is a mixed mode display of the trace buffer data resulting from the setup used in Fig. 12-23 while running the Test4 program. It shows the state of the address bits, the corresponding data bits, the R/w and D/i bits status, whether this term is an event, the state of the logic clips, and the time of occurrence for the first 16 frames. Note that the D/i column is 0 for those Frames that are the first byte of an instruction. That is, for Frames 1, 3, 6, 11 and 16 of this figure. Secondly, the R/w column is always a 1 (for read) except for Frame 15 where a data byte of 00 has been written to address $118. The analyzer is very useful to observe the steps in the processing of instructions, such as the BRCLR decision instruction starting at Frame 6. The processor knows after reading the instruction (0F) that it must read the next byte (Frame 7) to get an operand address. It then reads the data at that address in Frame 8. Note that the data read is $80 which means that Bit 7 is set. This tells the processor not to take the offset, which is the number shown in Frames 9 and 10, so the CPU goes to the next instruction at address $106. We do not have space to show what would happen if that bit 7 were not set, but it would have added the offset to the address and skipped over the next three bytes to address $109, thus, not storing the accumulator.

12-11.9 ▼ Using the Time-Tag Clock

The time-tag clock provides a means of timing the execution of one or more instructions. The user can select the source and the frequency of the time-tag clock. Entering the TIMETAG command calls up the TIMETAG window shown in Fig. 12-25. Scrolling up or down with the arrow keys and pressing ENTER allows the time-tag clock to be set to 1, 2, 4, 8, or 16 MHz, or to use the emulator clock, an external clock,

```
========================== Bus State Analyzer ==========================
Frame   Address   Data    RD   Term     POD B       POD A      Time tag       ↑
                          wi            gpbgyorb    gpbgyorb   abs:nSec
      1 STRT      AE03    LDX #3
      1 0100      AE      10   ....     00000000    00000000   5.00000000E+02
      2 0101      03      11   ....     00000000    00000000   1.00000000E+03
      3 ST1       F6      LDA ,X
      3 0102      F6      10   ....     00000000    00000000   1.50000000E+03
      4 0103      0F      11   ....     00000000    00000000   2.00000000E+03
      5 0003      00      11   ....     00000000    00000000   2.50000000E+03
      6 0103      0FF003  BRCLR 7,00F0,ST2
      6 0103      0F      10   ....     00000000    00000000   3.00000000E+03
      7 0104      F0      11   ....     00000000    00000000   3.50000000E+03
      8 00F0      80      11   ....     00000000    00000000   4.00000000E+03
      9 0105      03      11   ....     00000000    00000000   4.50000000E+03
     10 0105      03      11   ....     00000000    00000000   5.00000000E+03
     11 0106      C70118  STA 0118
     11 0106      C7      10   ....     00000000    00000000   5.50000000E+03
     12 0107      01      11   ....     00000000    00000000   6.00000000E+03
     13 0108      18      11   ....     00000000    00000000   6.50000000E+03
     14 0118      10      11   ....     00000000    00000000   7.00000000E+03
     15 0118      00      01   ....     00000000    00000000   7.50000000E+03
     16 ST2       5A      DECX
F1:"1" F2:"2" F3:Find F4:Disp F7:data F8:tt <ESC>:exit   △c:            ↓
= ALT-A,B,C,D,E,F1,F2,T:goto ALT-P:log c1<>c2 ALT-S:log scrn ALT-N:filename =
```

Figure 12-24 Bus Analyzer Buffer contents shown in Mixed Mode.

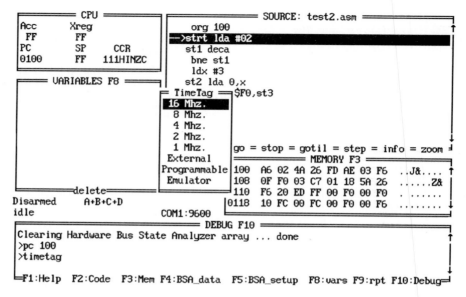

Figure 12-25 TIMETAG Window overlaying the Debug Window.

or a programmable clock. A lower-frequency clock should be chosen for timing relatively long instruction sequences. Higher-frequency clocks provide greater time resolution for timing faster operations. The time tag is displayed in seconds when the 1-, 2-, 4,- 8-, or 16-MHz clock is used.

To time the execution of a portion of the code, use either the raw bus cycle mode or the mixed mode of the BSA display with the absolute time-tag format. The cycle with which to begin execution timing is then selected. Pressing the Fl key marks that cycle. The user must also select the ending cycle and press the F2 key to mark it. The software then calculates the time between the two frames and the difference is displayed in the lower right corner of the screen. For example, if the beginning time-tag were 3.2677888E03 and the ending time-tag were 3.2677928E03, the difference would be 0.00000400 second, or 4 μs.

When the time-tag is represented in clock periods, the procedure is the same but the difference obtained is a number of time-tag clock cycles. Multiplying the result by the time-tag clock period gives elapsed time between the beginning and ending cycles.

EXAMPLE 12-14

Assume that the beginning time-tag value for a code segment is 219, the ending time-tag value is 234, and the time-tag frequency is 4 MHz. Find the elasped time of the segment

SOLUTION

The segment requires 15 time-tag cycles. At a time-tag clock frequency of 4 MHz, the time-tag clock period is 0.25 μs and the elapsed time is 3.75 μs. Had the same time-tag values been obtained with a time-tag clock frequency of 500 kHz (a clock period of 2 μs), the elapsed time would be 30 μs.

The time-tag clock provides a time reference value in each frame of the trace buffer and should be set up prior to any bus analysis.

12-11.10 ▼ Other Commands

Other MMDS05 commands apply to the MCU emulation; some are used during bus analysis, although they are not actually bus analyzer commands. We describe these commands in this section.

The ARM command is used to enable the capturing of bus states. Emulation (and capturing) begins when a G, GO, or GOTIL command is executed. Emulation continues until it is stopped by a breakpoint or by a STOP command. Bus capture is halted by the DARM command. The contents of the trace buffer can be displayed (1) as raw bus cycles, (2) as disassembled instructions only, (3) as mixed instructions and raw bus cycles, or (4) as source code. In the mixed display, each disassembled instruction is followed by the associated raw bus cycles.

The timer synchronization (TSYNC) command enables or disables synchronization of the start of emulation with the programmable timer of the MCU, which runs at one-fourth of the MCU clock frequency. When enabled, the system firmware records the value of the free-running timer counter each time emulation stops. Before restarting emulation (in response to a G or GO command), the system waits until the free-running timer reaches the value recorded at the previous stop. This is a valuable feature when debugging programs that use the timer.

12-11.11 ▼ Searching the Trace Buffer

To search the trace buffer for a frame that contains a special configuration of bits, the user can press the F3 key. The software displays the Find Pattern window shown in Fig. 12-26. Initially, or following a clear operation (F8) keyboard command, all fields are set to X (don't care). The arrow keys can be used to move to the desired field. The Frame field is a decimal field. The frame number field can only be used to scroll to a specified frame.

The Address and Data fields are hexadecimal fields. A range of addresses or data values can be specified by using the X (don't care) character for some digits. For example, 03XX in the Address field searches for addresses in the range of 0300 through 03FF. An X can be specified in any digit position to cause that digit to be ignored in the search. Because the *RwDi* field and the two pod fields are binary fields, a 0 or 1 can be entered for each bit to be used in the search, and an X for the bits to be ignored.

Bus cycles in which one or more terms are true can be found by entering A, B, C, or D in the Term field. When the search pattern has been defined completely, pressing F7

```
═══════════════════ Bus State Analyzer ═══════════════════
Frame  Address    Data     RD   Term     POD B      POD A     Time tag    ↑
                            wi           gpbgyorb   gpbgyorb  abs:nSec
   1 STRT       A602       LDA #2
   1 0100       10100110   10   ....     00000000   00000000  5.00000000E+02
════════════════════════ Find Pattern ════════════════════════
Frame  Address    Data     RD   Term     POD B      POD A
                            wi   ABCD     gpbgyorb   gpbgyorb

XXXX XXXX         XX        XX   XXXX     XXXXXXXX   XXXXXXXX

              F7:Find    F8:Clear    <ESC>:CANCEL

   8 0105       01001010   10   ....     00000000   00000000  4.00000000E+03
   9 0106       00100110   11   ....     00000000   00000000  4.50000000E+03
  10 0106       00100110   11   ....     00000000   00000000  5.00000000E+03
  11 0106       26FA       BNE ST1
  11 0106       00100110   10   ....     00000000   00000000  5.50000000E+03
  12 0107       11111010   11   ....     00000000   00000000  6.00000000E+03
  13 0107       11111010   11   ....     00000000   00000000  6.50000000E+03
  14 ST1        C70118     STA 0118
  14 0102       11000111   10   ....     00000000   00000000  7.00000000E+03
  15 0103       00000001   11   ....     00000000   00000000  7.50000000E+03
F1:"1" F2:"2" F3:Find F4:Disp F7:data F8:tt <ESC>:exit  ◦c:        ↓
═ ALT-A,B,C,D,E,F1,F2,T:goto ALT-P:log c1<>c2 ALT-S:log scrn ALT-N:filename ═
```

Figure 12-26 Find Pattern Window.

starts the search. The search begins at the first frame of the screen and proceeds toward the highest-numbered frame in the trace buffer.

12-11.12 ▼ Moving the Cursor

In the BSA data window, the cursor can be moved to the cycle corresponding to the next occurrence of a term, by pressing the Alt key while pressing the A, B, C, D, or E key. Alt-A, Alt-B, Alt-C, and Alt-D specify terms A, B, C, and D; Alt-E specifies any term. The same thing can be done by entering a NEXTA, NEXTB, NEXTC, NEXTD, or NEXTE command from the DEBUG window. The command displays the term bus cycle in the DEBUG window, but the user must press F4 to display BSA data to see the bus cycles that precede and follow the event cycle.

While in the DEBUG window, entering a SHOWTRIGGER command will display the trigger cycle. The cursor appears on the frame that triggered the analyzer. F4 will display the trigger cycle in the trace buffer. Alt-T will scroll the trigger cycle. The Home key moves the display cursor to frame 0, and the End key moves the display cursor to the end of the buffer. As described in Section 12-11.11, the F3 key (in the BSA data window) defines a pattern, and the F7 key moves the cursor to the next cycle that matches the pattern. (Because the Find operation does not wrap around to the start of the buffer, if the matching cycle precedes the currently selected cycle, the matching cycle is not found.)

12-11.13 ▼ Saving the Bus Display

The bus display can be saved in a disk file called a **log file** (see Section 12-10.3), along with the commands used in a session. Pressing the Alt and S key will copy the screen to the log file. The log can be written to a file by executing an LF (log file) command and specifying a pathname for the log file. If the file exists, the software prompts for overwriting or appending the entries to that file; otherwise, the LF command creates a new log file. The trace buffer frames are logged in the format in which they are displayed, according to the current view mode.

12-11.14 ▼ Scrolling the Display

The bus analysis display can be scrolled with the PgUp, PgDn, and arrow keys. However, scrolling of the BSA data display operates in conjunction with cursor bars. Initially, the horizontal cursor bar is at the top frame of the display. Scrolling downward moves the horizontal cursor bar downward; continuing to scroll downward when the horizontal cursor bar has reached the bottom of the display causes the entire display to scroll. Scrolling upward moves the horizontal cursor bar upward; scrolling the display begins when the bar reaches the top of the display. The display does not scroll to the left or right because the entire line is displayed.

12-11.15 ▼ Host Computer Requirements

The host PC for the MMDS05 must be hardware and software compatible with the IBM PC/XT/AT or PS/2 computers and must be running DOS 3.0 or later. It can be run under OS/2 using the DOS window. A memory size of at least 640K bytes is recommended because approximately 512K bytes is required for the host software. An asynchronous communications port is required, configured as either COM1, COM2, COM3, or COM4, for communications between the MMDS05 and the host.

Some additional system characteristics recommended for improved product performance and usability are: 80286- or 80386-based systems, a fixed disk drive, and a color monitor. The MMDS05 system software also supports a Microsoft, IBM, or Logitech mouse.

Although a Color Monitor is recommended, the MMDS05 will work with a monochrome display. In this case, when starting up the MDS, the command should be followed by the DOS BW command, as follows:

```
C:> MMDS05 BW
```

As many users may know, not all color combinations are readable in many color monitors. To help this situation, the MMDS05 has a COLORS command and display. This screen allows the user to select usable colors for each element of the display. Numbers should be entered for each line of the display, and the color choice is selected by pressing Enter. The new colors will not appear until the MMDS05.EXE file is executed again. Making the background of highlights and of help screens a different color sets these elements off from the main screen.

12-12 ▼ SUMMARY

In this chapter we described the process of designing, building, and testing MCU systems. The need to test both the software and hardware performance of a system under development was explained. Logic Analyzers were introduced and their role in testing hardware was discussed. Three Logic Analyzers made by prominent electronic instrumentation manufacturers were also described.

The Motorola Modular Development System (MMDSx) was introduced as a specialized instrument to develop software and to test hardware. MMDSs are now available for many of the MCUs in several MCU families. The MMDS05 development system made by Motorola to test systems that use a **6805** MCU was described in detail. This included explanations of Bus State Analysis and the techniques of Source-Level Debugging.

12-13 ▼ GLOSSARY

Assembler A program used to convert programmer's mnemonics to machine language.

Breakpoint A feature of debugging systems used to stop the execution of a user's program at a specific address and enter the debug program.

BSA Bus State Analyzer. A device to record the status of all the signal lines of the μP buses for each cycle of execution.

Capture The process of recording or saving the status of signals or data.

Command An instruction to a computer. Usually typed on the keyboard.

CRT terminal Stands for Cathode Ray Tube terminal. A data terminal with a TV-like screen.

Debug The process of finding and eliminating "bugs" or errors in hardware or software.

Diagnostics A type of program used to test hardware or systems.

Disassembler A program that converts machine language back into the mnemonics that were used to generate it.

Download The process of moving a file via a transmission path from a remote computer to the local computer.

Edit To use an EDITOR utility program to create or modify another program.

Emulation Ram RAM Memory in an emulator system used to hold programs for system testing before the regular memory is in place.

Emulator A device used to duplicate the operation of another device (such as an MCU).

Event Something that causes the bus analyzer to trigger.

Help One of the screens or environments of an MDS system.

Host A computer used for software development or as a source of data for another computer.

Invasive A term used to describe software or functions that interfere with or delay the normal operation of a computer.

Language A term used to distinguish between the different syntax used to describe the machine code for a computer. BASIC, Pascal, C, or FORTRAN are examples of "High-Level" Languages; Assembly language is provided by the μP manufacturers for each μP.

Map A screen or environment where the μP memory map to be used can be selected.

MDS Microcomputer Development System. A system tool to aid in the development of μC systems.

Menu A screen that lists selections that can be called up by a command or selected by a mouse.

Mnemonics The "English-like" statements used by programmers to specify the desired machine code or Symbol address of a software program.

Modem MODulator/DEModulator. A device used to convert digital signals to audio tones for transmission over a telephone channel, or vice versa. Most MODEMs will convert signals in both directions simultaneously (known as full-duplex).

Noninvasive A function or condition that does not interfere with the normal operation of a computer system.

One-line-assembler A COMMAND that will permit entries of mnemonics and will deposit the appropriate machine language into memory or a file one line at a time.

Patching A method of modifying the machine language of an object program without reassembling or recompiling it.

PC A Personal Computer; or Printed Circuit board; or Program Counter.

Personality pod Another name for a separate Emulator Module for a specific μC or MCU.

Protocols The rules, or format, or prescribed procedure.

Prototype A hand-made model of a system destined for production.

Screen A CRT display that is formatted in a prescribed way.

SLD Source-Level Debugger. A technique to display the operands or Symbols as well as the instructions of a program in mnemonic form.

STOP An emulator command used to stop execution of a user's program.

Term A set of specific conditions on the address bus, data bus, and other lines on an MCU.

Terminal emulation A program that will make a computer look and act like a specific terminal.

TRACE A COMMAND that causes one instruction to be executed and updates the register's display information.

Trigger A signal or condition that causes an action. The event can be a combination of terms.

Upload To move a program file from the local computer to a remote computer via the serial transmission link.

Window A technique to display a collection of data on a CRT screen.

Wirewrap A technique for constructing a prototype model of an electronic circuit that uses patented tools for wrapping wires around posts instead of soldering them.

12-14 ▼ REFERENCES

GREENFIELD, J. D., *Practical Digital Design,* 3rd ed., Prentice Hall, Englewood Cliffs, N.J. 1994.

MOTOROLA, *Evaluation Module User's Manual,* M68HC05EVM/AD6, Phoenix, Ariz., November 1990.

———, *Evaluation Module User's Manual,* M68HC11EVM/AD7, Phoenix, Ariz., October 1989.

———, *MMDS05 Software Operations Manual,* MMDS05OM/D, Austin, Texas, April 1993.

———, *HC05P9 Emulator Module User's Manual,* HC05P9EMUM/D, Austin, Texas, 1993.

12-15 ▼ PROBLEMS

12-1. Conceptually design the MCU system for a microwave oven.

12-2. In Fig. 12-9, where is the reference location and where is the cursor location? What is the data at REF+35? At REF-1?

12-3. How much time do the data samples in a Tektronix 1230 cover if the sample rate is:
(a) 2 μs?
(b) 100 ns?

12-4. A data line ocassionally has a 60-ns pulse on it. What must the sampling rate of a logic analyzer be to ensure that the logic analyzer detects the pulse? Explain why a longer sampling rate may cause the logic analyzer to miss the pulse.

12-5. In Fig. 12-17, what are the contents of each register in the **6805?**

12-6. In Fig. 12-18, what will happen when the instructions at $106 and $109 are executed?

12-7. In Fig. 12-20, what locations are assigned to RAM0?

12-8. In Fig. 12-22, what is the time difference between each frame?

12-9. The Bus Analyzer should trigger when three external signals are all 1s and the data on the lines is 34. How can the Bus Analyzer be set up to make this happen?

After attempting to solve these problems, try to answer the self-evaluation questions in Section 12-2. If any of them still seem difficult, review the appropriate sections of the chapter to find the answers.

REAL–WORLD APPLICATIONS AND INTERFACING TECHNIQUES

13-1 ▼ INSTRUCTIONAL OBJECTIVES

In this chapter we consider the problems of connecting or interfacing external system components to a μC. This may involve both digital and analog signals.

MCU systems that work properly in a prototype or laboratory setup may not function at all when connected to the real-world devices they were designed to control, due to electrical noise. Such an electrically noisy environment is often found in industry. Even when the internal design of the μC system is done well, the overall performance may not be acceptable unless the μC is properly interfaced to the external system components. *Electrical noise* consists of unwanted pulses or voltage variations on the power or signal lines that cause false operation.

After reading this chapter, the student should be able to:

1. Use noise reduction techniques such as twisted-pair wiring or electrostatic shielding where necessary.
2. Protect systems properly from electrical noise or damage.
3. Use input and output circuits designed to isolate μCs from high-power systems.
4. Connect A/D and D/A converters to μC systems.
5. Explain the *successive approximation* technique for converting analog signals to their digital equivalents.

13-2 ▼ SELF-EVALUATION QUESTIONS

Watch for the answers to the following questions as you read the chapter. They should help you to understand the material presented.

1. Why should the *grounds* for circuits meet only at one common point?
2. What are the advantages of *twisted-pair* wiring?
3. What are the advantages of isolated circuits over direct TTL coupling? Under what circumstances must input isolation be used?

4. What advantages do differential amplifiers have for the transmission of digital or analog signals?

5. What is a transducer?

6. When is it necessary to use A/D converters in a μC system?

13-3 ▼ USES OF μCs

Although the use of μCs (in Personal Computers) for *business applications* is increasing rapidly, the majority of μCs are still used in *automotive* and *industrial applications.* Automotive use alone has become a yearly market of millions of μCs.

Larger computers (known as *mainframes*) have been used for business applications for many years, but now thousands of new μC-based Personal Computers are being installed by businesses every year. The Personal Computers fall into two basic classes: those that use the Intel family of μPs, and those that use the Motorola **68000** family. There are many different companies making so-called IBM clones. (They use the MS-DOS operating system and Intel 80386 or 80486 μPs.) These companies include Tandy Corporation (Radio Shack), Hewlett-Packard, Compaq Computer, Dell Computer, and others. The principal **68000** family user is Apple Macintosh, although two smaller companies, Atari and Amiga, also use these Motorola μPs.

Because the IBM and clones all use the Intel μPs, their programs use the Intel machine language. Probably most programs for these PCs have been written in the C programming language, however. The Macintosh computers all use the Motorola **68000** family of μPs, so their programs are assembled or compiled in that language. Again, most are written in C.

These business μCs are complete stand-alone systems, but in many companies they are interconnected to form large distributed processing systems. This is called *networking,* and many companies, such as Novell, Inc., provide network hardware and software. These networks sometimes contain both IBM and Macintosh PCs. Macintosh PCs have a built-in network called Appletalk. Using modems and telephone lines, they can span the continent and even the world. Thousands of business software programs have been written. Almost all of the business μCs use either the DOS or the Macintosh operating system. These PCs with their well-designed network transmission systems generally are operated in an office environment.

As opposed to these systems that work with 16- and 32-bit μPs, most *industrial control* applications use 8-bit MCUs. Motorola has, however, introduced several 16- and 32-bit MCUs (see Chapter 16). All these MCUs use *bit-manipulation* programs that control machinery with individual signal wires. Each signal sent by the MCU is usually a command to turn external devices, such as motors, solenoids, and relays, ON or OFF. The signals received from the external hardware represent the *status* of the input sensors, such as mechanical limit switches, ON/OFF operator controls, or transducers. Because most industrial applications are unique, they present difficult and challenging problems for the designer.

Systems to turn devices ON or OFF as a result of discrete events can easily be implemented by TTL or CMOS logic. When *decisions* must be made, however, based on a calculated result of inputs, the computing power of a μC is needed. Many μC systems must also interpret a variable analog input signal or must output a similar variable control signal.

13-3.1 ▼ Real-World Electrical Interference

The internal bus structure of many μC systems has been discussed in previous chapters, but the real-world connections to external equipment that may be physically separated by many feet has not been described in detail. This interfacing is an important aspect of controller design. In a laboratory or business environment where the MCU is less than 10 or 20 feet away from the devices it is controlling, and no large power-operated devices are used, there are usually few problems with electrical interfacing. In a factory environment, however, electrical noise can cause many problems. In *process control* applications, for example, the equipment being controlled is often powered by high-current DC or high-power AC sources. Because of the inductive nature of motors or solenoids, large *voltage or current pulses* can be generated. Unless proper design techniques are used to interconnect the μC system to the power equipment, these pulses can be induced into the MCU or other digital circuits and cause system malfunctions. In some cases the pulses may be so powerful that the interfacing parts are damaged. Because externally powered control equipment may produce transient voltages exceeding several thousands of volts, it is obvious that semiconductor devices, designed for 5-V or even 12-V operation, can be damaged permanently.

13-4 ▼ NOISE REDUCTION IN DIGITAL INTERFACING

The I/O devices discussed in previous chapters were mostly TTL compatible, and an interfering voltage pulse greater than about 1.2 V can cause false operation by changing a 1 to a 0, or vice versa. CMOS devices are less susceptible to these interfering pulses but can still fail when pulses exceed 2.5 or 3 V. These induced noise pulses are usually termed *spikes* or *glitches*. When a μC is operated in an electrically noisy environment, special shielding and grounding precautions must be taken to prevent the introduction of interfering pulses (noise) into the μC signal lines.

13-4.1 ▼ Ground Coupling

Improper grounding of digital circuits is one of the principal causes of severe problems. Depending on how circuits are wired, currents from several different circuits can flow through the same ground path and can cause unwanted coupling even if there is only a fraction of an ohm in that path. If the currents are large enough (a current of 12 A through 0.1 ohm (Ω) produces a potential difference of 1.2 V), false operation can result in a typical TTL circuit.

An example of improper grounding is shown in the circuit of Fig. 13-1a. It uses two transistors to amplify the input signal V_{IN}. The problems occur because the ground line of transistor B is improperly connected to the ground of transistor A rather than directly to the system ground. Assume that the wire from the emitter of transistor A to the signal ground has a resistance of 0.1 Ω. If transistor B draws 12 A when it is ON, the emitter of A will be raised to 1.2 V, which will change its biasing dramatically and probably cause improper operation. Figure 13-1b shows the correct way to connect the grounds to eliminate coupling due to the common ground path. If all grounds for a system are brought to *only one point,* so that mutual resistance paths are avoided, coupling from this source is eliminated.

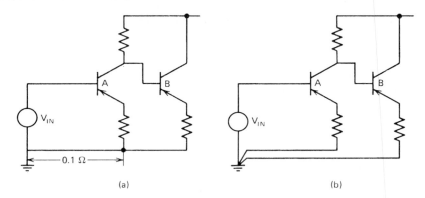

Figure 13-1 Grounding rules. (a) Improper grounding. (b) Proper grounding.

13-4.2 ▼ Capacitive and Inductive Coupling

Capacitive or inductive coupling between lines not actually connected to each other can also result in interference. Since digital signals are pulses, and like AC have changing levels, capacitive coupling can cause interfering voltages to be induced.

Capacitive coupling can result from two lines parallel to one another on a PC card or in a ribbon cable, or due to the closeness of the metallic cabinet to the interconnecting wiring. This coupling between lines is called *crosstalk*. Since the input impedance of some IC gates is as high as 100 kΩ, a capacitance of only a few picofarads (pF) can result in a signal large enough to cause trouble. It is particularly troublesome when the coupling exists to a line or surface that is hundreds of volts above ground, which can be true if the chassis and/or power supply grounds are not connected properly. Similarly, whenever there are large currents in wires, strong magnetic fields result. These fields can be inductively coupled to nearby circuits and produce unwanted glitches.

13-4.3 ▼ Techniques for Reduction of Noise

Several techniques are used to avoid interference resulting from capacitive, inductive, or ground circuit coupling. They are:

1. Capacitively coupled noise voltages are reduced greatly using *electrostatic shielding*. This consists of a grounded wire (or metallic screen) between the two circuits, or surrounding one of them. A coaxial cable, which is a cable consisting of a signal wire surrounded by a grounded metal sheath, is frequently used to carry digital signals whenever it is necessary to avoid possible capacitive interference. On a printed circuit board (see Section 13-11.1), a grounded line is frequently used between two signal lines. Ground lines are also used in a flat ribbon cable to provide this type of shielding.

2. Magnetic coupling between adjacent circuits can be reduced by using *twisted-pair wires*. This is a technique commonly used in telephone lines and other audio systems to eliminate audible crosstalk. If two lines are carrying equal and opposed polarity signals, such as a signal line and its ground return, proper twisting of these two wires (so that they are transposed several times) causes the magnetic fields to nearly cancel each other. This greatly reduces inductively generated interfering voltages. When combined with proper (right-angle) separation, magnetic coupling is effectively eliminated. Twisting a ground wire with a signal wire can also reduce capacitive coupling since it serves to provide electrostatic shielding and therefore reduces this form of crosstalk.

3. The use of optical coupling, described in Section 13-5.3, is one of the most effective ways to minimize grounding problems.

13-5 ▼ METHODS OF INTERFACING DIGITAL DEVICES

When connecting an MCU to an external electromechanical system, the MCU must *send* the control signals and *receive* the sensor feedback. But the power circuitry must be kept separate from the MCU circuitry to minimize digital errors due to electrical noise. Care must be taken to separate the wiring and components physically so that electrostatic, magnetic, or common ground coupling are all minimized.

To connect the TTL signals of an MCU to externally controlled equipment, the following methods are used:

1. Direct TTL or CMOS connections
2. Relays
3. Optically coupled DC circuits
4. Solid-state relays

13-5.1 ▼ TTL or CMOS Interfacing

A direct TTL-level connection can be used only if the equipment to be controlled is close (no more than a few feet) and the external power circuit grounds are very carefully planned to avoid passing high currents through the MCU circuit grounds. This is much easier if the system is located in a low-electrical-noise environment such as a laboratory or office.

13-5.2 ▼ Electromechanical Relays

A relay is basically a device consisting of a coil and a switch. Passing current through the coil creates a magnetic field that closes the switch. Thus the switch and its activation device, the coil, have no electrical connection and can be totally isolated from each other.

For years, relays have been used where isolation was needed between grounds and power sources. Many types of relays are available, including a growing number of types that can be mounted on PC cards. Figure 13-2 shows two types of relays: an electromechanical relay (commonly called just a "relay") and its semiconductor equivalent, the solid-state relay. Figure 13-2a shows that the electromechanical relay isolation qualities are excellent, because the coil circuit is not electrically connected to the contacts, but these relays are mechanical devices and will wear out or require adjustment in time. Converting to electronic switching is an answer to this problem, but care must be taken to avoid the coupling problems just mentioned. The solid-state relay, shown in Fig. 13-2b, uses optical coupling and transmits its signal using light waves.

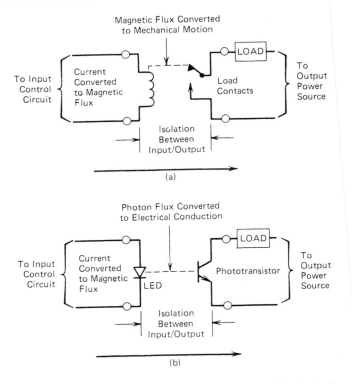

Figure 13-2   Two types of relays. (a) Electromechanical relay.
(b) Solid-State relay.

13-5.3 ▼ Optical Coupling

One of the best ways to avoid common ground problems is to use another semiconductor technology product known as an **optical coupler.** As shown in Fig. 13-3, an optical coupler consists of a *Light-Emitting Diode* (LED) and a *phototransistor.* Because the information is transmitted optically (i.e., light from the LED shines on the phototransistor to turn it ON), the input circuit is electrically isolated from the output and separate power sources or ground returns are possible. When optical couplers are installed properly, common ground and capacitive coupling are both avoided. One disadvantage is that the response time of *some* devices is very slow compared to that of standard TTL gates. Various types of optical couplers are now available to provide this circuit isolation, and some of them feature the ability to withstand up to 7500 V (rms) between input and output.

Optically coupled DC circuits are functionally equivalent to relays, and DC optical coupling is provided in single- or dual-transistor **(Darlington)** types. The dual-transistor amplifier has higher gain and thus will work with smaller input signals. They can be used in many applications where ground isolation is needed and large DC voltages or currents are involved.

When laying out the hardware, it is important to keep the wiring and components of the power equipment physically separated, and shielded if necessary, from the MCU circuits. Otherwise, electrostatic or magnetic coupling can still occur and defeat the purpose of the optical couplers.

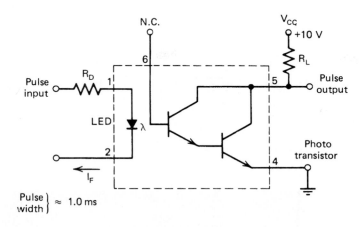

Figure 13-3 An optical coupler.

13-5.4 ▼ Solid-State Relays

Solid-State Relays (SSRs) are optically coupled semiconductor circuits that usually include TRIACs or Silicon-Controlled Rectifiers (SCRs) capable of switching AC circuits. A SSR circuit is shown in Fig. 13-4a. Figure 13-4b shows several packaged assemblies capable of controlling motors, heaters, or other AC-operated devices.

For SSRs the DC input to the LEDs controls the TRIACs or SCRs that turn AC-powered devices ON or OFF. These circuits can also include *zero-crossing* detection circuits (the circuit is opened or closed only when the AC voltage is at the zero point of the cycle) to minimize the generation of transient noise signals. Basic units are available that control up to 25 A with an isolated DC input of 1 to 10 mA. Depending on the sensitivity, they can be operated directly from the I/O lines from some of the MCU devices.

A typical application could employ three of these relays to control three-phase AC motors of considerable power with one TTL or MCU output signal line. The MCU control signal would be connected to the paralleled DC inputs of three SSRs. The three output circuits of the relays would be connected in series with each of the three AC power wires to the motor.

All the previous devices are used as output ON–OFF switches where isolation between the μC circuits and the controlled equipment is required. All except the AC versions of SSRs can also be used to connect input signals into the μC.

13-6 ▼ DIGITAL INTERFACE CIRCUITS

Digital circuits are frequently used to interface between external system devices and the μC. Each signal path must provide some form of isolation to prevent the problems described in Sections 13-3 and 13-4. Two types of circuits are described: output circuits that transfer the signals from the μC to the external system components, and input circuits that transfer signals from the remote system's sensors or switches to the μC circuits.

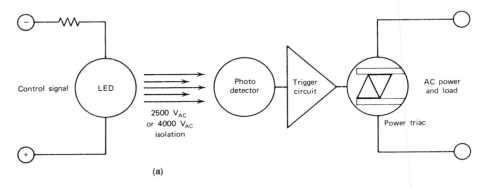

(a)

(b)

Figure 13-4 Typical Solid-State relays. (a) Functional block diagram. (b) Solid-State relays.

13-6.1 ▼ Digital Output Interface Circuits

Figure 13-5 is a block diagram showing one way to connect externally controlled circuits to an MCU. It uses four Burr-Brown-type MP701/MP702 modules. Each module consists of eight latches/drivers. The eight data bus lines from the MCU control the eight outputs of each module. Each output line is connected to a relay for isolation. A typical relay controlling a single line is shown in the upper right-hand corner of the figure. Each of the four modules has an enable line that is selected by the control logic circuit shown in the figure. Address bits A0 and A1 (which connect into the control logic) select the module to be controlled. The remainder of the address lines are used to select this particular set of circuits. When data is written to that address, the 1s turn ON the appropriate relays and the 0s turn them OFF. Example 13-1 explains how these modules might be used in a typical **6800** family system.

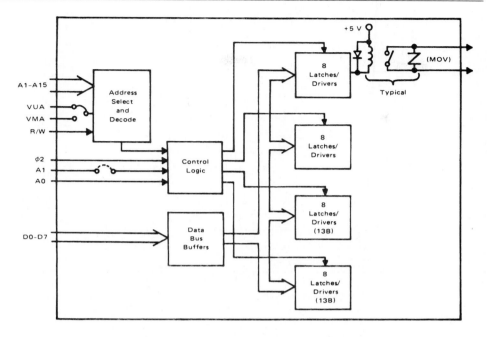

Figure 13-5   Isolated digital output module block diagram.
(Redrawn from information supplied by Burr-Brown.)

EXAMPLE 13-1

The modules shown in Fig. 13-5 occupy locations $8000 through $8003 on an MCU's address bus. If the third module down is to be selected, what address signal must be applied to the Address Select and Decode logic, and what signals must be applied to the Control Logic blocks?

SOLUTION

The address of the module selected is $8002. The binary value on Address lines A15 through A2, respectively, is 1000 0000 0000 00XX. When decoded in the Address Select Block, it will enable the Control Logic block. Because A1 is 1 and A0 is 0, the third of the four modules will be selected.

13-6.2 ▼ Digital Input Interface Circuits

The block diagram of Fig. 13-6 shows circuits that are used for isolated inputs (to the MPU) of digital (ON/OFF) signals. A typical input comes in through the optical isolator shown in the right-hand corner of the figure. It sets a bit in a buffer. When that buffer is enabled by the control logic and selected by the proper address, the bit that was set is read

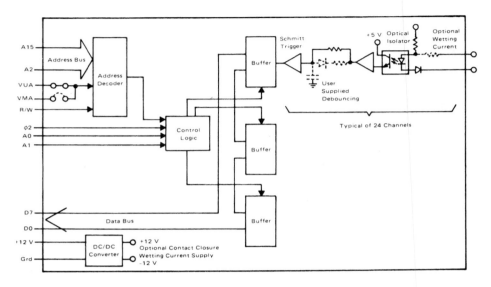

Figure 13-6 Isolated digital input module block diagram.
(Redrawn from information supplied by Burr-Brown.)

out on the data bus. Inputs can be isolated using optically coupled circuits as shown and, typically, can withstand voltage differences of at least 600 V between the external wires and the internal circuits. These methods are used in pressure or thermostat sensors, or limit switches.

13-7 ▼ APPLICATIONS OF DIGITAL INTERFACING

The circuits described previously can be used in a wide variety of applications. Several examples of their use are described in the following paragraphs.

13-7.1 ▼ Digital Temperature Controller

Figure 13-7 shows a simplified temperature controller subsystem using an MCU that can be assembled with standard digital circuits. This example uses the circuits just described,

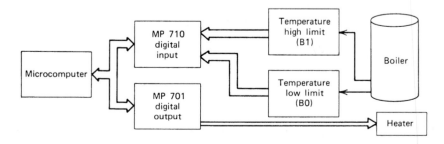

Figure 13-7 Temperature control subsystem.
(Redrawn from information supplied by Burr-Brown.)

with optically isolated digital inputs and reed-relay outputs. Temperature limit switches are used to provide the contact closures. The limit switch B1 closes when the temperature exceeds the HIGH limit, and the B0 switch closes when the temperature is too LOW, in accordance with Table 13-1.

Table 13-1   Operation of Temperature Limit Switches

INPUT[a]		PROCESS STATUS	CONTROL ACTION
B1	B0		
0	0	Temperature acceptable	No change required
1	0	Temperature too high	Turn OFF heater
0	1	Temperature too low	Turn ON heater
1	1	Controller malfunction	Sound alarm

[a]Closed contacts = 1.

Figure 13-8 shows the flow diagram of the system functions to be implemented in software. Note that this is an extremely simple example and could easily have been implemented in discrete TTL logic. A μC might be used, however, because it can perform other functions simultaneously. It gives the designer a great deal of flexibility, and modifications to the function can easily be made by changing the program.

13-7.2 ▼ Digital Mixture Controller

Figure 13-9 shows a mixture-control subsystem. Two solenoid valves control the flow of liquids into a vat. Two float switches close their contacts whenever levels A or B are reached. The μC starts a sequence with the vat empty. Valve A is opened and the A liquid flows in until level A switch closes. Valve B is then opened and the B liquid flows in until level B switch closes. The two liquids are then mixed and drained out by devices not shown. Level C is monitored at all times. If the liquid ever reaches this level, both valves are turned OFF and an alarm is sounded.

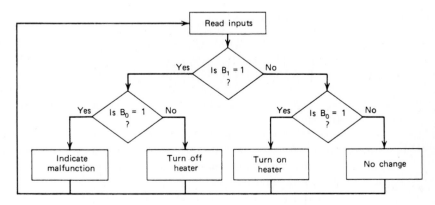

Figure 13-8   Flow diagram for temperature control system software. (Redrawn from information supplied by Burr-Brown.)

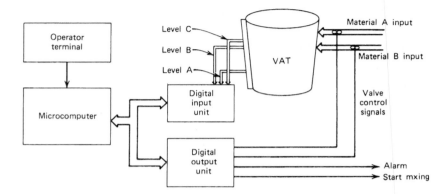

Figure 13-9 Mixture control system. (Redrawn from information supplied by Burr-Brown.)

Again this is a simple example just to show the application of the digital input/output circuits. Students can use their imagination to elaborate on the design. For example, several more float sensors could be added and a high- and low-speed flow could be used by switching to low speed for "topping off" when a level just under the desired level is reached. Alternatively, the mixture "recipe" could be changed by selecting switches at different levels.

13-8 ▼ ANALOG I/O FOR µC SYSTEMS

Microcomputer systems often must *generate* analog (or variable) control voltages, and must read or *sense* variable input voltages with high accuracy (possibly as high as 0.01%). In the fields of process control, industrial instrumentation, and medical electronics, a variety of physical parameters must be monitored. This is usually done using Transducers and Analog-to-Digital Converters (ADCs). ADCs are explained in Section 13-9.

13-8.1 ▼ Transducers

Transducers are devices that convert physical quantities to electrical voltages. They convert heat, motion, and position to an electrical signal proportional to their magnitude (i.e., they generate analog voltages). A pressure transducer may consist of a diaphragm connected to a strain gage whose resistance varies as the diaphragm is deflected by the pressure. Using the strain gage as one arm of a resistance bridge, a voltage proportional to the pressure is obtained.

The output of an analog transducer can range from millivolts to volts, and can also be in the form of a varying current. Fortunately, some standardization exists and most transducers have outputs falling within five major voltage/current categories: high- and low-level voltages, and three current ranges.

High-level voltage outputs may range up to several volts, generally not exceeding 10 V. Low voltages may be up to a few tens of millivolts, either positive or negative. In most cases the transducer outputs must be amplified before they can be used. The current ranges of most transducers are 0 to 20 mA, 4 to 20 mA, or 10 to 50 mA.

Frequently, it is possible to set up a typical analog input system that includes a number of transducers having similar output signal levels. In this case it is possible to use a *multiplexer* to switch the various transducers to the same input circuit (rather than using a duplicate amplifier and analog-to-digital converter for each channel).

Each of the components used in a data acquisition system has unique characteristics that must be understood before specifying or constructing an interface. Overall speed, accuracy, and noise immunity must all be considered in any system.

13-8.2 ▼ Interface Problems with Analog Signals

All the noise problems that affect digital inputs may be even more detrimental to analog signals. Because most analog signals are smaller than TTL digital signals, interference effects may be more severe. If a single wire (and ground) is used to input an electrical analog signal to a standard amplifier, the presence of noise is amplified by the same factor as the desired signal. This is shown in Fig. 13-10a.

When dealing with the low-level signals provided by most transducers, *amplifiers with differential inputs* are extensively used because they have the ability to separate the two signals. A differential amplifier is designed so that any signal impressed *in phase* on both inputs will be rejected. This signal is caused by electrostatic coupling and is considered to be noise. Only voltages that are placed *across* the input (out of phase), such as the transducer output, are amplified. Figure 13-10b shows the equivalent circuit for *differential* inputs. Figure 13-10c is a more detailed wiring diagram showing the proper shielded cable connections. The voltage that is common to both lines is known as the *common-mode* voltage and is shown as V_{cm}. The transducer output is shown as V_{DM}. The noise reduction achieved by this means is considerable and is measured by the ratio of the *Differential-Mode Gain* (DMG) to the *Common-Mode Gain* (CMG). Generally, this *Common-Mode Rejection Ratio* (CMRR) is expressed in decibels (dB) and is equal to $20 \log_{10}$ DMG/CMG. (See the article by Don Aldridge listed in Section 13-14.) Typically, values of CMRR range from 70 to 120 dB. A further explanation is given in Example 13-2.

EXAMPLE 13-2

A differential amplifier has a CMRR of 80. What is the ratio of its differential-mode gain to its common-mode gain?

SOLUTION

Here we have

$$80 = 20 \log_{10} \text{DMG/CMG} \text{ or } 4 = \log_{10} \text{DMG/CMG}$$

Thus the ratio is 10,000, and the signal, applied across the inputs of a differential amplifier, will be amplified 10,000 times more than a noise signal applied to both inputs simultaneously.

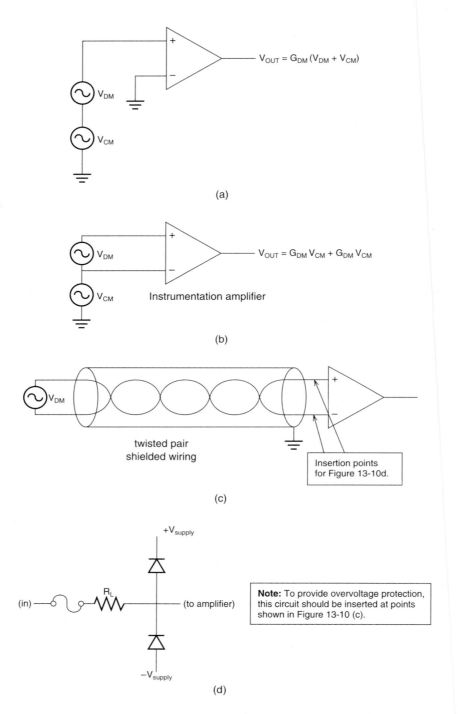

$V_{OUT} = G_{DM} (V_{DM} + V_{CM})$

(a)

$V_{OUT} = G_{DM} V_{CM} + G_{DM} V_{CM}$

Instrumentation amplifier

(b)

twisted pair
shielded wiring

Insertion points
for Figure 13-10d.

(c)

$+V_{supply}$

R_L

(in) (to amplifier)

Note: To provide overvoltage protection,
this circuit should be inserted at points
shown in Figure 13-10 (c).

$-V_{supply}$

(d)

Figure 13-10   Analog Amplifier input wiring. (a) Single-ended
connections. (b) Differential connections. (c) Cable wiring for
differential inputs. (d) Overvoltage protection circuit.

13-8.3 ▼ Overvoltage Protection

The most devastating event for an IC component is excessive voltage. In industrial installations, when dealing with long signal lines that go outside the equipment cabinets, special precautions are necessary. Low-level analog lines that connect to remote sensors are frequently required. These lines can easily come in contact with abnormal voltages, and therefore all inputs must be protected from damage from external sources, including lightning.

Any protection techniques, however, must not affect the accuracy of the voltage measurement in the normal range. One protection circuit is shown in Fig. 13-10d. It can be inserted in Fig. 13-10c. Here the maximum range of voltages is limited by diodes that conduct whenever their reverse bias is exceeded. To protect the diodes from damage in the event of an installation error or lightning stroke, a limiting resistor and a fuse are used. The series resistance must be low compared to the input impedance of the ICs so as not to degrade accuracy. Example 13-3 provides additional design information.

EXAMPLE 13-3

The input to the amplifier in Fig. 13-10d is to be limited to between 0 and +10 V. What must the supply voltages be?

SOLUTION

Assuming a normal diode drop of 0.7 V, the positive supply voltage should be 9.3 V. Then any voltage above 10 V would cause the upper diode to conduct and force the current to enter the power supply. But the voltage at the amplifier input could never rise above 10 V.

Technically, the minus supply voltage should be at +0.7 V. Then the diode will start to conduct when the input goes below 0 V. In most circuits, however, engineers simply tie the $-V_{supply}$ to ground.

13-9 ▼ ANALOG-TO-DIGITAL CONVERSION TECHNIQUES

An Analog-to-Digital converter is used to change analog (continuously varying amplitude) signals, such as the output of temperature or pressure transducers, to a digital signal that can be accepted by μCs. A typical A/D converter has:

1. An analog input
2. Digital outputs that represent the magnitude of the analog input signal voltage in digital form
3. A start-of-conversion (SOC) input from the μC that tells the A/D converter to start converting its analog input into a digital value
4. An end-of-conversion (EOC) output that tells the μC that the converter has finished and the data is available

Several techniques are used to convert analog transducer outputs to digital signals. When a fast conversion must be performed at a moderate price, *successive approximation* converters are almost always the choice. A block diagram of a simple 4-bit successive approximation circuit is shown in Fig. 13-11a. It shows the *comparator* (usually an *operational amplifier*) that adjusts the output of a Digital-to-Analog ladder attenuator in discrete steps until its output voltage closely approximates the analog input signal value. When the closest match is found (the comparator output is close to 0 V), an EOC signal is

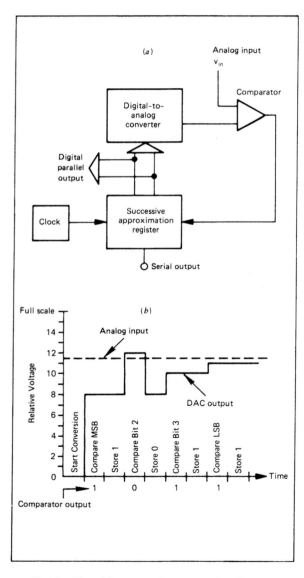

Figure 13-11 Four-bit successive-approximation converter. (a) Block diagram. (b) Waveforms.

activated (not shown), and the digital values of the steps are used to represent the unknown analog signal. This is shown in the graph of Fig. 13-11b for this 4-bit Digital-to-Analog (D/A) converter.* The Digital-to-Analog function is used directly to provide an analog control voltage output from an MCU where external devices require it.

13-9.1 ▼ Adding A/D Conversion to an MCU

When A/D conversion is required, the system designer has three choices:

1. A commercially available A/D converter with a parallel interface can be used. The interface between the converter and a **6800**-type μP must be designed.
2. An A/D converter IC that has an SPI interface can be used.
3. An MCU that has a built-in A/D converter can be specified.

The last choice is the simplest and is preferable in most cases. **68HC11** and **6805** μCs include A/D converters in many versions. This is discussed further in Section 13-9.3.

If the μC does not have an internal A/D converter, the user may make the first choice. Separate A/D-converter ICs made by several manufacturers have been available for many years. Most of them, however, have a parallel interface. Figure 13-12 shows a basic A/D converter** interfaced to a **6800** family μP. Internally, this type of ADC contains the ladder networks and comparators necessary for the conversion. It also includes a differential input. Its operation can be described only briefly in this book.

1. The analog signal comes into the converter on the $V_{IN}(+)$ pin, pin 6, and $V_{IN}(-)$ pin, pin 7, if the differential input, shown in Fig. 13-10b, is used. Otherwise, pin 7 is connected to ground for the single-ended connection.
2. The digital representation of the data is sent to the μP via the eight data lines, DB0 through DB7.
3. The four signals shown on the upper left of the A/D converter (pins 1, 2, 3, and 5) control the data transfer.

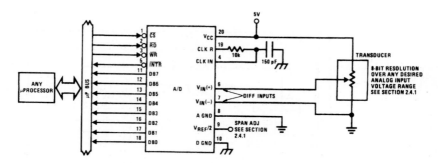

Figure 13-12   Basic A/D converter interfaced to an MCU.
(Courtesy of National Semiconductor)

---

*A more thorough discussion of comparators and A/D converters is given in *Practical Digital Design Using ICs,* 3rd ed., by J. Greenfield, published by Prentice Hall, Englewood Cliffs, N.J., 1994.

This figure applies to the **ADC0801, ADC0802, ADC0803, ADC0804, and **ADC0805** A/D converters, all manufactured by National Semiconductor, Inc. See their literature on these converters for further information.

The control signal functions follow:

1. Chip Select (CS) comes from the computer to the converter. It must be LOW to activate the converter. If it is HIGH, all other signals are ignored.
2. A LOW pulse on the WR (Write) input acts as a Start-Of-Conversion (SOC) signal. It causes INTR to go HIGH.
3. The falling edge of INTR acts as the End-Of-Conversion (EOC) signal. It indicates that the conversion is complete and the digital data can be read by the μP.
4. LOW levels on CS and RD enable the output data drivers, so the data can be sent out.

EXAMPLE 13-4

Figure 13-13 shows how an A/D converter can be connected to a PIA. Describe the program to read the output of the converter (see Section 8-6).

SOLUTION

1. During initialization, the PIA's data direction register must be set for input. CB2 should be set for pulse mode, and the PIA should respond to a falling edge on CB1.
2. Conversion is started by writing any data to the B data register of the PIA. The data being written is meaningless, but the pulse on CB2 will act as SOC.
3. The falling edge on INTR acts as EOC and can cause the output of the converter to be read into the mP via port B of the PIA.

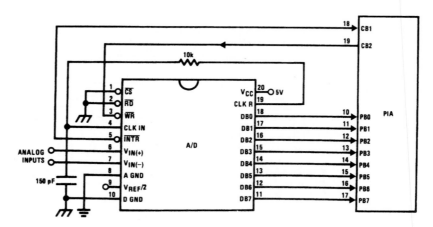

Figure 13-13 **ADC0801** interfaced to a **6821** PIA.
(Courtesy of National Semiconductor)

13-9.2 ▼ A/D Converters with SPI

The second choice for adding Analog-to-Digital capability is to use IC components designed to connect to the Serial Peripheral Interface (SPI). This interface has been described in previous chapters as a way for MCUs to communicate with each other, but it also provides the ability to add external functions to any MCU. A number of IC devices, such as Real-Time clocks and ADCs, are available that use the SPI.

Motorola makes at least four ADC ICs for this purpose. The **145041** is an 8-bit A/D converter with SPI. It is a 20-pin CMOS IC. The block diagram of the **145041** is shown in Fig. 13-14. This IC includes all of the components needed for an A/D converter, including an 11-input analog multiplexer. This IC is also compatible with National Semiconductor's MICROWIRE interface.

Figure 13-15a shows part of a schematic of a thermostat demonstration system that is designed to control the temperature in a room at better than usual accuracy. It uses two temperature sensors (one is outdoors). It uses the **145041** IC. The figure shows this 8-bit A/D converter interfaced to a **HC05** type of MCU. Only two of the 11 analog inputs are

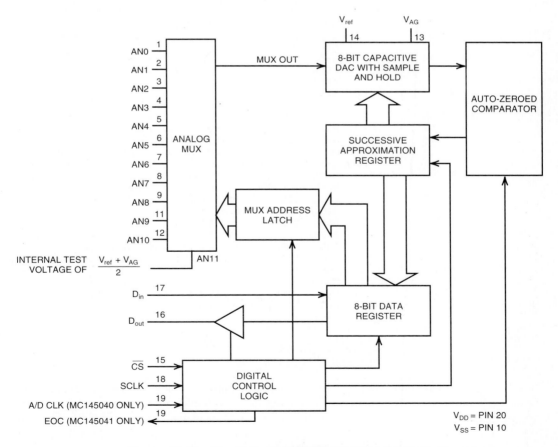

Figure 13-14 The Motorola **145041** A/D converter block diagram.

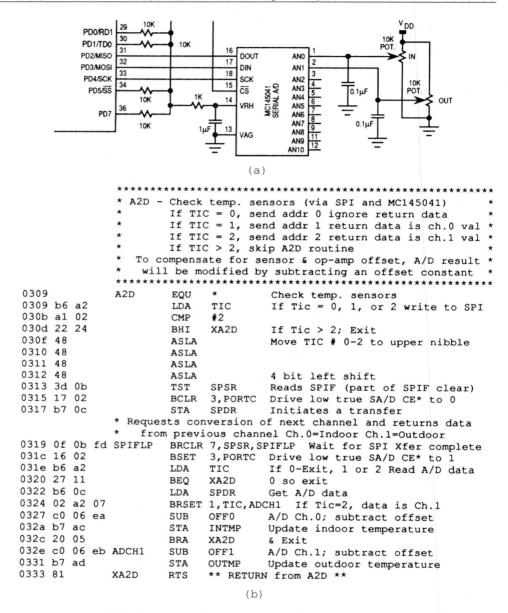

(a)

```
*****************************************************************
* A2D - Check temp. sensors (via SPI and MC145041)             *
*        If TIC = 0, send addr 0 ignore return data            *
*        If TIC = 1, send addr 1 return data is ch.0 val *
*        If TIC = 2, send addr 2 return data is ch.1 val *
*        If TIC > 2, skip A2D routine                          *
*   To compensate for sensor & op-amp offset, A/D result *
*    will be modified by subtracting an offset constant  *
*****************************************************************
0309            A2D     EQU     *         Check temp. sensors
0309 b6 a2              LDA     TIC       If Tic = 0, 1, or 2 write to SPI
030b a1 02              CMP     #2
030d 22 24              BHI     XA2D      If Tic > 2; Exit
030f 48                 ASLA              Move TIC # 0-2 to upper nibble
0310 48                 ASLA
0311 48                 ASLA
0312 48                 ASLA              4 bit left shift
0313 3d 0b              TST     SPSR      Reads SPIF (part of SPIF clear)
0315 17 02              BCLR    3,PORTC   Drive low true SA/D CE* to 0
0317 b7 0c              STA     SPDR      Initiates a transfer
             * Requests conversion of next channel and returns data
             *    from previous channel Ch.0=Indoor Ch.1=Outdoor
0319 0f 0b fd SPIFLP    BRCLR   7,SPSR,SPIFLP  Wait for SPI Xfer complete
031c 16 02              BSET    3,PORTC   Drive low true SA/D CE* to 1
031e b6 a2              LDA     TIC       If 0-Exit, 1 or 2 Read A/D data
0320 27 11              BEQ     XA2D      0 so exit
0322 b6 0c              LDA     SPDR      Get A/D data
0324 02 a2 07           BRSET   1,TIC,ADCH1  If Tic=2, data is Ch.1
0327 c0 06 ea           SUB     OFF0      A/D Ch.0; subtract offset
032a b7 ac              STA     INTMP     Update indoor temperature
032c 20 05              BRA     XA2D      & Exit
032e c0 06 eb ADCH1     SUB     OFF1      A/D Ch.1; subtract offset
0331 b7 ad              STA     OUTMP     Update outdoor temperature
0333 81       XA2D      RTS     ** RETURN from A2D **
```

(b)

Figure 13-15 Thermostat application. (a) Schematic.
(b) ADC and SPI programming.

used in this application, and for development purposes, they are shown connected to potentiometers rather than temperature sensors. This allows the designer to simulate temperature changes. In a final installation, an actual temperature sensor such as shown in Fig. 13-16 would be used. This precision temperature sensor is a LM34C National Semiconductor component in a TO-92 package.

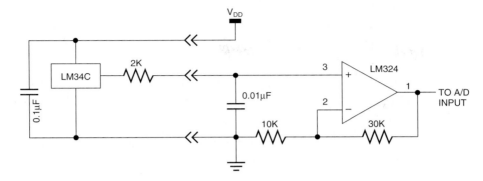

Figure 13-16 Precision temperature sensing circuit
for use with the Thermostat application.

The software routine for an application that measures both indoor and outdoor temperatures is shown in Fig. 13-15b. This is just one of the subroutines used in the thermostat example. The software variable TIC used in the routine keeps track of time. Each tick is equal to 50 ms. When it reaches 20 it is cleared and seconds are incremented (20 ticks = 1 second). The temperatures are only checked every second. The ADC Channel 0 is for the indoor thermostat and channel 1 is for outdoor. Thus if the program is studied, it will be seen that the first three lines of the program will bypass the routine if TIC is greater than 2. When the TIC is 0 or 1, the routine reads or writes to the SPI registers identified by their mnemonics as SPSR and SPDR. The BRCLR instruction on line 319 loops on itself until the SPI transfer is complete. The SPI lines MISO, MIS1, and SCK are used to communicate between the ADC IC and the MPU. The indoor temperature is stored in the INTMP variable at address $AC, and the outdoor temperature is stored in OUTMP at address $AD. These are displayed by routines not shown.

This demonstration system is described in detail in the **68HC05** applications guide (68HC05AG/AD) referenced in Section 13-14. The newer **145050** or **145051** A/D converter ICs are pin-for-pin replacements for the **145040** or **145041,** and upgrade the A/D system from 8-bit to 10-bit resolution.

13-9.3 ▼ A/D Converters inside MCUs

The third choice is to use an MCU that includes an ADC. A number of today's MCUs have built-in A/D circuitry. They provide eight or more inputs and 8- or 10-bit resolution. The **68HC11E9,** for example, as shown in Fig. 13-17a, contains an eight-channel, 8-bit, multiplexed-input converter, which internally includes the multiplexer, analog converter, digital control, and storage registers for the results of the conversions on all channels.

An electrical model of one of the analog input circuits is shown in Fig. 13-17b. The incoming analog signal goes through the protection circuit and charges the capacitor. The voltage on this capacitor is converted to digital by the internal A/D converter. The inclusion of all this A/D circuitry in the MCU provides a very significant reduction in complexity of many controller systems.

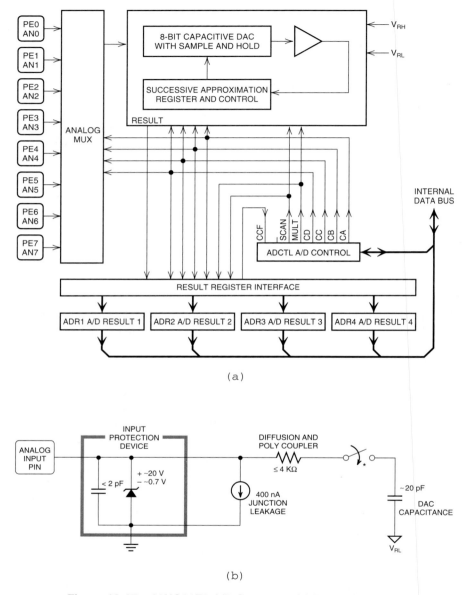

(a)

(b)

Figure 13-17   68HC11E9 A/D Converter. (a) Block diagram.
(b) Electrical model of an input pin (Sample Mode).

13-9.4 ▼ Programming A/D Converters

In any A/D converter system, the method of handling the A/D conversion must be considered. The simplest method, after the process has been started, is for the program to check the EOC signal continually to determine when the conversion is finished. This is inefficient, however, and wastes valuable μP time since nothing else is accomplished during this period.

A better method uses the μP's *interrupt* system to report the end of conversion. During the conversion time, other segments of the program can be executed until the end-of-conversion signal interrupts the μP. Although this approach may appear efficient, caution should be used when interfacing very fast converters to an MCU system. The overhead time associated with servicing the interrupt may take the μP longer than the time required for the conversion. The net effect is that the overall throughput is slower than when looping and waiting for the end-of-conversion signal.

The analog system can be connected in such a way that it places the μP in a WAIT state during the conversion process. This provides the highest throughput speed for programmed data transfers while considerably reducing the electrical noise generated by the digital system. An additional benefit can be found in those processors, such as the **6800,** that can be halted in midcycle to wait for slow memory. With the **6800,** the entire conversion process is carried out during the course of a single memory-read instruction, with the timing of the operation totally transparent to the programmer. For all its merits, this method has one serious drawback. The μP is totally blind to any other outside events during the conversion. Where μP response times (for external events) are required to be shorter than the conversion time, this method cannot be used.

When several channels are to be converted before the data is processed, or a block of channels must be scanned continually, direct memory access (DMA) should be considered as the interfacing method. Although more complicated from a hardware point of view, this method maximizes channel throughput with a minimum of software. In one mode of operation, a segment of memory can be updated continually by continuous automatic operation of the analog system and the transfer of digital data performed between processor cycles. There is only a slight reduction in software execution speed and the data is fetched from memory without regard to the details of the analog interface. Another mode of operation might allow several channels to be processed and then an interrupt generated to signal the software that the block of data is available.

13-10 ▼ A/D APPLICATIONS

An example of a typical MCU application might be found in a large process control facility. A large computer could direct the overall operation of the plant through the activities of μC systems placed strategically throughout the plant. As shown in Fig. 13-18, one such μC system might be assigned the sole task of monitoring combustion in a boiler. Inputs would originate from flame-temperature transducers, effluent-gas analyzers, and fuel-flow meters. Outputs would control fuel and oxygen flow and drive a small strip-chart recorder to make a permanent record of the burner's operation. The main plant supervisory computer would direct the μC system to set the burner for a specified (desired) flame temperature. With this information, the μC's control algorithm would make the necessary adjustments to fuel flow and mixture to attain the required temperature while maintaining minimum combustion pollutants and maximum fuel economy.

At the analog interface, the signals must undergo an A/D conversion before they are suitable for processing. Since there is more than one input, either multiple A/D converters must be used, or if all transducers provide the same range of output, these inputs can be connected to a single A/D converter through a multiplexer switch. The latter method is currently the least expensive and is used almost universally.

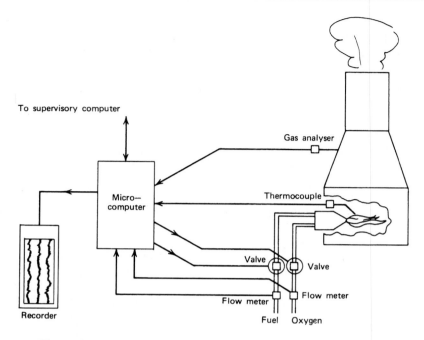

Figure 13-18 μC boiler control system with an analog interface.

Before these low-level signals can go through the conversion process, they must be amplified. All modern A/D-converter designs require inputs of several volts. A differential-input instrumentation amplifier is used for this purpose. Not only is amplification performed, but through the return of both signal lines from the transducers as a differential connection, high common-mode noise rejection can also be attained (see Section 13-8.2). An application design problem is described in Example 13-5.

EXAMPLE 13-5

A transducer provides an output range from 0 to 10 mV. If it is to be connected to an A/D converter whose input range is 0 to 5 V, as is typical for the converter in a 68HC11, what must the difference mode gain of the differential amplifier be?

SOLUTION

The required gain is simply the largest input voltage to the A/D converter divided by the largest output signal of the transducer. This is 5 V divided by 10 mV or 500.

In the system of Fig. 13-18, electrically operated proportionally controlled fuel and mixture valves are adjusted through their voltage inputs. The analog output modules produce these voltages through a separate D/A converter for each transducer.

13-11 ▼ METHODS OF CONSTRUCTION FOR μC SYSTEMS

The various hardware IC components that are needed to assemble a μC system have been described from a functional or electrical point of view in this and in previous chapters, but little has been said about the mechanical construction. There are an unlimited number of ways that the parts can be assembled, but certain methods have evolved that are relatively well standardized.

Most ICs are soldered into plated through-holes in an insulated board that has *printed circuit* wiring. In recent years, however, a new technique called **surface mount** is becoming more common. The ICs are much smaller and have solder pads instead of pins. The pads are spaced much closer together and, as a result, the printed circuit assemblies are also much smaller. The IC assemblies are, in many cases, made by automated or robotic machines. In some cases the ICs are plugged into sockets that are soldered to the board. The connections between components are made by copper strips that are also plated onto the insulated board. The board material is usually fiberglass. Originally, these boards were made by copper plating one or both sides of a $\frac{1}{16}$-inch fiberglass sheet and then chemically etching away the unwanted material, leaving only the desired paths between pins.

Today, these *Printed Circuit Boards* (PCBs) are made with very thin layers and sandwiched together so as to be about $\frac{1}{16}$-inch thick overall. They are called *multilayer boards* and provide multiple *ground planes* or voltage levels anywhere on the board. Up to 10 layers are possible, but typically, only two to four are used. More layers make them expensive but also allow very dense placement of parts.

Two basic styles of system construction are used. One is to place all the parts on one specialized PCB that is then mounted into some sort of protective case. The other method is to divide the ICs and associated discrete parts (such as capacitors and resistors) into functional circuit groups that are placed on separate boards and called *modules.*

13-11.1 ▼ Printed Circuit Modules

The designer may decide to use the single-board method, but if devices such as optical couplers or solid-state relays are included on the same board as the μC, noise problems may arise due to the need to bring the high-power lines into the same area where the μC lines exist. It may be preferable to place the high-power devices on separate modules that can be separated slightly and shielded.

These modules are connected together to form a complete computer by plugging them into a *motherboard.* The motherboard is also a PC board and has many connectors that are linked together by other printed circuit lines, which form a bus. These lines are used to tie the address, data, and control pins of the connectors together. The same pins are used for the same purpose on each connector so that the modules can be plugged into any position. For 8-bit μCs there are 16 address lines, 8 data lines, and various control lines that run parallel between connectors. This is similar to plugging a board into one of the slots in a personal computer.

13-11.2 ▼ Standard μC Buses

A *bus standard* defines the electrical characteristics of the interconnecting signal lines, which pins are connected to which lines, the type of connectors, and the mechanical dimensions of the modules that are expected to work together. These factors must all be compatible so that the modules of each family can be assembled into various combinations to form different systems. Unfortunately, each family is different.

The methods of construction for μC control systems have been evolving for years, so several standard module families have been designed by various manufacturers. One of the current standards is the *VME bus*. A *chassis* (or Card Cage) was designed and used for assembling various combinations of modules. These chassis are made to mount in a standard 19-inch rack, a type that is frequently used in many industrial installations.

Motorola and four other manufacturers collaborated to develop the *VMEbus,* while Intel developed *Multibus II.* These buses have become very popular, and dozens of companies are busy designing new modules. Not all types of modules are provided by the semiconductor companies, however. To interface high-power external peripherals such as machinery, other companies, including Analogic and Burr-Brown, have provided modules for use on these popular buses. Some of these modules provide an isolated digital interface, and others do the same for analog signals (see Sections 13-6 and 13-7). We cannot devote any space in this book to the advantages or disadvantages of the various buses.

13-12 ▼ SUMMARY

The problems of real-world interfacing of MCUs to external electromechanical hardware have been discussed. This includes digital as well as analog circuits. Particular emphasis was placed on minimizing electrical noise, which frequently interferes with proper computer operation in an industrial environment.

The use of transducers and A/D converters to determine how a system is operating, and the use of D/A converters to control such a system, were also considered. Finally, the problems of constructing the hardware were described.

13-13 ▼ GLOSSARY

AC Alternating Current.

Analog Resembling the original. In electronics, it usually refers to a voltage that varies in direct relationship to some physical property.

DAC A Digital-to-Analog Converter.

DC Direct Current.

DIP Dual In-line Package. Standard package for integrated circuits with pins on a 0.1-inch grid pattern.

Electrostatic shield A conductive screen placed between or around an electrical circuit to drain off unwanted charges.

Ground Earth potential. The point to which the frame or chassis is connected.

Multiplexer An electronic switch to select any of a number of inputs or outputs.

Ohm A unit of measure of electrical resistance. Voltage drop (in Volts) = Current (in Amperes) times the resistance (in Ohms) (Ohm's Law).

Optical coupling A semiconductor device that uses a light-emitting diode (LED) whose output is detected by a phototransistor.

PC card A Printed Circuit (on a card).

Picofarad A unit of capacitance equal to 10^{-12} farad.

Reed relay A relay that uses vacuum encapsulated contacts operated by magnetic field.

Solenoid valve An electrically operated valve, using a DC magnetic actuator.

Solid-state relay Semiconductor devices connected so that the optically coupled output turns on a TRIAC or Silicon-Controlled-Rectifier (SCR) for control of AC motors, lights, and so on.

Successive approximation A technique of determining equality by comparing with progressively smaller values.

Transducer A converter to change physical parameters to electrical signals, or vice versa.

TRIAC A semiconductor device that can be "triggered" ON or OFF for control of AC-powered units.

13-14 ▼ REFERENCES

ALDRIDGE, DON, *Analog-to-Digital Conversion Techniques with the* **M6800** *Microprocessor System,* Application Note AN-757, Motorola, Phoenix, Ariz., 1975.

BURR-BROWN, *Digital Output (Contact Closure) Microperipherals for Motorola Microcomputers,* MP701, MP702, PDS 381, Tucson, Ariz., 1977.

———, *Microcomputer Digital Input System,* MP710, PDS 386, Tucson, Ariz., 1978.

GREENFIELD, JOSEPH D., *Practical Digital Design,* 3rd ed., Prentice Hall, Englewood Cliffs, N.J., 1994.

KOSTOPULOS, GEORGE K., *Digital Engineering,* Wiley, New York, 1975.

MORRISON, ROBERT, *Data Acquisition and the Microcomputer,* Burr-Brown Research Corporation, Tucson, Ariz., 1977.

TEEPLE, C. R., *Isolated Digital Input/Output Microcomputer Peripherals Solve Industrial Problems,* Burr-Brown Research Corporation, Tucson, Ariz., 1977.

13-15 ▼ PROBLEMS

13-1. A transducer is to be designed to measure the outdoor temperature in your area. What range of temperatures must this transducer accommodate? Conceptually design such a transducer.

13-2. A differential amplifier has a CMRR of 100 dB. What is the ratio of its common differential-mode gain to its common-mode gain?

13-3. A signal line has 0.1 V of signal in difference mode and 10 V of common-mode noise. If it is put through a differential amplifier with a CMRR of 120 dB, what is the ratio of signal to noise at the output?

13-4. For the circuit of Fig. 13-13, assume that the PIA is at \$8004 through \$8007 and that A/D conversions are to be performed every 5 ms until they fill the buffer from \$C100 through \$C1FF. Write the program using a WAI instruction and allowing the PIA to interrupt at EOC.

13-5. Figure 13-12 shows the direct connections between a **6800** μP and an A/D converter. Explain how it works.

After attempting to solve these problems, try to answer the self-evaluation questions in Section 13-2. If any of them still seem difficult, review the appropriate sections of the chapter to find the answers.

68000 FAMILY

14-1 ▼ INSTRUCTIONAL OBJECTIVES

In this chapter we introduce the 16-bit microprocessors of the Motorola **68000** family. These 16-bit μPs are also descendants of the **6800** but are more powerful and more versatile. The features and operation of the **68000,** Motorola's basic 16-bit μP, are explained. More advanced versions of the **68000** family are discussed in Chapter 15. After reading this chapter, the student should be able to:

1. List the advantages and disadvantages of a 16/32-bit μC as compared to an 8-bit μP or MCU.
2. Describe the advantage of a 24 or 32-bit address bus over a 16-bit bus.
3. List the registers in the **68000,** and explain their function.
4. Calculate the effective address of an instruction in all modes.
5. Write programs for the **68000.**
6. Define the function of each pin on the **68000.**
7. List the error conditions that cause *exception processing* in **68000** family systems.

14-2 ▼ SELF-EVALUATION QUESTIONS

Watch for the answers to the following questions as you read the chapter. They should help you to understand the material presented.

1. A **68000** has 23 address pins but addresses 16M bytes of memory, which requires a 24-bit address. How is this possible?
2. Why can the data registers be used as accumulators, but not the address registers?
3. How does the **68000** determine which of the two registers labeled A7 is the stack pointer?
4. What is a privileged instruction? What types of instructions are privileged?

5. What are the limitations of QUICK instructions? What are their advantages?

6. What are the differences between a MOVE-to-address-register instruction and a MOVE-to-data-register instruction?

7. Why is it desirable to increase the word size in a computer system?

8. What new hardware techniques are used in the new generations of 16/32-bit μPs?

9. What new programming techniques are supported by the 16/32-bit μPs?

14-3 ▼ INTRODUCTION

This book is devoted primarily to the subject of Microcontrollers (MCUs). As mentioned in Section 10-3, Motorola builds MCUs and μPs other than the 8-bit versions discussed previously. One of the principal families is the **68000** family of 16- and 32-bit μPs. It has also been very successful and has produced a number of very high-performance μPs.

Motorola has combined the microprocessor (μP) and microcontroller (MCU) in a synergistic way. This marriage has resulted in the development of two more advanced families of MCUs, the **68HC16** and **68300**. They contain 16-bit and 32-bit μPs, respectively.

Because these high-performance MCUs use many of the techniques and features of the **68000** family, the reader should become familiar with this family of μPs before attempting to understand the **68HC16** or **68300** MCUs, which are described in Chapter 16.

The **68000** is Motorola's basic 16-bit μP. As the technology advanced, more powerful μPs were added to the product line, such as the **68020, 68030, 68040,** and **68060.** These are described in Chapter 15.

The **68000,** with its 32-bit registers, 16-bit data bus, and 24-bit address bus, is the first in a family of processors that implement a comprehensive extendable computer architecture. The more advanced Motorola μPs, such as the **68020, 68030, 68040,** and **68060,** and the **68HC16** and **68300** MCUs, are extensions of the **68000.** Their programming and architecture are similar.

After the success of the **68000,** the **68008** was added. It has an 8-bit data bus and 20-bit address bus (in the 48-pin package) or a 22-pin address bus (in the 52-pin package). Both ICs are otherwise compatible with the **68000.** The **68008** allows the design of cost-effective systems using the less expensive 8-bit peripherals and byte-wide memories, while providing the benefits of a 32-bit μP architecture. The performance of the **68008** is comparable to that of the 8-bit **6809** μP and superior to that of several other 16-bit units. Complete compatibility with the **68000** instruction set is maintained by the **68008,** with 56 instruction types.

The **68010** is the third member of the family and was first available in the spring of 1983. It is object code-compatible with the **68000** and has the same pinouts. However, it has new instructions, new registers, and several other enhancements described in Chapter 15. The **68008** and **68010** are rarely used these days because they have been superseded.

The **68000,** which forms the basis for all of Motorola's 16/32-bit μPs, is discussed in this chapter. The **68010, 68020,** and **68030,** with their advanced features, and the even more powerful **68040** and **68060,** are covered in Chapter 15. The emphasis of this book has been to teach systems design, so the hardware features of the μPs are covered as well as the programming.

14-3.1 ▼ Eight-bit vs. 16-bit vs. 32-bit μCs

Its longer word size gives the **68000** a significant advantage over its 8-bit predecessors. Eight-bit data bytes, ASCII characters, and BCD arithmetic can be handled with little difficulty in an 8-bit system, but other mathematical operations are time consuming because it is necessary to handle larger values a byte at a time. Consider, for example, the problem of adding two 32-bit numbers. In an 8-bit μP such as the **6800** or **68HC05,** it requires four operations and about 12 instructions. The **68000** architecture uses 32-bit registers so that operations with larger numbers are much faster. A **68020**-type μP can add two 32-bit numbers using a single instruction.

The **68000** has eight data registers, which can operate as accumulators or index registers, and eight address registers, which greatly facilitate programming. The **68000** uses a 16-bit ALU and I/O data path, so it is properly called a 16-bit μP. However, the 32-bit registers (see Section 14-5) and associated instructions provide many advantages when compared to other 16-bit μPs, such as the Intel **8086.** Also, the internal 32-bit architecture uses software that is *upwardly compatible* with the full 32-bit designs of the **68020, 68030, 68040,** and **68060.** That means that programs written for the **68000** will run on all of the later upgrades, such as the **68040** or **68060** μPs. That has always been one of the guidelines followed by Motorola designers to preserve the large data bank of software. This has been estimated at worth over $8 billion, not to mention the time saved.

Another limitation in an 8-bit system is in the amount of *addressable memory.* Typical 8-bit systems are limited to 64K bytes, unless bank switching is used, and bank switching is also slow. In modern computers where inefficient high-level languages are being used increasingly, larger memory sizes are required to speed the execution of large programs, such as word processors, spreadsheets, and relational databases. The **68000** μP uses an address bus of 24 bits and can therefore address up to 16 megabytes of memory. The **68020, 68030, 68040,** and **68060** (described in Chapter 15) have a full 32-bit address bus and can address 4 gigabytes.

When an 8-bit op code is increased to 16 or 32 bits, more functions can be performed inside the processor *in parallel* and thus are done simultaneously. Multiply and divide instructions for 16- or 32-bit numbers are also provided instead of subroutines. These save considerable time.

The 16-bit op codes available in 16-bit μPs means that many more instructions, modes, and options are possible. Figure 14-1 shows a comparison of the op codes for the ADD instruction in the **6800** and **68000** μPs. The number of bits in a **6800** op code are limited to 8. Because more bits allow parallel operations, it is obvious that the 16-bit op codes for the **68000,** with their ability to use so many more registers and address modes, are much more powerful.

There are also some disadvantages to 16-bit μPs. Their larger word size requires more memory, more gates in the IC buffers, and more address and data lines on the PC boards. The 8-bit μPs and μCs are, therefore, less expensive.

The 16-bit μPs are used where their increased computational power is important. This includes use in controllers where high-speed Analog-to-Digital conversions are necessary, in multiuser systems, in robotics, and in artificial intelligence. They also have been found to be desirable in all of the newer personal computers where customer appeal depends on the power of their μPs. The Macintosh, Amiga, and Atari computers all use the **68000** family.

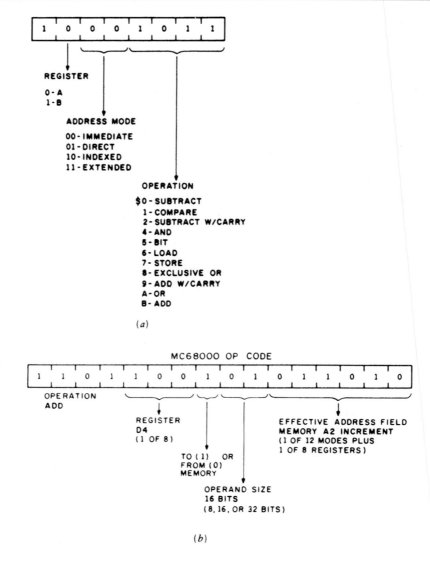

Figure 14-1   Comparisons of 8 vs 16 bits. (a) Op code organization for the **6800.** (b) The **68000** ADD instruction op code.

Where the faster performance is not a requirement, a low-cost 8-bit system may be the best choice. They can be used very effectively in many smaller industrial or process control systems. In fact, in the majority of computer applications (some engineers estimate at least 90%), the increased speed of the 16- or 32-bit instructions is not necessary and the added power of the larger-word-size systems is not needed. The sales of 8-bit MCUs has continued to grow, and judging by the success of the **68HC11** and **68HC05** systems that have been built, these MCUs will continue to be a dominant factor in the microcontroller world. The 8-bit market will be driven by the industrial automation applications segment, which will require a large part of the systems produced. At the present time, an entire PC board assembly using an 8-bit μC can be built for less than the cost of a 32-bit μP.

14-3.2 ▼ New Features of the 68000 Family

The knowledge the reader has acquired by studying the **6800** family is directly applicable to the 16-bit μPs. But there are also many new and unique features that have been introduced for the **68000** family of μPs. These include:

1. Asynchronous data bus and Bus Arbitration
2. User and Supervisory processing states
3. Internal eight-level Priority Interrupt system
4. Interface with **6800** peripherals (using the **68008**)
5. Virtual Memory/Machine concepts
6. HCMOS process with 200,000 transistors
7. Cache Memory
8. Coprocessors
9. Pipelining

The first four of these are explained in this chapter and the more advanced features (items 5 through 9) are covered in Chapter 15.

One of the most important features of the **68000** family is that the basic instructions are the same for all members of the family, and programs written for a **68000** will run on all of the current advanced processors and also on those planned for the future.

14-4 ▼ PROCESSING STATES

In addition to the many hardware differences between the 8- and 16-bit μPs, the **68000** family has many differences in internal operation. One difference is the use of *Processing States.* The **68000** is always in one of three processing states: *Normal, Exception,* or *Halted.*

The *Normal processing state* occurs when the program is proceeding in normal sequence through the instructions, including the bus cycles to fetch instructions, or operands, or to store the results. A special case of the normal state is the *stopped state,* which the processor enters when a STOP instruction is executed. In this state, no further memory references are made until an interrupt occurs that restarts the processor. This is similar to the stopped state in the **68HC11.**

The *Exception processing state* is associated with resets, interrupts, trap instructions, tracing, and other *exceptional* conditions. This expression has been shortened throughout the **68000** family literature to the word *exception.* This state may be generated internally by an instruction or by an unusual condition arising during the execution of an instruction. Exception processing is described in Section 14-12.

The *Halted processing state* is an indication of catastrophic hardware failure. For example, if a bus error occurs (see Section 14-11.8) it causes the **68000** to jump to the *bus error vector* and start an exception process (see Section 14-12.2). If during the execution of this routine another bus error occurs (a double bus fault), the processor assumes that the system is unusable and halts. Only an *external RESET* can restart a halted processor. Note that a processor in the stopped state is not in the halted state, or vice versa.

14-4.1 ▼ Privilege Levels

Another innovation in the **68000** operation is the use of *privilege levels*. The processor operates at one of two levels of privilege: the *User* or the *Supervisor* level. The supervisor level is a higher level of privilege. Not all processor instructions can be executed in the lower-privileged user state, but all are available in the supervisor state.

The register set of the **68000** is described in Section 14-5. It contains two stack pointers, a **Supervisory Stack Pointer** (SSP) and a **User Stack Pointer** (USP). The USP register is called A7 and the SSP register is called A7'. The privilege level is used internally by the processor to choose between the USP and the SSP during operand references, and it can be used by external memory management devices to control and translate addresses for memory accesses (see also Chapter 15).

The privilege level is a mechanism for providing security in a computer system. This is achieved in two ways: the *Supervisor* and *User* distinction, and the allocation of separate memory for data and instructions. These allocations are controlled by an external *Memory Management Unit* (MMU) in conjunction with the *Function Control pins* (FCX). (see Sections 14-4.4 and 14-11 and Chapter 15). For example, in a multiuser system, the executive program that controls the computer operates in the *Supervisor* mode while the users operate in the more restricted *User* mode, so that their programs cannot interfere with the system operation or the programs of other users. In addition, all programs access only their own data areas of memory, and are prevented from accessing information that they do not need and must not modify. The techniques for doing this are discussed in detail in Chapter 15.

14-4.2 ▼ Supervisor State

The **Supervisor state** is the more privileged of the normal processing modes. For instruction execution, the Supervisor state is selected by *setting* the S bit of the status register (see Section 14-5.4). All instructions can be executed in the supervisor state. The bus cycles generated by instructions executed in the supervisor state are classified as *Supervisor references*. While the processor is in the supervisor privilege state, those instructions that either use the system stack pointer implicitly or address register seven (A7) explicitly access the SSP. All *exception processing* is done in the Supervisor state, regardless of the setting of the S bit. All stacking operations during exception processing use the SSP (see Section 14-12).

14-4.3 ▼ User State

The **User state** is the lower state of privilege. The S bit of the status register is cleared when the processor is executing instructions in the User state. Most instructions execute identically in the User state and in the Supervisor state. However, some instructions which have important system effects are made *privileged* (i.e., they will only work in the supervisor mode). User programs are not permitted to execute the *STOP* instruction or the *RESET* instruction. To ensure that a user program cannot enter the Supervisor state, users are not allowed to set the *S* bit of the status register. To aid in debugging programs that are to be used as **operating systems** (programs that supervise and control computers) in the Supervisor mode, the MOVE USP *(MOVE to User Stack Pointer)* instruction is provided.

While the processor is in the User state, those instructions that use either the System Stack Pointer implicitly or address register seven (A7) explicitly access the USP.

14-4.4 ▼ Function Codes and Address Space Types

There are three **Function Code** (FCX) pins on the **68000** μP (see Section 14-11). The processor indicates the cycle type being executed during each bus cycle by setting the state of these pins. Table 14-1 lists the types of access and their respective address space encoding. The bus cycles generated by an instruction executed in the user state, for example, are classified as *user references* (Function Code cycles 1 and 2). Referencing the state of these pins allows external translation of addresses, control of access to different areas of memory, and differentiation of special processor states such as *interrupt acknowledge*. This allows an external *memory management* device to translate the address and control access to protected portions of the address space (see Chapter 15).

14-5 ▼ 68000 REGISTERS

One of the major features of the **68000** is its large register set. Because most of the registers can be used in more than one way, the **68000** has much more flexibility and versatility than that of any 8-bit μP. Even in single-precision operations, the **68000** data registers can handle numbers between $+2^{31}$ and -2^{31}.

These features greatly simplify the writing of programs and make the computer more powerful. The registers in the **68000** are shown in Fig. 14-2.

The *User* mode of all **68000** family devices has:

- Eight 32-bit data registers (D0–D7)
- Seven 32-bit address registers (A0–A6)
- One User Stack Pointer (USP) register (A7)
- A 32-bit Program Counter (PC)
- An 8-bit Condition Code Register (CCR)

TABLE 14-1 Function Codes for Classification of Address Space

Function Code Output			Cycle Type
FC2	FC1	FC0	
Low	Low	Low	(Undefined, Reserved)
Low	Low	High	User Data
Low	High	Low	User Program
Low	High	High	(Undefined, Reserved)
High	Low	Low	(Undefined, Reserved)
High	Low	High	Supervisor Data
High	High	Low	Supervisor Program
High	High	High	CPU Space

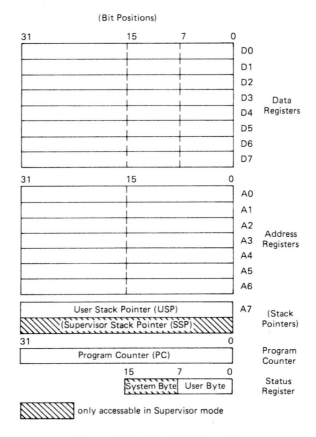

Figure 14-2 The **68000** registers.

When the **68000** μPs are in the Supervisor mode, the registers shown crosshatched in Fig. 14-2 are also provided. The SSP is substituted for the USP and the upper or *system* byte of the status register is made available.

14-5.1 ▼ Data Registers

The top eight registers shown in Fig. 14-2 are the data registers (D0–D7). They are used as accumulators or as index registers. The vertical dashed lines show their ability to handle byte (8-bit), word (16-bit), and **long-word** (32-bit) operations. Byte operands occupy the low-order 8 bits of the register, word operands occupy the low-order 16 bits, and long-word operands occupy the entire 32 bits. The least significant bit is bit 0 and the most significant bit is bit 31.

14-5.2 ▼ Address Registers

The second set of eight registers in Fig. 14-2 consists of the seven address registers (A0–A6), and depending on whether the processor is in the User or Supervisor mode, the

USP or the SSP. They hold the memory addresses of operands or data and may be used as additional software stack pointers or base address registers. The address registers may be used for word and long-word operations. If a word is used as a source operand, it occupies the low-order bits of the register. Address registers do not support byte-sized operands. All seven of the address registers may also be used as index registers.

14-5.3 ▼ Program Counter

The **68000** contains a 32-bit Program Counter (PC) that holds the address of the next instruction to be executed. The **68000** instructions occupy from one to five words in memory. All instructions must start at even addresses. The **68000** op codes are always 16 bits wide, and any arguments that the **68000** requires are always stored as one or more additional 16-bit words (even if the argument is only a byte quantity). Because of this, code that starts on an even-byte boundary will stay on an even-byte boundary and thus will be accessed at the fastest rate possible.

14-5.4 ▼ Status Register

The status register, shown in Fig. 14-3, contains two bytes. The lower or *user byte* includes the condition code bits; the N (negative), Z (zero), V (overflow), and C (carry) flags that are similar to the **6800** flags; and the X (extend) bit. The X bit is similar to the carry bit with some differences. Most instructions affect the X and C bits in the same way. The differences are:

1. LOGIC, MOVE, MULTIPLY, and DIVIDE instructions clear the C bit but do not affect X.

2. X and C behave differently for some SHIFT and ROTATE instructions.

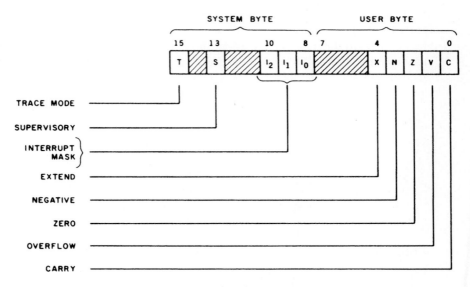

Figure 14-3   The status register.

3. ADD WITH CARRY and SUBTRACT WITH CARRY in the **6800** have become ADD WITH EXTEND (ADDX) and SUBTRACT WITH EXTEND (SUBX) in the **68000.**

The MS byte of the status register is the **System Byte.** It contains the *interrupt mask* (eight levels available; see Section 14-13.1); the *Trace* (T) bit, which will cause the program to single-step if it is set (see Section 14-14); and the *Supervisor state bit* (S), which selects User or Supervisor mode. When it is set, the system is in the Supervisor state.

The System Byte is accessible only in Supervisor mode. Proper computer system design must allow only a supervisor to control the system. If the system byte were available in the User mode, a user could change the S bit and then execute any privileged instruction, thus taking control of the entire system.

14-6 ▼ DATA ORGANIZATION AND ADDRESSING

Memory for the **68000** is organized in words, as shown in Fig. 14-4. Bytes can be addressed with the high-order byte having an even address the same as a word. The low-order byte has an odd address that is one count higher than the word address. Instructions and multi-byte data are accessible only on word (even-byte) boundaries. If a long word is located at address n (n even), the second word of that long word is located at address n + 2.

Five basic data types are supported:

1. Bits
2. BCD digits (4 bits)
3. Bytes (8 bits)
4. Words (16 bits)
5. Long words (32 bits)

Each of these types is put into memory as shown in Fig. 14-5. The numbers indicate the order in which the data would be accessed by the processor. Note that addresses increase in a downward direction. Figure 14-5a shows bit data, addressed as bit n of the byte at location m. Figure 14-5b shows byte addressing in a long word. The MSB is byte 0. The sequence of addressing three words is shown in Fig. 14-5c, and the addressing of three long words is shown in Fig. 14-5d.

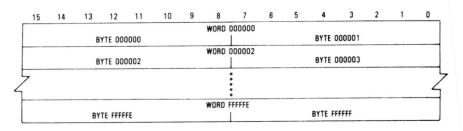

Figure 14-4 Word organization in memory.

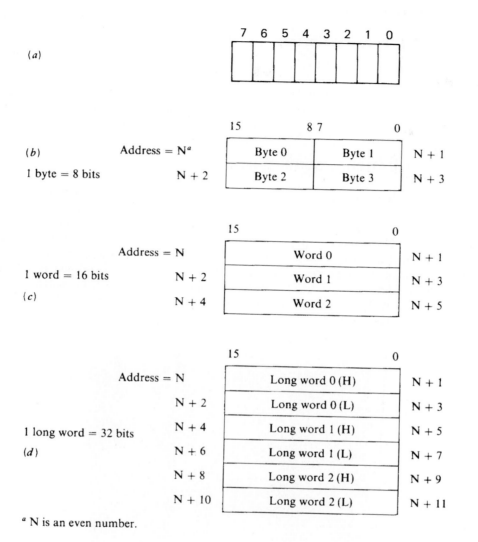

(a)

(b) Address = N[a]
1 byte = 8 bits

(c) 1 word = 16 bits
Address = N

(d) 1 long word = 32 bits

[a] N is an even number.

(e) Decimal Data
2 Binary Coded Decimal Digits = 1 Byte

MSD = most significant digit
LSD = least significant digit

Figure 14-5 Data organization in memory. (a) Bits. (b) Bytes. (c) Words. (d) Long words. (e) BCD.

14-6.1 ▼ BCD Data in Memory

The organization of Binary-Coded Decimal (BCD) is shown in Fig. 14-5e. In the **68000,** BCD digits are encoded two to a byte. This is called *packed* BCD. The BCD instructions operate on one byte (two BCD digits) at a time. In a byte, BCD0 is the most significant digit (MSD), followed by BCD1. Figure 14-5e shows the arrangement of eight BCD digits in a long word. Here BCD0 is the MSD and BCD7 is the LSD.

14-7 ▼ 68000 EDUCATIONAL COMPUTER BOARD

Motorola produced an Educational Computer Board (ECB) in the late 1980s for use as a training aid in colleges and universities. Motorola no longer builds it, however, and it has been replaced with a third-party board made by Arnewsh, Inc. of Ft. Collins, Colorado. This board is nearly identical to the ECB but has additional features, including the ability to add floppy disk drives. It uses the same TUTOR program originally developed by Motorola, and thus test programs written for the old ECB will run on the new board. The new version of the board is called the SBC68K, and it is also available through Motorola. Because the new board is so similar, it will be referred to in this book as the ECB. The board is shown in Fig. 14-6.

Figure 14-6 SBC68K **68000** Educational Computer Board.
(Courtesy of Arnewsh, Inc. Fort Collins CO 80524.)

The ECB is capable of examining memory or registers and is therefore very helpful in creating and debugging **68000** programs. It provides an excellent learning tool for understanding the operation of the **68000** and its instructions. The student is encouraged to try out each of the **68000** instruction features as they are presented. The board contains a **68000** μP, 64K of RAM, a debugger program in ROM called TUTOR (similar to, but much more sophisticated than, the BUFFALO monitor program used in the **68HC11** EVB), and several types of peripheral I/O ICs. It only needs to be connected to a display terminal and a power supply (+5 V, +12 V, and –12 V) to become an operational computer.

The major features of the TUTOR program are the ability to:

1. Set and display all the registers in the **68000.**
2. Write to and display sections of memory.
3. Run or trace (single-step) a program.
4. Set breakpoints.
5. Use a one-line assembler or disassembler.

The assembly/disassembly feature allows the user to write programs in assembly mnemonics. TUTOR converts them to machine language and stores them in memory. The user can also *download* a program from a Host computer, disassemble the machine language, and display it in assembly language mnemonics. Programs can also be saved after they are patched and *uploaded* to the Host.

Figure 14-7a shows the use of the DF (Display Formatted registers) command in TUTOR. In response to the DF command, the first line lists the contents of the PC, the status register, and the system and user stack pointers. The status register contents are shown in hex and also in ASCII format. The ASCII format displays the status register in the following order: trace bit, status bit, interrupt vector, and the X, N, Z, V, and C bits of the condition codes. Dots indicate that the bit is 0, or not set.

```
TUTOR  1.32> DF
PC=00002006  SR=2704=.S7..Z.. US=6379 1CFF SS=0000077A
D0=FFFF7E38  D1=CDFF3EFB D2=7FFF79FF D3=FFFFBF7F
D4=5CE37DFF  D5=FDFF3EFF D6=4FBF5EDF D7=B9DB7FFF
A0=FF6FFF    A1=FCFD0FFF A2=EFF73FDF A3=7DBF7EFB
A4=00003500  A5=FFEF6FFF A6=FFFFFFFC A7=0000077A
----------              ---002006      00000000      OR.B    #0,D0
```

(a)

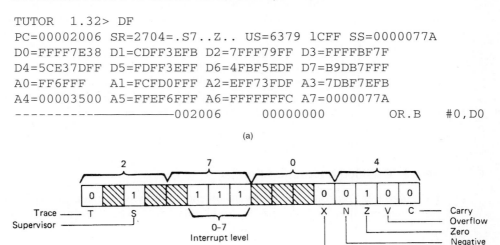

(b)

Figure 14-7   (a) TUTOR'S Register display. (b) Interpretation of status register.

EXAMPLE 14-1

In Fig. 14-7, what are the contents of the status register in both hex and ASCII?

SOLUTION

Translation of the system bytes into ASCII letters or numbers is shown in Fig. 14-7b. The figure shows that the status register contents are

$$2704 = .S7..Z..$$

The hex value is $2704. This corresponds to .S7..Z.. in an ASCII format. The dots indicate that the T, X, N, V, and C bits are off. The S and Z bits are set and the interrupt mask bits are 111.

The contents of the eight data registers and eight address registers are then displayed. Because the **68000** is in Supervisor mode, A7 is the SSP. The last line lists the instruction pointed to by the PC in both machine language and in its disassembled form.

Details on the setup and use of the board, and on TUTOR, are given in the *SBC68K User's Manual* (see Section 14-17).

14-8 ▼ 68000 INSTRUCTION FEATURES

Many new software techniques have been developed to work with the advanced register set and instruction modes of the **68000.** Among these are methods for organizing and moving data. All of the old LOAD, STORE, PUSH, PULL, and I/O instructions from other µPs were combined into one very powerful and flexible MOVE instruction in the **68000.** The MOVE instruction can move 8-, 16-, or 32-bit data from any location to any other. Data from the top of the stack can be moved to or from any register, another stack, a queue,* or any I/O location, all in one simple operation.

Direct memory-to-memory moves are also possible. There are 10 different memory-addressing modes (see Section 14-9) to select from for the source operand and seven for the destination. Each addressing mode can use any of the eight address registers, further increasing the versatility of these MOVE instructions.

14-8.1 ▼ 68000 Instruction Format

Each **68000** instruction has a one-word op code, followed by extension words, if necessary, to specify absolute addresses, immediate data, and so on. This is shown in Fig. 14-8.

---

*A queue is a programming technique for a special type of buffer where data is added at the end (pointed to by one pointer) and read from another location (pointed to by another pointer). The concept is similar to the normal meaning of standing in line while waiting to be served. In a multiuser program, for example, queues are frequently provided to sequence properly the use of a common routine.

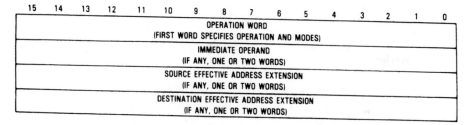

Figure 14-8 The **68000** μP instruction format.

The op code defines the instruction, its length (B, W, or L), the source field, and the destination field.

Instructions for the **68000** contain two kinds of information: the type of function to be performed and the location of the operand(s) on which to perform the function. Instructions specify an operand location in one of three ways:

1. **Register specification.** The type of the register (address or data) is specified in the op code. The number of the register is given in the register field of the instruction.

2. **Implicit reference.** The definition of certain instructions implies the use of specific registers.

3. **Effective Address (EA).** Specifying the address of the operand using one of the address modes. This needs further explanation (see Section. 14-9).

The various instructions are described in the following sections, and a detailed description of each instruction is also given in the *M68000 Microprocessors Programmer's Reference Manual*, described in Section 14-17. Figure 14-9 is a page of this manual that defines the ADD instruction. A typical manual page consists of four major parts, as shown in Fig. 14-9:

1. A description of the instruction

2. The effect of the instruction on the condition codes or flags

3. The format of the instruction word

4. Definitions of the fields in the instruction format

14-8.2 ▼ Register Notation

To understand the operation of the **68000** instructions, a standard *register notation* has been adopted. This is used in the description of the instruction operation and in the Assembler syntax. It shows the various logic operations. The following mnemonics are used to identify the registers:

An	Address register (n is register #)
Dn	Data register (n is register #)
Rn	Any register, Address or Data (n is register #)
Xn	Any Index register: can be Address or Data (n is register #)
PC	Program Counter
SR	Status Register
CCR	Condition Code Register

ADD

ADD   Add   **ADD**

Operation: Source + Destination → Destination

Assembler   ADD <ea>,Dn
Syntax: ADD Dn,<ea>

Attributes: Size = (Byte, Word, Long)

Description: Add the source operand to the destination operand using binary addition, and store the result in the destination location. The size of the operation may be specified to be byte, word, or long. The mode of the instruction indicates which operand is the source and which is the destination as well as the operand size.

Condition Codes:

X	N	Z	V	C
*	*	*	*	*

N   Set if the result is negative. Cleared otherwise.
Z   Set if the result is zero. Cleared otherwise.
V   Set if an overflow is generated. Cleared otherwise.
C   Set if a carry is generated. Cleared otherwise.
X   Set the same as the carry bit.

The condition codes are not affected when the destination is an address register.

Instruction Format:

15	14	13	12	11	10	9	8	7	6	5	4	3	2	1	0
1	1	0	1	Register Dn			Op-Mode			Effective Address					
										Mode			Register		

Instruction Fields:

Register field — Specifies any of the eight data registers.

Op-Mode field —

Byte	Word	Long	Operation
000	001	010	<ea> + <Dn> → <Dn>
100	101	110	<Dn> + <ea> → <ea>

Effective Address Field — Determines addressing mode:
a. If the location specified in a source operand, the all addressing modes are allowed as shown:

Addr. Mode	Mode	Register
Dn	000	reg. number:Dn
An*	001	reg. number:An
(An)	010	reg. number:An
(An) +	011	reg. number:An
– (An)	100	reg. number:An
(d16,An)	101	reg. number:An
(d8,An,Xn)	110	reg. number:An

Addr. Mode	Mode	Register
(xxx).W	111	000
(xxx).L	111	001
#<data>	111	100
(d16,PC)	111	010
(d8,PC,Xn)	111	011

*Word and Long only.

b. If the location specified is a destination operand, then only alterable memory addressing modes are allowed as shown:

Addr. Mode	Mode	Register
Dn	—	—
An	—	—
(An)	010	reg. number:An
(An) +	011	reg. number:An
– (An)	100	reg. number:An
(d16,An)	101	reg. number:An
(d8,An,Xn)	110	reg. number:An

Addr. Mode	Mode	Register
(xxx).W	111	000
(xxx).L	111	001
#<data>	—	—
(d16,PC)	—	—
(d8,PC,Xn)	—	—

Notes: 1. If the destination is a data register, then it cannot be specified by using the destination <ea> mode, but must use the destination Dn mode instead.
2. ADDA is used when the destination is an address register. ADDI and ADDQ are used when the source is immediate data. Most assemblers automatically make this distinction.

Figure 14-9   The **68000** ADD instruction page from the Programming Manual.

SP   Stack Pointer
USP   User Stack Pointer
SSP   Supervisor Stack Pointer
d   Displacement value
N   Operand size in bytes (1, 2, 4)

As described in Section 14-8.1, all **68000** instructions must specify a word length, the source operand, and then the destination operand. The instruction ADD.B would be used to designate a byte-sized operand; ADD.W, a word operand; and ADD.L, a long-word operand.

Use of the ECB helps clarify the operation of these instructions. It is very educational to enter the byte option (.B) and observe the resulting machine language code and then enter the word option (.W) to see the difference. It is also interesting to run the instruction to see the effect on the registers. Even more clarification of the μP operations can be seen if negative numbers are used. This will demonstrate how the various-sized entries are *sign* extended.

EXAMPLE 14-2

What does the **68000** instruction ADD.W D1,D3 do?

SOLUTION

This instruction can be entered into memory at any location ($2000, for example) using the ECB's assembler/disassembler command (MM $2000;DI). If ADD.W D1,D3 is entered and then executed (by placing $2000 in the PC and entering T to run one instruction), it causes the 16 LSBs of D1 to be added to the 16 LSBs of D3, and the result is placed in the 16 LSBs of D3. The condition codes are set in accordance with the 16-bit results. All of D1 and the 16 MSBs of D3 are unchanged. Even if there is a carry out of the addition, it will not affect the MSBs of D3, but it will affect the condition codes.

EXAMPLE 14-3

What does the machine language instruction $D019 do?

SOLUTION

The instruction is disassembled as shown in Fig. 14-10. Bits 12 through 15 are a hexadecimal D, which indicates an ADD instruction. Bits 9 through 11 determine that data register 0 is the data register involved in this instruction. The op mode of this instruction is also 0. This indicates that:

1. The data length is a byte.
2. Register 0 is one of the operands. The contents of the byte referenced by the effective address comprise the other operand, and register 0 is also the destination, where the results will reside.

   Bits 0 through 5 determine the address and mode of the other operand. Address modes are discussed in Section 14-9. The operand mode in this case is 011 (see Table 14-2 in Section 14-9), and the address register involved is address register 1.
   The effect of this instruction is to ADD the number in data register 0 to the number in the memory location pointed to by address register 1. The results go to data register 0. Also, the mode is auto-incrementing, so that address register 1 is incremented at the end of the instruction. Thus the disassembled instruction is

   ```
   ADD.B (A1)+,D0
   ```

14-8.3 ▼ Assemblers

The reverse of the disassembly procedure of Example 14-3 is called *hand assembly*. It requires the user to look up the machine language code for every instruction used. This process is so tedious and laborious that it is rarely done. Some hand assembly may be necessary during the hardware debug phase of a project to determine if the signals on the various data and address lines are correct, but software for the **68000** is rarely written in machine language.

Much of the labor in Example 14-3 is eliminated by using an Assembler or the ECB, which will assemble single instructions. **68000** Assemblers are available from Motorola and many other software vendors. In addition to making programming easier, they will detect and flag invalid instructions and addressing modes. We recommend that the programmer use one of these Assemblers or the ECB (see Section 14-7) to ensure the correctness of the code before attempting to run the program. Note that when dealing with addresses and data, most Assemblers require a distinction between decimal and hex numbers. Motorola uses the $ (dollar sign) to mean hex. Some commands of the ECB and some assemblers assume that the number is decimal unless the $ sign is included.

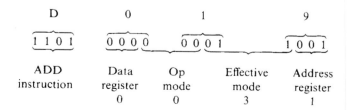

Figure 14-10 Disassembling the op code D019.

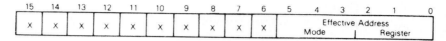

Figure 14-11 The Effective Address field format.

14-9 ▼ ADDRESS MODES

Most instructions specify the location of an operand by using a 6-bit field within the instruction word that is called the *Effective Address* (EA) *field.* Three bits are used to specify the addressing mode and 3 bits are used to specify a register, as shown in Fig. 14-11. The address mode and register are used together to calculate the actual address of the data or operand. This is known as the *Effective Address* (EA) of the instruction. The Effective Address is listed as <ea> in Fig. 14-9 and other places in the literature.

The effective address field may require additional information to fully specify the operand. This additional information, called the effective address extension, is contained in a word (or words) following the op code and is considered part of the instruction, as shown in Fig. 14-8. The effective address modes are grouped into three categories: register direct, memory addressing, and special.

The effective addressing modes are shown in Table 14-2. They include these basic types:

- Register Direct
- Register Indirect
- Absolute

TABLE 14-2 Effective Address Mode Categories

Address Modes	Mode	Register	Data	Memory	Control	Alterable	Assembler Syntax
Data Register Direct	000	reg no	X	–	–	X	Dn
Address Register Direct	001	reg no	–	–	–	X	An
Address Register Indirect	010	reg no	X	X	X	X	(An)
Address Register Indirect with Postincrement	011	reg no	X	X	–	X	(An)+
Address Register Indirect with Predecrement	100	reg no	X	X	–	X	–(An)
Address Register Indirect with Displacement	101	reg no	X	X	X	X	(d_{16}, An, n) or $d_{16}(An)$
Address Register Indirect with Index	110	reg no	X	X	X	X	(d_8, An, Xn) or $d_8(An, Xn)$
Absolute Short	111	000	X	X	X	X	(xxx).W
Absolute Long	111	001	X	X	X	X	(xxx).L
Program Counter Indirect with Displacement	111	101	X	X	X	–	(d_{16}, PC) or $d_{16}(PC)$
Program Counter Indirect with Index	111	011	X	X	X	–	(d_8, PC, Xn) or $d_8(PC, Xn)$
Immediate	111	100	X	X	–	–	#<data>

- Immediate
- Program Counter Relative (PCR)

Included in the register indirect addressing modes is the capability to do postincrementing, predecrementing, offsetting, and indexing. Program Counter Relative (PCR) mode addresses can also be modified via indexing and offsetting.

Some modes (those designated by 111 in the mode field) do not need to specify a register. In these cases the register field is used to define the mode further. Each of the addressing modes is considered in the following sections.

14-9.1 ▼ The Register Direct Mode

The general format of a **68000** data instruction is

```
<op code.X> <source>,<destination>
```

where X is the *length* of the instruction (B, W, or L). In *data register direct* mode, the source or destination (or both) is a data register. For example, the instruction CLR.B D3 is a *data register direct* instruction that needs only one operand. The .B specifies that it is a byte instruction. It clears bits 0 through 7 of D3.

14-9.2 ▼ Address Register Direct Mode

In *Address Register Direct* mode, the source or destination (or both) is an address register. These must be word or long-word operands; address registers do not work with byte operands. The instruction MOVE.W A3,D4, for example, uses address register direct mode for the source and data register direct for the destination; it copies the 16 LSBs of A3 into D4.

14-9.3 ▼ Address Register Indirect

Address Register Indirect is a very popular addressing mode. It uses the contents of an address register as the memory address. Its assembler syntax is (An), where n specifies the address register being used. If, for example, A5 contains $2004, the instruction MOVE.B (A5),D3 will move the byte at $2004 into the LS byte of D3. $2004 is the *Effective Address* of this instruction.

There are two other address register indirect modes: *predecrement* and *postincrement.* In *predecrement mode,* the contents of the selected address register are first decremented and then used as an address. Although the **68000** does not contain PUSH or PULL instructions, this is essentially what happens during a PUSH instruction, when putting data on the stack. Its syntax is – (An).

In *postincrement mode* the selected register is used as an address and then it is incremented. This is similar to a PULL instruction. Its syntax is (An)+. The equivalent of a PUSH from data register Dn can be obtained by the instruction MOVE.X Dn, –(An), and the corresponding PULL can be obtained by MOVE.X (An)+,Dn. This adds flexibility to the **68000** because any vacant address register can be used for PUSH or PULL functions.

EXAMPLE 14-4

What does the following program do?

```
MOVEA.L   #$2004,A4
MOVE.W    (A4)+,D2
MOVE.W    D2,(A4)
```

SOLUTION

The first instruction is an *Immediate* instruction that moves the number $2004 into address register A4. The source mode of the second instruction is address register indirect with postincrement and the destination mode is data register direct. This instruction moves the contents of $2004 and $2005 into D2 and increments A4 to $2006 because it is a word-length instruction. The third instruction writes the contents of D2 into $2006. Thus the program has copied the contents of $2004 and $2005 into $2006 and $2007.

14-9.4 ▼ Address Register Indirect with Displacement

In the *Address Register Indirect with Displacement* mode, the *Effective Address* is the sum of the contents of the designated address register plus a *displacement*. The operation of this mode is shown in Fig. 14-12. The displacement is a 16-bit word that is added to the instruction (a number larger than 32767_{10} or smaller than -32768_{10} cannot be used). The addition is a 32-bit addition of the contents of the address register and the *extended* displacement. The displacement is extended as follows:

- If the MSB of the 16-bit displacement is a 0, leading 0s are added to fill out the 32 bits.
- If the MSB of the displacement is 1, leading 1s are added to fill out the 32 bits.

This allows the displacement to be either a positive or a negative number.

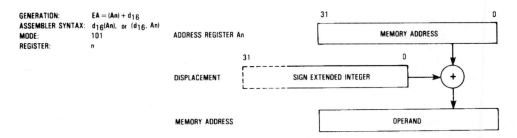

GENERATION: EA = (An) + d_{16}
ASSEMBLER SYNTAX: d_{16}(An), or (d_{16}, An)
MODE: 101
REGISTER: n

Figure 14-12 Address Register Indirect instruction with displacement.

EXAMPLE 14-5

If A4 contains $20004, what is the effective address of the following expressions?

(a) `$1234(A4)`

(b) `-2(A4)`

(When testing with the ECB it will be found that the −2 must be replaced with the 32-bit equivalent, FFFFFFFE. Also, the effective address must be an even address or it will cause an error.)

SOLUTION

(a) Here the displacement is positive. The EA is

```
 $00020004
+$00001234
 $00021238
```

The result is a higher address.

(b) Here the displacement is negative, because the MSB of the displacement is 1. The displacement is extended by adding leading Fs (1s). The EA is

```
 $00020004
+$FFFFFFFE
 $00020002
```

The result is a lower address.

14-9.5 ▼ Address Register Indirect with Index

The *Address Register Indirect with Index* mode is the **68000** equivalent of the index mode in the **6800.** The way the EA is generated and the Assembler syntax are shown in Fig. 14-13. This mode uses an 8-bit displacement that is extended to 32 bits and then added to the sum of the selected address register and the selected index register. The size of the index register does not affect the execution time of the instruction.

A one-word extension to the instruction is required, as shown in Fig. 14-13a. This extension word defines the register to be used as an index and whether the index register is to be taken as a word, in which case it is extended to 16 bits, or as a long word (extended to 32 bits). The extension word also includes the 8-bit displacement integer.

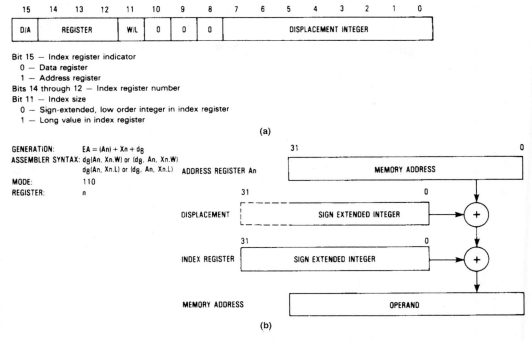

Bit 15 — Index register indicator
  0 — Data register
  1 — Address register
Bits 14 through 12 — Index register number
Bit 11 — Index size
  0 — Sign-extended, low order integer in index register
  1 — Long value in index register

(a)

GENERATION: $EA = (An) + Xn + d_8$
ASSEMBLER SYNTAX: $d_8(An, Xn.W)$ or $(d_8, An, Xn.W)$
                  $d_8(An, Xn.L)$ or $(d_8, An, Xn.L)$
MODE: 110
REGISTER: n

(b)

Figure 14-13 Address Register Indirect instruction with index. (a) Extension word. (b) Generation of Effective Address and assembly syntax.

EXAMPLE 14-6

If `A4` contains `$20004`, `A6` contains `$ABCD`, and the displacement is -99, find the effective address of the expression `-99(A4,A6.W)`.

SOLUTION

The extension word to the instruction is `$E09D` (see Section 14-9), and the EA is the sum of the three numbers:

```
 $00020004
 $FFFFABCD = 32-bit sign extension of $ABCD
+$FFFFFF9D = -99₁₀
 $0001AB6E
```

Note that since A6 is defined as a word, the number entered in A6 can be $ABCD, which is sign extended by the instruction to $FFFFABCD. If A6 is defined as a long word by specifying A6.L, the entry in A6 must be $FFF-FABCD. The resulting EA is lower than the address in A4 because of the negative value in the index register (A6) and also because of the negative displacement.

EXAMPLE 14-7

If A4 contains an address of $3500, A6 contains –4, and the displacement is –128, find the EA for the expression –128(A4,A6.W).

SOLUTION

This can be solved as in Example 14-6 to give $347C. The EA can also be found without manual calculations by using the DC (Data Conversion) command of the ECB, as shown in Fig. 14-14. This figure shows the execution results using the ECB.

To verify the results, a MOVE immediate instruction was created using the one-line assembler to place $222 into memory at the EA calculated by the expression. The instruction was entered using the command MM 2000;DI as shown on the top line. It created the machine language and mnemonics as shown in line 2 when the instruction MOVE #$222, –128(A4,A6) shown in the last part of line 2 was entered. The MM command was then exited by entering a period, as shown on line 3. The register values were then entered as shown on lines 4, 5, and 6, and the instruction was traced (by the T command, line 7). Normally, the register display would have been examined using the DF command, before executing the instruction and it would show that the registers involved have been set to the proper values and the instruction to be executed is displayed. (We skipped that step to save space.)

After tracing one instruction, the registers were displayed. It is not obvious from this display that the instruction did what was intended, so the EA was calculated using the DC command. Note that the ECB creates a 32-bit value for –4. Also note that the ECB uses Hex values for registers or addresses in the DC command, but defaults to decimal for other numbers when it disassembles the instructions. It shows the EA to be $347C. When that address was examined, by displaying the line at $3470, it was seen to contain the number $222.

14-9.6 ▼ Absolute Addressing

Absolute addressing uses a specific number to specify the address. This mode should be avoided when relocatable programs are being written, but it is necessary when addressing peripherals, such as PIAs, that reside at fixed addresses. The instruction, MOVE.B $2004,D0 is an example of absolute source addressing and direct data addressing for the destination.

There are two types of absolute addressing, short and long. Short absolute addressing requires a one-word extension to the instruction and can specify any address from $0000 to $FFFF. Long absolute addressing uses a two-word extension, giving it a 32-bit address field, and can access any memory location. The longest **68000** instructions use

```
TUTOR  1.32> MM 2000;DI
002000    39BC0222E080        MOVE      #$222,-128(A4,A6)
002006    0000000             OR.B      #0,D0 ?.


TUTOR  1.32> .PC 2000

TUTOR  1.32> .A4 $3500

TUTOR  1.32> .A6 -4

TUTOR  1.32> T
PHYSICAL ADDRESS=00002000
PC=00002006 SR=2700=.S7..... US=63791CFF SS=0000077A
D0=FFFF7E38 D1=CDFF3EFB D2=7FFF79FF D3=FFFFBF7F
D4=5CE37DFF D5=FDFF3EFF D6=4FBF5EDF D7=B9DB7FFF
A0=BFFF6FFF A1=FCFD0FFF A2=EFF73FDF A3=7DBF7EFB
A4=00003500 A5=FFEF6FFF A6=FFFFFFFC A7=0000077A
--------------------002006    0000000             OR.B      #0,D0

TUTOR  1.32:> DC $3500-&128-4
$347C=&13436

TUTOR  1.32> MD 3470
003470    AE FF FF FF EF FF FF FF  AE FF FF FF 02 22 FF FF    ....o........"..

TUTOR  1.32> _
```

Figure 14-14   ECB display results for Example 14-7.

one word of op code, an absolute long source address, and an absolute long destination address. This is the worst case and results in a five-word instruction.

14-9.7 ▼ Program Counter Relative Modes

There are two *Program Counter Relative* (PCR) modes in the **68000.** These modes are often used in relocatable programs because the Effective Addresses are relative to the PC and change when the starting address of the program changes.

The *Program Counter with Displacement* mode is shown in Fig. 14-15. Its operation appears similar to the Address Register Indirect mode except that the PC is used instead of an address register and the Assembler syntax is the reverse of what might be expected from the previous figures. The displacement is a sign-extended integer in an extension word to the instruction, and the address of that extension word is used as the PC component of the addition. When entering the mnemonic into a source program for assembly into TUTOR's one-line assembler, or into another similar debugger, the number in front of the parentheses is the *actual destination* address instead of the displacement. Typically, in an assembly program, a *label* would be used to designate the destination address. When testing with TUTOR, it is therefore necessary to substitute the absolute address that is equivalent to the label. This makes sense since when testing loops or jumps, the absolute addresses must be used instead of the label. Only data-alterable addressing modes (see Section 14-9.9) are allowed for the destination EA field.

EXAMPLE 14-8

The machine language for the instruction MOVE.W $3002(PC),D3 is in memory starting at $3004. What is this assembler-generated code, and how is the displacement calculated?

SOLUTION

In the program counter relative mode, the reader must distinguish between the *Assembler syntax* and the *displacement* (or offset) calculated by the assembler. In the instruction MOVE.W $3002(PC),D3, the assembler interprets the $3002 as the Effective Address of the source of the data, or the *actual source address.* The (PC) tells the assembler that this is a *Program Counter Relative* instruction. The assembler then knows to calculate the *displacement,* and includes it in the machine language. In this mode each instruction consists of an op code and an extension word. The effective address is the result of adding the displacement to the address of the extension word. In this example we have been told the EA is $3002, and we know the address of the extension word ($3006), so the assembler calculates the displacement or difference between $3006 and $3002 or –4 ($FFFC). The assembler listing created for this instruction is

```
ADDR            CODE                INST.
003004          363AFFFC    MOVE.W $3002(PC), D3
```

Here 363A (at location $3004) is the op code for MOVE.W in the PC relative mode, and the displacement created by the Assembler of TUTOR or other Motorola Assemblers is $FFFC (at location $3006). If MOVE.B had been used, the op code would have been 163A. The EA as calculated by the μP is

```
 $00003006  Location of extension word
+$FFFFFFFC  displacement integer (extended)
 $00003002
```

The *Program Counter with Index* mode is similar to the Indirect Address with Index mode and is shown in Fig. 14-16. It also takes a one-word extension, as shown in Fig. 14-16a, which contains an 8-bit displacement byte. Again, the assembler syntax requires the actual destination address (or a Label) to be entered preceding the (PC) rather than the displacement as in other instructions [i.e., MOVE.B $3008(PC,D6),D3 entered at location $3000 will generate 103B6006, where 06 is the displacement]. It adds this to the contents of the index register (D6, in this case) plus the PC address+2 and the EA will be $3008 (if D6 is zero). Note that the address preceding the parentheses in the assembler syntax (or the label location) cannot be more than $7F (+127) bytes above the extension word's address, or less than $80 (–128) below that address.

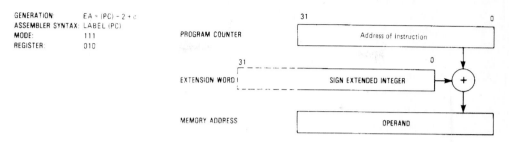

Figure 14-15 Program Counter (with displacement) instruction generation and assembler syntax.

14-9.8 ▼ Immediate Mode

The *Immediate* mode uses either one or two extension words to provide the data for the instruction, depending on the size selected for the operation. The extension word formats for byte, word, and long word are shown in Fig. 14-17. The immediate mode can be a source but never a destination. For example, the instruction `MOVE.W #$1234,-4(A4,A6)`

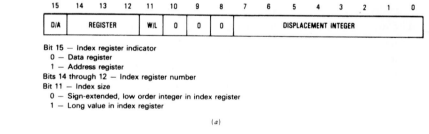

Bit 15 — Index register indicator
 0 — Data register
 1 — Address register
Bits 14 through 12 — Index register number
Bit 11 — Index size
 0 — Sign-extended, low order integer in index register
 1 — Long value in index register

(a)

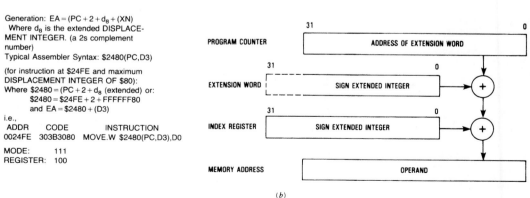

Generation: EA = (PC + 2 + d_8 + (XN)
 Where d_8 is the extended DISPLACE-
 MENT INTEGER. (a 2s complement
 number)
Typical Assembler Syntax: $2480(PC,D3)

(for instruction at $24FE and maximum
DISPLACEMENT INTEGER OF $80):
 Where $2480 = (PC + 2 + d_8 (extended) or:
  $2480 = $24FE + 2 + FFFFFF80
  and EA = $2480 + (D3)
i.e.,

ADDR	CODE	INSTRUCTION
0024FE	303B3080	MOVE.W $2480(PC,D3),D0

MODE: 111
REGISTER: 100

(b)

Figure 14-16 Program Counter (with index) instruction generation and assembler syntax. (a) Extension word. (b) Effective Address calculation.

moves the first extension word (the hex number 1234) into the address that is the sum of the address in A4, plus the contents of A6, plus the displacement (second extension word), which in this case is also negative. This instruction has an immediate mode source and an address register indirect with index destination.

The Immediate mode can be specified as byte, word, or long word, but the immediate extension to the instruction must be at least one word long. In byte-length mode, only bits 0 through 7 are used. Word sizes use the entire word and long-word sizes require two extension words to the instruction.

14-9.9 ▼ Address Categories

Effective Address modes may be categorized by the ways in which they may be used. Table 14-3 shows the various categories to which each of these effective addressing modes belong. Addresses fall into one or more of four categories:

1. **Data.** If an effective address mode may be used to refer to *data operands* (the contents of a data register), it is considered a *data addressing* effective address mode.

2. **Memory.** If an effective address mode may be used to refer to *memory operands,* it is considered a *memory addressing* effective address mode.

3. **Alterable.** If an address mode may be used to refer to alterable (writable) operands, it is considered to be an *alterable addressing* effective address mode. All addressing modes that do not involve the PC are alterable.

4. **Control.** If an Effective Address mode may be used to refer to memory operands without an associated size, it is considered a *control addressing* Effective Address mode. For example, the JMP instruction uses the control addressing modes, meaning those modes where the Effective Address is a memory location. The JMP instruction does not perform postincrement or predecrement. The addressing modes

```
GENERATION:        OPERAND GIVEN
ASSEMBLER SYNTAX:  # xxxx or # <data>
MODE:              111
REGISTER:          100
```

The extension word formats are shown below:

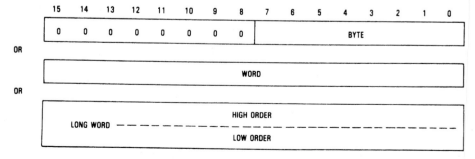

Figure 14-17   Immediate Mode instructions.

TABLE 14-3 Effective Address Encoding
Summary

Addressing Mode	Mode	Register
Data Register Direct	000	Register Number
Address Register Direct	001	Register Number
Address Register Indirect	010	Register Number
Address Register Indirect with Postincrement	011	Register Number
Address Register Indirect with Predecrement	100	Register Number
Address Register Indirect with Displacement	101	Register Number
Address Register Indirect with Index	110	Register Number
Absolute Short	111	000
Absolute Long	111	001
Program Counter with Displacement	111	010
Program Counter with Index	111	011
Immediate	111	100

allowed are consistent with the nature of the instruction. The program should be allowed to jump to a location, but not to a register.

To determine the allowed addressing mode for a specific instruction, determine the addressing category from the instruction set summary shown in Tables 14-7 through 14-15 in the following sections; then look up the allowed addressing modes in Table 14-3. The addressing modes that fall into each of these categories are defined with an "X" in the appropriate column. The **68000** *Programmer's Reference Manual* also shows the condition codes and the allowable modes for each instruction.

EXAMPLE 14-9

What address modes can be used with the instruction NEGX? (Create the 2s-complement negative of a value with the sign bit extended.)

SOLUTION

This instruction appears in Table 14-10 and the allowable addressing modes are "data alterable." This means that the addressing modes in Table 14-3 that have an "X" in both the data and the alterable columns are allowed. Looking at Table 14-3, we can see that the NEGX instruction can take all addressing modes except Address Register Direct, Immediate, Program Counter with Displacement, and Program Counter with Index. This allows the user to negate data registers and memory operands.

14-10 ▼ 68000 INSTRUCTION SET

A summary of the **68000** instructions is shown in Table 14-4. Some additional instructions are variations or subsets of these and they appear in Table 14-5. The instruction set supports structured high-level languages to facilitate ease of programming. Each instruction, with a few exceptions, operates on bytes, words, and long words, and most instructions can use any of the 12 addressing modes. By combining instruction types, data types, and addressing modes, over 1000 useful instructions are provided. These instructions include BCD arithmetic, signed and unsigned, multiply and divide, "Quick" arithmetic operations, and expanded operations (through traps). In the following sections we describe many of the **68000** instruction modes and illustrate their uses.

14-10.1 ▼ Quick Instructions

There are three instructions in the **68000** instruction set known as *Quick* instructions. An ADD Quick or SUBTRACT Quick instruction is a one-word immediate instruction that deals with a small value in the operand. These instructions use a 3-bit field that contains the numbers 0 through 7. If a number from 1 through 7 is found in that field, it is the immediate operand used by the instruction. If the field contains 0, the instruction uses 8 as its immediate operand. The advantage of Quick instructions is that they require only one word in the program, and thus save time and space. The ADD Quick (ADDQ) and SUBTRACT Quick (SUBQ) instructions allow the user to add or subtract the numbers 1 through 8 from a register or memory.

TABLE 14-4 MC68000 and MC68008 Instruction Set Summary

Mnemonic	Description	Mnemonic	Description
ABCD	Add Decimal With Extend	MOVE	Move
ADD	Add	MULS	Signed Multiply
AND	Logical And	MULU	Unsigned Multiply
ASL	Arithmetic Shift Left	NBCD	Negate Decimal with Extend
ASR	Arithmetic Shift Right	NEG	Negate
Bcc	Branch Conditionally	NOP	No Operation
BCHG	Bit Test and Change	NOT	One's Complement
BCLR	Bit Test and Clear	OR	Logical Or
BRA	Branch Always	PEA	Push Effective Address
BSET	Bit Test and Set	RESET	Reset External Devices
BSR	Branch to Subroutine	ROL	Rotate Left without Extend
BTST	Bit Test	ROR	Rotate Right without Extend
CHK	Check Register Against Bounds	ROXL	Rotate Left with Extend
CLR	Clear Operand	ROXR	Rotate Right with Extend
CMP	Compare	RTE	Return from Exception
DBcc	Test Condition, Decrement and Branch	RTR	Return and Restore
DIVS	Signed Divide	RTS	Return from Subroutine
DIVU	Unsigned Divide	SBCD	Subtract Decimal with Extend
EOR	Exclusive Or	Scc	Set Conditional
EXG	Exchange Registers	STOP	Stop
EXT	Sign Extend	SUB	Subtract
JMP	Jump	SWAP	Swap Data Register Halves
JSR	Jump to Subroutine	TAS	Test and Set Operand
LEA	Load Effective Address	TRAP	Trap
LINK	Link Stack	TRAPV	Trap on Overflow
LSL	Logical Shift Left	TST	Test
LSR	Logical Shift Right	UNLK	Unlink

TABLE 14-5   Variations of Instruction Types

Instruction Type	Variation	Description	Instruction Type	Variation	Description
ADD	ADD	Add	MOVE	MOVE	Move
	ADDA	Add Address		MOVEA	Move Address
	ADDQ	Add Quick		MOVEM	Move Multiple Registers
	ADDI	Add Immediate		MOVEP	Move Peripheral Data
	ADDX	Add with Extend		MOVEQ	Move Quick
AND	AND	Logical AND		MOVE from SR	Move from Status Register
	ANDI	AND Immediate		MOVE to SR	Move to Status Register
	ANDI to CCR	AND Immediate to Condition Codes		MOVE to CCR	Move to Condition Codes
	ANDI to SR	AND immediate to Status Register		MOVE USP	Move User Stack Pointer
			NEG	NEG	Negate
CMP	CMP	Compare		NEGX	Negate with Extend
	CMPA	Compare Address	OR	OR	Logical OR
	CMPM	Compare Memory		ORI	OR Immediate
	CMPI	Compare Immediate		ORI to CCR	OR Immediate to Condition Codes
EOR	EOR	Exclusive OR		ORI to SR	OR immediate to Status Register
	EORI	Exclusive OR Immediate			
	EORI to CCR	Exclusive OR Immediate to Condition Codes	SUB	SUB	Subtract
	EORI to SR	Exclusive OR Immediate to Status Register		SUBA	Subtract Address
				SUBI	Subtract Immediate
				SUBQ	Subtract Quick
				SUBX	Subtract with Extend

EXAMPLE 14-10

There is no decrement instruction in the **68000**. Show how to decrement register D4.

SOLUTION

The simplest way is to use the instruction:

```
SUBQ #1,D4
```

Note that a memory location could also have been decremented in this way by using the memory location as the destination of the instruction.

The MOVEQ instruction is the third Quick instruction. It is discussed in Section 14-10.3.

14-10.2 ▼ Address Register Destination Instructions

Instructions that specify an address register as a destination are somewhat special. They may only use word or long-word operands, and most of them do not affect the condition codes. The four address destination words are MOVEA, ADDA, SUBA, and CMPA. Of these, only the COMPARE sets the condition codes; it subtracts the destination address register from the source, which can be a register, a memory location, or an immediate value, and sets the condition codes accordingly without changing the registers.

MOVE   Move Data from Source to Destination   # MOVE

Operation: Source — Destination

**Assembler
Syntax:**   MOVE <ea>,<ea>

Attributes: Size = (Byte, Word, Long)

Description: Move the content of the source to the destination location. The data is
examined as it is moved, and the condition codes set accordingly. The size of the
operation may be specified to be byte, word, or long.

Condition Codes:

X	N	Z	V	C
—	•	•	0	0

N Set if the result is negative. Cleared otherwise.
Z Set if the result is zero. Cleared otherwise.
V Always cleared.
C Always cleared.
X Not affected.

Instruction Format:

15	14	13	12	11	10	9	8	7	6	5	4	3	2	1	0
0	0	Size		Destination						Source					
				Register			Mode			Mode			Register		

Instruction Fields:

Size field — Specifies the size of the operand to be moved:
01—byte operation.
11—word operation.
10—long operation.
Destination Effective Address field — Specifies the destination location. Only data
alterable addressing modes are allowed as shown:

Addr. Mode	Mode	Register
Dn	000	reg. number:An
An	—	—
(An)	010	reg. number:An
(An) +	011	reg. number:An
– (An)	100	reg. number:An
(d16,An)	101	reg. number:An
(d8,An,Xn)	110	reg. number:An

Addr. Mode	Mode	Register
(xxx).W	111	000
(xxx).L	111	001
#<data>	—	—
(d16,PC)	—	—
(d8,PC,Xn)	—	—

Source Effective Address field — Specifies the source operand. All addressing
modes are allowed as shown:

Addr. Mode	Mode	Register
Dn	000	reg. number:Dn
An*	001	reg. number:An
(An)	010	reg. number:An
(An) +	011	reg. number:An
– (An)	100	reg. number:An
(d16,An)	101	reg. number:An
(d8,An,Xn)	110	reg. number:An

Addr. Mode	Mode	Register
(xxx).W	111	000
(xxx).L	111	001
#<data>	111	100
(d16,PC)	111	010
(d8,PC,Xn)	111	011

*For byte size operation, address register direct is not allowed.

Notes: 1. MOVEA is used when the destination is an address register. Most assemblers
automatically make this distinction. .
2. MOVEQ can also be used for certain operations on data registers.

Figure 14-18   Manual Page for the MOVE instruction.

14-10.3 ▼ MOVE Instructions

MOVE instructions move data from a register or memory location (the source) to another register or memory location (the destination). They replace LOADs, STOREs, PUSHes, PULLs, and so on. The page of the manual for MOVE instructions is shown in Fig. 14-18. The instruction format contains an op code field that declares it to be a MOVE instruction and specifies the size of the operand. The page shows that any instruction where the two MSBs are 0 are MOVE instructions. They all have a 6-bit field to define the destination and another 6-bit field to define the source.

EXAMPLE 14-11

Table 14-6 shows the location of data in memory for this example. What data ends up in data register D0 after executing each of the following instructions?

(a) MOVE.B $2004,D0
(b) MOVE.B $2005,D0
(c) MOVE.W $2004,D0
(d) MOVE.W $2005,D0
(e) MOVE.L $2004,D0

SOLUTION

(a) The instruction MOVE.B $2004,D0 moves the byte at $2004 to D0. The 8 LSBs of D0 become AA; the remaining bytes of D0 are unchanged.
(b) The byte at $2005 is moved to D0. Its 8 LSBs become BB; the remaining bytes are unchanged.
(c) This instruction moves the word at $2004 to D0. The 16 LSBs of D0 become AABB; the remainder of the bits are unchanged.
(d) This instruction is illegal. Word or long-word transfers cannot specify odd addresses.
(e) This is a long-word transfer. The contents of D0 become AABBCCDD.

Space limitations preclude giving as thorough a description of each instruction as found in the *M68000 Programmer's Reference Manual* (see Section 14-17). Each **68000** instruction is covered here, however, in Tables 14-8 through 14-16. Between the tables

TABLE 14-6 Data for Example 14-11

Memory	
Byte Addresses	Data
2004	AA
2005	BB
2006	CC
2007	DD

and the descriptions we will present in the following paragraphs, we hope to provide enough information so that the reader can use the instructions. The tables give the instruction, the allowable sizes of its operands, its operation, its notation, and its allowable Effective Address modes. Using the notation provided in the table and the address notation provided in Section 14-8, the reader should be able to specify an Assembler instruction for an Assembler or TUTOR. The effect of the instruction on the condition codes is not given in these tables, but Table 14-7 shows how the various instructions affect the codes.

Characteristics of the MOVE group of instructions in the **68000** are shown in Table 14-8. The MOVE instruction copies data from the source, which can be any of the modes, to the destination, which can be any mode except an address register with displacement,

TABLE 14-7 Condition Code Computations

Operations	X	N	Z	V	C	Special Definition
ABCD	•	U	?	U	?	C = Decimal Carry $Z = Z \wedge \overline{Rm} \wedge \ldots \wedge \overline{R0}$
ADD, ADDI, ADDQ	•	•	•	?	?	$V = Sm \wedge Dm \wedge \overline{Rm} \vee \overline{Sm} \wedge \overline{Dm} \wedge Rm$ $C = Sm \wedge Dm \vee \overline{Rm} \wedge Dm \vee Sm \wedge \overline{Rm}$
ADDX	•	•	?	?	?	$V = Sm \wedge Dm \wedge \overline{Rm} \vee \overline{Sm} \wedge \overline{Dm} \wedge Rm$ $C = Sm \wedge Dm \vee \overline{Rm} \wedge Dm \vee Sm \wedge \overline{Rm}$ $Z = Z \wedge \overline{Rm} \wedge \ldots \wedge \overline{R0}$
AND, ANDI, EOR, EORI, MOVEQ, MOVE, OR, ORI, CLR, EXT, NOT, TAS, TST	–	•	•	0	0	
CHK	–	•	U	U	U	
SUB, SUBI, SUBQ	•	•	•	?	?	$V = \overline{Sm} \wedge Dm \wedge \overline{Rm} \vee Sm \wedge \overline{Dm} \wedge Rm$ $C = Sm \wedge \overline{Dm} \vee Rm \wedge \overline{Dm} \vee Sm \wedge Rm$
SUBX	•	•	?	?	?	$V = \overline{Sm} \wedge Dm \wedge \overline{Rm} \vee Sm \wedge \overline{Dm} \wedge Rm$ $C = Sm \wedge \overline{Dm} \vee Rm \wedge \overline{Dm} \vee Sm \wedge Rm$ $Z = Z \wedge \overline{Rm} \wedge \ldots \wedge \overline{R0}$
CMP CMPI, CMPM	–	•	•	?	?	$V = \overline{Sm} \wedge Dm \wedge \overline{Rm} \vee Sm \wedge \overline{Dm} \wedge Rm$ $C = Sm \wedge \overline{Dm} \vee Rm \wedge \overline{Dm} \vee Sm \wedge Rm$
DIVS, DIVU	–	•	•	?	0	V = Division Overflow
MULS, MULU	–	•	•	?	0	V = Multiplication Overflow
SBCD, NBCD	•	U	?	U	?	C = Decimal Borrow $Z = Z \wedge \overline{Rm} \wedge \ldots \wedge \overline{R0}$
NEG	•	•	•	?	?	$V = Dm \wedge Rm, C = Dm \vee Rm$
NEGX	•	•	?	?	?	$V = Dm \wedge Rm, C = Dm \vee Rm$ $Z = Z \wedge \overline{Rm} \wedge \ldots \wedge \overline{R0}$
BTST, BCHG, BSET, BCLR	–	–	?	–	–	$Z = \overline{Dn}$
ASL	•	•	•	?	?	$V = Dm \wedge (\overline{Dm - 1V} \ldots V \overline{Dm - r})V\overline{Dm} \wedge (Dm - 1V \ldots + Dm - r)$ $C = \overline{Dm - r + 1}$
ASL (r=0)	–	•	•	0	0	
LSL, ROXL	•	•	•	0	?	$C = Dm - r + 1$
LSR (r=0)	–	•	•	0	0	
ROXL (r=0)	–	•	•	0	?	$C = X$
ROL	–	•	•	0	?	$C = Dm - r + 1$
ROL (r=0)	–	•	•	0	0	
ASR, LSR, ROXR	•	•	•	0	?	$C = Dr - 1$
ASR, LSR (r=0)	–	•	•	0	0	
ROXR (r=0)	–	•	•	0	?	$C = X$
ROR	–	•	•	0	?	$C = Dr - 1$
ROR (r=0)	–	•	•	0	0	

– = Not Affected	Rm	= Result Operand – most significant bit
U = Undefined, result meaningless	R	= Register Tested
? = Other – See Special Definition	n	= Bit Number
• = General Case	r	= Shift Count
$\quad X = C$	LB	= Lower Bound
$\quad N = Rm$	UB	= Upper Bound
$\quad Z = \overline{Rm} \wedge \ldots \wedge \overline{R0}$		= Boolean AND
Sm = Source Operand – most significant bit	V	= Boolean OR
Dm = Destination Operand – most significant bit	$\overline{Rm}$	= NOT Rm

TABLE 14-8 Data Movement Instructions

Instruction	Operand size	Operation	Notation	Allowable effective address modes
MOVE	8,16,32	(SOURCE) → DESTINATION	MOVE ⟨ea⟩, ⟨ea⟩	SOURCE ALL DEST DATA ALTERABLE
MOVE from SR	16	SR → DESTINATION	MOVE SR, ⟨ea⟩	DATA ALTERABLE
MOVE to CC	16	(SOURCE) → CCR	MOVE ⟨ea⟩, CCR	DATA
MOVE to SR	16	(SOURCE) → SR	MOVE ⟨ea⟩, SR	DATA
MOVE USP	32	USP → An or An → USP	MOVE USP, An MOVE An, USP	—
MOVEA	16,32	(SOURCE) → REGISTERS	MOVEA ⟨ea⟩, An	ALL
MOVEM	16,32	REGISTERS → DESTINATION (SOURCE) → REGISTERS	MOVEM REGISTER LIST ⟨ea⟩	ALTERABLE CONTROL AND PREDECREMENT
			MOVEM ⟨ea⟩ REGISTER LIST	CONTROL AND POST INCREMENT
MOVEP	16,32	(SOURCE) → DESTINATIC	MOVEP Dx, d(Ay) MOVEP d(Ay), Dx	—
MOVEQ	32	IMMEDIATE DATA → DESTINATION	MOVEQ # data, Dn	—
EXG	32	Rx ↔ Ry	EXG Rx,Ry	—
SWAP	16	Dnhw ↔ Dnhw	SWAP Dn	—

or a PC with displacement (control) mode. The MOVE instruction is the only instruction in the group that accommodates byte instructions. It sets the N and Z flags, clears C and V, and does not affect X. Most of the other instructions do not affect the condition codes at all. The MOVE instruction has been used in Examples 14-5, 14-9, and 14-11. The other instructions in the move group are described below.

MOVEA. This instruction is used when an address register is a destination. Many assemblers will convert a MOVE to a MOVEA where appropriate.

EXAMPLE 14-12

Write a program to transfer the words in $1000–$11FE to $2000–$21FE. This is a block transfer program.

SOLUTION

The program is very short using **68000** instructions.

```
        MOVEA.L #$1000,A1
        MOVEA.L #$2000,A2
LOOP    MOVE.W  (A1)+,(A2)+
        CMPA #$1200,A1
        BNE LOOP
        ....CONTINUE
```

where the CMPA and BNE are the basic *CoMPare Address register* and *Branch if Not Equal* instructions.

MOVE to CCR. This instruction specifies a 16-bit source moved into the 8-bit condition codes. The lower byte of the source is moved and the upper byte is ignored. Of course, this instruction affects all the condition codes.

MOVE from SR. This instruction moves the contents of the status register to a data register or memory so that the program can examine and use it.

MOVE to SR. This is the converse of MOVE from SR. This instruction alters both the condition codes and the system byte. It is a privileged instruction (usable only in the supervisor mode) because it can change the S-bit.

MOVE USP (Move User Stack Pointer). This instruction moves the user stack pointer (USP) to or from another address register. It can be used only in supervisor mode. It allows the executive program to set the USP before turning control over to the user.

MOVEM (Move Multiple registers). This instruction moves a group of address or data registers to or from memory. It uses a 16-bit extension word to define which of the eight data and eight address registers are to be moved. Only word or long word operations are allowed. Its syntax is

```
MOVEM.X <list> source, destination
```

where <list> is the list of registers to be moved. In the list a slash (/) separates the registers; a dash can be used to specify a group of inclusive registers.

EXAMPLE 14-13

Write a program segment to move register D1 through D5, D7, A2, and A3 into memory starting at location $1000. Assume that register A4 is available.

SOLUTION

The instructions are

```
MOVEA.L #$1000,A4
MOVEM.L D1-D5/D7/A1/A2,(A4)
```

These two instructions move the contents of the eight registers into $1000 through $101F.

MOVEP (Move to Peripherals). This instruction is designed to move data so it can be used with 8-bit peripherals, such as a PIA. This is discussed in Section 14-11.12.

MOVEQ. The Move Quick instruction must have a data register as its destination. It will move 8 bits into the selected data register, and then *sign extend* it to 32 bits.

As a result of MOVEQ, the data register will contain a number between $+127_{10}$ and -128_{10}.

EXCHANGE. This instruction is used to exchange data between any two registers. Its syntax is

```
EXG Dx,Dy
EXG Ax,Ay
EXG Dx,Ay
```

Only long-word exchanges are permitted.

SWAP. The SWAP instruction exchanges words in a register instead of between registers. For example, if D4 contains 1234ABCD, a SWAP D4 instruction will change it to ABCD1234. The N and Z condition codes are set by SWAP while C and V are cleared.

14-10.4 ▼ Logic Instructions

The logic instructions in the **68000** are given in Table 14-9. They are AND, OR, EOR (Exclusive OR), and NOT. Address registers cannot be the source or destination in a logic instruction. An example would be

```
AND.W D0,(A0)
```

which ANDs the 16 LSB contents of D0 and memory, and puts the results in memory. The AND, OR, and EOR instructions each have three submodes:

1. **Immediate.** This can be byte, word, or long word.

2. **Immediate to CCR.** This byte instruction allows the user to set or clear various bits in the CCR.

3. **Immediate to SR.** This word instruction allows the programmer to control the entire SR. It is a privileged instruction because it can change the S bit.

TABLE 14-9 Logic Instructions

Instruction	Operand Syntax	Operand Size	Operation
AND	<ea>,Dn Dn,<ea>	8, 16, 32 8, 16, 32	Source ∧ Destination ◆ Destination
ANDI	#<data>,<ea>	8, 16, 32	Immediate Data ∧ Destination ◆ Destination
EOR	Dn,<ea>	8, 16, 32	Source ⊕ Destination ◆ Destination
EORI	#<data>,<ea>	8, 16, 32	Immediate Data ⊕ Destination ◆ Destination
NOT	<ea>	8, 16, 32	~ Destination ◆ Destination
OR	<ea>,Dn Dn,<ea>	8, 16, 32	Source ∨ Destination ◆ Destination
ORI	#<data>,<ea>	8, 16, 32	Immediate Data ∨ Destination ◆ Destination

---

EXAMPLE 14-14

Write an instruction to clear the V bit of the CCR. All other bits must remain unchanged.

SOLUTION

The V bit is bit 1 (see Fig. 14-3). The instruction is

```
ANDI.B #$FD,SR.
```

The NOT instruction complements a data register or memory location. Byte, word, or long word may be used. The NOT instruction cannot be used to complement an address register.

14-10.5 ▼ ADD and SUBTRACT Instructions

The ADD and SUBTRACT instructions in the **68000** are shown in Table 14-10. The ADD instructions are

ADD
ADDA   Add to an address register.
ADDI   Add Immediate.
ADDQ   Add Immediate (immediate value is between 1 and 8).
ADDX   Add with the extend (X) bit; add 1 if the X bit is set.

TABLE 14-10 Integer Arithmetic Instructions

Instruction	Operand size	Operation	Notation	Allowable effective address modes
ADD	8,16,32	(DESTINATION) + (SOURCE) → DESTINATION	ADD Dn, <ea>	ALTERABLE MEMORY
			ADD <ea>, Dn	ALL
ADDA	16,32	(DESTINATION) + (SOURCE) → DESTINATION	ADD <ea>, An	ALL
ADDI	8,16,32	(DESTINATION) + IMMEDIATE DATA → DESTINATION	ADDI # <data>, <ea>	DATA ALTERABLE
ADDQ	8,16,32	(DESTINATION) + IMMEDIATE DATA → DESTINATION	ADDQ # <data>, <ea>	ALTERABLE
ADDX	8,16,32	(DESTINATION) + (SOURCE) + X → DESTINATION	ADDX Dy, Dx ADDX –(Ay). –(Ax)	–
SUB	8,16,32	(DESTINATION) – (SOURCE) → DESTINATION	SUB Dn, <ea>	ALTERABLE MEMORY
			SUB <ea>, Dn	ALL
SUBA	16,32	(DESTINATION) – (SOURCE) → DESTINATION	SUBA <ea>, An	ALL
SUBI	8,16,32	(DESTINATION) – IMMEDIATE DATA → DESTINATION	SUBI # <data>, <ea>	DATA ALTERABLE
SUBQ	8,16,32	(DESTINATION) – IMMEDIATE DATA → DESTINATION	SUBQ # <data>, <ea>	ALTERABLE
SUBX	8,16,32	(DESTINATION) – (SOURCE) – X → DESTINATION	SUBX Dy, Dx SUBX –(Ay). –(Ax)	–

The SUBTRACT instructions are similar to the ADD instructions. The subtraction operation is

$$\text{Destination} - \text{Source} < \text{Destination}$$

EXAMPLE 14-15

Write a program to subtract the 6-byte number in $4000 from the 6-byte number in $3000 and store the result in $5000. The LSBs of the numbers are in $3005, $4005, and $5005, respectively.

SOLUTION

The minuend is in $3000 through $3005 and the subtrahend is in $4000 through $4005. Because the LSBs are in the highest locations, it would be most efficient to use the auto-predecrement mode. Three pointers are needed: a minuend pointer, a subtrahend pointer, and a destination pointer. The program runs in word mode and the pointers are each set one word higher than the data because the addresses will be decremented before they are used. The program uses the SUBX instructions, because borrows must be accommodated.

```
        MOVEA    #$4006,A4    Set subtrahend pointer
        MOVEA    #$5006,A5    Set destination pointer
        ADDI     #0,D3        This instruction does not
                              change D3, *but it clears
                              the X bit
LOOP    MOVE.W   -(A3),D3     Move minuend to D3
        MOVE.W   -(A4),D4     Move subtrahend to D4
        SUBX.W   D4,D3        Subtract: the difference
                              goes to D3
        MOVE.W   D3,-(A5)     Place result in memory
        CMPA.W   #$3000,A3    Done?
        BNE      LOOP         No if not equal to zero.
        ...      CONTINUE
```

14-10.6 ▼ BCD Instructions

To use Binary-Coded Decimal (BCD) instructions, the data must first be in BCD form with two BCD digits to a byte. There are three BCD instructions as shown in Table 14-11. They all operate only on bytes, so a length specification is unnecessary. They all use the X bit. Both the BCD add and subtract instructions (ABCD and SBCD) require that both the source and destination be either in data registers or in memory. If in memory, they can be accessed only in the auto-predecrement mode. The negate BCD (NBCD) produces the 10s complement of the destination if X is 0, and the 9s complement if X is 1 (see Section 4-8.4).

TABLE 14-11 BCD Operations

Instruction	Operand Syntax	Operand Size	Operation
ABCD	Dn,Dn −(An), −(An)	8 8	$Source_{10}$ + $Destination_{10}$ + X ♦ Destination
NBCD	<ea>	8	0 − $Destination_{10}$ − X ♦ Destination
PACK	−(An), −(An) #<data> Dn,Dn,#<data>	16 ♦ 8 16 ♦ 8	Unpackaged Source + Immediate Data ♦ Packed Destination
SBCD	Dn,Dn −(An), −(An)	8 8	$Destination_{10}$ − $Source_{10}$ − X ♦ Destination
UNPK	−(An),−(An) #<data> Dn,Dn,#<data>	8 ♦ 16 8 ♦ 16	Packed Source ♦ Unpacked Source Unpacked Source + Immediate Data ♦ Unpacked Destination

---

EXAMPLE 14-16

If D3 contains 46 in its LS byte, what is the result of the instruction NBCD D3?

SOLUTION

If X is clear, D3 will contain the 10s complement of 46, or 54, and if X is set it will contain the 9s complement, or 53.

14-10.7 ▼ Other Arithmetic Instructions

The other arithmetic instructions in the **68000** are given in Table 14-12. Most of them are very simple, but the MULTIPLY and DIVIDE instructions are more complex. The CLEAR instruction is used to clear a byte, word, or long word in a data register or memory. An address register cannot be used. It sets Z and clears N, C, and V of the condition codes. X is not affected.

The EXT instruction *extends* the sign of a byte in a data register to a word, or the sign of a word to a long word. To extend a byte to a word, for example, it places either 00 or $FF in the upper byte, depending on whether the MSB of the lower byte was 0 or 1.

The NEG instruction negates (2s complements) the contents of a data register or memory location by subtracting the contents from zero. The results affect all the condition code bits; the X bit is set the same as the C bit. The NEGX instruction is similar, but it subtracts 1 if X is set. It is used where multiple-word 2s complementing is required.

The MULTIPLY instructions multiply a word-length source by a word in the destination register. The result is a long word that fills the entire destination register. The source word can be in a data register, memory, or an immediate value. The destination must be a data register. The MULU instruction treats the words as unsigned, or positive integers, regardless of their MSB. The MULS (signed multiply) instruction treats the numbers as signed numbers.

TABLE 14-12 Other Arithmetic Instructions

Instruction	Operand size	Operation	Notation	Allowable effective address modes
EXT	16,32	(DESTINATION) Sign-EXTENDED → DESTINATION	EXT Dn	
MULS	16	(SOURCE) × (DESTINATION) → DESTINATION	MULS \<ea>, Dn	DATA
MULU	16	(SOURCE) × (DESTINATION) → DESTINATION	MULU \<ea>, Dn	DATA
NEG	8,16,32	0 − (DESTINATION) → DESTINATION	NEG \<ea>	DATA ALTERABLE
NEGX	8,16,32	0 − (DESTINATION) − X → DESTINATION	NEGX \<ea>	DATA ALTERABLE
CLR	8,16,32	0 → (DESTINATION)	CLR \<ea>	DATA ALTERABLE
DIVS	16	(DESTINATION) ÷ (SOURCE) → DESTINATION	DIVS \<ea>, Dn	DATA
DIVU	16	(DESTINATION) ÷ (SOURCE) → DESTINATION	DIVU \<ea>,Dn	DATA

EXAMPLE 14-17

The number in D4 is $FFFE. What number appears in D4 after the following instructions?

(a) MULU D4,D4
(b) MULS D4,D4

SOLUTION

This instruction squares the number. For part (a), where the numbers are treated as unsigned integers, the result is FFFC0004. For part (b), we simply have $(-2)^2$, and the result in D4 is 00000004.

The division instructions start with a long-word dividend in a data register. The divisor is the source word and can be in another data register, memory, or an immediate operand. The division places the 16-bit quotient in the lower word of the destination register and the 16-bit remainder in the upper word. The DIVU treats the numbers as unsigned and the DIVS assumes that the numbers are signed. Two possible errors can occur in a division operation:

1. The quotient may be longer than 16 bits.
2. The divisor may be zero.

The first condition sets the V bit and the second condition causes a *trap* (see Section 14-12.3).

EXAMPLE 14-18

If the number in D4 is 1D, what appears in D4 after a DIVU #4,D4 instruction?

SOLUTION

The results of dividing 1D $(29)_{10}$ are a quotient of 7 and a remainder of 1. The number in D4 is, therefore, 00010007.

14-10.8 ▼ COMPARE and TEST Instructions

The COMPARE instructions, shown in Table 14-13, all subtract the source from the destination and then discard the results. They do *not* change the contents of any memory locations or registers, but they do affect the N, V, Z, and C condition codes. *They do not affect the X bit.* The CMP instruction must have a data register as the destination, or minuend for the subtraction. The CMPA instruction uses an address register for the minuend. The CMPA instruction has already been used in Examples 14-12 and 14-15.

The CMPI can be used to compare an immediate value with memory or a register. The CMPM compares two memory locations, but each location must be specified in the auto-postincrement mode.

EXAMPLE 14-19

Write a program segment to compare the contents of $1000 and $2000.

SOLUTION

The segment is

```
MOVEA  #$1000,A3
MOVEA  #$2000,A4
CMPM.B (A3)+,(A4)+
```

At the end of the segment, the contents of A3 and A4 will be $1001 and $2001. The C bit will be set if the absolute value of the contents of $1000 is greater than the contents of $2000.

The TEST instruction simply subtracts zero from a register or memory location and sets the N and Z bits accordingly. It can be used to determine the characteristics of the destination (is it positive, negative, or zero?).

TABLE 14-13 COMPARE and TEST Instructions

Instruction	Operand size	Operation	Notation	Allowable effective address modes
CMP	8,16,32	(OPERAND2) – (OPERAND1)	CMP ⟨ea⟩, Dn	ALL
CMPA	16,32	(OPERAND2) – (OPERAND1)	CMPA ⟨ea⟩, An	ALL
CMPI	8,16,32	(OPERAND) – IMMEDIATE DATA	CMPI # ⟨data⟩,⟨ea⟩	DATA ALTERABLE
CMPM	8,16,32	(OPERAND2) – (OPERAND1)	CMPM (Ay) + ,(Ax) +	
TST	8,16,32	(DESTINATION) – 0 (DESTINATION) TESTED → CC	TST ⟨ea⟩	DATA ALTERABLE

14-10.9 ▼ BIT TEST Instructions

The BIT TEST group of instructions is given in Table 14-14. The function of the BTST instruction is to test a bit in a data register or memory, and set or clear the Z flag if the bit selected is 0 or 1. All other bits of the CCR are unaffected. There are two allowable forms of the BTST instruction:

```
BTST      Dn,<EA>
BTST      #<data>,<EA>
```

In either form <EA> is the effective address of the byte or long word being tested. If <EA> specifies a memory address, only bits 0 through 7 can be tested. This is a byte-length instruction. If <EA> is a data register, however, any of its 32 bits can be tested. This is the long-word form of the instruction.

The first form of the instruction is sometimes called the *dynamic* form. The number of the bit to be tested is contained in Dn. The second form is called the *static* form. The number of the bit to be tested is specified immediately.

The BSET instruction is identical to the BTST instruction except that it sets the bit after testing it. After a BSET instruction, the bit is a 1, but the Z flag gives the status of the bit before it was changed. The BCLR works like the BSET instruction, except that the bit is cleared after the test, and the BCHG instruction also works the same way except that the bit is changed (inverted) after the test. These three instructions can also be used to set or clear a bit in a location, as Example 14-20 shows.

TABLE 14-14 Bit-Manipulation Instructions

Instruction	Operand Syntax	Operand Size	Operation
BCHG	Dn,<ea> #<data>,<ea>	8, 32 8, 32	~ (<Bit Number> of Destination) ◆ Z ◆ Bit of Destination
BCLR	Dn,<ea> #<data>,<ea>	8, 32 8, 32	~ (<Bit Number> of Destination) ◆ Z; 0 ◆ Bit of Destination
BSET	Dn,<ea> #<data>,<ea>	8, 32 8, 32	~ (<Bit Number> of Destination) ◆ Z; 1 ◆ Bit of Destination
BTST	Dn,<ea> #<data>,<ea>	8, 32 8, 32	~ (<Bit Number> of Destination) ◆ Z

EXAMPLE 14-20

Bits 0 through 6 of location $2000 contain an ASCII character. Write a program to set bit 7, if necessary, so that the parity of the byte is odd (it contains an odd number of 1s).

SOLUTION

The following program will set the parity:

```
        MOVEA   #$2000,A4
        CLR.B   D3
        BSET    #7,(A4)     Set the parity bit
LOOP    BTST    D3,(A4)     Test a bit in $2000
        BEQ     CONT        If the tested bit is a 1,
        BCHG    #7,(A4)     change the parity bit.
CONT    ADDQ    #1,D3       Increment D3 to get the next
                            bit
        CMP.B   #7,D3       Done?

        BNE     LOOP
        ....                CONTINUE
```

The program starts by setting the parity bit, bit 7 of $2000, to 1. It then tests bit 0 of the byte in location $2000 and changes the parity bit if the tested bit is a 1. It then increments D3, so it will test bit 1 of $2000 on its second time through the loop. This continues until the program has tested bits 0 through 6 and changed the parity bit each time it finds a 1. Note that the parity bit was originally set to a 1 because if all the bits tested were 0, there would be no changes. It should be a 1 in this case.

14-10.10 ▼ SHIFT and ROTATE Instructions

The SHIFT and ROTATE instructions in the **68000** are shown in Table 14-15, and the diagrams in the table show what each instruction is doing. The Arithmetic Shift Left (ASL) brings 0s into the vacated LSBs, while the Arithmetic Shift Right (ASR) replicates the MSB to preserve the sign. The logical shifts, LSL and LSR, bring 0s into the vacated positions. All the SHIFT instructions put the last bit shifted out into both C and X.

The ROTATE instructions (ROL, ROR) simply rotate the operand, placing the last bit both in the other end of the operand and in the carry flag. The rotate-with-extend instructions (ROXL, ROXR) rotate the combination of the operand and the X flag. The last bit shifted out also goes into the carry flag.

The operand to be shifted or rotated can be in a data register or in memory. If the operand is in a data register, a single shift or rotate instruction can cause it to be shifted several places instead of just one place as in the **6800**. There are three forms of the shift and rotate instruction:

TABLE 14-15   SHIFT and ROTATE Instructions

Instruction	Operand size	Operation	Notation	Allowable effective address modes
ASL ASR	8,16,32 / 16	ASL / ASR	ASd Dx, Dy	—
			ASd # ⟨data⟩, Dy	—
			ASd ⟨ea⟩	MEMORY ALTERABLE
LSL LSR	8,16,32 / 16	LSL / LSR	LSd Dx, Dy	—
			LSd # ⟨data⟩, Dy	—
			LSd ⟨ea⟩	MEMORY ALTERABLE
ROL ROR	8,16,32 / 16	ROL / ROR	ROd Dx, Dy	—
			ROd # ⟨data⟩, Dy	—
			ROd ⟨ea⟩	MEMORY ALTERABLE
ROXL ROXR	8,16,32 / 16	ROXL / ROXR	ROXd Dx, Dy	—
			ROXd # ⟨data⟩, Dy	—
			ROXd ⟨ea⟩	MEMORY ALTERABLE

1. **ASL.X Dx,Dy.** This is the dynamic form. The number of shifts is contained in data register X and the data to be shifted is contained in data register Y. An example would be ASL.B D2,D3. If D2 contained a 4, the LS byte of D3 would be shifted left by 4 bits.

2. **ASL.X #n,Dy.** This is the static or immediate form. The immediate number (n) specifies the number of bits to be shifted.

3. **ASL.W <EA>.** This is the memory form. The contents of <EA> are shifted. This form is restricted to a 1-bit shift and to word size.

In the previous examples ASL was used for illustration only. Any shift or rotate instruction operates similarly.

EXAMPLE 14-21

If data register D3 contains C5 and X is 1, what will D3 contain after each of the following instructions?

(a) `ASL.B    #3,D3`

(b) `ASR.B    #3,D3`

(c) `LSL.B    #3,D3`

(d) `LSR.B    #3,D3`

(e) ROL.B   #3,D3
(f) ROR.B   #3,D3
(g) ROXL.B   #3,D3
(h) ROXR.B   #3,D3

SOLUTION

The results are:

(a) 28
(b) F8
(c) 28
(d) 18
(e) 2E
(f) B8
(g) 2F
(h) 78

The results are best explained by referring to Fig. 14-19. It also shows the contents of C and X after each instruction.

```
                              C    5
                            ⏞    ⏞
                            11000101      Original Data

ASL.B  #3,D3   X=0          00101000    < 3 Bit Shift
               C=0

                                         X=1
ASR.B  #3,D3                11111000    C=1 > 3 Bit Shift (sign preserved)

LSL.B  #3,D3   X=0          00101000    < 3 Bit Shift
               C=0

LSR.B  #3,D3                00011000    X=1 > 3 Bit Shift
                                        C=1

ROL.B  #3,D3   C=0          00101110    < 3 Bit Rotate

ROR.B  #3,D3                10111000    C=1 > 3 Bit Rotate

ROXL.B #3,D3   X=0          00101111    < 3 Bit Rotate Through X
               C=0

ROXR.B #3,D3                01111000    X=1 > 3 Bit Rotate Through X
                                        C=1
```

Figure 14-19   Action of the C and X bits for Example 14-21.

EXAMPLE 14-22

There are two BCD digits in location $2000. This is packed BCD. For example, the digits might be 57. The ASCII equivalent of these digits is to be put in locations $3000 and $3001 in order to be sent to a terminal. The ASCII equivalent of a digit is obtained by prefixing the digit with a 3, so in the example $3000 and $3001 will contain $35 and $37, respectively. Write a program to translate the packed BCD to ASCII.

SOLUTION

The program proceeds as follows:

```
MOVE.B    $2000,D3     Move data to D3
LSR.B     #4,D3        Shift upper digit to lower
ORI.B     #$30,D3      Add the prefix of 3
MOVE.B    D3,$3000     Store data
MOVE.B    $2000,D3     Move data to D3
ANDI.B    #$F,D3       Zero upper byte; keep lower byte

ORI.B     #$30,D3      Add prefix
MOVE.B    D3,$3001     Store data
```

In this program we have chosen to use absolute addressing instead of address registers.

14-10.11 ▼ Program Control Instructions

The program control instructions are shown in Table 14-16. They will be discussed in order of simplicity rather than in alphabetical order as they are presented in the table.

The NOP (No OPeration) instruction (4E 71) does nothing. After encountering it, the program simply goes to the next instruction. NOPs can be used to fill voids in programs, which might be left when an instruction is deleted. They can also be used to increase the time of a time-delay loop (see Section 9-9). Some programmers deliberately write NOPs into their code at various places so that if an instruction has to be added during debugging, it can replace the NOPs.

The Jump instruction is of the form JMP <EA>.It loads the PC with the effective address. Only the control addressing modes are allowed. The effective address may be in an address register or in the PC. Indexing and displacement are allowed, but predecrementing and postincrementing are not.

The Jump to SubRoutine (JSR <EA>) is similar to the JMP. The addressing modes are the same. During a JSR the 4 bytes containing the address of the next instruction are put on the stack, and the stack pointer (A7) is decremented by 4.

The ReTurn from Subroutine (RTS) is the converse of the JSR. It pulls the return address off the stack, places it in the PC, and increments the stack pointer by 4 bytes. The JSR and RTS are similar to the **6800** instructions (see Section 5-5).

TABLE 14-16 Program Control Instructions

Instruction	Operand Syntax	Operand Size	Operation
Integer and Floating-Point Conditional			
Bcc, FBcc	<label>	8, 16, 32	If Condition True, Then PC + d_n ➡ PC
DBcc, FDBcc	Dn,<label>	16	If Condition False, Then Dn − 1 ➡ Dn If Dn ≠ −1, Then PC + d_n ➡ PC
Scc, FScc	<ea>	8	If Condition True, Then 1's ➡ Destination; Else 0's ➡ Destination
Unconditional			
BRA	<label>	8, 16, 32	PC + d_n ➡ PC
BSR	<label>	8, 16, 32	SP − 4 ➡ SP; PC ➡ (SP); PC + d_n ➡ PC
JMP	<ea>	none	Destination ➡ PC
JSR	<ea>	none	SP − 4 ➡ SP; PC ➡ (SP); Destination ➡ PC
NOP	none	none	PC + 2 ➡ PC (Integer Pipeline Synchronized)
FNOP	none	none	PC + 4 ➡ PC (FPU Pipeline Synchronized)
Returns			
RTD	#<data>	16	(SP) ➡ PC; SP + 4 + dn ➡ SP
RTR	none	none	(SP) ➡ CCR; SP + 2 ➡ SP; (SP)➡PC; SP + 4➡SP
RTS	none	none	(SP) ➡ PC; SP + 4 ➡ SP
Test Operand			
TST	<ea>	8, 16, 32	Set Integer Condition Codes
FTST	<ea> FPn	B, W, L, S, D, X, P X	Set Floating-Point Condition Codes

Letters cc in the integer instruction mnemonics Bcc, DBcc, and Scc specify testing one of the following conditions:

CC—Carry clear	GE—Greater than or equal
LS—Lower or same	PL—Plus
CS—Carry set	GT—Greater than
LT—Less than	T—Always true*
EQ—Equal	HI—Higher
MI—Minus	VC—Overflow clear
F—Never true*	LE—Less than or equal
NE—Not equal	VS—Overflow set

*Not applicable to the Bcc instructions.

The ReTurn and Restore condition codes (RTR) instruction assumes that the condition codes of the program were pushed onto the stack immediately after a JSR or BSR was encountered [i.e., MOVE CCR –(A7) is the first instruction of the subroutine]. The RTR first pulls the condition codes off the stack, and then the PC.

The BRAnch instruction (BRA) operates like the **6800** BRA, in that it adds a displacement to the PC and branches there. The displacement can be either 8 bits (short branch) or 16 bits (long branch). The assembler form is BRA <label>, and assemblers will calculate the value of the displacement. In TUTOR, one can use BRA <$address> because it cannot handle labels. Most of the previous examples used branch instructions.

The Branch to SubRoutine (BSR) instruction preserves the address of the next instruction on the stack before branching to a subroutine.

The Bcc is the Branch-on-Condition-Code instruction. Here cc represents a condition code as shown in Table 14-17. This is just a different way to represent the Conditional branch instructions. They function the same as in the **6800** (BNE, BEQ, etc.) except that the instruction format allows for a 16-bit displacement, if desired. If the 8-bit displacement field is set to zero, an additional word (16-bit) is used to designate the offset.

TABLE 14-17 Conditional Tests

Mnemonic	Condition	Encoding	Test
T*	True	0000	1
F*	False	0001	0
HI	High	0010	$\bar{C} \wedge \bar{Z}$
LS	Low or Same	0011	$C \vee Z$
CC(HI)	Carry Clear	0100	$\bar{C}$
CS(LO)	Carry Set	0101	C
NE	Not Equal	0110	$\bar{Z}$
EQ	Equal	0111	Z
VC	Overflow Clear	1000	$\bar{V}$
VS	Overflow Set	1001	V
PL	Plus	1010	$\bar{N}$
MI	Minus	1011	N
GE	Greater or Equal	1100	$N \wedge V \vee \bar{N} \wedge \bar{V}$
LT	Less Than	1101	$N \wedge \bar{V} \vee \bar{N} \wedge V$
GT	Greater Than	1110	$N \wedge V \wedge \bar{Z} \vee \bar{N} \wedge \bar{V} \wedge \bar{Z}$
LE	Less or Equal	1111	$Z \vee N \wedge \bar{V} \vee \bar{N} \wedge V$

NOTES:

$\bar{N}$ = Logical Not N
$\bar{V}$ = Logical Not V
$\bar{Z}$ = Logical Not Z
*Not available for the Bcc instruction.

The Set-according-to-condition (Scc) sets an entire byte to all 1s if the condition specified by cc is true, and to all 0s if it is false. The condition table is the same as for the Bcc instruction. The byte can be in a data register or memory location.

Other instructions in Table 14-16, such as RTE, TRAP, and TRAPV, are discussed in Sections 14-12.4 and 14-12.6.

14-10.12 ▼ Other 68000 Instructions

There are three other **68000** instructions that do not fit conveniently into categories that have been discussed in this section. The test condition Decrement and Branch (DBcc) is a powerful instruction for controlling loops. Again cc is a *condition* and Table 14-17 shows the conditions for this instruction. The syntax of the DBcc is DBcc Dn,<label>. It uses a data register, Dn, that contains a loop count. Dn, specified by the DBcc, must be word sized.

The instruction operates as follows:

1. It first tests the condition. If the condition is true, the program falls through (does not branch).
2. If the condition is false, it decrements Dn.
3. If Dn now equals –1, the program falls through. Otherwise, it branches to <label> (loops back).

A program that uses the DBeq is given in Example 14-23.

EXAMPLE 14-23

There is a block of 20 words of data starting at location $2000. Write a program to move them to a block starting at $3000 provided that none of the words is equal to zero. If a zero is found, terminate the block move.

SOLUTION

The list must be examined, a byte at a time, to determine if a zero occurs. This suggests the use of a postincrementing register.

```
         MOVE.W    #20,D2        Put count into D2
         MOVEA.L   #$2000,A0     Put source address in A0
         MOVEA.L   #$3000,A1     Put destination in A1
LOOP     MOVE.W    (A0)+,(A1)+   Move word and increment pointers
         DBEQ      D2,LOOP       Branch if not zero and D2 not = -1
HERE     TST.W     D2            Does D2 = -1?
         BPL       FOUND         No; a word = zero was found
         BRA       *             End of list; none found
FOUND    BRA       *             Save it and exit
```

The DBcc instruction assumes a branch displacement of -4 (FFFC), and therefore, the branch must be to a one-word instruction preceding the DBcc instruction. After the word is moved, the DBeq instruction tests the Z bit, and if it is not set, and if D2 is not = to -1, the program branches to LOOP. The label HERE is reached either because a zero value has been found or because D2 = -1. D2 is then tested to determine which condition exists. If D2 does equal -1, the list has been exhausted and no zero was found. Then the program drops through the BPL and continues.

To test this routine with the ECB, BRA * (branch to self) has been used. After stepping through the instructions, they can be allowed to execute by placing breakpoints at these branch addresses. Also note that this instruction has been improved in the **68010** and this improvement is discussed in Chapter 15.

The Load Effective Address (LEA) instruction calculates the effective address <EA> for an instruction and stores it in an address register instead of using it as an address. The instruction is long word only (because it calculates a 24-bit address) and the destination must be an address register. The LEA can be used to preserve the results of a complex address calculation (such as address register indirect with indexing and displacement) which may be used more than once.

EXAMPLE 14-24

What does the instruction LEA $7A(A2,D2.W),A3 do if address register A2 contains $22 and data register D2 contains $ABCD0003?

SOLUTION

First the LEA calculates the effective address. In this example the index with offset address mode is used. The effective address is the sum of the offset (7A), the contents of A2 (22), and the word in D2 (0003). The result, $9F, is placed in address register A3.

EXAMPLE 14-25

The proper use of the LEA can lead to more efficient coding. Suppose that we are required to transfer a block of 100 words of data from a table located by using an address of $2000 in A2, with D1 as an index register, to location $3000 (in A1).

SOLUTION

One way to do this might be:

```
        MOVE.W   #4, D7           Set up loop counter
        MOVE.W   #$2000,A2        Set up base address
        MOVE.W   #$3000,A1        Set up destination
LOOP    MOVE.W   (A2,D1.W),(A1)+  Move data
        ADDQ.W   #2,A2            Increment source
                                  address
        DBF.L    D7,LOOP          Loop until data ends
        ....     ......
```

where the DBF is the Decrement-and-Branch-if-False instruction. The DBF is another example of the DBcc instruction. It is always false, however, so the DBF instruction loops back continually until the data register it references decrements to −1. The same block transfer program might be written

```
        MOVE.W   #4, D7           Set μP loop count
        MOVE.W   #$2000,A2        Set μP base address
        MOVE.W   #$3000,A1        Set μP destination
        LEA.L    (A2,D1.W),A3     Put effective address
                                  in A3
LOOP    MOVE.W   (A3)+,(A1)+      Move Data
        DBF.L    D7,LOOP          Until count = -1
        ....     ......
```

The second program is more efficient because it uses many fewer cycles. It calculates the effective address only once, using the LEA, and stores it in A3. The first program has to calculate the effective address each time around the loop. The second program loop also includes one less instruction.

The Push-Effective-Address (PEA) instruction works like the LEA except that it pushes the effective address onto the stack instead of into an address register. Figure 14-20 shows how the LEA and PEA instructions can replace three and four instructions, respectively.

14-11 ▼ 68000, 68008, AND 68010 PINOUTS AND SIGNALS

In addition to the programming aspects of the **6800** family, an engineer interested in system design must understand the many new hardware features of the **68000, 68008,** and **68010.** (The **68010** is included here because its pinouts are the same as the **68000** and **68008.**)

```
Motorola M68000 ASM Version  1.90 BILL:0.    LEA.SA 08/06/87 11:55:32

   1                            LLEN      100
   2        00001000            ORG       $1000
   3                     *
   4        0000000A     OFFSET  EQU       10
   5                     *
   6                     * COMPARISON OF LEA AND PEA
   7                     *
   8                     * INPUT : (A0.L) = ADDRESS OF TABLE
   9                     *         (D0.W) = INDEX INTO TABLE
  10                     *         OFFSET = BYTE WITHIN ELEMENT OF PREDEFINED TABLE
  11                     *
  12                     * OUTPUT : (A1.L) = EFFECTIVE ADDRESS (LEA)
  13                     *
  14                     * OPERATION OF THE LEA TO LOAD THE ADDRESS OF AN ELEMENT
  15                     *
  16 00001000 43F0000A           LEA       OFFSET(A0,D0.W),A1
  17                     *
  18                     * LOAD THE ADDRESS OF AN ELEMENT WITHOUT USING LEA
  19                     *
  20 00001004 2248               MOVE.L    A0,A1
  21 00001006 D2C0               ADDA.W    D0,A1
  22 00001008 D2FC000A           ADDA.W    #OFFSET,A1
  23                     *
  24                     * OPERATION OF THE PEA TO SAVE AN ADDRESS
  25                     *
  26 0000100C 4870000A           PEA       OFFSET(A0,D0.W)
  27                     *
  28                     * SAVE AN ADDRESS WITHOUT USING THE PEA
  29                     *
  30 00001010 2248               MOVE.L    A0,A1
  31 00001012 D2C0               ADDA.W    D0,A1
  32 00001014 D2FC000A           ADDA.W    #OFFSET,A1
  33 00001018 2F09               MOVE.L    A1,-(SP)
  34                     *
  35                            END

****** TOTAL ERRORS     0--    ****** TOTAL WARNINGS     0--

SYMBOL TABLE LISTING

SYMBOL NAME     SECT    VALUE        SYMBOL NAME     SECT    VALUE

OFFSET                  0000000A
```

Figure 14-20 Comparison of LEA and PEA instructions. From Thomas Harmon and Barbara Lawson, *The MC68000 Microprocessor Family,* Prentice Hall, 1985. (Copyright 1985 by Prentice Hall Inc., Englewood Cliffs, New Jersey.)

The pin connections and signals can be functionally organized into groups as shown in Fig. 14-21. The following paragraphs provide a description of these signals and a reference (if applicable) to other paragraphs that contain more detail. The readers are advised that this data is only brief and they should refer to the advanced information booklets listed in Section 14-17 for added details on each processor type.

14-11.1 ▼ Address Bus (A1 through A23)

Although the Address Registers in the **68000** are 32 bits wide, only 24 bits are used, thus providing a bus capable of addressing 16 megabytes of memory. Because the memory is organized as words or long words, only even addresses are needed. Therefore, line A0 is not provided on the IC package and the address bus actually has only 23 lines. It is unidirectional and three-state and provides the addresses for bus operation for all cycles except interrupt cycles. During interrupt cycles, address lines A1, A2, and A3 provide information about what level of interrupt is being serviced while lines A4 through A23 are all set to a logic HIGH.

14-11.2 ▼ Data Bus (D0 through D15)

The 16-bit bidirectional three-state bus is the general-purpose data path. It can transfer and accept data in either word or byte lengths. During an interrupt acknowledge cycle (see Section 14-13.3), the external device supplies the vector number on data lines D0 through D7.

14-11.3 ▼ Asynchronous Bus Control

The **68000** address and data lines are not multiplexed and operate independently, which provides superior performance compared to multiplexed buses. A major innovation for the **68000** family is that the data bus is asynchronous. This eliminates the need to

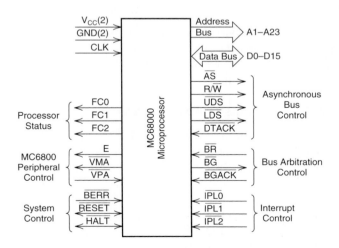

Figure 14-21 **68000** Signal lines.

provide synchronizing signals around the system. The use of handshaking signals, such as Data Transfer ACKnowledge (DTACK), allows devices and memories with large variations in response time to be connected to the processor bus. The processor can wait an arbitrary amount of time until the device or memory signals that the transfer is complete. If no device responds or if the access is invalid, external control logic asserts BERR (see Section 14-11.8) or BERR and HALT, to abort or retry the cycle. This μP bus architecture is also convenient for connecting to system buses of varying lengths.

Asynchronous data transfers are handled using the following control signals:

- Address Strobe (AS)
- Read/Write (R/W)
- Upper and Lower Data Strobes (UDS, LDS)
- Data Transfer ACKnowledge (DTACK)
- Bus ERRor (BERR)
- Halt (HALT)

These signals, shown in the Asynchronous Bus Control and System Control groups in Fig. 14-21 are explained in the following paragraphs.

14-11.4 ▼ Address Strobe

The Address Strobe (AS) signal indicates that there is a valid address on the address bus. It is one of five lines that make up the asynchronous bus control function shown in Fig. 14-21.

14-11.5 ▼ Read/Write

The Read/Write (RW) signal defines the data bus transfer as a read or write cycle. A write signal is a logic 0. The R/W signal also works in conjunction with the data strobes, as explained in the following paragraph.

14-11.6 ▼ Upper and Lower Data Strobe

The Upper and Lower **Data Strobe** (UDS, LDS) lines control the flow of data on the data bus, as shown in Table 14-18. When the R/W line is high, the processor will read from the data bus as indicated. When the R/W line is low, the processor will write to the data bus as shown.

14-11.7 ▼ Data Transfer Acknowledge

The Data Transfer ACKnowledge (DTACK) input indicates that the data transfer is completed. When the processor initiates a memory cycle, it must wait for DTACK to terminate it. Each memory or peripheral in the system must have some means of generating DTACK. Figure 14-22 shows the circuit used in the Educational Computer Board for the TUTOR ROMs. It is simply an **LS175** IC counter. It is wired to provide a delay sufficient for the data to be stable (based on the access time of the parts used). The counter is reset each time the ROMs are enabled and is clocked by the 8-MHz clock. When the processor recognizes DTACK during a read cycle, data is latched and the bus cycle terminated.

TABLE 14-18 Data Strobe Control of Data Bus

UDS	LDS	R/W	D8-D15	D0-D7
High	High	—	No Valid Data	No Valid Data
Low	Low	High	Valid Data Bits 8-15	Valid Data Bits 0-7
High	Low	High	No Valid Data	Valid Data Bits 0-7
Low	High	High	Valid Data Bits 8-15	No Valid Data
Low	Low	Low	Valid Data Bits 8-15	Valid Data Bits 0-7
High	Low	Low	Valid Data Bits 0-7*	Valid Data Bits 0-7
Low	High	Low	Valid Data Bits 8-15	Valid Data Bits 8-15*

*These conditions are a result of current implementation and
may not appear on future devices.

14-11.8 ▼ Bus Error

In a bus architecture that requires a handshake from an external device such as the asynchronous bus used in the **68000** family, the handshake may not always occur. A bus error input is provided to terminate a bus cycle in error when the expected DTACK signal does not arrive. Different devices within the same system may require different maximum-response times. External circuitry can be provided to assert the bus error signal (BERR) after the appropriate delay following the assertion of AS.

EXAMPLE 14-26

Explain, conceptually, how a circuit to generate BERR might work.

SOLUTION

The circuit might use a counter, similar to the **74LS175** in Fig. 14-22. The appearance of address strobe could start the counter, and DTACK should clear the counter. If no device responds, so that DTACK does not occur after a predetermined amount of time, the counter will reach a specified count. If it does this, it could generate BERR, to indicate to the **68000** that no device is responding to its bus request.

14-11.9 ▼ HALT

HALT performs a halt/run/single-step operation similar to the halt operation of a **6800.** When HALT is asserted by an external device, the processor halts and remains halted as long as the signal remains asserted.

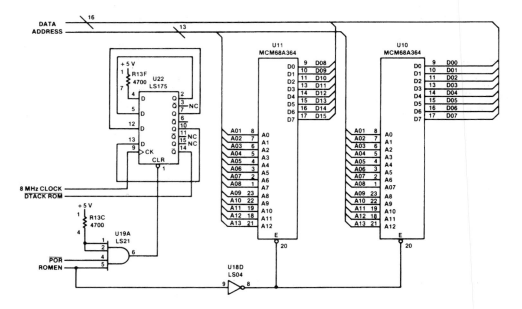

Figure 14-22   ROM DTACK schematic.

While the processor is halted, the address and data bus signals are placed in the high-impedance state. Bus Arbitration is performed as usual. Should a bus error occur while HALT is asserted, the processor retries the preceding cycle using the same function codes, address, and data (for a write operation).

The HALT line is bidirectional, and when the processor stops executing instructions, such as in a double bus fault condition, the HALT line is driven by the processor to indicate to external devices that the processor has stopped.

14-11.10 ▼ Bus Arbitration Control

Another innovative feature of the **68000** family processors is *Bus Arbitration.* In a multiprocessor system some means is needed to transfer control when another processor or a Direct Memory Access (DMA) device such as a Disk Controller needs to access the common bus. Any number of μPs or DMA devices can be installed on the system bus provided that *bus arbitration* is used to allow them to access the bus, one at a time, in an orderly fashion. Bus Arbitration is controlled by three signal lines: bus request, bus grant, and bus grant acknowledge (explained below). These signals are interconnected in a bus arbitration circuit to determine which device will be the **bus master** (the bus device that currently is transferring data to or from the data bus).

14-11.11 ▼ Bus Request

The **Bus Request** (BR) input is wire-ORed with all other devices that could be bus masters. When asserted, this input indicates to the processor that some other device wishes to become the *bus master.*

14-11.12 ▼ Bus Grant

The **Bus Grant** (BG) output signal line, when true (LOW), indicates to all other potential bus master devices that the processor will release bus control at the end of the current bus cycle.

14-11.13 ▼ Bus Grant Acknowledge

When the **Bus Grant ACKnowledge** (BGACK) input is true (LOW), it indicates that some device has become the bus master. A device that is making a request to become a bus master should not assert BGACK until the following four conditions are met:

1. A BG has been received.
2. AS is inactive, which indicates that the μP is not using the bus.
3. DTACK is inactive, which indicates that neither memory nor peripherals are using the bus.
4. BGACK is inactive, which indicates that no other device is still claiming bus mastership.

14-11.14 ▼ Peripheral Control

When the **68000** was introduced, there were very few 16-bit peripheral ICs that could be used with it to make up a system. To avoid waiting for the development of other 16-bit devices, an 8- bit interface was included in the design. Devices such as the ACIA or PIA from the **6800** family, and the other **6800** peripherals described in previous chapters, could then be used. The **68000, 68008,** and **68010** μPs all have provisions for using 8-bit peripheral ICs. Many 16-bit peripherals are available now and new ones are continually being developed.

The interface is specifically designed to work with the **6800** family of peripherals, and three pins of the **68000** have been dedicated to provide the required signals. These are

- Enable (E)
- Valid Memory Address (VMA)
- Valid Peripheral Address (VPA)

Enable corresponds to phase 2 of the **6800** clock. The bus frequency is one-tenth of the incoming **68000** clock frequency. The timing of E allows 1-MHz peripherals to be used with 8-MHz **68000**s. Enable has a 60/40 duty cycle; that is, it is low for six input clocks and high for four input clocks.

VMA is used by **6800** μP peripherals. It should be noted that the **68000** VMA signal is active LOW, contrasted with the active HIGH **6800** VMA. This allows the **68000** to put its buses in the high-impedance state on DMA requests without inadvertently selecting the peripherals.

VPA is an input signal that tells the **68000** μP that the address on the bus is the address of a **6800** device (or an area reserved for **6800** devices) and that the bus should conform to the phase 2 transfer characteristics of the **6800**. A valid Peripheral Address is derived by decoding the address bus, conditioned by Address Strobe.

Figure 14-23 shows a portion of the ECB circuit that is used to interface to the ACIAs and the **68230** Parallel Interface and Timer (PIT). Gate U45C is drawn like an

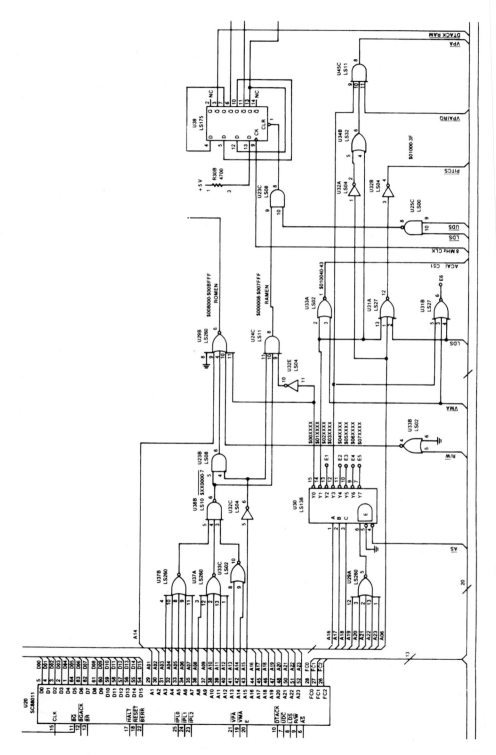

Figure 14-23 Schematic of the **68000** interface showing address decoding.

AND gate, but since the signals are negative true, it functions as an OR gate. If the address of a peripheral appears on the address lines, VPA should go low. This means that if an address for the ACIA appears on Y1 of U30, or, the address for the PIT is present, OR the VPAIRQ signal goes true (low), a true VPA signal will result. When the processor sees it, it will produce a VMA signal. Gate U33A will then generate the chip select (CS1) for the ACIA's OR gate; U31A will do the same thing for the **68230** (PIT). When the VPA is asserted, the **68000** will assert VMA and thereby complete a normal **6800** read cycle. The processor will then use an internally generated autovector that is a function of the interrupt being serviced (see Section 14-13).

14-12 ▼ EXCEPTION PROCESSING

As mentioned in Section 14-4, the exception processing state is entered when the processor is reset, experiences an interrupt, executes a trap instruction, encounters a bus error, or has some other exceptional condition. Exception processing is designed to provide an efficient *context switch* so that the processor may handle unusual conditions quickly and gracefully. A context switch is the name given to the process of saving all the registers and flags that define the state of the system at the moment, and replacing them with values that will cause the processor to process a different portion of the program. A context switch is caused by an exception, and another context switch occurs when returning to the main program after an exception. The second context switch basically restores the registers to the state they were in when the exception occurred. All of the causes of exception processing are described in the following sections.

14-12.1 ▼ Entering the Exception State

Before discussing the details of interrupts, traps, tracing, and reset, a general description of exception processing is in order. After an exception is initiated, its processing occurs in four steps:

1. A temporary internal copy of the status register is made, and the S bit is set.
2. The Exception Vector is determined.
3. The current processor context is saved.
4. A new context is obtained and the processor switches to instruction processing.

14-12.2 ▼ Exception Vectors

Exception Vectors are addresses of routines that will handle exceptions. They are kept in prescribed locations for each type of exception. Thus the processor can fetch the proper address to respond to a particular exception. Table 14-19 shows the table of exception vector addresses, and Fig. 14-24 shows the vector format. All exception vectors are two words in length except for the reset vector, which is four words (see Section 14-13.8).

When an interrupt is caused by a peripheral, it provides an 8-bit vector number to the processor on data bus lines D0 through D7, as a part of the interrupt acknowledge cycle. This is shown in Fig. 14-25. When multiplied by 4 (by left shifting two bit positions), and the upper order bits are filled with zeros to obtain a full 32-bit address, this number becomes the address of an exception vector as shown in Fig. 14-26. Vector numbers are generated internally or externally, depending on the cause of the exception, as explained in Section 14-13.3.

TABLE 14-19 Exception Vector Assignment

Vector Number(s)	Vector Offset (Hex)	Assignment
0	000	Reset Initial Interrupt Stack Pointer
1	004	Reset Initial Program Counter
2	008	Access Fault
3	00C	Address Error
4	010	Illegal Instruction
5	014	Integer Divide by Zero
6	018	CHK, CHK2 Instruction
7	01C	FTRAPcc, TRAPcc, TRAPV Instructions
8	020	Privilege Violation
9	024	Trace
10	028	Line 1010 Emulator (Unimplemented A-Line Opcode)
11	02C	Line 1111 Emulator (Unimplemented F-Line Opcode)
12	030	(Unassigned, Reserved)
13	034	Coprocessor Protocol Violation
14	038	Format Error
15	03C	Uninitialized Interrupt
16–23	040–05C	(Unassigned, Reserved)
24	060	Spurious Interrupt
25	064	Level 1 Interrupt Autovector
26	068	Level 2 Interrupt Autovector
27	06C	Level 3 Interrupt Autovector
28	070	Level 4 Interrupt Autovector
29	074	Level 5 Interrupt Autovector
30	078	Level 6 Interrupt Autovector
31	07C	Level 7 Interrupt Autovector
32–47	080–0BC	TRAP #0 – 15 Instruction Vectors
48	0C0	FP Branch or Set on Unordered Condition
49	0C4	FP Inexact Result
50	0C8	FP Divide by Zero
51	0CC	FP Underflow
52	0D0	FP Operand Error
53	0D4	FP Overflow
54	0D8	FP Signaling NAN
55	0DC	FP Unimplemented Data Type (Defined for MC68040)
56	0E0	MMU Configuration Error
57	0E4	MMU Illegal Operation Error
58	0E8	MMU Access Level Violation Error
59–63	0EC–0FC	(Unassigned, Reserved)
64–255	100–3FC	User Defined Vectors (192)

14-12.3 ▼ Instruction Traps

Traps are exceptions caused by *instructions.* They cause the program to depart from the normal sequence of executing instructions and go to a t*rap handler routine,* which is the same as an interrupt service routine. The function of the trap handler is to respond to the abnormal condition or instruction that caused the trap. A TRAP instruction has a vector number associated with it that determines the routine the processor will execute in response to the trap.

Exception processing for traps follows the steps outlined previously. A vector number is internally generated for the TRAP #n instruction. Part of the vector number comes

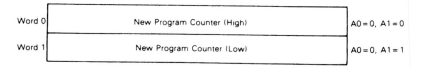

Figure 14-24 Exception Vector format.

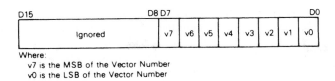

Where:
  v7 is the MSB of the Vector Number
  v0 is the LSB of the Vector Number

Figure 14-25   Peripheral vector number format.

from the instruction itself. The trap vector offset, the Program Counter, and the copy of the Status Register are saved on the Supervisor Stack. The value of the program counter saved is the address of the instruction after the instruction that generated the trap. Finally, instruction execution begins at the address contained in the *exception vector*.

EXAMPLE 14-27

A program encounters a TRAP #1 instruction. What does the **68000** do in response?

SOLUTION

First the **68000** will enter the Supervisor mode and stack the address of the next instruction on the supervisor's stack. Table 14-19 shows that vector numbers 32 through 47 are for TRAPs #0 through #15. The Trap Vector Offset is thus 32 + the TRAP number (1 in this example). Thus the trap vector number is 33. This is multiplied by 4 to give an address of 132_{10} or 84_{16}. The system will go to location $84, where it will find a jump to the start of the trap handler routine.

14-12.4 ▼ Return from Exception Instruction

Most trap handler routines end with a ReTurn from Exception (RTE) instruction. The RTE is a privileged instruction that can be executed only in Supervisor mode, but because traps place the μP in Supervisor mode, this is usually not a problem. The RTE restores the status register and PC (the context) to the values they had before the trap occurred, and allows the program to resume at the point where the trap occurred.

14-12.5 ▼ The TRAP 14 Handler in TUTOR

The monitor program in the ECB, TUTOR, contains many useful functions. Users can access these functions for inclusion in their own programs by moving a function number into D7 and then executing a TRAP #14 instruction.

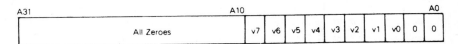

Figure 14-26   Address translated from 8-bit vector number **(68000/68008).**

The TRAP 14 handler is a system call within TUTOR that allows user to access selected routines contained within the firmware, including ASCII–hex conversion, input routines, output routines, and so on. Users need not reproduce these functions in their own programs. Table 14-20 is a summary of the available functions. They are used by including a calling sequence in the user's program as follows:

```
MOVE.B   #<function number>,D7
TRAP     #14
```

where <function number> is a number from 0 through 254, which represents the selected function. Calls to functions not defined result in the message "UNDEFINED TRAP 14" and program control is passed to TUTOR. The appropriate function number is placed in the least significant byte of register D7 before executing the TRAP instruction.

EXAMPLE 14-28

Write a program to input a series of characters from the terminal into memory starting at $7000.

SOLUTION

Some of the details for this problem are contained in the *MC68000 Educational Computer Board User's Manual* (see Section 14-17). The function we need is PORTIN1: input string from port 1, which is #241 in Table 14-20. The User's manual shows that the buffer starting address must be in A5. At the beginning it must also be in A6. As each character is entered, A6 increments. A carriage return ($0D) terminates the TRAP. The program is as follows:

```
MOVEA.L    #$7000,A5    Set starting addresses in A5 and A6
MOVEA.L    A5,A6
MOVE.B     #241,D7      Put function number in D7
TRAP       #14
```

The computer now goes to the input routine to wait for data from the terminal.

14-12.6 ▼ Other Traps

The TRAPV and CHK instructions force an exception if the user program detects a run-time error, which may be an arithmetic overflow or subscript value out of bounds. The TRAPV instruction causes a trap if the prior instructions cause an overflow to occur (setting the V flag).

The CHK instruction checks the low-order word in a data register against an upper *bound* (a number that should not be exceeded) or to see if it is negative. The upper bound is specified in the instruction as an Immediate value or in an operand. If the number in the data register is negative or exceeds the bound, a CHK trap will occur. For example, the instruction CHK D3,(A5) will cause a trap if the word in D3 is negative, or if it is greater than the word in memory pointed to by A5.

TABLE 14-20   TRAP 14 Function Summary

Function	Function Name	Function Description
255	—	Reserved function—end of table indicator.
254	—	Reserved function—used to link tables.
253	LINKIT	Append user table to TRAP 14 table.
252	FIXDADD	Append string to buffer.
251	FIXBUF	Initialize A5 and A6 to "BUFFER."
250	FIXDATA	Initialize A6 to "BUFFER" and append string to buffer.
249	FIXDCRLF	Move "CR," "LF" string to buffer.
248	OUTCH	Output single character to port 1.
247	INCHE	Input single character from port 1.
246	—	Reserved function.
245	—	Reserved function.
244	CHRPRINT	Output single character to port 3.
243	OUTPUT	Output string to port 1.
242	OUTPUT21	Output string to port 2.
241	PORTIN1	Input string from port 1.
240	PORTIN20	Input string from port 2.
239	TAPEOUT	Output string to port 4.
238	TAPEIN	Input string from port 4.
237	PRCRLF	Output string to port 3.
236	HEX2DEC	Convert hex value to ASCII-encoded decimal.
235	GETHEX	Convert ASCII character to hex.
234	PUTHEX	Convert 1 hex digit to ASCII.
233	PNT2HX	Convert 2 hex digits to ASCII.
232	PNT4HX	Convert 4 hex digits to ASCII.
231	PNT6HX	Convert 6 hex digits to ASCII.
230	PNT8HX	Convert 8 hex digits to ASCII.
229	START	Restart TUTOR; perform initialization.
228	TUTOR	Go to TUTOR; print prompt.
227	OUTICR	Output string plus "CR," "LF" to port 1.
226	GETNUMA	Convert ASCII-encoded hex to hex.
225	GETNUMD	Convert ASCII-encoded decimal to hex.
224	PORTININ	Input string from port 1; no automatic line feed.
223–128	—	Reserved.
127–0	—	User-defined functions.

EXAMPLE 14-29

Using the ECB, write a program to test the function of the CHK instruction.

SOLUTION

A program using the CHK instruction was written and is shown in Fig. 14-27. When the program is executed with an "out-of-bound" value in the D3 register, it causes the program to go to the CHK exception vector. A look at the vector table shows that vector to be in location 24 ($18). To illustrate how this instruction might be used, the TRAP 14 function #237 (PRCRLF) was used to print an "out-of-range" message on the printer when such a number is found in the D3 register. The upper bound was set to 16_{10} (or 10_{16}), by the CHK.W #16,D3 instruction, which also defines the register to be D3. The program writes a new vector to location $18 that jumps the program to the TRAP 14 routine located at $201C. The first two instructions are used to set the buffer pointers to the location of the message. The first command shown in Fig. 14-27 is MD (Memory Display), which shows the program after it was entered with the one-line assembler using the MM nnnn;DI command. Next, the PC was set to the start at $2000. Breakpoints have been entered previously and are shown by the BR command. The DF (Display Formatted) command was used to show the contents of the registers prior to running the program. We can see that a value of $11 is in register D3, and the first instruction is displayed at the bottom of the register display. The contents of the memory from $3000 to $300F are shown next by the MD command.

When the G is entered, the program runs until it sees the breakpoint at $2022, and the message "Out of Range" will be printed on the ECB printer. If a value from 0 to $10 had been in D3, the program would have gone to the breakpoint at $2014 since the trap would not have occurred. If a value less than 0 is used, such as $FFFC (word length required), the "Out of Range" message would also be printed.

```
TUTOR  1.3 > md 2000 29;di
002000     3A7C3000              MOVE.W  #12288,A5
002004     3C7C300F              MOVE.W  #12303,A6
002008     21FC0000201C0018      MOVE.L  #8220,$00000018
002010     47BC0010              CHK.W   #16,D3
002014     4E71                  NOP
002016     4E71                  NOP
002018     4EF82014              JMP.S   $00002014
00201C     3E3C00ED              MOVE.W  #237,D7
002020     4E4E                  TRAP    #14
002022     4E71                  NOP
002024     4E71                  NOP
002026     4EF82022              JMP.S   $00002022

TUTOR  1.3 > .pc 2000

TUTOR  1.3 > br

BREAKPOINTS
002014     002014
002022     002022


TUTOR  1.3 > df
PC=00002000 SR=2004=.S0..Z.. US=00000782 SS=0001DBF2
D0=00434E21 D1=00000000 D2=00014E75 D3=00000011
D4=00018000 D5=FFFFFFFF D6=00000008 D7=000000ED
A0=00008902 A1=0000832C A2=00000414 A3=00000428
A4=601A0000 A5=00003000 A6=0000300D A7=0001DBF2
-------------------002000     3A7C3000              MOVE.W #12288,A5

TUTOR  1.3 > md 3000
003000     4F 75 74 20 6F 66 20 52  61 6E 67 65 21 0D 0A FF  Out of Range!...

TUTOR  1.3 > g
PHYSICAL ADDRESS=00002000

AT BREAKPOINT
PC=00002022 SR=2004=.S0..Z.. US=00000782 SS=0001DBEC
D0=00434E0A D1=00000000 D2=00014E75 D3=0000000A
D4=00018000 D5=FFFFFFFF D6=00000008 D7=000000ED
A0=00008902 A1=0000832C A2=00000414 A3=00000428
A4=601A0000 A5=00003000 A6=0000300F A7=0001DBEC
-------------------002022     4E71                  NOP

TUTOR  1.3 >
```

Figure 14-27   Program to illustrate the CHK instruction for Example 14-28.

The TRAPV instruction can also be tested easily in the ECB by writing the one-line instruction (TRAPV) at a location ($2500, for example), and then tracing it. If the overflow bit (V) of the condition codes is set, it will trap and the address in the PC for the next instruction will be in $1C (the TRAPV vector). If the V bit was not set, the trap does not occur and the PC will be at the next instruction in sequence ($2502, in this case). The DIVS and DIVU instructions can be tested similarly. They force an exception if a division operation is attempted with a divisor of zero.

14-13 ▼ INTERRUPTS

External hardware devices can cause interrupts of the normal program processing by means of signals on the three interrupt (IPL) lines. These lines use negative logic; a low level corresponds to a logic 1. When these lines are encoded with a value greater than 000, that is not *masked* (see the following section); an interrupt is made pending. Pending interrupts are serviced between instruction executions. When this occurs, the interrupt vector is fetched and the **68000** enters an interrupt exception processing routine. There are two types of interrupts; *auto-vectored* interrupts, discussed in Section 14-13.3, and user interrupts, discussed in Section 14-13.4.

14-13.1 ▼ Interrupt Priority Levels

Seven levels of interrupt priority are provided. They are numbered from 1 through 7, with level 7 being the highest priority. The status register contains a 3-bit mask that indicates the current processor interrupt priority. Figure 14-28 shows how the interrupt mask bits in

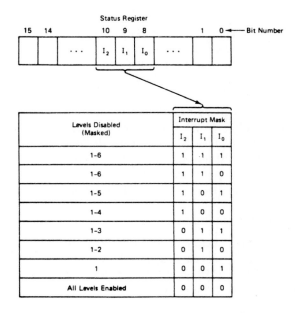

Figure 14-28 Interrupt mask for the **68000**. From Thomas Harmon and Barbara Lawson, *The MC68000 Microprocessor Family,* Prentice Hall, 1985. (Copyright 1985 by Prentice Hall Inc., Englewood Cliffs, New Jersey.)

the status register determine the various priority levels. An interrupt request is made to the processor by encoding an interrupt level other than 000 on the interrupt request lines. 000 means that all IPL lines are high; this is the state where no interrupts are requested. If any IPL line goes low, an interrupt is requested on some level.

Interrupt requests arriving at the processor do not force immediate exception processing, but are made *pending*. Pending interrupts are detected between instruction executions. If the priority of the pending interrupt is lower than, or equal to, the current processor priority, execution continues with the next instruction and the interrupt request is ignored. The recognition of level 7 is slightly different, as explained in Section 14-13.5.

EXAMPLE 14-30

A **68000** has 0s (logic low levels) on IPL0 and IPL2 and a 1 on IPL1. What is the level of interrupts being requested? What must the interrupt mask be for this interrupt to be enabled?

SOLUTION

The IPL lines read 010. But this is inverted logic, so the interrupt level is 101 or 5. The mask bits in the status register (see Fig. 14-28) must be 100 (4) or lower for this interrupt to be recognized.

The most common method of placing the proper signals on the IPL lines is to use a **74LS148** priority encoder as shown in Fig. 14-29. A signal on one of the input lines will cause the **74LS148** to convert it to the proper IPL levels. If a low level is received on input 4, as shown in the figure, the **74LS148** will cause IPL2 to be low and IPL0 and IPL1 to be high.*

Several devices may be assigned to interrupt at the same level by *daisy chaining* them as shown in Fig. 14-29. If three devices are assigned to interrupt on line IRQ4, for example, they would all be at a higher priority than those on lines IRQ0 through IRQ3, but there would also be priority among those three devices because the one closest to the μP would have priority over all others on that line. By this means, an unlimited number of external devices can be connected to interrupt the processor.

14-13.2 ▼ Interrupt Processing

If the priority of the pending interrupt is greater than the current processor priority, the exception processing sequence is started. A flowchart of this process is shown in Fig. 14-30. The sequence is slightly different for user interrupts, and auto-vectored interrupts, as described on the next page.

---

* The **74148** priority encoder is discussed in the second and third editions of *Practical Digital Design Using ICs* by J. D. Greenfield, published by Prentice Hall, Englewood Cliffs, N. J., 1983, 1994.

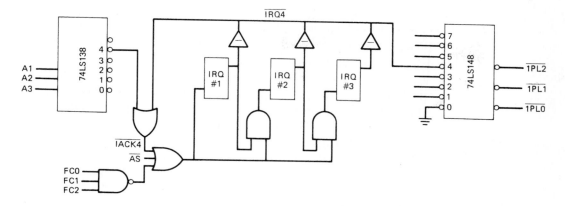

Figure 14-29 Daisy-chained interrupt lines.

14-13.3 ▼ Auto-vectored Interrupts

An auto-vectored interrupt is caused by asserting an interrupt level on the IPL lines and generating an active VPA signal during the interrupt acknowledge cycle. Figure 14-31 shows a hardware configuration to generate both auto-vectored and user interrupts. In the

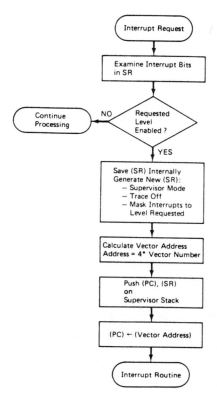

Figure 14-30 Interrupt processing. From Thomas Harmon and Barbara Lawson, *The MC68000 Microprocessor Family,* Prentice Hall, 1985. (Copyright 1985 by Prentice Hall Inc., Englewood Cliffs, New Jersey.)

figure, controller 1, connected to I/O$_1$, generates a user interrupt, and controller 2, connected to I/O$_2$, generates an auto-vectored interrupt.

To generate an auto-vectored interrupt, the following events must occur:

1. Controller 1 is not trying to generate a user interrupt.
2. Controller 2 generates a level 3 auto-vectored interrupt by taking its interrupt request line low. This forces one input of the **74LS32** low and brings the INT3 input to the **74LS148*** low. In the absence of other requests, the **74LS148** places a level 3 interrupt on the interrupt input pins (IPL0, IPL1, and IPL2).
3. When the processor decides to honor the level 3 interrupt, it enters an interrupt acknowledge cycle by setting the three function control lines (FC0, FC1, FC2) to all 1s and placing the number 3 on address lines A1, A2, and A3. With the three FC lines at 1, the highest output of the first **74LS138** decoder goes low. This enables the second **74LS138**. Because the address inputs to it contain the number 3, the signal IACK$_3$ (interrupt acknowledge 3) goes low.
4. When IACK$_3$ goes low, both inputs to the **74LS32** are low and VPA goes low. The **68000** is now acknowledging a level 3 interrupt with VPA low. The fact that VPA is low during the interrupt acknowledge cycle tells the μP that it is acknowledging an auto-vectored interrupt. The processor internally generates a vector number which is determined by the interrupt level number.
5. The μP goes to the level 3 interrupt auto-vector to find the address of the service routine for that interrupt. The vector allocation map (Table 14-19) shows that this vector is at memory address $6C.
6. After reading the auto-vector at $6C, the μP jumps to that address and starts executing the service routine.

14-13.4 ▼ User Interrupts

Figure 14-31 also shows the hardware required to generate a user interrupt. A user interrupt is generated by putting the interrupt request level on the IPL inputs and leaving VPA high. When the request is honored, the **68000** goes to one of the 192 user interrupt vector locations to find the address of the proper starting routine (The vector is put there by the initialization routine.)

Again referring to Fig. 14-31, a user interrupt is generated as follows:

1. Controller 1 brings the INT5 input to the **74148** low. This puts a 5 on the IPL lines to the processor.
2. When the processor responds with an interrupt acknowledge cycle and address lines A1, A2, and A3 have a 5 on them, IACK$_5$ is produced.
3. IACK$_5$ gates the box labeled "ENABLE VECTOR NUMBER" to put the proper vector number (a number between $40 and $FF) on the data bus.
4. The μP knows that this is a user interrupt because VPA is high. It multiplies the vector number by 4 to get the vector address. It then goes to that address to get the starting address of the service routine. The controller must also generate DTACK to terminate the interrupt acknowledge cycle.

---

* The **74148** priority controller IC is discussed in Section 17-5.4 of *Practical Digital Design Using ICs,* 2nd ed., by Joseph D. Greenfield, published by Wiley, New York, 1983.

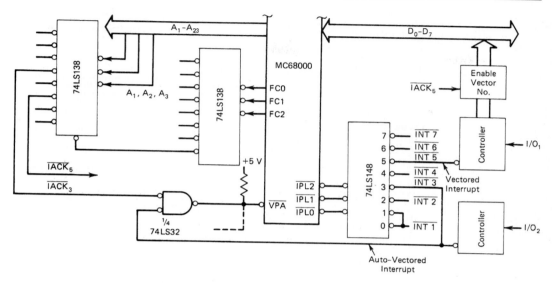

Figure 14-31 **68000** vectored and auto-vectored interrupt logic.

Table 14-19 shows that the seven auto-vectored interrupts are vectors 25 to 31, and the user interrupts are vectors 64 to 255.

EXAMPLE 14-31

A **6821** Peripheral Interface Adapter (PIA) is wired into a circuit similar to Fig. 14-31. It can interrupt on level 3 and is therefore assigned auto-vector number 27_{10}. The interrupt service routine for this PIA starts at location $7000. Explain what happens when the PIA interrupts.

SOLUTION

The PIA's IRQ line is connected into an interrupt priority detector circuit that places a 3 on the IPL lines when an interrupt is generated. External circuitry then monitors the FC and address lines until it detects an interrupt acknowledge cycle with the PIA's proper address on A1, A2, and A3.

To service the interrupt, the processor then fetches the level 3 auto-vector (number 27_{10}) from location $6C, where it finds $7000. It places this in the PC and starts the service routine, which ends with an RTE instruction. A flowchart for the interrupt acknowledge sequence is given in Fig. 14-32, a timing diagram is given in Fig. 14-33, and the interrupt processing sequence is shown in Fig. 14-34. The service routine must cause the PIA to terminate its interrupt request.

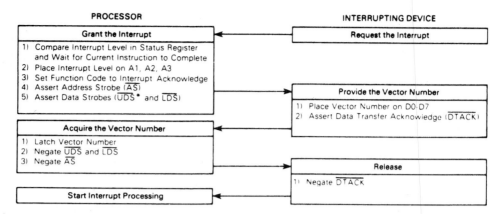

PROCESSOR | INTERRUPTING DEVICE

Grant the Interrupt | **Request the Interrupt**

1) Compare Interrupt Level in Status Register and Wait for Current Instruction to Complete
2) Place Interrupt Level on A1, A2, A3
3) Set Function Code to Interrupt Acknowledge
4) Assert Address Strobe ($\overline{AS}$)
5) Assert Data Strobes ($\overline{UDS}$* and $\overline{LDS}$)

Provide the Vector Number
1) Place Vector Number on D0-D7
2) Assert Data Transfer Acknowledge ($\overline{DTACK}$)

Acquire the Vector Number
1) Latch Vector Number
2) Negate $\overline{UDS}$ and $\overline{LDS}$
3) Negate $\overline{AS}$

Release
1) Negate $\overline{DTACK}$

Start Interrupt Processing

*Although a vector number is one byte, both data strobes are asserted due to the microcode used for exception processing. The processor does not recognize anything on data lines D8 through D15 at this time.

Figure 14-32 Interrupt Acknowledge Sequence.

14-13.5 ▼ Nonmaskable Interrupt

The reader may have noticed in Fig. 14-28 that a level 7 interrupt cannot be masked by any setting of the status register. A level 7 interrupt (all IPL lines low) is a **NonMaskable Interrupt** (NMI), and should be used for things that cannot logically be interrupted, such as clock timing pulses or emergency situations.

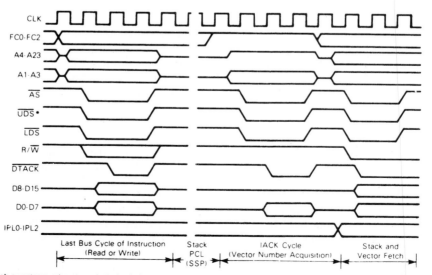

*Although a vector number is one byte, both data strobes are asserted due to the microcode used for exception processing. The processor does not recognize anything on data lines D8 through D15 at this time.

Figure 14-33 Interrupt Acknowledge cycle timing diagram.

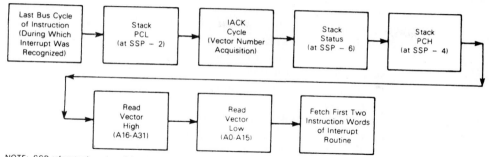

NOTE: SSP refers to the value of the supervisor stack pointer before the interrupt occurs.

Figure 14-34 Interrupt processing sequence.

14-13.6 ▼ Uninitialized Interrupt

One of the **68000** family design rules states that the peripheral devices must have internal logic that initializes their internal vector register to a value of $0F when a Power-On Reset (POR) occurs. It is the responsibility of the system initialization program to change that register value so that the correct vector can be fetched to point to the peripheral's interrupt service routine. During an *interrupt acknowledge cycle* an interrupting device asserts Valid Peripheral Address (VPA), a Bus Error (BERR), or provides an interrupt vector number and asserts DTACK. If, however, an interrupt should occur before the initialization routine is completed and the peripheral's vector register has not been updated (initialized), the $0F will be fetched, and the vector from that location will be used by the processor. This is an **uninitialized interrupt**. The interrupt mask is set to 7 at the beginning of the initialization process. If it is not lowered until the end of the initialization routine, this possibility would be minimized.

14-13.7 ▼ Spurious Interrupt

If during the interrupt acknowledge cycle, no device responds by asserting DTACK or VPA, the Bus Error line (BERR) should be asserted by external logic to terminate the vector acquisition. This is a **spurious interrupt.** The processor separates the processing of this error from bus error by fetching the *spurious interrupt vector* instead of the *bus error vector.* The processor then proceeds with the usual exception processing.

14-13.8 ▼ RESET

The RESET line is a hardware input very much like an interrupt, except that it only uses one pin on the μP. When it is taken low, it provides the highest exception level. The RESET signal is designed for system initiation (startup) or recovery from catastrophic failure. Any processing in progress at the time of the reset is aborted and cannot be recovered. The processor is forced into the supervisor state, the trace state is forced off (see Section 14-14), and the processor *interrupt priority mask* is set to level seven (see Section 14-13.1). The vector number is internally generated to reference the *reset exception vector* at location 0 in memory. Because no assumptions can be made about the validity of register contents, in particular the supervisor stack pointer, neither the program counter nor the status register is saved. The reset exception vector contains four words that are fetched from ROM and placed in registers as follows. The address contained in the first two words of the *reset exception vector* is the initial supervisor stack pointer, and the address in the higher two words of the vector is the initial program counter. Finally, instruction execution is started at the address in the program counter. The power/up restart (system initialization) code should be pointed to by the initial program counter.

The reset *instruction* does not fetch the reset vector but does assert the RESET line to reset external devices. This allows the software to reset the system to a known state and then continue processing with the next instruction.

14-14 ▼ TRACING

As an aid to program development, the **68000** family of μPs includes a feature to allow instruction-by-instruction **tracing.** In the trace state, an exception is forced after each instruction. This allows a debugger program to examine the registers or memory after each instruction is traced and thus to analyze the user's program's progress. This feature is used in the ECB's TUTOR program.

The trace facility uses the T bit in the supervisor portion of the status register. If the T bit is clear (off), tracing is disabled and instruction execution proceeds as normal. If the T bit is set (on) at the beginning of the execution of an instruction, a trace exception will be generated as the execution of the instruction is completed. If the instruction is not executed, either because an interrupt is taken, or the instruction is illegal or privileged, the trace exception does not occur. The trace exception also does not occur if the instruction is aborted by a reset, bus error, or address error exception. If the instruction is indeed executed and an interrupt is pending on completion, the trace exception is processed before the interrupt exception. If, during the execution of the instruction an exception is forced by that instruction, the forced exception is processed before the trace exception. This process is illustrated in the flowchart of Fig. 14-35.

As an extreme illustration of the rules above, consider the arrival of an interrupt during the execution of a TRAP instruction while tracing is enabled. First the trap exception is processed, then the trace exception, and finally, the interrupt exception. Instruction execution resumes in the interrupt handler routine.

14-15 ▼ SUMMARY

In this chapter we introduced the **68000** and explained the basic features. Differences between the **6800** and the **68000** were shown, and the merits of 8–, 16–, and 32-bit systems were explained. The register set within the **68000** was discussed first, followed by an explanation of the various addressing modes. A major part of the chapter was devoted to discussing the instruction set, and many programming examples were presented. The pinout and signal functions of the **68000** were described for the **68000** system designer. Finally, exceptions, traps, and interrupts were discussed. The more advanced features of the newer Motorola μPs are presented in Chapter 15.

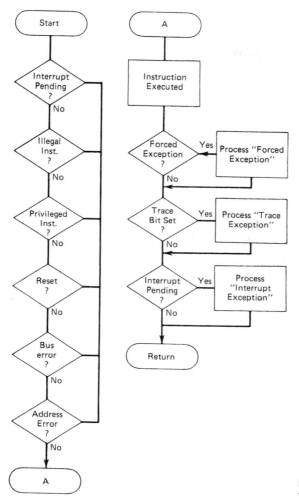

Figure 14-35 Flow chart showing trace exception.

14-16 ▼ GLOSSARY

BERR A bus error signal indicating that an invalid bus operation is being attempted.

Bus Arbitration The use of three signals—Bus Request, Bus Grant, and Bus Grant Acknowledge—to determine which device will be the bus master.

Bus Grant (BG) An output signal that indicates to all other potential bus master devices that the processor will release bus control at the end of the current bus cycle.

Bus Grant ACKnowledge (BGACK) This signal indicates that some other device has become the bus master.

Bus master The device that currently is transferring data to or from the bus.

Bus Request (BR) A bus signal output by a device indicating a desire to become the master.

Context switch Saving all the registers and flags that define the state of the system at the moment and substituting other values that will cause the processor to execute a different part of the program, such as an exception handler routine.

Data Strobes Signals that control the flow of data on the data bus. The **68000** μPs have Upper Data Strobe (UDS) and Lower Data Strobe (LDS), except the **68020**, which has only one DS signal line.

Exception processing A state associated with interrupts, trap instructions, tracing, and other exceptional conditions.

Exception Vector A pointer (address) used by the processor to fetch the address of a routine that will handle an exception.

Function Code lines Three of the signal lines on **68000** family μPs (FC1, FC2, and FC3) that indicate the state (Supervisor or User) and the cycle type currently being executed.

Interrupt acknowledge cycle The sequence of events during which the processor initiates interrupt processing beginning with fetching the interrupt vector. It then saves current conditions on the stack and executes the interrupt service routine.

Long word A word containing 32 bits.

NonMaskable Interrupt (NMI) A Level 7 interrupt. It cannot be masked.

Operating System The software program that supervises and controls the operation of a computer.

Spurious interrupt An event that occurs during the Interrupt Acknowledge cycle. If no device responds, the bus error line is asserted to terminate the vector acquisition, and the μP fetches the spurious interrupt vector instead of the bus error vector.

Supervisor Stack Pointer (SSP) An address kept in a register in the **68000** family μP and used to control storage of data in the Supervisor Stack area memory.

Supervisor State or Mode The more privileged of the normal processing modes.

System Byte The most significant byte of the status word. It contains the Supervisor state (S) and Trace (T) mode status bits, and the interrupt mask bits.

Uninitialized interrupt vector The address of a service routine kept in vector location $3C that is fetched when a peripheral's interrupt vector register has not been properly initialized.

Trap An exception that is caused by the TRAP instruction. It is useful for system calls.

User Stack Pointer (USP) An address kept in a register in the **68000** family μP that points to the User's stack area of memory.

User State or Mode The less privileged processing state of the 68000 family μPs.

Word 16 bits or two bytes in a **68000** μP.

14-17 ▼ REFERENCES

ARNEWSH, INC., *SBC68K User's Manual,* Rev. 1.1, 2nd ed., Fort Collins, Colo., 1991.

GREENFIELD, JOSEPH, Ed., *Microprocessor Handbook,* Wiley, New York, 1985.

———— *Practical Digital Design Using ICs,* 3rd ed., Prentice Hall, Englewood Cliffs, N. J., 1994.

HARMAN, THOMAS L., AND BARBARA LAWSON, *The Motorola MC68000 Microprocessor Family,* Prentice Hall, Englewood Cliffs, N. J., 1985.

MOTOROLA, *M68000 Family Programmer's Reference Manual,* M68000PM/AD—1992.

———— *MC68000 16/32-Bit Microprocessor,* ADI 814R6, Austin, Texas, 1985.

———— *MC68000 Educational Computer Board User's Manual, 2nd Ed.,* Phoenix, Ariz., 1982.

———— *M68000 Family Fact Sheet,* BR249 Rev. 2, Phoenix, Ariz., 1985.

———— *MC68008 8/32-Bit Microprocessor with 8-Bit Data Bus,* ADI 939R2, Austin, Texas, 1985.

———— *MC68HC000 Low Power HCMOS 16/32-Bit Microprocessor,* BR275 Rev. 1, Phoenix, Ariz., 1986.

14-18 ▼ PROBLEMS

14-1. The following registers contain

$$(D1) = 1\ 2\ 3\ 4\ A\ B\ C\ D$$
$$(D2) = 3\ 5\ 6\ 7\ 4\ 4\ 4\ 5$$
$$(A3) = 0\ 0\ 0\ 0\ 2\ 0\ 0\ 0$$

and the contents of $2000 are $1456. What are the contents of these registers and $2000 after the following instructions?

(a) MOVE.B   D1,D2
(b) MOVE.W   D2,D1
(c) ADDA.W   D2,A3
(d) ADD.L   D1,D2
(e) ADD.W   D2,D1
(f) ADD.B   D2,D1
(g) MOVEA.W   D2,A3
(h) MOVE.L   A3,D1
(i) MOVE.W   D1,(A3)
(j) MOVE.B   D2,(A3)+
(k) MOVE.B   A3,D2

14-2. The following registers contain

$$(D1) = 0\ 0\ 0\ 0\ 2\ 0\ 0\ A$$
$$(D5) = 0\ 0\ 0\ 0\ 1\ 1\ 1\ 1$$
$$(A4) = 0\ 0\ 0\ 0\ 3\ 0\ 0\ 0$$

The PC is at $5100. What is the Effective Address for the course of each of the following instructions?

(a) MOVE.L   –(A4),D0
(b) MOVE.B   –(A4),D0
(c) MOVE.W   139(A4),D0
(d) MOVE.B   AB(A5,D1.W),D0
(e) MOVE.W $F900(PC),D0
(f) MOVE.W $25(PC),D5.W,D0

14-3. What do the following machine language instructions do?

(a) D822
(b) 3115
(c) 1E38
(d) 1008

14-4. Hand assemble the following instructions.

(a) MOVE.B   D2,(A5)
(b) ADD   (A6)+,D3

14-5. In Fig. 14-7, what are the contents of A2, A3, and the A7 register? Which stack is in use?

14-6. Data register D2 contains AAAABBBB. What does it contain after the following instructions?

(a) ADD.W   #$1234,D2
(b) ADDQ.B   #3,D2
(c) ADDQ.B   #0,D2

14-7. Write a program to move the numbers in A0 through A9 into registers D0–D2, D5, and A1. Use word-size transfers and only one instruction.

14-8. Use the register definitions of Problem 14-1. What are the results after the following instructions are executed?

(a) EXG   D1,D2
(b) EXG   D2,A3
(c) SWAP   S2

14-9. Write a program to add the bytes in $3000 through $3020. Place the sum in D3.

14-10. There is a 12-digit BCD number in $2000 through $2005 and another one in $2010 through $2014. Write a program to add them and put the results in locations $2020 through $2025.

14-11. Multiply 3A by 2B using the **68000** MULTIPLY instruction.

14-12. If 1A2 is divided by 15, using a DIVIDE instruction, what are the results?

14-13. Write a program to test the byte in $2003. Go to $3000 if the parity is even and go to $4000 if the parity is odd.

14-14. Write an assembly language program to subtract one multiple word number from another. The number of words in each number is stored in the word at memory location $002FF0. The first number is stored in memory, starting at location $003000. The second number is stored in memory, starting at location $004000. The result should be stored in memory starting at location $005000. Both numbers and the result are stored MS word first. Subtract the second number from the first. Try your program with the following data:

$$002FF0 = 4$$
$$\text{first number} = 10F3689400A16184$$
$$\text{second number} = 09A2547400902071$$

14-15. There is a TRAPV instruction in location $2006. The overflow exception routine is to start at $4000. How must the vector table be altered to allow this to occur?

14-16. Using the ECB, write the following program:
- **(a)** Place the number $11 in D1
- **(b)** Add $17 to it.
- **(c)** Use a TRAPV instruction. If the trap is not taken, repeat steps (b) and (c). If the trap is taken, return to the monitor and examine the registers. Explain your results.

14-17. In Fig. 14-30, if both devices interrupt at the same time, which gets priority, and why?

14-18. Modify Fig. 14-30 so that controller 2 can generate a second auto-vector interrupt on level 6.

After attempting to solve these problems, try to answer the self evaluation questions in Section 14-2. If any of them still seem difficult, review the appropriate sections of the chapter to find the answers.

ADVANCED FEATURES OF THE NEWER MEMBERS OF THE 68000 FAMILY

15-1 ▼ INSTRUCTIONAL OBJECTIVES

In this chapter we continue the description of the **68000** family of microprocessors by discussing the newer and more capable μPs, the **68010, 68020, 68030, 68040,** and the **68060.** Some of the many lower-cost variations of these advanced μPs, such as the **68EC0x0** family, the *Embedded Controller* versions, will also be described because of our primary interest in Microcontrollers. Other variations, such as the **68HC000** and **68HC001** will also be discussed.

After reading this chapter, the student should be able to:

1. Describe the new features that make the **68010** superior to the **68000.**
2. Explain Virtual Memory and Memory Management.
3. Discuss the methods used in the **68020** to increase its performance.
4. Discuss how the **68030** uses cache and memory management technologies to further improve performance.
5. Explain how the enhanced Loop Mode instruction speeds table or block moves.
6. Describe an Embedded Controller.

15-2 ▼ SELF-EVALUATION QUESTIONS

Watch for the answers to the following questions as you read the chapter. They should help you to understand the material presented.

1. How many words does the **68000** μP store on the stack when it is interrupted? How many for the **68010?**
2. What is the purpose of the Vector Base Register?
3. What added features does the **68020** have?

4. How does the **68020** execute instructions in zero time?

5. How does having the Memory Management Unit on-chip improve performance of the **68030**?

6. How does the data cache work to improve the performance of the **68030**?

7. Why is the **68EC0x0** family less expensive?

15-3 ▼ INTRODUCTION TO THE ADVANCED 16/32-BIT μPS

Several references have been made to the newer members of the **68000** μP family in Chapter 14. In this chapter we start by describing the **68010** and discuss the **68020, 68030, 68040,** and **68060** in the later sections. Each of these μPs has substantial performance improvements over their earlier relative, and each has become more complex as more circuitry was included within the μP. The newer enhancements to the μP, such as the use of virtual memory and caches, will be explained.

The **68010** was introduced in 1983. It is pin and software compatible with the **68000.** It has several added features, such as the support of *virtual memory techniques* and *enhanced instruction execution timing,* that improve its performance. Today, the **68010** is rarely used because these features have been incorporated in the newer μPs, where they function in the same way.

Although the **68000, 68008,** and **68010** have 32-bit registers, the internal data paths were 16 bits wide. Many 32-bit operations had to be handled in two steps. The **68020** μP, introduced in 1984, has full 32-bit implementation of registers, internal data paths, and external address and data buses. Thus it is Motorola's first full 32-bit μP. It retains the virtual memory features of the **68010** and adds many new features, such as the *internal instruction cache,* the *coprocessor interface,* and *pipelined internal architecture,* that provide remarkable performance capabilities.

In September 1986 a still more powerful member of the **68000** μP family was added. It is the **68030,** and also supports virtual memory operation. It is based on the **68020** core but has numerous enhanced performance features. Increased *internal parallelism* is provided by *multiple* internal data and address buses and a versatile built-in bus controller. An on-chip *Paged Memory Management Unit* (PMMU) reduces the minimum physical bus cycle time and the *internal pipelining* provides this memory management with *zero* translation time for addresses.

The **68030** with its built-in Memory Management Unit (MMU) was in production in 1987 and the **68040** followed in 1989. The **68040** has many features to make it faster and more powerful. It includes a *Floating-Point Unit* (FPU) and optimized instructions plus improved caches and MMUs. The **68060** introduced in 1992 has even greater performance improvements, achieved by multiple internal buses and execution units. It has three times the performance of a 25-MHz **68040.** The features of these newer μPs are described in Sections 15-7, 15-12, 15-13, and 15-14.

In 1991, Motorola reengineered many of these μPs to streamline feature sets and minimize costs for embedded applications. The **68EC0x0** family was the result. The **68EC040,** for example, is a simplified version of the **68040** that does not include the FPU or the MMU. Embedded microcontrollers are discussed in Section 15-15.

The **68000** was built using HMOS technology, but the **68020** and later μPs were implemented using HCMOS to conserve power. The newer **68HC000** and **68HC001** are a rework of the **68000** μP in HCMOS and they use one-tenth as much power. The original **68000** had the ability to work with 8-bit peripherals because of the VPA pin and so does the **68HC000**. The **68HC001** brings out a VPA, a MODE, and an A0 pin, which gives it added flexibility to work with both 8- and 16-bit data buses. It eliminates the need for the **68008,** an early 16-bit μP that had an 8-bit data bus, which was compatible with Motorola's 8-bit peripheral family. All of these newer chips still qualify as members of the **68000** family because the software is upwardly compatible (i.e., **68000** programs will run on all the newer μPs).

15-4 ▼ HCMOS TECHNOLOGY

The **68000** family of μPs were made possible by the continuing developments in semiconductor processing technology. Although the **68000** had processing improvements over the **6800** and **6809,** the **68020** achieved even more from the features available in the HCMOS technology of 1984. By 1986, HCMOS has been made still smaller and faster, making the **68030** possible. With circuits as complex as those in the **68020** and **68030,** the transistor density, chip size, speed, power consumption, and manufacturability are all critical considerations.

Motorola's experience with High-density Complementary Metal-Oxide Semiconductors (HCMOSs) made it possible to design nearly 200,000 transistors into the **68020,** nearly 300,000 transistors into the **68030,** and with 0.8-μm HCMOS technology, more than 1.2 million into the **68040.** The **68060** has slightly more complexity. The HCMOS process also provides the necessary combination of high-speed performance with very low power consumption. By using this advanced process, production can be maintained at high volumes with proper yields. The resulting μPs are greatly enhanced over the processing power of the **68000,** yet they consume less power. The **68060** has several new features which reduce power consumption by 40 to 60% over that of similar μPs.

15-5 ▼ VIRTUAL MEMORY

Because memory is expensive, most **68000** family μP systems provide physical memory for only a fraction of the 16 megabytes addressable by the 24-bit address bus. A technique called *virtual memory* has been used for several years in large mainframe computers and more recently in minicomputers to allow programs larger than the size of the physical memory to be executable. This concept was introduced in the **68010** μP and is available in all of the more advanced μPs of the **68000** family. Virtual memory is a concept where, by means of added hardware and software, the full addressable range of memory *appears* to be present even though only a smaller block of RAM is actually available. This is done by using address translation hardware to switch the block of physical memory quickly to the address requested. The memory therefore can appear to be at an address different from the actual *physical* address. The virtual memory is said to occupy the **logical address space,** whereas the RAM is the real **physical memory.**

Programmers can then write programs that require several megabytes, even if, for example, only 1 Mbyte of RAM is actually available. Then, when execution is started, 1 Mbyte of the program would be loaded into the RAM and the rest must remain on the disk.

If the program addresses a memory location that is already in RAM, execution progresses with no delays. If, however, the program addresses a location that is in the portion stored on disk, *swapping* must occur. Part of the program in physical memory must be written from RAM to the disk. Then the part of the program on disk that contains the addressed location must be written into the RAM before execution can continue. Virtual memory systems contain circuits that determine whether each addressed location is already in physical memory or on the disk.

15-5.1 ▼ Page Faults

Virtual memory systems subdivide their memory into *pages*. A page is a specific amount of memory. A typical page might be 4K bytes in size. The physical memory has room for a finite number of these pages in the RAM. The logical address space, however, can contain many more pages, up to the limit that the computer can address.

EXAMPLE 15.1

A programmer is writing a program that will require 16 Mbytes of memory. Assume that the memory is divided into 32K-byte pages and that 1 MB of physical memory is available.

(a) How many address bits does the programmer need?

(b) How many address bits does each page have?

(c) How many pages can be in memory, and how many must remain on the disk?

SOLUTION

(a) An address space of 16 Mbytes contains 2^{24} bytes and therefore requires 24 address bits.

(b) Each page has 32K bytes of memory and will require 15 address bits. This leaves 9 address bits available for determining the page selected. This system contains 512 pages of 32K bytes each, to make up a total address space of 16 Mbytes.

(c) Because there is only 1 M byte of physical memory available, 32 pages can be in memory at any time. The other 480 pages must reside on the disk.

When the processor attempts to access a memory location, it can do so directly if that location is present in the physical memory. A *page fault* occurs, however, if that page is not currently residing in the physical memory. When memory that is outside the current range is accessed, a page fault is generated by hardware external to the μP. This causes a Bus ERRor (BERR) signal to occur and a Bus Error Exception Process is started, which:

1. Makes a copy of the Status Register.
2. Obtains the exception vector.
3. Saves the system status. In a virtual memory system, the current processor status is saved on the stack in a new long format that is used only for Bus Error or address error exceptions (see Section 15-5.3).
4. Runs the Exception handler. A virtual memory system must have routines to fetch the address that caused the page fault from the stacked information and then run a disk/RAM page swap. The disk/RAM page swap sends the least used page in the RAM to the disk and replaces it with a new page, read from the disk, that contains the instructions or data at the required address.
5. Executes a revised RTE. Restore the long format status (see Section 15-5.4) and resume normal instruction execution, which reruns the instruction that caused the page fault.

There are two ways to implement swapping: *instruction restart* and *instruction continuation*. With instruction restart, the processor must remember the exact state of the system *before each instruction is started* in order to restore that state should a page fault occur during its execution. Then, after the page fault has been *repaired* (a new memory page loaded), the entire instruction that caused the fault is reexecuted.

Using *instruction continuation,* however, the μP stores its internal state on the supervisor stack whenever a bus cycle is terminated with a *bus error,* which indicates that a page fault has occurred. It then loads the program counter from *Exception Vector Table entry number two* (offset $008). This vector points to the bus error routine, and program execution begins again at that new address. When the bus error exception handler routine has completed execution, by swapping pages, an RTE instruction is executed using the long format exception stack frame, which reloads the μP with the internal state stored previously on the stack, reruns the *faulted bus cycle,* and continues the suspended instruction.

Instruction continuation is accomplished by a change in the way the Exception Stack Frame (see Section 15-5.3) and the RTE instruction (see Section 15-5.4) are implemented in the **68010** and later μPs. Virtual memory performs almost as well as physical memory because of the way programs operate. Statistically, it has been found that most memory accesses are made to a nearby address and thus to a page that is already in physical memory.

15-5.2 ▼ Virtual Machines

A Virtual Machine is an extension of the virtual memory concept, which not only simulates memory but also simulates the input/output devices of a physical machine. One typical use for this type of system is in the development of software, such as an operating system, to work with hardware that is also under development and not available for programming use. In such a system, which typically has memory-mapped input/output devices (i.e., hardware registers for printers, disk drives, or A/D converters), the governing operating system emulates this hardware and allows the operating system under development to be executed and debugged as though it were running on the new hardware. Such an emulated system is called a *Virtual Machine.*

Instruction continuation is the necessary choice to support virtual I/O devices in memory-mapped input/output systems. Assume, for example, that an instruction reads a register in a PIA (see Chapter 7) and when the data is being written to memory, a page fault occurs. It is *not* possible to restart the instruction since the status bits in the PIA have already been reset. Therefore, the instruction must be *continued* after the page fault has been corrected in order for the results to be proper.

Suppose also that a system is under development and will use I/O devices that are not yet installed. The registers in these I/O devices will occupy specific locations in memory. Again, the PIA can be used as an example. The **68010** and the other advanced **68000** family μPs and their programs can be set up so that any attempted reference to these locations causes a page fault. The page fault will cause an exception, and the exception routine can be written to *simulate* the action of these registers. Thus the operating system program can be tested before the I/O ICs are actually installed.

Because the new operating system is controlled by the governing operating system, the new one must execute at a lower privilege level than the governing operating system. A virtual machine may be fully supported by running the new operating system in the *User* mode and the governing operating system in the *Supervisor* mode, so that any attempts to access supervisor resources or execute privileged instructions by the new operating system will cause a trap to the governing operating system.

Different operating systems (such as UNIX and CPM-68K) could be running simultaneously under the main operating system. Note that the systems are not emulating instructions but are executing **680x0** instructions at full clock rates. Any disk swapping will, however, slow things a little compared to a fully implemented physical system.

To fully support a Virtual Machine, the μP must protect the supervisor resources from access by user programs. The one supervisor resource that is not fully protected in the **68000** is the *system byte* of the Status Register. In the **68000,** the *MOVE from SR* instruction allows user programs to test the S bit (in addition to the T bit and interrupt mask) and thus determine that they are running in the *User* mode. For full virtual machine support, a new operating system must not be aware that it is running in the User mode and thus should not be allowed to access the S bit. For this reason, the MOVE from SR instruction *has been made privileged* in the **68010** and later μPs to allow only supervisor programs unhindered access to the system byte of the Status Register. By making this instruction privileged, a trap to the governing operating system will occur when the new operating system, which is running in User mode, attempts to access the S bit.

15-5.3 ▼ Exception Stack Frame

As a part of the changes necessary to provide Virtual Memory capability, the advanced versions of the **68000** family μPs have a different stacking procedure that is used when Bus Error Exception Processing is required. Exception processing for the **68000** was described in Section 14-12. One of the steps in this procedure is to save the *current* processor state, called the **context,** on the top of the supervisor stack. This context is organized in a format called the *Exception Stack Frame.* The information in this frame varies for the type of exception and in the **68000** is three words in length as shown in Fig. 15-1a. It contains the Status Register contents (one word) and the Program Counter values (two words) that existed when the exception occurred. One of the features added to

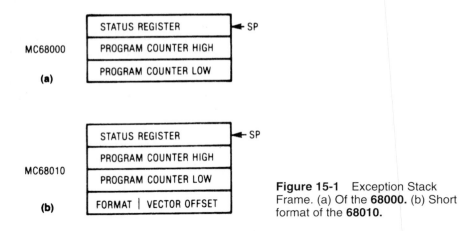

Figure 15-1 Exception Stack Frame. (a) Of the **68000**. (b) Short format of the **68010**.

the **68010** and the other advanced μPs to provide for virtual memory is the use of a *long* and a *short* format in saving the *Exception Stack Frame*. As shown in Fig. 15-1b, the short format for the **68010** contains four words as compared to three in the **68000** stack frame. The added word includes a 4-bit field to define the *format*. The remaining bits make up the *vector offset* for the exception being processed (see Section 14-12.2). In the **68010** there are only two valid stack formats, A format field of 0000 is for the normal four-word format, and 1000 is used for the long format. Other formats are identified as illegal by the

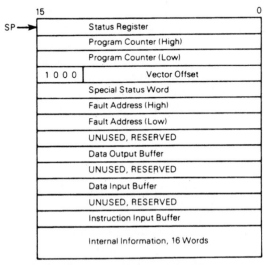

NOTE: The stack pointer is decremented by 29 words, although only 26 words of information are actually written to memory. The three additional words are reserved for future use by Motorola.

Figure 15-2 **68010** Exception stack frame (long format) for a bus and address error.

68010 and cause a *format error* exception. The more advanced μPs to be described later in this chapter, however, use some of these other formats. The **68020** and **68030** μPs provide six different stack frames, each identified by a unique format code. The details of these can be found in the User's Manuals for these μPs, listed in Section 15-18.

The long format is needed to allow *instruction continuation* that is used to recover from a *page fault* (see Section 15-5.1). When a long format exception occurs, during a Bus or Address Error, additional words are written to the stack. Figure 15-2 shows the makeup of the long format Exception Stack Frame for the **68010,** where the format is 1000 and 29 additional words are written to the stack. The additional information describes the internal state of the processor at the time of the bus error. The value of the program counter saved does not necessarily point to the instruction that was executing when the bus error occurred, but may be up to five words later. This is due to the prefetch mechanism in the Motorola μPs, which always fetches a new instruction word as each previously fetched instruction word is used.

Enough information is placed on the stack for the bus error exception handler routine to determine why the bus fault occurred. This additional information includes the address that was being accessed, the Function Codes for the access, whether it was a read or write, and what internal register was included in the transfer. The fault address can be used by an operating system to determine what virtual memory location is needed so that the page of data requested can be brought into physical memory. The RTE instruction (explained below) is then used to reload the processor's internal state at the time of the fault. The faulted bus cycle will then be rerun and the suspended instruction completed. If the faulted bus cycle was a read–modify–write, the entire cycle will be rerun whether the fault occurred during the read or the write operation.

15-5.4 ▼ Return-from-Exception Instruction

The use of different formats when data is saved on the stack means that the ReTurn-from-Exception (RTE) instruction must be expanded for the **68010** and later μPs so that the proper number of words are reloaded and the type of exception associated with the stack frame determined so that the appropriate restorative action can be taken.

Execution of the RTE on these newer μPs occurs as follows: The processor reads four words, which contain the status register, program counter, and stack format into the machine. The format bits are then evaluated. If the short stack format is found, only the PC and SR are restored, and normal processing resumes at the address indicated by the restored program counter. If a long stack format is present, the remaining words must be read from the stack and restored to the appropriate location before execution can continue in the main program at the point of the exception.

15-5.5 ▼ Enhancements in the Advanced μPs

The advanced μPs contain several other new features not found in the **68000.** One is an additional CPU register called the **Vector Base Register** (VBR). In the **68000,** the *Exception Vector Table* starts at address 0. To support Virtual Memory or Virtual Machine systems, additional vector tables can be installed and the VBR used to determine their starting or base address. When another operating system is implemented it is likely that at least some of the Exception vector handling routines will be different. Rather than attempting to copy or write in all the Exception handling routines during a context switch, another group of routines is provided during initialization and accessed by just changing the VBR. One vector table must be at location 0. When an exception vector is fetched, the processor translates the 8-bit **vector number** to a full 32-bit **offset,** which is added to the contents of the VBR to get the correct **vector table base address.** Because the VBR is initialized to zero during reset, these advanced μPs are fully compatible with **68000** programs.

In the **68000** μP, the switch to the supervisor mode allows access to two additional CPU registers, the Supervisor Stack Pointer and the MSB of the 16-bit status register. In the **68010** and the other advanced μPs, three more CPU control registers were added that are accessible only in the supervisory mode. These are the 32-bit VBR, already described, and two 3-bit alternate Function Code Registers, SFC (Source Function Code), and DFC (Destination Function Code). These registers, along with some new *MOVE* instructions, allow the supervisor to access any address space. Function Codes were described in Section 14-4.4 (see also Sections 15-6 and 15-10.1). The following instructions have been added or changed for use with these registers:

- Two instructions have been added for the supervisory mode: MOVES and MOVEC.
- Two have been added for use in both modes: MOVE to/from CCR and RTD.
- Changes have been made in the MOVE to/from SR and RTE instructions.

Because MOVES and MOVEC are usable only in the Supervisory mode, they are known as Privileged instructions.

MOVES (move to alternate address space) copies data from the specified general register to a location within the address space specified by the DFC register, or it moves the data from a location within the address space specified by the SFC register to the specified general register.

These 3-bit registers alter the Function Code bits (FC2, FC1, and FC0) put out by the processor and thus will select the appropriate address space as determined by the MMU logic or by the logic included in a custom Function Code decoder (see Section 15-6).

The data can be a byte, word, or long word. Thus an operating system running in the supervisory mode can exchange data between users. MOVES allows crossing Function Code boundaries or moving between Supervisor and User memory areas.

The assembler syntax is

```
MOVES Rn,<EA>    or
MOVES <EA>,Rn
```

where Rn is the specified general register and EA specifies the source or destination location within the alternate address space.

The MOVEC instruction copies the contents of a specified control register to the specified general register or copies the contents of the specified general register to the specified control register. The control registers are identified by the three LS bytes of the instruction format. In the **68010** programmer's manual the listed options are:

HEX	Control Register
000	Source Function Code (SFC) register
001	Destination Function Code (DFC) register
800	User Stack Pointer (USP)
801	Vector Base Register (VBR)

This is always a 32-bit transfer even though the control register may be implemented with fewer bits. Unimplemented bits are read as zeros. The reader should refer to the *Programmer's Reference Manual* (see Section 15-18) for more details on these new advanced μP instructions.

EXAMPLE 15-2

Show how to set up a new Exception Vector Table with a base address of $100000.

SOLUTION

The following instructions would be used:

```
MOVE.L   #$100000,D0    Set up new VBR value
MOVEC    D0,VBR         Change VBR
```

EXAMPLE 15-3

A **68010** is being used as a virtual machine to emulate another system and it has set up a new Exception Vector Table at location $C000. Assume that a TRAP 1 instruction is encountered. How does the system respond?

SOLUTION

When a new emulation environment is set up, a set of alternative exception routines and an alternative vector table must be loaded (at some address other than 0). Thereafter, when the emulated operating system is executed, and runs its initialization routines, one of its first requirements is to write the address of the special vector table into the VBR.

In Section 14-12.3 and Example 14-27 we describe how a TRAP 1 instruction is handled by a **68000** μP. If the same instruction is encountered in an advanced μP, the solution will proceed as described in Example 14-27 except that the address calculated will be added to the number in the VBR. Instead of totaling $84, it will be $C084. The exception processing routine at that address will be entered.

15-5.6 ▼ Loop Mode Operation

Although essentially obsolete now, the **68010** has a feature that is interesting because it is the precursor to the cache memory concepts used in the **68020** and later μPs (see Section 15-8). This is an enhanced DBcc looping instruction, where cc is one of the conditions shown in Table 14-17. The cc also has the same meaning as in the Bcc or Scc instructions described in Section 14-10.11. The DBcc instruction for the **68000** was described in Section 14-10.12. The *loop mode* enhancement instruction included in the **68010** dramatically reduces the number of μP cycles required for the DBcc instruction and thereby speeds its execution. The unique feature of this **68010** loop mode is that the single-word instruction that precedes the DBcc instruction and the first word of the DBcc instruction (both within the loop) will only be fetched twice, first when the loop is entered and then when the DBcc loop conditions fail. When we study the more advanced μPs, we will see how this feature is accomplished in a different way (see Section 15-8).

15-6 ▼ MEMORY MANAGEMENT UNITS

In the **68000** or even the **6800** or **6809** μC systems we considered previously, the μP is connected directly to memory. Any program can therefore read or write to any part of memory available. This type of system has many applications but is unsuitable for execution of *multiple concurrent tasks,* as required in **multiuser systems,** because there is no mechanism to protect the memory of one task from interference by another task. It is also unsuitable for hosting virtual systems programs that are larger than the physical address space available.

The **68000** family processors and other *bus-master* devices (i.e., DMA controllers, or network controllers) provide an indication of the context in which they are operating on a cycle-by-cycle basis through the *Function Code* outputs. The Function Codes indicate the current mode of the bus master (Supervisor or User) and the type of operand that is being accessed (program or data). These Function Codes make it possible to designate portions of memory for specific uses, and to *protect* them from unauthorized accesses.

A new family of devices has been developed to handle these problems. They are known as *Memory Management Units* (MMUs) (Section 15-6) or, as explained later, *Paged Memory Management Units* (PMMUs) (Section 15-10). They provide an integrated hardware implementation of the memory selection and Bus Error functions needed for a Virtual Memory or Virtual Machine system and additionally make use of the Function Codes to provide memory segregation or protection.

EXAMPLE 15-4

A μP system that has been programmed to handle virtual memory has 256K bytes of hardware memory. A 512K program is started with 64K byte page size. What would happen?

SOLUTION

The operating system program must separate the memory into pages for all programs that it loads from disk. Assume that page 1 is occupied by the operating system, which must remain in the physical memory at all times. Thus no more than three pages of the 512K application program can be loaded when the program is started. The program would have a total of eight pages, so at least five of them would have to be kept on disk and be swapped out as required when the program runs.

User processes can be completely unaware of this swapping. The operating system controls the allocation of pages to page frames (called *mapping*).

Paging is a desirable method for memory allocation because it means that the entire code of data segments (consisting of many pages) need not be resident in physical memory at the same time. Only those pages that are currently being used by the process must be in memory. Since pages are all the same size, they can easily be swapped between memory and the disk.

The term *demand* means that a process does not need to specify in advance what areas of its logical address space it requires. An access to an address is interpreted by the system as a request to provide that memory. In a demand paged system, new pages are loaded by the operating system when the processor addresses a location that is within one of them. This requires a processor with a virtual memory capability, as provided in the **68010** and later μPs. The **68010** and **68020** also require external logic in one or more ICs to form a MMU or subsystem, to control the memory allocations. One new IC that has been developed for this function is the **68851** PMMU described in Section 15-10.

The MMU is inserted into the address bus between the CPU or μP, and memory, as shown in Fig. 15-3. Although the basic functions of a MMU also includes memory protection/privilege selections by using the Function Codes, only the *memory mapping* or *address translation* function of MMUs is discussed here. (see Section 15-10.1 for the other aspects of MMUs.)

When a MMU is used, the address bus is divided into two parts: a *logical address bus* and a *physical address bus*. The μP drives the logical address bus that connects to the MMU. The physical address bus is the path that the MMU uses to communicate with the rest of the system.

An *Address Translation Cache* (ATC) is internal to the MMU. The ATC is a fast memory containing entries composed of *logical* information (Logical address and Function Codes) and *physical* information (physical address and protection bits). During every cycle, the logical addresses and Function Codes are compared against the entries in the ATC. If one of the entries matches the stored physical address (and Function Code) from the ATC, this is called a cache *hit*. The address is placed onto the physical address bus and access information is gated to *access checking* circuitry. If the MMU detects no exceptional conditions, it then asserts *Physical Address Strobe* (PAS). If the ATC entries do not match the bus status during an attempted access, a *page fault* has occurred and the page containing the desired instructions or data is *swapped* from the disk into memory

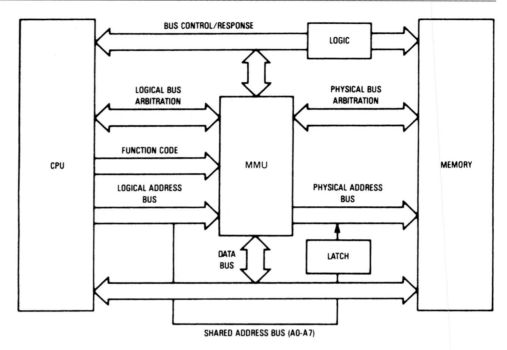

Figure 15-3 MMU block diagram.

and the ATC table is updated. Some type of external hardware is needed to generate the fault and subsequent Bus Error. This is included in typical MMU ICs.

15-7 ▼ 68020 MICROPROCESSOR

The **68020** μP was introduced in 1984. It retains all the features of the **68000** and **68010,** except that it does not have the special pins (signal lines) for support of 8-bit peripherals. It is a more powerful μP that uses the more advanced technology that became available at that time. The **68020** is the first full 32-bit implementation of a μP for the **68000** family.

The **68010** improved on the **68000** by adding virtual memory, which is needed for large programs. The **68020** also has virtual memory but improves on its predecessors by adding several significant new features:

1. It has a 32-bit address bus. Thus the **68020** can address 4 gigabytes of memory space instead 16 MB.

2. It has a 32-bit data bus. This means that memory data can be acccessed twice as fast compared to a 16-bit μP such as the **68000** or **68010.**

3. It includes an on-chip **cache** memory (see Section 15-8).

4. It can accommodate a **coprocessor** (see Section 15-9).

5. It has enhanced pipelining (see Section 15-11).

6. The Arithmetic/Logic Unit (ALU) and all internal data paths are also 32 bits wide.

The functional groups of lines that make up the bus interface are shown in Fig. 15-4.

The **68020** is available in a Pin Grid Array package (see Fig. 15-5) with 114 pins. The pinouts are identified in the **68020** User's Manual referenced in Section 15-18.

The **68020** User registers shown in Fig. 15-6a are the same as in the **68000** and **68010.** (It will execute **68000** or **68010** User mode programs.) However, the **68020** has several new supervisor registers as shown in Fig. 15-6b. A number of new control registers have been added, including two new registers for the Cache. The Supervisor Stack Pointer (SSP) has been renamed the Interrupt Stack Pointer (ISP) and an additional Stack Pointer, the Master Stack Pointer (MSP), has been added. The primary advantage of having two supervisor stack pointers rather than just one is for switching between tasks. The master stack pointer (MSP) can point to a task control block (TCP) and the interrupt stack pointer (ISP) can point to an interrupt stack. The processor sets the M bit before switching tasks. Therefore, all exceptions other than interrupts will use the MSP. For example, when a timer interrupt initiates a switch to another task, it does not change the MSP, since it has its own pointer. Therefore, the MSP is not changed when a task is changed and this pointer does not have to be saved—thereby saving some overhead.

The SFC, DFC, and VBR control registers that were explained in Section 15-5.5 are retained. The privileged MOVES and MOVEC instructions can also be used in **68020** programs, but the new control registers can also be accessed. For these the following control register fields of the MOVEC instruction are added to those described for the **68010** (Section 15-5.5):

HEX	CONTROL REGISTER
002	CAche Control Register (CACR)
802	CAche Address Register (CAAR)
803	Master Stack Pointer (MSP)

Many new **68020** instructions have been implemented and some are upgraded for 32-bit operation. New addressing modes and data types are also provided.

15-8 ▼ CACHE MEMORY CONCEPTS

As a means of improving the performance of the processor, the **68020** incorporates an on-chip *instruction cache* memory. This is a block of 64 long words of high-speed memory within the μP. The cache control logic stores instructions in the cache as they are being fetched for execution. Studies have shown that typical programs spend most of their time in main routines or program loops. Therefore, once instructions are stored in high-speed cache memory, it is likely that the next instruction is in the cache and can be fetched without going through the bus structure to main memory. Thus the total program execution time is significantly improved. In addition to the faster fetch from high-speed memory instead of from the slower system's DRAM, the major benefit of using the cache is that the processor's external bus activity is greatly reduced. In a system with more than one master (such as a processor and a DMA device) or a multiprocessor system, more of the bus time is available to the alternate bus masters without a major degradation in the

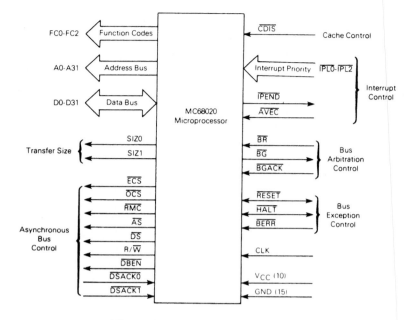

Figure 15-4 **68020** bus interface.

	MILLIMETERS		INCHES	
DIM	MIN	MAX	MIN	MAX
A	34.18	34.90	1.345	1.375
B	34.18	34.90	1.345	1.375
C	2.67	3.17	.100	.150
D0	.46	.51	.017	.019
G	2.54 BSC		.100 BSC	
K	4.32	4.82	.170	.190
V	1.74	2.28	.065	.095

MC68020
RC Suffix Package
Preliminary
Mechanical
Detail

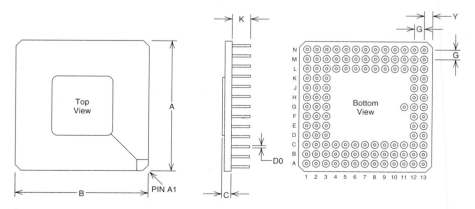

Figure 15-5 The **68020** μP showing the 114 pin
Plastic Gate Array (PGA) package.

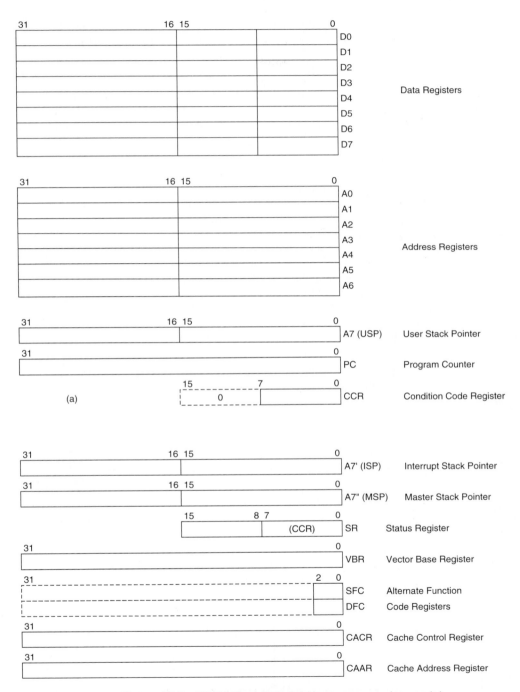

Figure 15-6   68020 Registers. (a) User programming model.
(b) Added registers for Supervisor programming model.

(a)

(b)

performance of the system. The **68020** can fill the cache rapidly because it can write from main memory to the cache while the program is decoding and executing instructions.

15-8.1 ▼ Cache Organization

Each time the processor attempts to read a 16-bit instruction, it checks to see if it is already in the cache memory. If not, it reads the instruction and the following word from the main memory and writes it into the cache. The words are not necessarily kept in order in the 64-long word block but are written into the location that has been used least recently. Each cache entry consists of a *tag* field made up of the upper 24 address bits, the FC2 Function Code (user/supervisor) bit, one *valid* bit, and 32 bits (two words) of instruction code. Figure 15-7 shows a diagram of the **68020** on-chip cache.

The **68020** employs a 32-bit data bus and fetches instructions on long-word address boundaries. Hence each 32-bit instruction fetch brings in two 16-bit instruction words that are written into the on-chip cache.

The process of checking for a word is started by first using the (A2–A7) field of the address as an index. This selects one of the 64 entries in the cache. Next, the address bits (A8–A31) and the FC2 bit are compared to those of the selected entry. If there is a match and the valid bit (Section 15-8.2) is set, a cache *hit* has occurred. Address bit A1 is then used to select the proper word from the cache entry and the cycle ends. If there is no match, or the valid bit is clear, a cache *miss* occurs and the instruction is fetched from external memory. This new instruction is written into the cache automatically, and the valid bit is set, unless the freeze cache bit (Section 15-8.4) has been set in the cache control register. Since the processor always prefetches instructions externally with long word aligned bus cycles, both words of the entry will be updated, regardless of which word caused the miss.

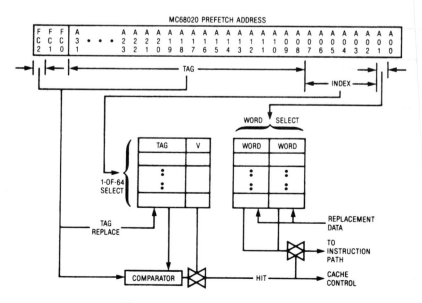

Figure 15-7 68020 on-chip cache.

15-8.2 ▼ Valid Bit

The valid bit, shown as "V" in Fig. 15-7, is a vital part of the mechanism for handling the Cache entries. It is *set* whenever new data is fetched from main memory and written into a cache entry. It is *reset* (or cleared) by the following events:

1. The *setting* of the Clear Entry or Clear Cache bits in the Cache Address Control Register (CACR) as explained in the following sections.
2. A JUMP or BRANCH to a section of the program that has a different tag.
3. A tag overflow, which moves the program to a different tag. If the instruction at 123456FE, for example, is executed, the next instruction will be at 12345700. These instructions have different tags, so the valid bits must be cleared and the cache reloaded.

EXAMPLE 15-5

An instruction is located at address 123456AA.

(a) What is its tag?
(b) What is its index?
(c) What instructions are written into the cache?

SOLUTION

(a) The cache tag is the upper 24 bits of the instruction or $(123456)_{16}$ plus the FC2 bit.
(b) The index is the next 6 bits of the instruction. Here it is $(101010)_2$.
(c) The instructions at memory locations 123456AA and 123456AC will become the words at this cache entry.

EXAMPLE 15-6

A **68020** has a program segment that starts at 123456F8. The program contains a loop. Eight instructions later, at 12345708, the program loops back. Why is this program slow? How can it be made faster?

SOLUTION

The program is slow because the loop covers two cache tags, and the cache must be reloaded constantly. It will execute faster if NOPs are placed at 123456F8, A, C, and E. Then the program segment can start at 12345700 and the branch back will then be at 12345710. The entire loop will be contained in the same tag and the program will execute faster.

15-8.3 ▼ Cache Control Register

The cached instructions and associated data are accessible only by the internal **68020** control unit. The user has no direct method to read or write individual entries (e.g., tag, instructions, or *valid* bits). This data can be manipulated, however, by a set of control functions available in the *Cache Control Register* (CACR). The CACR is a 32-bit register that is organized as shown in Fig. 15-8. Only the 4 least significant bits in the CACR are defined; the rest always read as zeros. Access to the CACR is provided by means of the privileged instruction, *MOVE Control register* (MOVEC). The bits are defined as described below.

Enable Cache. This bit determines whether the cache is to be used. It is necessary to be able to disable the cache to permit *system debug and emulation*. This bit is cleared automatically whenever the processor is reset, and therefore the user must set this bit during initialization to enable the cache for normal program operation. Clearing this bit will disable the cache, suppress fills, and force the processor to access external memory. The cache will remain disabled as long as this bit is clear.

The cache can also be disabled by a low level on the *Cache Disable Input* (CDIS) pin on the **68020.** The CDIS pin is used to disable the cache dynamically. The input signal on this pin is synchronized with the clock by internal logic before being used to control the internal cache. The cache is disabled on the first cache access after the synchronized CDIS signal is recognized as being asserted. The cache will be reenabled on the first cache access after the synchronized CDIS signal is recognized as being negated. This pin disables the cache independent of the enable bit in the CACR and therefore can be used by external emulator hardware to force the **68020** to make all accesses via the external bus.

Freeze Cache. The freeze bit keeps the cache enabled, but cache *misses* are not allowed to replace valid cache data. This bit can be used by emulators to freeze the cache during system testing.

Clear Entry. When the clear entry bit is set, the index field (bits 2 through 7 in the cache address register) specifies the associated entry that is to be invalidated. It clears the valid bit in the cache, regardless of whether or not it provides a hit (i.e., whether the tag field in the cache address register matches the cache tag or not). This function will occur only when a write to the cache control register is performed with the CE bit set. This bit always reads as a zero and the operation is independent of the state of the E (cache enable) or F (cache freeze) bits, or the external CDIS pin.

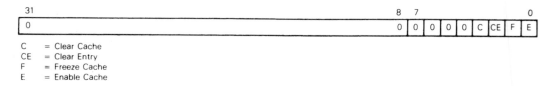

```
31                                                    8  7              0
 0                                                   | 0 | 0 | 0 | 0 | 0 | C | CE | F | E |
```

C   = Clear Cache
CE = Clear Entry
F   = Freeze Cache
E   = Enable Cache

Figure 15-8   The **68020** cache control register.

Clear Cache. The *clear cache* bit is used to invalidate all entries in the cache. This function is necessary for operating systems and other software which must clear old data from the cache whenever a context switch is required. The setting of the clear cache bit in the cache control register causes all *valid* bits in the cache to be cleared, thus invalidating all entries. This function occurs only when a write to the cache control register is performed with the C bit set. This bit always reads as a zero.

During processor reset, the cache is cleared by resetting all the *valid* bits. The CACR enable (E) and Freeze (F) bits are also cleared.

15-8.4 ▼ Cache Address Register

The CAche Address Register (CAAR) is a 32-bit register that provides an address for cache control functions. It is shown in Figure 15-9. The **68020** uses this register only for the clear entry (CE) function. These bits specify the tag and address of the entry to be cleared. Access to the CACR and CAAR registers is provided by the MOVE Control Register (MOVEC) privileged instruction.

15-9 ▼ COPROCESSOR CONCEPTS

The **68000** family of general-purpose μPs provides a level of performance that satisfies a wide range of computer applications. *Coprocessors* allow the capabilities and performance of a general-purpose processor to be enhanced for a particular application without unduly encumbering the main processor.

A coprocessor is a special-purpose processor that is used *in conjunction* with the main processor to provide added capabilities. Coprocessors generally execute special-purpose instructions that are not recognized by the main processor. Coprocessors with different features can be designed and can be used separately or in combination. The processing capabilities of a system can be tailored to a specific application by utilizing a general-purpose main processor and the appropriate coprocessor(s).

The coprocessor must be interfaced to the main processor so that the special instructions that pertain to the coprocessor can be communicated to it. This **68000** family coprocessor interface is an integral part of the design of the **68020** and the various coprocessors. Coprocessors such as the **68881** Math Coprocessor or the **68851** MMU can be used. Each processor in a system has an instruction set that implements its special function, whether it be floating-point math, memory management, or another unique purpose.

These special coprocessor instructions may be executed merely by placing the instruction op code and parameters in the **68020** instruction stream. The **68020** detects the coprocessor instruction, initiates bus communication with the registers of the target coprocessor to pass the instruction, and tests for conditions requiring further action. The **68020** performs activity to support the execution of the instruction (e.g., address calcula-

31   8 7   2 1 0

| Cache Function Address | Index | |

Figure 15-9 The **68020** cache address register.

tion or data transfer) at the request of the coprocessor. The interchange of information and the division of responsibility between the main processor and the coprocessor are controlled by the coprocessor interface, and this process is completely transparent to the user. The addition of a coprocessing unit to a **68020** system supplements the instruction set executable by the processor. The register set of the coprocessor is perceived by system programmers to be a direct extension of the main processor registers.

No knowledge of the communication protocol between the main processor and the coprocessor is required of the programmer since this protocol is implemented in the **68020** hardware. Thus the coprocessor can provide capabilities to the user without appearing as hardware external to the main processor.

In contrast, standard peripheral hardware is generally accessed through the use of interface registers mapped into the memory space of the main processor. When coprocessors are used with the **68000** or **68010,** they function in this way. In this case, the programmer must use standard processor instructions to access the peripheral or coprocessor interface registers and utilize services provided by that device. While these units can conceivably provide capabilities equivalent to the built-in coprocessor interface for many applications, the programmer must provide the communication protocol between the main processor and the external hardware.

15-9.1 ▼ 68881 Floating-Point Coprocessor

The **68881** floating-point coprocessor implements the IEEE Standard for Binary Floating-Point Arithmetic (P754) for use with the **68000** family of μPs. It uses VLSI technology to provide remarkable performance in a physically small device.

Intended primarily for use as a coprocessor to the **68020,** the **68881** provides a logical extension to the main μP's integer data processing capabilities. It does so by providing a very high-performance floating-point arithmetic unit and a set of floating-point data registers that are utilized in a manner analogous to the use of the integer data registers. It can be interfaced to the **68020** via a 32-, 16-, or 8-bit data bus configuration. These bus size differences are controlled by the connections to the A0 and SIZE pins of the **68881.** Diagrams are shown in the **68881/882** *Coprocessor User's Manual* referenced in Section 15-18.

The **68881** instruction set is fully upward compatible with all earlier members of the **68000** family and supports all of the addressing modes of the host μP. Due to the flexible bus interface of the **68000** family, the **68881** can be used with any of μP devices of the family, such as the **68000, 68008,** or **68010.** In these cases the **68881** is connected as a peripheral via a 16- or 8-bit data bus as shown in the User's Manual referred to above. It may also be used as a peripheral to non-**68000** processors.

The major features of the **68881** are:

- Eight general-purpose floating-point data registers, each supporting a full 80-bit extended-precision real data format (a 64-bit mantissa plus a sign bit, and a 15-bit biased exponent)
- A 67-bit ALU to allow very fast calculations, with intermediate precision greater than the extended precision result
- A 67-bit Barrel Shifter for high-speed shifting operations (for normalizing)
- 46 instruction types, including 35 arithmetic operations

- Full conformity with the IEEE P754 Standard (Draft 10.0), including all requirements and suggestions
- Supports functions not defined by the IEEE Standard, including a full set of trigonometric and logarithmic function
- Supports seven data types:
  - Byte, word, and long integers
  - Single, double, and extended-precision real numbers
  - Packed binary-coded-decimal string real numbers
- Support of virtual memory/machine operations
- Efficient mechanisms for procedure calls, context switches, and interrupt handling
- Fully concurrent instruction execution with the main processor
- Compatibility with any host processor on an 8-, 16-, and 32-bit data bus

15-9.2 ▼ 68882 Floating-Point Coprocessor

The **68882** *enhanced* floating-point coprocessor was introduced in September 1986. It is pin compatible with the **68881,** offers the same strict conformity to the IEEE 704 specification, and is software compatible with the **68881.** The **68882** has a superior internal architecture that provides more concurrent operations. By simply removing a **68881** and replacing it with the **68882,** a 50% performance increase is obtained. For those designs that optimize the software, the **68882** is nearly twice as fast as the **68881.**

From the standpoint of applications software, the two coprocessors are identical, right down to the results that are generated by calculations. The instruction set is also the same.

15-10 ▼ 68851 PAGED MEMORY MANAGEMENT UNIT

Another HCMOS coprocessor introduced in 1986 is the **68851** *Paged Memory Management Unit* (PMMU). It is a high-performance VLSI IC designed for efficient support of the **68020** 32-bit μP. The **68851** is optimized to perform very fast *logical-to-physical address translation,* to provide a comprehensive access control and protection mechanism for the installed memory, and to provide extensive support for *paged virtual systems.*

The **68851** functions as a coprocessor in systems where the **68020** is the main processor via the coprocessor interface. It can function as a peripheral in systems where the main processor is a **68010** or any other processor with virtual memory capabilities.

A powerful and complete memory management system is assured by using the following **68851** features:

- 32-bit logical and physical addresses and 4 Function Code bits
- Eight available page sizes from 256 bytes to 32K bytes
- A fully associative 64 entry on-chip Address Translation Cache
- Address Translation Cache support for multi tasking
- Hardware maintenance of external translation tables and an on-chip cache
- A **68020** instruction set extension and instruction-oriented communication using the **68000** family coprocessor interface

- Hierarchical protection mechanism with up to eight levels of protection
- Instruction breakpoints for software debug and program control
- Support for a logical and/or a physical data cache
- Support for multiple logical and/or physical bus masters

The primary system functions provided by the **68851** are logical-to-physical address translations (described in Section 15-6), implementing the protection/privilege mechanism, and supporting the breakpoint operations.

15-10.1 ▼ PMMU Protection Mechanism

The **68851** PMMU provides facilities to protect address spaces from access by the wrong user. This protects the supervisor from user tasks, user tasks from each other, and user tasks from themselves.

The **68851** also has two protection mechanisms that can be used either independently or together to provide a comprehensive memory protection scheme. The primary mechanism uses the Function Code outputs of the logical bus master to define address space based on the current operating mode of the master (Supervisor or User) and the type of operand (program or data) being accessed. The second mechanism is a more comprehensive protection method that subdivides the logical address space of user mode tasks into regions of privilege.

The **68851** completely supports the **68020** module call return functions (CALLM/RTM instructions), which include a mechanism to change privilege levels during module operations. Details can be obtained from the **68851** PMMU User's Manual cited in Section 15-18.

15-10.2 ▼ PMMU Instruction Set Extensions

The **68851** implements an extension to the **68000** μP family instruction set using the coprocessor interface. These added instructions provide control functions for:

- Loading and storing of MMU registers
- Testing access rights and conditionals based on the results of this test
- MMU control functions

There are 15 additional instructions provided for the **68851.** Since we are limited in space, the reader is again referred to the **68851** PMMU user's manual referenced in Section 15-18 for complete descriptions.

15-11 ▼ PIPELINED ARCHITECTURE

The concept of **pipelined architecture** inside a μP is not new. Internal connections that *pipe* the data directly to a register or part of the μP control unit, where it can be processed at the same time other events are occurring, is the basis of the concept. For example, in a pipelined system, while an instruction is in the process of being executed, the next instruction will be fetched from memory or the cache.

The **68020** has several pipeline mechanisms, but the primary pipeline is a *three-stage instruction pipe*, as shown in Fig. 15-10. Instructions are loaded from the on-chip cache or from external memory into stage B. The instructions are sequenced from stage B through stage C to D. Stage D presents a fully decoded and validated instruction to the control unit for execution. Instructions with *immediate data* or *extension words* will find these words already loaded in stage C, thus speeding the execution times.

The benefit of the pipeline is to allow concurrent operations to occur on up to three words at a time. They could all be part of the same instruction or could be three separate consecutive instructions. This technique is most efficient when dealing with instructions in normal program sequence. Since two short instructions can be processed concurrently even though they were fetched sequentially, it gives rise to the statement that some instructions are processed in *zero* time. When a change-of-flow instruction (i.e., a branch) occurs, however, the words following a jump or branch are fetched but must be ignored. Another three words must be fetched before processing can continue.

The depth of the instruction pipe was increased from two to three words on the **68020,** since it was observed that there is no performance penalty for the third element during a change-of-flow instruction on a 32-bit bus. This is true because it is always possible to fetch three words in two accesses. Because of the possibility of branching to an odd-word address, in which case two accesses are required to fetch either two or three words, the minimum number of accesses required to branch is two. A demonstration of

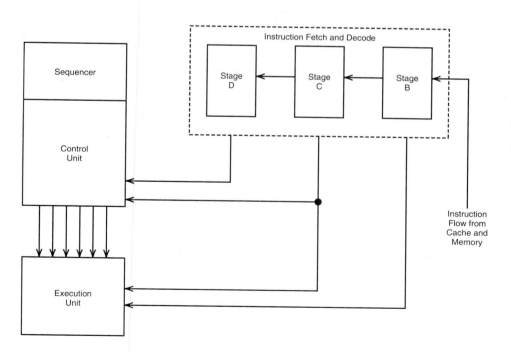

Figure 15-10 **68020** pipeline.

EVEN ALIGNED

$00	A	B
$04	C	D
$08	E	

ODD ALIGNED

$00		A
$04	B	C
$08	D	E

Figure 15-11 Two memory configurations for the instruction stream A, B, C, D, E.

the stubborn consistency of this principle is given by Fig. 15-11, which depicts two memory configurations for the instruction stream A, B, C, D, E. (These can be separate one-word instructions or five words of a single instruction, or, more likely, a mixture of one- and two- word instructions.)

If a branch is made to the first example (even aligned), only one access is required to fetch two words. However, in the other case (odd aligned), two accesses must occur to fetch the first two words. Once it is determined that two accesses need to be made to fill the pipe, it can be observed that it is always possible to fetch the first three words with two memory accesses. Thus there is no penalty for increasing the depth of the instruction pipe from two to three words.

As described above, the greater depth of the instruction pipe, while improving performance of in-line code, has a detrimental effect on change-of-flow instructions. By using a three-word pipe, the **68020** optimizes the performance.

15-12 ▼ 68030 MICROPROCESSOR

The **68030** is a newer, more powerful, and faster µP than the **68020.** Features of the **68030** over and above those in the **68020** are:

- More internal buses so that address and data can be fetched at the same time

- An *on-chip* PMMU that reduces the minimum physical bus cycle time to two cycles and provides *zero* translation time by virtue of the parallel pipelining

- The ability to enable or disable the PMMU by software

- A 256-byte instruction cache and a 256-byte data cache that can be accessed simultaneously

- Two transparent segments that allow untranslated blocks to be defined for systems that transfer large blocks of data to predefined addresses, as in graphics applications

- Pipelined architecture with increased parallelism that allows accesses from internal caches to occur in parallel with bus transfers and multiple instructions to be executing concurrently

- An enhanced Bus Controller that supports asynchronous bus cycles, synchronous bus cycles that can operate in two clock cycles, and burst data transfers that can operate in one clock cycle, all with physical addresses

The functional signal groups of the **68030** bus interface can be seen in Fig. 15-12.

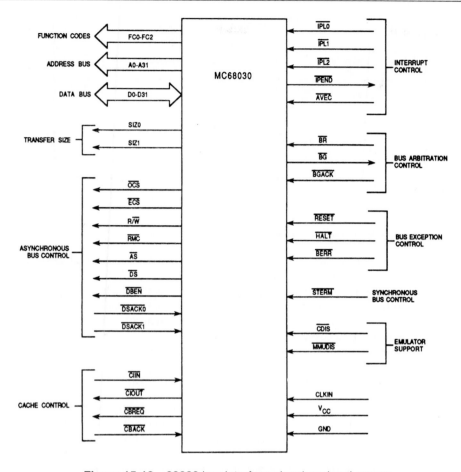

Figure 15-12 **68030** bus interface showing signal groups.

15-12.1 ▼ On-Chip Instruction and Data Caches

The **68030** is the first 32-bit μP to offer both an on-chip **instruction cache** and a **data cache**. A block diagram is shown in Fig. 15-13. The caches (high-speed temporary storage) are used to increase the performance by providing immediate access to instructions and data for the CPU execution unit. The two 256-byte on-chip caches serve to boost the data flow to the CPU, typically a major performance bottleneck, and enhance overall throughput. Operating from the caches not only reduces access times but also reduces the overall bus requirements since the μP spends less time on the bus accessing data. Bus access time is reduced further by the *burst fillable cache mode,* allowing high-speed data fills of both the data and instruction caches. These features increase bus availability for other bus masters that are used in multiprocessor systems, Local Area Networks (LANs), disks and so on. Simulation studies on 17 million bus cycles of data captured from engineering workstations indicates that the combination of a 256-byte instruction cache and a 256-byte data cache is optimum when evaluating silicon die size, and performance increases.

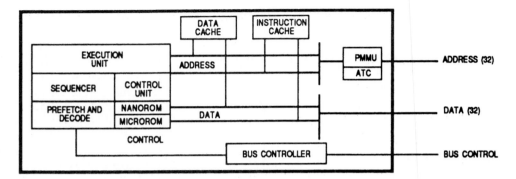

Figure 15-13 **68030** block diagram.

15-12.2 ▼ Harvard Style Architecture

Harvard style architecture has been used for many years in several super- and mainframe computers allowing parallel access of data and instructions. Two independent 32-bit address buses and two 32-bit data buses allow the CPU, caches, the (PMMU), and the bus controller to operate in parallel. These parallel instruction and data paths provide the processor an internal *bus bandwidth* of greater than 80 Mbytes/second. The **68030** can simultaneously access an instruction from the instruction cache, data from the data cache, and instructions or data from external memory.

15-12.3 ▼ Asynchronous and Synchronous Bus Interfaces

The **68030** is suitable for many types of systems from low-end ($2000 to $3000) to high-performance (greater than $50,000) systems with much of the difference due to the choice of memory configuration. Low-end systems typically interface directly to low-cost DRAM using only the internal caches, while high-performance systems use a multilevel hierarchy of memory that range from high-speed static to slow dynamic RAMs. To support these features, the **68030** supports both a synchronous bus interface (with a minimum two clock access times), which allows maximum access time to a cache subsystem, as well as an asynchronous interface (such as that on the **68020**) for slower memories, peripherals, and other **68020**-compatible subsystems. This interface supports synchronous or asynchronous accesses on a cycle-by-cycle basis as determined by the memory subsystem used. Like the **68020,** compatibility is maintained by supporting the existing asynchronous dynamic bus sizing feature which allows interfaces to 8-, 16-, or 32-bit devices.

In addition, this bus interface provides the low-end system designer with increased performance by taking advantage of the shorter access times offered by the paged mode and nibble mode in DRAM technology (see AN986 in Section 15-18). Here the **68030** can request a burst fill to the internal caches. Since data in the cache is organized in rows of four long words, up to three additional long words may be loaded during the access. The **68030** will request a burst fill and the system can then, in as little as one clock cycle per subsequent access, supply the **68030** with the successive data obtained from the memory.

15-12.4 ▼ Summary of 68030 Performance Enhancements

The **68030** gains in performance are made possible by including the function of memory management on-chip and using a Harvard style architecture (parallel address and data bus accesses). The relative performance increases of the **68030** over prior devices can be seen in Fig. 15-14. The dual bus structure offers 80 Mbytes of bandwidth and allows the MMU to be efficiently integrated on-chip. In doing this, the time to translate logical addresses to physical addresses can be hidden during cache access, so that the system will see no performance degradation due to MMU translations. In addition, the on-chip MMU is coupled to the instruction and data caches so that accesses to the on-chip caches are performed in parallel. Also, the MMU is not utilized unless required.

The MMU portion of the **68030** provides a high-powered set of functions that are a subset of those available on the **68851** Paged Memory Management Unit. These include multiple page sizes, multilevel translation trees, and on-chip Address Translation Cache (ATC). The MMU on the **68030,** like the **68851,** will automatically search the main memory for address translations when they are not found in the ATC. The on-chip MMU reduces the minimum physical bus cycle time to two clocks, half the time required by the **68020** and **68851.** Internal pipelining permits the MMU to avoid adding any translation time to any bus cycle and physical accesses are just as fast as logical accesses. The 22-entry, fully associative, on-chip ATC helps maximize performance. ATC *hit* rates will be greater than 99% for 4K pages and about 98% for 1K pages.

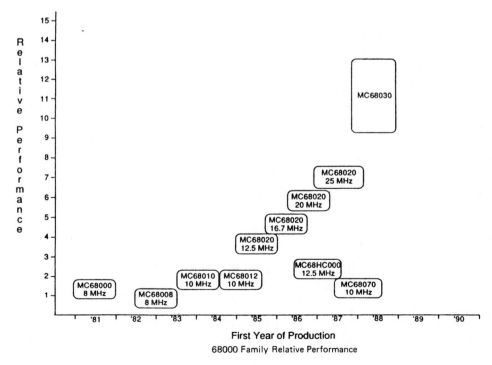

Figure 15-14   68000 family relative performance.

The **68030** supports the same powerful **68020**-compatible coprocessors: the **68851** PMMU, the **68881** Floating-Point Coprocessor (FPCP), or the new enhanced FPCP, the **68882.** Unique dynamic disabling of the address translation provides for off-chip MMUs as well as for the times when translations must be disabled for emulation support.

Occasionally, a system cannot afford the time required to search tables for a correct translation when referencing memory. For example, if the **68030** is sharing the graphics function in a low-cost system, and if a translation in the ATC should miss, drawing a line may appear erratic as the tables are searched. To eliminate this problem, the **68030** provides the feature of *transparent memory windows* that can be used to bypass the MMU and thereby map the logical addresses directly through to the physical address space. In this way, no overhead is incurred for time-critical portions of the application. These windows can be as small as 16 Mbytes or as large as the entire 4-gigabyte address space supported by the **68030.**

15-13 ▼ 68040 μP

The **68040** is Motorola's third generation of **68000**-compatible, high-performance, 32-bit μPs. Very high performance is achieved by employing multiple concurrent execution units in this Virtual Memory monolithic HCMOS device. A **68030**-compatible Integer Unit is integrated with two fully independent instruction and data demand-paged MMUs, an IEEE 754–compatible Floating-Point Unit (FPU), and independent 4K-byte instruction and data caches, all on a single chip. Multiple internal buses and multiple independent execution pipelines are combined with Harvard architecture to achieve parallel instruction execution. Both instruction and data accesses include separate physical caches. The **68040** also directly supports cache coherency (Section 15-13.1) in multimaster applications with dedicated on-chip bus snooping logic (see Section 15-13.1). The **68040** is implemented in Motorola's latest HCMOS technology. Figure 15-15 is a simplified block diagram of the **68040.** Instruction execution is pipelined in both the Integer Unit (IU) and FPU. Independent data and instruction MMUs control the main caches and the address translation caches (ATCs). The ATCs speed up logical-to-physical address translations by storing recently used translations.

The main features of the **68040** are as follows:

- 20-MIP Integer performance
- 3.5-MFLOP Floating-Point performance
- An IEEE 754-compatible FPU
- Independent Instruction and Data MMUs
- A 4K-byte Physical Instruction Cache and a 4K-byte Physical Data Cache accessed simultaneously
- 32-Bit, nonmultiplexed external address and data buses with synchronous interface
- User-object-code compatible with all earlier **68000** μPs
- Multimaster/multiprocessor support via Bus Snooping
- Concurrent Integer Unit, FPU, MMU, Bus Controller, and Bus Snooper Operation all maximize throughput

- 4-Gbyte Direct Addressing range
- Software support, including Optimizing C Compiler and UNIX* System V port

The **68040** is user-object-code compatible with previous members of the **68000** family and is specifically optimized to reduce the execution time of compiler-generated code.

15-13.1 ▼ Cache Coherency

As in every new development, different techniques are introduced and new expressions need to be explained. With new capabilities, additional operating modes are possible. As shown in Fig. 15-15, the **68040** has two independent 4K-byte on-chip caches. One is used for instructions and the other for data. Accessing instruction words and data simultaneously through separate caches increases instruction throughput. The data cache improves system performance by providing cached data to the on-chip execution unit with very low latency. Also, the separate units allow systems with alternate bus masters increased bus availability. This is the reason for concern about cache coherency. Cache coherency means that the data in the cache and in memory are the same. When the **68040** is the only bus master, differences can easily be avoided, but when a DMA device or another processor

* UNIX is a registered trademark of AT&T Bell Laboratories.

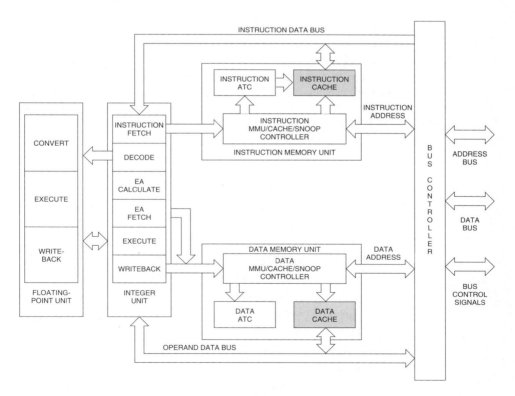

Figure 15-15   68040 block diagram.

are installed on the bus with commonly accessed memory, problems can arise. To solve this, as also shown in Fig. 15-15, the **68040** implements a Bus Snooper function in the cache controller that maintains cache coherency by monitoring an alternate bus master's access and performing cache maintenance operations as requested by the alternate master.

Another point about the use of 4K-byte caches is that because they bring in large blocks of instructions or data at a time, fewer accesses are necessary. Therefore, the access time of the main memory can be slower, which can significantly reduce the cost of the system while causing little performance degradation.

There are many more aspects of these dual caches that need discussion when designing or programming a new system, but they are too complex to be included in this book. For detailed information on the **68040,** refer to MC68040UM/AD, The MC68040 32-bit microprocessor User's Manual, listed in Section 15-18.

15-14 ▼ 68060 μP

The **68060** is a 32-bit-μP with three times the performance of a 25-MHz **68040.** It also has various ways to operate with reduced power. It provides *dual execution pipelines* in the instruction execution controller (called superscalar design), allowing simultaneous execution of instructions, thus processing more than one instruction during each machine cycle. This feature can be disabled in software, turning off the second execution pipeline for debugging.

The **68060** is fully compatible with all previous members of the **68000** family in user mode. The **68060** features *dual* on-chip caches, fully independent demand-paged MMUs for both instructions and data, dual integer execution pipelines, an on-chip FPU, and a branch target cache. Parallel instruction execution is achieved through the use of a full internal Harvard architecture, multiple internal buses, independent execution units, and dual instruction issues within the instruction execution controller. Figure 15-16 is a block diagram of the **68060.**

Complete code compatibility with the **68000** family allows the designer to draw on existing code and past experience to bring products to market quickly. The **68060**'s high level of integration results in high performance while reducing overall system power consumption.

The following is a list of primary features for the **68060:**

- 100% User-Mode compatible with **68040**
- Three times the performance of a 25-MHz **68040**
- Superscalar implementation of **68000** architecture
- Dual integer instruction execution for improved performance
- IEEE-compatible on-chip FPU
- a Branch target cache to minimize branch latency
- Independent instruction and data MMUs
- Dual 8-Kbyte on-chip Caches
  - Separate Data and Instruction Caches
  - Simultaneous access

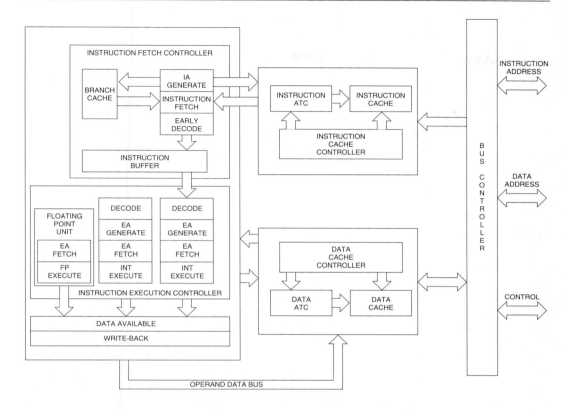

Figure 15-16 **68060** simplified block diagram.

- Bus Snooping
- Full 32-bit nonmultiplexed Address and Data Bus
  - 32-Bit bus to maximize data throughput
  - Nonmultiplexed bus to simplify design
  - Four-deep write buffer to maximize write bandwidth
  - **68040**-Compatible bus to provide a simple hardware migration path
- Concurrent operation of Integer Unit, MMUs, Caches, Bus Controller, Integer Pipelines, and FPU to provide high performance
- Power consumption control
  - Static HCMOS technology to reduce power in normal operation
  - Low-voltage operation at 3.3 V
  - LPSTOP to provide an idle state for lowest standby current
- 50- and 66-MHz clock operation
- Packaging
  - Ceramic Pin Grid Array (PGA) package
  - Ceramic Quad Flat Pack (CQFP) package

15-14.1 ▼ Power Consumption Management

Perhaps the most innovative feature in the **68060** μP, in addition to the improved performance attributable to multiple execution units, is the unique power consumption control. The **68060** is very power efficient due to static logic and power management designed into the basic architecture. Each stage of the integer and floating-point unit's pipelines draws power only when an access is made. The FPU, Caches, and integer execution pipeline can be disabled to save power. An LPSTOP instruction is available on the **68060** to put the μP in a comatose mode and thereby save power. It shuts down the active circuits in the processor, halting instruction execution. Power consumption in this standby mode is very low. An interrupt resets the processor restoring normal operation and power consumption. Low-voltage operation at 3.3 V reduces current by 40 to 60% over μPs using 5 V.

15-15 ▼ EMBEDDED CONTROLLERS

Motorola has been striving to include more and more functions into the **68000** family μP chips, to increase their performance in general-purpose systems. At the same time, as we have been describing in previous chapters, there is a big demand for μC controllers for dedicated applications. Some applications do not require all the features available in the highly integrated modern μPs and some can be omitted to keep the costs down. In controller applications, the tasks are frequently limited and can be defined precisely. Only a small amount of memory may be needed. Thus, for a dedicated application, an 8K or 16K ROM may be adequate. Certainly, in this case, an MMU is not needed. Similarly, the FPU in the **68040** provides outstanding performance for some applications, but it is an unnecessary expense in many other systems. Thus it has been found desirable to provide cost-reduced versions of these top-of-the-line processors. The term *Embedded Controllers* has been created to describe the types of μC systems that are built into industrial products or processes to provide transparent control. Motorola has reengineered all the **680x0** families to minimize costs while maintaining performance, and has generated a new μP family to meet the demands for this class of systems.

The **68EC000, 68EC020, 68EC030,** and **68EC040** μPs offer all the integer performance of the corresponding **68000** family μPs at a fraction of the cost. They are also software compatible and can use the available development tools.

Embedded Controllers have integrated Cache memories, Bus Controllers, and clock circuits, but do not have the I/O ports, Timers, A/D converters, and so on, integrated into the chip as we have seen in the MCUs of Chapter 10. These **68EC0x0** μPs do offer high performance, however, in specialized Embedded Controller systems. They can be used with devices such as the **68901** multifunction peripheral chip, which provides a timer and serial and parallel I/O. If, for example, a **68EC000** is used with the **68901** plus a ROM and RAM, the four-chip system is a high-performance Embedded Controller system.

Where the very high performance of these new μPs is not required, Motorola has created the **68300** family of integrated MCUs, which include the CPU32 processor based on the **68020**. It and the **68300** family of MCUs are described in Chapter 16.

15-16 ▼ SUMMARY

In this chapter we have introduced the **68010, 68020, 68030, 68040,** and **68060** members of the **68000** family of 16/32-bit µPs. The features supported by these µPs, such as Virtual Memory, PMMUs, Cache memory, Coprocessors, and/or FPUs, were described. These features and the µPs themselves are of such complexity that only a brief description has been possible in this single chapter. Students are referred to the manuals and data sheets listed in Section 15-18.

15-17 ▼ GLOSSARY

Addressable memory Memory that is accessible to the programmer.

Barrel Shifter A hardware structure in the chip that will rotate or shift a 32-bit long word any number of positions in one clock cycle.

Base address The beginning address of a table of addresses or of a block of memory.

Cache coherency Maintaining the contents of the cache memory the same as the contents of main memory.

Cache hit A match between the parameters of a memory access and those of a cache entry, when an instruction fetch occurs.

Cache memory A small high-speed memory that holds a group of instructions so that they can be accessed directly by the CPU without the need to fetch them individually from main memory.

Cache miss The fetch of an instruction that is not in the cache, and must be fetched from external memory.

Context switch The process of saving the contents of all registers that represent the complete state of the machine, so that other code can be executed, or of restoring the original conditions and resuming execution of the main program.

Coprocessor A special-purpose processor that is used in conjunction with a main processor to provide added capabilities.

Coprocessor Interface Provision to connect a specialized processor to the main processor and communicate with it for enhanced overall performance. The coprocessor serves to add registers and instructions that are transparent to the programmer.

Demand-Paged A Type of Virtual Memory system where paged code segments can be loaded when needed without specifying areas of logical address space in advance.

Instruction Cache The cache memory used for storing a small group of instructions.

Logical addresses Program addresses put out by the µP that are outside the range of the physical memory and are translated by the MMU into addresses of the actual physical memory.

Loop Mode operation A special feature of the **68010** µP that provides efficient program loop operation.

Memory Management Unit (MMU) An IC circuit or device that provides address translation to implement Virtual Memory concepts. Function codes are also used to distinguish between the User and Supervisor address spaces, and between data and program spaces within them.

Multiuser system A μC system that can execute concurrent tasks by several users. Users may not be aware that other users are present.

Paging The subdivision of physical memory into equal-sized blocks called page frames.

Physical addresses Addresses determined by the MMU with the aid of the Function Codes. The actual addresses of the memory ICs used by the MMU.

Physical memory Real memory that is located at the addresses on the physical address bus.

Pipelined architecture Parallel bus structure within the μP that allows concurrent operations to occur.

Snooping A technique of monitoring the bus during accesses by alternate bus masters to avoid cache coherency problems.

Tag field The upper 24 address bits in each cache memory entry.

Valid Bit A bit in each cache memory entry that is set when an instruction is entered into that cache entry.

Vector Base Register (VBR) A register in the **68010,** and later μPs, that points to the base address of the 1K-byte Exception Vector Table. It is initialized to 0 so that **68000** programs will work.

Vector number An 8-bit number that when multiplied by 4 gives the offset of an exception vector.

Vector offset A 32-bit number that when added to the Vector Base address gives the actual vector address.

Vector Table Entry An address pointer to the exception service routines.

Virtual Machine An emulated μC that appears to have I/O and memory at virtual locations.

Virtual Memory Memory that appears to be at a location different than that selected by the physical address bus.

Wired-ORed The technique whereby open-collector or open-drain transistor circuits are paralleled and used with one pull-up resistor so that any one of the circuits can pull down the line to provide the interrupt signal.

15-18 ▼ REFERENCES

ARNEWSH, INC., *Single Board Computer* SBC68K Rev. 1.1, Fort Collins, Colo., 1991.

HARMAN, THOMAS L. *The Motorola MC68020 and 68030 Microprocessors,* Prentice Hall, Englewood Cliffs, N.J., 1989.

MOTOROLA, *020bug Resident Package*, M68K2RBBUG4, ADI 1109, Phoenix, Ariz., 1984.

———— *Built-in Tight-Loop Mode Raises μP's Performance*, AR-211, Motorola reprint from *Electronic Design*, Vol. 31, No. 22, 1983.

———— *Design Philosophy behind Motorola's MC68000*, AR208, Austin Tex., 1983.

———— *Low Power HCMOS 16/32 Bit Microprocessor MC68HC000*, MC68HC000/D Rev. 4, Phoenix, Ariz., 1990.

———— *M68000 Family Reference Manual*, M68000FR/AD, Phoenix, Ariz., 1990.

———— *MC68008 8/32-Bit Microprocessor with 8-Bit Data Bus*, AD1939R2, Phoenix, Ariz., April 1985.

———— *MC68008 Minimum Configuration System*, AN897, Phoenix, Ariz., 1984.

———— *MC68010/68012 16-/32-Bit Virtual Memory Microprocessors*, ADI942R2, Phoenix, Ariz., May 1985.

———— *MC68020 32-Bit Microprocessor User's Manual, 2nd ed.*, MC68020UM/AD Rev. 1, Motorola, Phoenix, Ariz., and Prentice Hall, Englewood Cliffs, N.J., 1985.

———— *MC68030 Enhanced 32-Bit Microprocessor User's Manual*, 2nd ed., MC68030UM/AD Rev. 1, Austin, Texas, 1989.

———— *MC68040, MC68EC040, MC68LC040 Microprocessors User's Manual*, MC68040UM/AD, Austin, Texas, 1992.

———— *MC68851 Paged Memory Management Unit*, 2nd ed., MC68881UM/AD Rev. 1, Phoenix, Ariz., 1989.

———— *MC68882 HCMOS Enhanced Floating Point Coprocessor* Technical Data Sheet, BR509/D, Phoenix, Ariz., 1986.

———— *Memory Management Chip for 68020 Translates Addresses in Less Than a Clock Cycle*, AR238, Motorola reprint from *Electronic Design*, Vol. 34, No. 11, 1986.

———— *Multiprocessing Capabilities of the MC68020 32-Bit Microprocessor*, AR220, WESCON, Austin, Texas 1984.

———— *Page, Nibble, and Static Column Modes*, AN986, Phoenix, Ariz., 1988.

———— *Programmer's Reference Manual (Includes CPU32 Instructions)*, MC68000PM/AD, Phoenix, Ariz., 1992.

———— *Virtual Memory and the MC68010 AR209*, Motorola reprint from *IEEE Micro*, Vol. 3, pp. 24–29, June 1983.

MOTOROLA *68881/882 Floating-Point Coprocessor User's Manual* MC68881UM/AD Rev. 2 1989.

16- AND 32-BIT MICROCONTROLLERS

16

16-1 ▼ INSTRUCTIONAL OBJECTIVES

In previous chapters we have described the **68HC11** and **68HC05** MCU families of 8-bit MCUs. Chapters 14 and 15 have been devoted to discriptions of the **68000** family of 16- and 32-bit μPs. Application of the features and techniques of the high-performace **68000** μPs has resulted in advances in MCU products. The marriage of the 8-bit MCU product line and the more advanced μPs has produced two other MCU families, the **68HC16** and the **68300.** These are, respectively, 16- and 32-bit MCUs, and are the subject of this chapter. After reading this chapter, the student should be able to:

1. Explain the function of each port on the **68HC16Z1.**
2. Set up the **68HC16Z1** MCU to use chip selects or function control signals.
3. Insert the proper number of wait states in DSACK.
4. Use the A/D converter on the **68HC16Z1.**
5. Understand the Background Debug Mode.
6. Use the **68HC16Z1EVB.**

16-2 ▼ SELF-EVALUATION QUESTIONS

Watch for the answers to the following questions as you read the chapter. They should help you to understand the material presented.

1. Explain the function of the K register in the **68HC16.**
2. Why can't port F be used for I/O in a system that allows peripherals to interrupt?
3. How many Chip Selects are available if the Function Code and bus arbitration signals are used in a **68HC16** MCU?
4. What effect does the MM bit of the System Integration Module's Module Configuration Register have?

5. The **68HC16Z1** has several causes of reset. How can a program determine the cause of the latest reset?

6. What are the functions of the QSM?

7. How many memories are in the RAM of the QSM? What are their functions?

16-3 ▼ INTRODUCTION

The development of 16- and 32-bit μPs allowed Motorola to develop more powerful microcontroller units (MCUs), whose primary function is to control a system rather than to perform computations. In developing the 16- and 32-bit versions of these MCUs, a new modular architecture has been created. It uses standardized submodules that communicate with each other via an on-chip bus called the *InterModule Bus (IMB)*. This concept facilitates the rapid design of new devices. The IMB was first introduced in the **68332** (see Section 16-14.2) and is being used in the other members of the **683xx** 32-bit family as well as in the **68HC16Z1**, **68HC16Z2**, **68HC16X1**, and **68HC16Y1** MCUs of the **68HC16** 16-bit family. The IMB is discussed in Section 16-5. A newly designed CPU core module called the **CPU16** is used in all the **HC16** versions and a simplified **68020** CPU core called the **CPU32** is used in the **683xx** MCUs. We will first describe the 16-bit versions of MCUs, starting with the **68HC16Z1**.

16-4 ▼ 68HC16Z1 MCU

The **68HC16Z1** was Motorola's first 16-bit MCU and appeared in 1991. Figure 16-1 shows the **68HC16Z1**'s block diagram. A number of new modular features (with new acronyms) are shown and are explained in the following sections. Internally, the **68HC16Z1** consists of several new modules. They are connected together by the InterModule Bus (IMB), which controls the transfer of data between the modules. The modules within the **68HC16Z1** include:

- The CPU16 Module
- The System Integration Module (SIM)
- An Analog-to-Digital Converter module (ADC)
- A General-Purpose Timer module (GPT)
- The Queued Serial Module (QSM)
- A Static RAM Module (SRAM)

All of these, except the CPU, SIM, and IMB, are new standardized submodule versions of functions previously found in the **68HC11** and **68HC05** MCUs. The documentation of these new modules has also been modularized, and most of them have a separate Reference Manual that describes them in detail. The exceptions at the time of this writing are the SIM, which is described in the *68331 User's Manual*, and the SRAM, which is described in the *68HC16Z1 Users Manual*.

In the sections to follow we provide a simplified description of each of these features, but it is recommended that the reference manuals listed in Section 16-19 be used for register bit functions and other details.

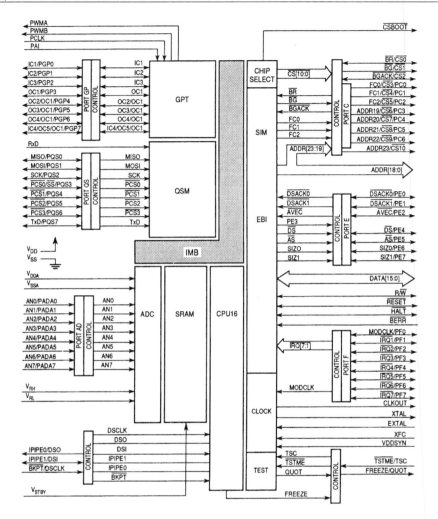

Figure 16-1 68HC16Z1 block diagram.

16-4.1 ▼ Ports on the 68HC16Z1

Figure 16-1 shows that there are six ports on the **68HC16Z1.** Each port has lines to connect the MCU to external devices and a control register that controls its functions and mode of operation. The ports along the left side of the figure connect directly to the internal modules. They are:

- **Port GP.** This port is used for input captures and output compares by the GPT (see Section 16-9) or as an I/O port. As in the **68HC11,** these lines may have more than one function, depending on the mode of operation.
- **Port QS.** This port is connected to the QSM (see Section 16-10). It is used for serial I/O and for master–slave operations.

- **Port AD.** This port is for analog inputs to the A/D converter (see Section 16-8).

Ports C, E, and F are shown on the right side of the figure, and because they all connect to the SIM, they are discussed in Section 16-7.

16-4.2 ▼ Other I/O Lines

Besides the ports, Fig. 16-1 shows that the MCU has several other lines connecting it to the external world. The most important are:

- **The 16-bit data bus.** D(0:15).
- **The 24-bit address bus.** Bits A0 through A18 have their own dedicated lines. Bits A19 through A23 come out of port C (see Section 16-7.2).
- **The R/W line.** As in other MCUs, a 1 indicates a read operation.
- **MCU control.** These include RESET, HALT, and BERR.
- **Timing lines.** These include XTAL, EXTAL, and CLKOUT.

Other I/O lines are discussed in conjunction with the modules to which they are connected.

16-4.3 ▼ Packaging

The **68HC16Z1** is fabricated using the submicron HCMOS process and packaged in a 132-pin PQFP package.

16-5 ▼ INTERMODULE BUS

The modules in the **68HC16** and **68300** MCUs use the InterModule Bus (IMB) to communicate with each other and with external components via the SIM's *External Bus Interface* (EBI) (see Fig. 16-1 and Section 16-7.2). The EBI handles the transfer of information between the IMB and external devices.

The IMB has circuitry to support multiple interrupt levels, vectored interrupts, address space partitioning, and exception processing (all are concepts borrowed from the **68000** family; see Sections 14-11, 14-12, and 14-13). The IMB is really an on-chip circuit module that provides a standardized interface to the modules within the chip and is analogous to a backplane for plug-in modules in a computer.

The IMB concept allows quick development of new integrated modules, and because it has been established as a Motorola standard, the modules and software of the **68HC16** and **68300** families can be shared. These new MCU families are derivatives of the **68HC11** and **68000** families, and in many cases, software (source code) already developed can also be used.

16-6 ▼ CPU16

The CPU16 is a newly designed high-speed 16-bit processor module with architecture that is a superset of the **68HC11**. It has two 16-bit general-purpose accumulators and three 16-bit index registers. The CPU16 supports 8-bit (byte), 16-bit (word), and 32-bit

Table 16-1 HC16 Implementation of 68HC11 instructions.

M68HC11 Instruction	CPU16 Implementation
BHS	BCC only
BLO	BCS only
BSR	Generates a different stack frame
CLC	Replaced by ANDP
CLI	Replaced by ANDP
CLV	Replaced by ANDP
DES	Replaced by AIS
DEX	Replaced by AIX
DEY	Replaced by AIY
INS	Replaced by AIS
INX	Replaced by AIX
INY	Replaced by AIY
JMP	IND8 addressing modes replaced by IND20 and EXT modes
JSR	IND8 addressing modes replaced by IND20 and EXT modes Generates a different stack frame
LSL, LSLD	Use ASL instructions*
PSHX	Replaced by PSHM
PSHY	Replaced by PSHM
PULX	Replaced by PULM
PULY	Replaced by PULM
RTI	Reloads PC and CCR only
RTS	Uses two-word stack frame
SEC	Replaced by ORP
SEI	Replaced by ORP
SEV	Replaced by ORP
STOP	Replaced by LPSTOP
TAP	CPU16 CCR bits differ from M68HC11 CPU16 interrupt priority scheme differs from M68HC11
TPA	CPU16 CCR bits differ from M68HC11 CPU16 interrupt priority scheme differs from M68HC11
TSX	Adds 2 to SK : SP before transfer to XK : IX
TSY	Adds 2 to SK : SP before transfer to YK : IY
TXS	Subtracts 2 from XK : IX before transfer to SK : SP
TXY	Transfers XK field to YK field
TYS	Subtracts 2 from YK : IY before transfer to SK : SP
TYX	Transfers YK field to XK field
WAI	Waits indefinitely for interrupt or reset Generates a different stack frame

*Motorola assemblers automatically translate ASL mnemonics

(long-word) load and store operations, as well as special instructions to handle 16- and 32-bit signed (+ or –) fractional number operations. Program diagnosis is aided by the use of the *Background Debugging Mode* explained in Section 16-6.8.

The CPU16 also has new enhanced addressing modes. The **68HC11** direct mode addressing has been replaced by a special form of indexed addressing that uses the new IZ register and a reset vector to provide greater flexibility. Initial IZ values are included in the RESET exception vector, so that IZ can be used as a direct page pointer immediately after reset (Section 16-6.3).

The CPU16 instruction set is optimized for high performance. One of the principal improvements in the CPU16, however, is the increased speed of execution. The **68HC16Z1** MCU has a system clock operating at 16.78 MHz. The interrupt response time is six times faster than a **68HC11.**

16-6.1 ▼ 68HC11 Compatibility

CPU16 architecture is a superset of **68HC11** architecture. All **68HC11** resources are available in the new CPU16 module. The **68HC11** instructions that have been replaced with an equivalent form, or are directly implemented, are shown in Table 16-1. The instruction sets are source code compatible, but some instructions are executed differently in the CPU16. These instructions are mainly related to interrupt and *exception processing* (see Section 14-12). **68HC11** code that processes interrupts, handles stack frames, or manipulates the condition code register must be rewritten. Execution times and number of cycles for all instructions are different, so that routines that depend on the number of cycles may be affected.

Because MCUs all contain a timer module, such as the General-Purpose Timer (GPT) (See Section 16-9) in the **68HC16Z1,** software delay routines should not be used to avoid tying up the CPU unnecessarily. However, instruction cycle times are important, especially in some Interrupt Service Routines (ISR). The CPU16 does not execute more than one instruction at a time. The total time required to execute a particular instruction stream can be calculated by summing the individual execution times of each instruction in the stream. Details are included in the CPU16 manual referenced in Section 16-19.

16-6.2 ▼ 68000 Compatibility

The **CPU16** also has many features of the **68000** family. They include:

- An eight-level priority interrupt structure
- Exception Processing
- An Asynchronous Data Bus
- Address map partitioning

These subjects were discussed at length in Chapter 14 but are described further in subsequent sections where applicable.

16-6.3 ▼ CPU16 Programmer's Model

The register configuration for the **16HC16Z1** CPU is shown in Fig. 16-2. It is similar to the **68HC11,** but there are several innovations as well as familiar features. First, the A and B registers are concatenated to form register D in the same way as in the **68HC11.** A new 16-bit E accumulator has been added that can be used in the same way as accumulator D, and it also extends CPU16 capabilities because it allows more data to be held within the CPU16 during many operations. Accumulator E also simplifies 32-bit arithmetic and digital processing and provides a practical 16-bit accumulator offset indexed addressing mode.

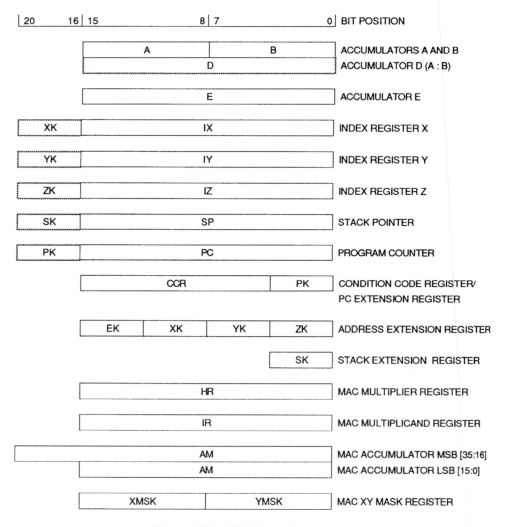

Figure 16-2 CPU16 Register Model.

The CPU16 has three 16-bit index registers (IX, IY, and IZ). Each index register has an associated 4-bit extension field (XK, YK, and ZK), as does the Stack Pointer (SP), the Program Counter (PC), and accumulator E to allow for operation with up to 1 Mbyte of memory. Index registers IX and IY can perform the same operations as **68HC11** registers of the same names, but the CPU16 instruction set provides additional indexed operations. IZ can perform the same operations as IX and IY, and also provides an additional indexed addressing capability that replaces **68HC11** direct addressing mode. Initial IZ and ZK extension field values are included in the RESET exception vector, so that the 20-bit value can be used as a direct page pointer immediately after reset.

EXAMPLE 16-1

The Y index register is to contain the number ABCDE. What must be done to make this happen?

SOLUTION

The instruction LDY #$BCDE will load the 16 LSBs into the IY register, while LDAB #$A followed by the new instruction TBEK will transfer the $A into the YK register.

The Condition Code Register (CCR) is a 16-bit register that contains condition flags, the interrupt priority mask, and the program counter address extension field. Finally, a major addition is the last four MAC (Multiply and ACcumulate) registers. They are used for Digital Signal Processing (DSP) support (see Section 16-6.5).

16-6.4 ▼ Address Map

Although the **68HC16Z1** has 16-bit registers, it was deemed necessary to provide more than 64K bytes of memory. This was accomplished by a combination of *bank switching* and *address space partitioning.*

Figure 16-3 shows the memory map, which also identifies the register blocks for the various submodules. Although there are 24 IMB address lines, the CPU16 only uses 20 of them so that it can address 1 MB of memory (from $00000 to $FFFFF). In the **68HC16Z1,** the MSB address lines (ADDR22–ADDR20) follow the logic state of ADDR19 unless externally driven. ADDR23 is controlled by the module mapping (MM) bit in the SIMCR register of the SIM module (Section 16-7).

Control registers for all the modules in the microcontroller are mapped into a 4K-byte block as shown in Fig. 16-3. The state of the MM bit in the SIM module configuration register (SIMCR) determines where the control registers block is located in the system memory map. When MM = 1, and the register block is being addressed, ADDR19 will be a 1 so that the address bits of ADDR23 through ADDR20 will be an F and the register addresses will range from $FFF000 through $FFFFFF. Those address bits represent the MS byte of the address so that it is now a six-digit number. If the MM bit is cleared, the SIM maps IMB modules into address space $7FF000 through $7FFFFF, which is inaccessible to the CPU16 until reset occurs. The reset state of MM is one, but the bit is one-time writable. Initialization software should make certain that it remains set. The RAM array is positioned by the base address register in the RAM CTRL block. Reset disables the RAM array.

Memory space can be implemented in several ways. If the Function Code signals (see Section 16-7.2) are decoded, separate 1 MB data and program spaces can be provided.

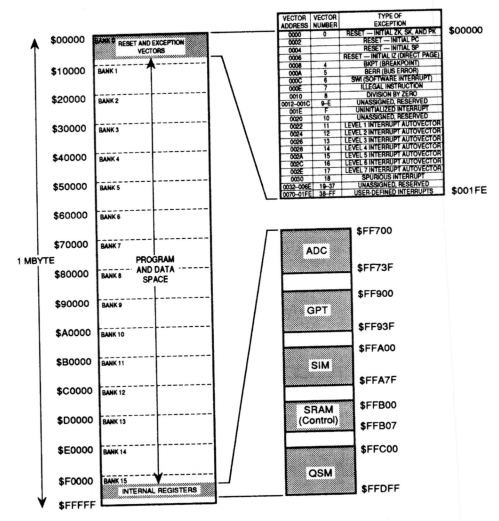

VECTOR ADDRESS	VECTOR NUMBER	TYPE OF EXCEPTION
0000	0	RESET — INITIAL ZK, SK, AND PK
0002		RESET — INITIAL PC
0004		RESET — INITIAL SP
0006		RESET — INITIAL IZ (DIRECT PAGE)
0008	4	BKPT (BREAKPOINT)
000A	5	BERR (BUS ERROR)
000C	6	SWI (SOFTWARE INTERRUPT)
000E	7	ILLEGAL INSTRUCTION
0010	8	DIVISION BY ZERO
0012–001C	9–E	UNASSIGNED, RESERVED
001E	F	UNINITIALIZED INTERRUPT
0020	10	UNASSIGNED, RESERVED
0022	11	LEVEL 1 INTERRUPT AUTOVECTOR
0024	12	LEVEL 2 INTERRUPT AUTOVECTOR
0026	13	LEVEL 3 INTERRUPT AUTOVECTOR
0028	14	LEVEL 4 INTERRUPT AUTOVECTOR
002A	15	LEVEL 5 INTERRUPT AUTOVECTOR
002C	16	LEVEL 6 INTERRUPT AUTOVECTOR
002E	17	LEVEL 7 INTERRUPT AUTOVECTOR
0030	18	SPURIOUS INTERRUPT
0032–006E	19–37	UNASSIGNED, RESERVED
0070–01FE	38–FF	USER-DEFINED INTERRUPTS

Figure 16-3 68HC16 Addressing with combined Program and Data spaces.

16-6.5 ▼ DSP Instructions

The CPU16 core includes instructions and hardware to implement control-oriented *Digital Signal Processing* (DSP) functions with a minimum of interfacing to permit applications such as the following:

- Data Averaging (i.e., Digital Filters)
- Closed-loop control
  - Disk head positioning
  - Adaptive suspension

Table 16-2 68HC16Z1 DSP Instruction Summary.

Mnemonic	Function	Operation
ACE	Add E to AM[31:15]	$(AM[31:15]) + (E) \Rightarrow AM$
ACED	Add concatenated E and D to AM	$(E:D) + (AM) \Rightarrow AM$
ASLM	Arithmetic Shift Left AM	C ← [b35 ... b0] ← 0
ASRM	Arithmetic Shift Right AM	[b35 ... b0] → C
CLRM	Clear AM	$\$000000000 \Rightarrow AM[35:0]$
LDHI	Initialize HR and IR	$(M:M+1)_X \Rightarrow HR$ $(M:M+1)_Y \Rightarrow IR$
MAC	Multiply and Accumulate Signed 16-Bit Fractions	$(HR) * (IR) \Rightarrow E:D$ $(AM) + (E:D) \Rightarrow AM$ Qualified $(IX) \Rightarrow IX$ Qualified $(IY) \Rightarrow IY$ $(HR) \Rightarrow IZ$ $(M:M+1)_X \Rightarrow HR$ $(M:M+1)_Y \Rightarrow IR$
PSHMAC	Push MAC State	MAC Registers $\Rightarrow$ Stack
PULMAC	Pull MAC State	Stack $\Rightarrow$ MAC Registers
RMAC	Repeating Multiply and Accumulate Signed 16-Bit Fractions	Repeat until $(E) < 0$ $(AM) + (H) * (I) \Rightarrow AM$ Qualified $(IX) \Rightarrow IX$; Qualified $(IY) \Rightarrow IY$; $(M:M+1)_X \Rightarrow H$; $(M:M+1)_Y \Rightarrow I$ $(E) - 1 \Rightarrow E$
TDMSK	Transfer D to XMSK : YMSK	$(D[15:8]) \Rightarrow XMSK$ $(D[7:0]) \Rightarrow YMSK$
TEDM	Transfer E and D to AM[31:0] Sign Extend AM	$(D) \Rightarrow AM[15:0]$ $(E) \Rightarrow AM[31:16]$ $AM[32:35] = AM31$
TEM	Transfer E to AM[31:16] Sign Extend AM Clear AM LSB	$(E) \Rightarrow AM[31:16]$ $\$00 \Rightarrow AM[15:0]$ $AM[32:35] = AM31$
TMER	Transfer AM to E Rounded	Rounded $(AM) \Rightarrow Temp$ If $(SM \bullet (EV + MV))$ then Saturation $\Rightarrow E$ else Temp$[31:16] \Rightarrow E$
TMET	Transfer AM to E Truncated	If $(SM \bullet (EV + MV))$ then Saturation $\Rightarrow E$ else AM$[31:16] \Rightarrow E$
TMXED	Transfer AM to IX : E : D	$AM[35:32] \Rightarrow IX[3:0]$ $AM35 \Rightarrow IX[15:4]$ $AM[31:16] \Rightarrow E$ $AM[15:0] \Rightarrow D$

- Servomotor control
- Automatic gain control
- Signal translation from Time Domain to Frequency Domain for analysis
- Linearization of sensor readings

The data to be analyzed can be digital inputs generated internally or externally, or they can be analog and be converted by the **68HC16**'s ADC module. DSP requires a large amount of computation and the **68HC16Z1** has a group of instructions for this purpose. These instructions are shown in Table 16-2. A *Multiply and ACcumulate* (MAC) unit provides the capability to multiply signed 16-bit fractional numbers and store the resulting fixed-point product in a 36-bit accumulator.

16-6.6 ▼ HLL Instructions

The use of High-Level Languages (HLL), primarily the C language, is increasing as controller applications become more complex and control programs become larger. High-level language aids the rapid development of software with less error and is readily portable to other CPUs by recompiling with the appropriate compiler. The **CPU16** instruction set has the following features that improve compiler efficiency.

- New addressing modes
  - 16-Bit signed offset
  - AccE offset indexing
  - 16-Bit-long relative branch
- New instructions
  - AIS   Add immediate to stack pointer
  - ADix   Add AccD to IX/IY/IZ
  - AEix   Add AccE to IX/IY/IZ
  - Tixix   Transfer index register IX/IY/IZ to IX/IY/IZ
- New registers
  - 16-Bit general-purpose accumulator E
  - Z index used as frame pointer in same bank as stack pointer

16-6.7 ▼ STOP and WAIT Instructions

There are two instructions that put the CPU16 in an inactive state. Both require that either an interrupt or a reset exception occur before normal execution of instructions resumes. However, they operate differently. LPSTOP minimizes MCU power consumption. Normal operating current for the **68HC16Z1** is approximately 110 mA. This is reduced to about 350 μA in LPSTOP mode. The CPU16 initiates a stop, but as explained in Section 16-7, it and other controller modules are deactivated by the MCU's System Integration Module (SIM). Reactivation is also handled by the SIM. The Interrupt Priority field (IP) from the CPU16 condition code register is copied into SIM control logic, then the system clock to the processor is stopped. When a reset or an interrupt of higher priority than the IP value occurs, the SIM activates the CPU16, and the appropriate exception processing sequence begins.

WAI idles the CPU16 but does not affect operation of other MCU modules. The Interrupt Priority field of the Condition Code Register is not copied to the SIM. System clocks continue to run. The processor waits until a reset or an interrupt of higher priority than the IP value occurs, then begins the appropriate exception processing sequence. Because the SIM does not restart the CPU16, interrupts are acknowledged more quickly following WAI than following LPSTOP. To make certain that conditions for termination of LPSTOP and WAI are correct, interrupts are not recognized until after the instruction following ANDP, ORP, TAP, and TDP executes. This prevents interrupt exception processing during the period after the mask changes but before the following instruction executes.

16-6.8 ▼ Background Debug Mode

Background Debug Mode (BDM) is another new feature included in the **CPU16** and **CPU32** CPU core modules. Microcomputer development systems generally provide a debugger, implemented in software, for system analysis at the lowest level. The *Background Debug Mode* in these CPUs is unique in that the debugger program has been implemented in CPU microcode. When the BDM is invoked (by resetting with BKPT held LOW), the Breakpoint (BKPT) and Instruction Pipeline pins (IPIP0 and IPIP1) become a serial interface to send commands and receive data from the MCU. Registers can be viewed and/or altered, memory can be read or written to, and test features can be invoked. Incorporating these capabilities *on-chip* simplifies the debug environment.

Background Debug Mode (BDM) Operation

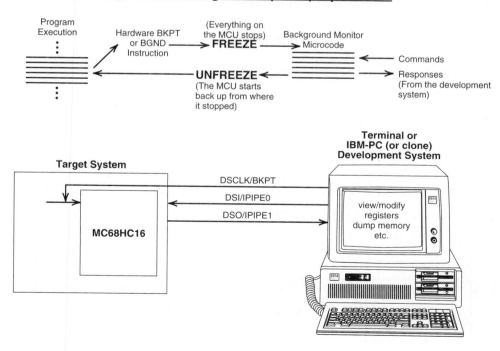

Figure 16-4   Background Debug Mode (BDM) Operation.

With an integrated debugger, the traditional emulator configuration may be replaced by a terminal or by a PC acting as a terminal as shown in Fig. 16-4. The PC simply communicates directly with the CPU microcode internally via a serial link, whereas the traditional in-circuit emulator replaces the processor in the target system with hardware in the emulator. In this case all external bus traffic must traverse the cable between the emulator and the target system, and because of the propagation delays, this method does not work properly in some time-critical situations.

In the BDM, as each command is accumulated in the serial shifter, a microaddress is generated which points to the microcode routine corresponding to that command. If addresses or operands are required, the microcode waits as each word is assembled. Result operands are loaded into the output shift register to be shifted out as the next command is read. Table 16-3 summarizes the command set available in the microcode for the background debug mode.

Two Evaluation Boards (the 68HC16Z1EVB and the 68332EVS) which use the BDM are available from Motorola (Section 16-16). The MS-DOS programs provided with them use these commands to display the registers and data or instructions on the screen of a host PC. Many more details on the BDM are given in the Reference Manual CPU16RM/AD, listed in Section 16-19.

16-7 ▼ SYSTEM INTEGRATION MODULE

The System Integration Module (SIM) is an on-chip module that includes all the hardware circuits and lines needed to interface the external system devices typically used in a control system, to the IMB, and thus to the internal MCU on-chip modules. It has many

Table 16-3   BDM Command Summary.

Command	Mnemonic	Description
Read Registers from Mask	RREGM	Read contents of registers specified by command word register mask
Write Registers from Mask	WREGM	Write to registers specified by command word register mask
Read MAC Registers	RDMAC	Read contents of entire Multiply and Accumulate register set
Write MAC Registers	WRMAC	Write to entire Multiply and Accumulate register set
Read PC and SP	RPCSP	Read contents of program counter and stack pointer
Write PC and SP	WPCSP	Write to program counter and stack pointer
Read Data Memory	RDMEM	Read byte from specified 20-bit address in data space
Write Data Memory	WDMEM	Write byte to specified 20-bit address in data space
Read Program Memory	RPMEM	Read word from specified 20-bit address in program space
Write Program Memory	WPMEM	Write word to specified 20-bit address in program space
Execute from current PK : PC	GO	Instruction pipeline flushed and refilled; instructions executed from current PC – $0006
Null Operation	NOP	Null command — performs no operation

programmable configuration features that eliminate or minimize the need for external interfacing components.

The SIM includes the following submodules:

- External Bus Interface (EBI)
- Chip Selects
- System Configuration and Protection
- System Clock Synthesizer
- Factory test capability

Each of these involves many registers and associated external lines. Table 16-4 shows the addresses, mnemonics and, descriptions of all the registers in the SIM.

Table 16-4 SIM Address Map.

Address	15 8	7 0
YFFA00	MODULE CONFIGURATION (SIMCR)	
YFFA02	FACTORY TEST (SIMTR)	
YFFA04	CLOCK SYNTHESIZER CONTROL (SYNCR)	
YFFA06	NOT USED	RESET STATUS (RSR)
YFFA08	MODULE TEST E (SIMTRE)	
YFFA0A	NOT USED	NOT USED
YFFA0C	NOT USED	NOT USED
YFFA0E	NOT USED	NOT USED
YFFA10	NOT USED	PORTE DATA (PORTE0)
YFFA12	NOT USED	PORTE DATA (PORTE1)
YFFA14	NOT USED	PORTE DATA DIRECTION (DDRE)
YFFA16	NOT USED	PORTE PIN ASSIGNMENT (PEPAR)
YFFA18	NOT USED	PORTF DATA (PORTF0)
YFFA1A	NOT USED	PORTF DATA (PORTF1)
YFFA1C	NOT USED	PORTF DATA DIRECTION (DDRF)
YFFA1E	NOT USED	PORTF PIN ASSIGNMENT (PFPAR)
YFFA20	NOT USED	SYSTEM PROTECTION CONTROL (SYPCR)
YFFA22	PERIODIC INTERRUPT CONTROL (PICR)	
YFFA24	PERIODIC INTERRUPT TIMING (PITR)	
YFFA26	NOT USED	SOFTWARE SERVICE (SWSR)
YFFA28	NOT USED	NOT USED
YFFA2A	NOT USED	NOT USED
YFFA2C	NOT USED	NOT USED
YFFA2E	NOT USED	NOT USED
YFFA30	TEST MODULE MASTER SHIFT A (TSTMSRA)	
YFFA32	TEST MODULE MASTER SHIFT B (TSTMSRB)	
YFFA34	TEST MODULE SHIFT COUNT (TSTSC)	
YFFA36	TEST MODULE REPETITION COUNTER (TSTRC)	
YFFA38	TEST MODULE CONTROL (CREG)	
YFFA3A	TEST MODULE DISTRIBUTED (DREG)	
YFFA3C	NOT USED	NOT USED
YFFA3E	NOT USED	NOT USED
YFFA40	NOT USED	PORT C DATA (PORTC)
YFFA42	NOT USED	NOT USED

Table 16-4 SIM Address Map *(Continued)*

Address	15 8	7 0
YFFA44	CHIP-SELECT PIN ASSIGNMENT (CSPAR0)	
YFFA46	CHIP-SELECT PIN ASSIGNMENT (CSPAR1)	
YFFA48	CHIP-SELECT BASE BOOT (CSBARBT)	
YFFA4A	CHIP-SELECT OPTION BOOT (CSORBT)	
YFFA4C	CHIP-SELECT BASE 0 (CSBAR0)	
YFFA4E	CHIP-SELECT OPTION 0 (CSOR0)	
YFFA50	CHIP-SELECT BASE 1 (CSBAR1)	
YFFA52	CHIP-SELECT OPTION 1 (CSOR1)	
YFFA54	CHIP-SELECT BASE 2 (CSBAR2)	
YFFA56	CHIP-SELECT OPTION 2 (CSOR2)	
YFFA58	CHIP-SELECT BASE 3 (CSBAR3)	
YFFA5A	CHIP-SELECT OPTION 3 (CSOR3)	
YFFA5C	CHIP-SELECT BASE 4 (CSBAR4)	
YFFA5E	CHIP-SELECT OPTION 4 (CSOR4)	
YFFA60	CHIP-SELECT BASE 5 (CSBAR5)	
YFFA62	CHIP-SELECT OPTION 5 (CSOR5)	
YFFA64	CHIP-SELECT BASE 6 (CSBAR6)	
YFFA66	CHIP-SELECT OPTION 6 (CSOR6)	
YFFA68	CHIP-SELECT BASE 7 (CSBAR7)	
YFFA6A	CHIP-SELECT OPTION 7 (CSOR7)	
YFFA6C	CHIP-SELECT BASE 8 (CSBAR8)	
YFFA6E	CHIP-SELECT OPTION 8 (CSOR8)	
YFFA70	CHIP-SELECT BASE 9 (CSBAR9)	
YFFA72	CHIP-SELECT OPTION 9 (CSOR9)	
YFFA74	CHIP-SELECT BASE 10 (CSBAR10)	
YFFA76	CHIP-SELECT OPTION 10 (CSOR10)	
YFFA78	NOT USED	NOT USED
YFFA7A	NOT USED	NOT USED
YFFA7C	NOT USED	NOT USED
YFFA7E	NOT USED	NOT USED

16-7.1 ▼ External Bus Interface

Because the **68HC16** family architecture is modeled after the **68000** family, the bus operation is asynchronous. The External Bus Interface (EBI) of the SIM handles the transfer of information between the internal MCU modules and the external memory or peripheral devices.

The external interchange involves the following signal lines:

- The 20-bit Address Bus (A19–A0)
- The 16 bit Data Bus (D15–D0)
- The Function Code lines (FC2–FC0)
- The Size pins (SIZ1–SIZ0)
- The Address Strobe (AS)
- The Data Strobe (DS)
- The Data Strobe ACKnowledge pins (DSACK1–DSACK0)

Table 16-5 SIZE signal encoding.

SIZ1	SIZ0	Transfer Size
0	1	Byte
1	0	Word
1	1	3 Byte
0	0	Long Word

- The Bus Arbritration pins (BR, BG, BGACK)
- The Interrupt ReQuest pins (IRQ7–IRQ1)
- The Chip Select pins (CS10–CS0)
- The Bus Error pin (BERR)
- Read/Write (R/W)
- Autovector (AVEC)
- Halt (HALT)

The pins carrying these signals are shown on the right-hand side of Fig. 16-1.

The MCU architecture supports byte, word, and long-word operands. In addition to the usual read and write transfer operations that are similar to those of the **68000,** the EBI must be concerned with dynamic sizing for byte, word, or long-word transfers. The maximum number of bits transferred during an access is referred to as port width. Widths can be 8 or 16 bits. In an asynchronous bus cycle, the CPU drives the SIZE pins to indicate how many bytes need to be transferred during an operand cycle. Table 16-5 shows the encoding used for these pins.

During normal bus transfers, external devices then assert the Data Strobe ACKnowledge signals (DSACK1 and DSACKO) to acknowledge the port width to the MCU. During a read cycle, these signals tell the MCU to terminate the bus cycle and to latch data. During a write cycle, the signals also indicate that an external device has successfully stored data and that the cycle may terminate. DSACK can also be supplied internally by Chip-Select logic (Section 16-7.3).

DSACKx inputs are shown in Table 16-6. Multiple bus cycles may be required for a dynamically sized transfer. For example, if the MCU is executing an instruction that reads a long-word operand from a 16-bit port, the MCU latches the 16 bits of valid data and then runs another bus cycle to obtain the other 16 bits. The operation for an 8-bit port is similar but requires four read cycles. A 16-bit device always returns DSACK1 = 0 and DSACK0 = 1 (for a 16-bit port) regardless of whether the bus cycle is a byte or word operation.

Table 16-6 DSACKx signal encoding.

DSACK1	DSACK0	Result
1	1	Insert Wait States in Current Bus Cycle
1	0	Complete Cycle — Data Bus Port Size is 8 Bits
0	1	Complete Cycle — Data Bus Port Size is 16 Bits
0	0	Reserved

Dynamic bus sizing requires that the portion of the data bus used for a transfer to or from a particular port size be fixed. A 16-bit port must reside on data bus bits [15:0], and an 8-bit port must reside on data bus bits [15:8]. This minimizes the number of bus cycles needed to transfer data and ensures that the MCU transfers valid data.

The MCU always attempts to transfer the maximum amount of data on all bus cycles. For a word operation it is assumed that the port is 16 bits wide when the bus cycle begins. Operand bytes are designated as shown in Fig. 16-5. OP0 is the most significant byte of a long-word operand, and OP3 is the least. The 2 bytes of a word-length operand are OP0 (most significant) and OP1. The single byte of a byte-length operand is OP0.

The Bus ERRor (BERR) signal is also a bus cycle termination indicator and can be used in the absence of DSACKx to indicate a bus error condition. It can also be asserted in conjunction with DSACKx to indicate a bus error condition, provided that it meets the appropriate timing requirements. BERR and HALT must not be asserted simultaneously; the CPU16 does not support the resulting bus condition.

The internal bus monitor can be used to generate the BERR signal for internal and internal-to-external transfers. An external bus master must provide its own BERR generation and drive the BERR pin, because the internal BERR monitor has no information about transfers initiated by an external bus master.

Finally, the auto-vector signal (AVEC) can be used to terminate external IRQ pin interrupt acknowledge cycles. AVEC indicates that the MCU will internally generate a vector number to locate an interrupt handler routine. If it is continuously asserted, auto-vectors will be generated for all external interrupt requests. AVEC is ignored during all other bus cycles.

16-7.2 ▼ EBI External Line Selections

Many lines controlled by the EBI have dual functions. The 11 lines connected to port C, shown in the upper right-hand corner of Fig. 16-1, can be either Chip Select lines or can function as Bus Arbitration, Function Codes, and additional addresses. Chip Select is discussed in the following section. Port E can be used as an 8-bit I/O port or can be used to transmit the bus control signals connected to it, such as DACKx and the SIZE lines. Similarly, port F can be used as an 8-bit I/O port or can be used to accept interrupts. If the MCU must be interrupted by one or more external peripherals, port F cannot be used for I/O.

The way these lines function is determined by the logic levels on the 16-bit Data Bus at reset. When *reset* is asserted, the **68HC16Z1** pulls all data lines high, but external

Operand	Byte Order			
	31 24 23 16	15 8	7 0	
Long Word	OP0	OP1	OP2	OP3
Three Byte		OP0	OP1	OP2
Word			OP0	OP1
Byte				OP0

Figure 16-5 Operand byte order.

Table 16-7 SIM Reset Mode selection.

Mode Select Pin	Default Function (Pin Left High)	Alternate Function (Pin Pulled Low)
DATA0	$\overline{\text{CSBOOT}}$ 16-Bit	$\overline{\text{CSBOOT}}$ 8-Bit
DATA1	$\overline{\text{CS0}}$ $\overline{\text{CS1}}$ $\overline{\text{CS2}}$	$\overline{\text{BR}}$ $\overline{\text{BG}}$ $\overline{\text{BGACK}}$
DATA2	$\overline{\text{CS3}}$ $\overline{\text{CS4}}$ $\overline{\text{CS5}}$	FC0 FC1 FC2
DATA3 DATA4 DATA5 DATA6 DATA7	$\overline{\text{CS6}}$ $\overline{\text{CS7}}$–$\overline{\text{CS6}}$ $\overline{\text{CS8}}$–$\overline{\text{CS6}}$ $\overline{\text{CS9}}$–$\overline{\text{CS6}}$ $\overline{\text{CS10}}$–$\overline{\text{CS6}}$	ADDR19 ADDR[20:19] ADDR[21:19] ADDR[22:19] ADDR[23:19]
DATA8	$\overline{\text{DSACK0}}$, $\overline{\text{DSACK1}}$, $\overline{\text{AVEC}}$, $\overline{\text{DS}}$, $\overline{\text{AS}}$, SIZE	PORTE
DATA9	$\overline{\text{IRQ7}}$–$\overline{\text{IRQ1}}$ MODCLK	PORTF
DATA11	Test Mode Disabled	Test Mode Enabled
MODCLK	VCO = System Clock	EXTAL = System Clock
$\overline{\text{BKPT}}$	Background Mode Disabled	Background Mode Enabled

circuitry can hold bits low to achieve a specific configuration. The **68HC16Z1** reads the data bus pin information and switches the EBI pin functions accordingly, as shown in Table 16-7. The Chip Selects are the default choice. But, for example, if DB1 is held low during reset, the Bus Arbitration lines will become active instead of CS0, CS1, and CS2.

Function code signals FC2 through FC0 are optional in place of three Chip Selects. When activated, they are automatically generated by the CPU16. The Function Codes can be considered address extensions that automatically select one of eight address spaces to which an address applies. This is another **68000** feature (see Section 14-4.4). These spaces are designated as either *user* or *supervisor,* and *program* or *data* spaces. Because the CPU16 always operates in supervisor mode (FC2 always = 1), only the address spaces shown in Table 16-8 are used. CPU space is used for control information not normally associated with read or write bus cycles. Function Codes are valid while AS is asserted. Figure 16-6 shows how the Function Code lines are used to implement separate Program and Data maps by selecting either an EPROM or a RAM.

Table 16-8 Function Code address space encoding.

FC2	FC1	FC0	Address Space
1	0	0	Reserved
1	0	1	Data Space
1	1	0	Program Space
1	1	1	CPU Space

Example of using separate program and data maps.

- Function Code Lines 0 & 1 are driven by CPU16
- User may use chip select logic (in SIM) to decode FC0 & FC1 internally, or
- User may decode FC0 & FC1 externally
- If FC0 & FC1 are not decoded, or decoded internally (in the SIM) then the pins may be used as CS3 and CS4

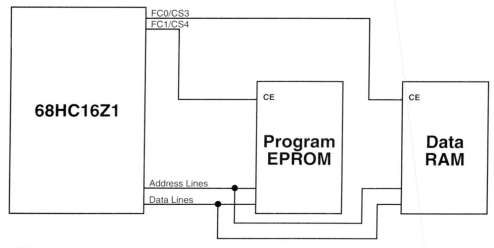

- FC1 is active during fetches based on the PC.
- FC0 is active during address calculations based on IX, IY, IZ, SP and extended addressing mode.

Figure 16-6 Function Code selection of Program and Data Maps.

EXAMPLE 16-2

A **68HC16Z1** is to be set up so that the Bus Arbitration signals and the Function Codes must appear at the outputs. It does not need addresses A19 through A23, however, because there are no devices with addresses higher than 512K bytes. How can the EBI select this configuration?

SOLUTION

The correct levels must be set up on the Data Bus lines prior to reset. Table 16-7 shows that DB1 must be pulled low to enable the three Bus Arbitration lines and DB2 must also be pulled low to enable the Function Codes. Lines DB3 through DB7 should be left open. These pins can then be used by the MCU as five Chip Select lines (CS6 through CS10).

16-7.3 ▼ Chip Selects

Typical μC systems require external hardware to decode addresses or an inverter IC to select external peripheral devices. The Chip-Select submodule of the SIM integrates these

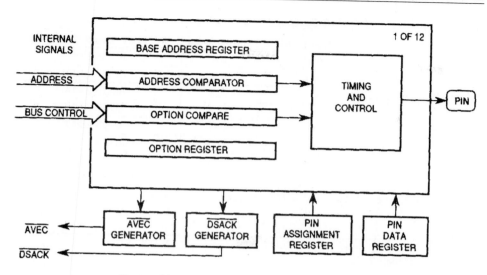

Figure 16-7 Chip-Select circuit block diagram.

functions on-chip. These Chip-Select signals can be used to enable a memory IC or a peripheral when its address is on the bus and eliminates the need for external address decoders or inverters.

A block diagram of the Chip-Select mechanism is shown in Fig. 16-7. It indicates that there are two registers (a Base Address and an Option register) associated with each of the 11 Chip-Selects (CSBARx and CSORx). These 11 pairs of registers are part of the SIM register set shown in Table 16-4.

The configuration of the Chip-Select Base Address Registers is shown in Fig. 16-8. It shows that each register consists of the 13 MSBs of the address and 3 bits that determine the size of the block of I/O that is being selected. The block sizes are given in Table 16-9.

D.4.25 CSBARBT — Chip Select Base Address Register Boot ROM   **$YFFA48**

15	14	13	12	11	10	9	8	7	6	5	4	3	2	1	0
ADDR 23	ADDR 22	ADDR 21	ADDR 20	ADDR 19	ADDR 18	ADDR 17	ADDR 16	ADDR 15	ADDR 14	ADDR 13	ADDR 12	ADDR 11	BLKSZ		

RESET:

0	0	0	0	0	0	0	0	0	0	0	0	0	1	1	1

D.4.26 CSBAR[0:10] — Chip Select Base Address Registers **$YFFA4C–$YFFA74**

15	14	13	12	11	10	9	8	7	6	5	4	3	2	1	0
ADDR 23	ADDR 22	ADDR 21	ADDR 20	ADDR 19	ADDR 18	ADDR 17	ADDR 16	ADDR 15	ADDR 14	ADDR 13	ADDR 12	ADDR 11	BLKSZ		

RESET:

0	0	0	0	0	0	0	0	0	0	0	0	0	0	0	0

Figure 16-8 Chip-Select Base Address Register configurations.

Table 16-9 Chip-Select block size encoding.

BLKSZ[2:0]	Block Size	Address Lines Compared
000	2 K	ADDR[23:11]
001	8 K	ADDR[23:13]
010	16 K	ADDR[23:14]
011	64 K	ADDR[23:16]
100	128 K	ADDR[23:17]
101	256 K	ADDR[23:18]
110	512 K	ADDR[23:19]
111	512 K	ADDR[23:20]

ADDR[23:20] = ADDR19 during normal operation.

EXAMPLE 16-3

In a **68HC16Z1** MCU system, an 8K-byte RAM is to be used starting at address $AB000. Chip-Select CS2 is to be used to select this RAM.

(a) What should be written into its base address register?

(b) Where is this register?

SOLUTION

(a) The register should contain $AB001. The 13 MSBs of this register specify that the starting address is $AB000. The 3 LSBs, (001) specify an 8K-byte block size. Thus CS2 will go low for any address between $AB000 and $AB1FF and can be used to select the RAM.

(b) The address of the base register for CS2 is given in Table 16-4 as $FFA54.

16-7.4 ▼ Internal DSACK

When a peripheral is addressed, it can terminate the bus cycle by sending DSACK0 or DSACK1 to the MCU as shown in Table 6-6. Alternatively, DSACK may be generated internally by the MCU. If port E is to be used for I/O, selected by holding DB8 low during reset (see Table 16-7), DSACK cannot come through the port and must be generated internally.

When DSACK is to be generated internally, up to 13 wait states can be inserted during an access. The process of holding off the DSACK assertion (to wait for slow memory or peripheral devices) is called inserting *wait states*. A wait state has a duration of one clock cycle. Figure 16-9 shows the Option Register that accompanies each of the Chip-Select Base Address Registers. Space limitations preclude a detailed description of each field, but there are 4 bits in the DSACK field that give the user the option of selecting any number of wait states from 0 to 13 or to specify that the external DSACK0 and

D.4.27 CSORBT — Chip Select Option Register Boot ROM $YFFA4A

15	14	13	12	11	10	9	8	7	6	5	4	3	2	1	0
MODE	BYTE		R/W̄		STRB		DSACK			SPACE		IPL			AVEC

RESET:

| 0 | 1 | 1 | 1 | 1 | 0 | 1 | 1 | 0 | 1 | 1 | 1 | 0 | 0 | 0 | 0 |

D.4.28 CSOR[0:10] — Chip Select Option Registers $YFFA4E–$YFFA76

15	14	13	12	11	10	9	8	7	6	5	4	3	2	1	0
MODE	BYTE		R/W̄		STRB		DSACK			SPACE		IPL			AVEC

RESET:

| 0 | 0 | 0 | 0 | 0 | 0 | 0 | 0 | 0 | 0 | 0 | 0 | 0 | 0 | 0 | 0 |

Figure 16-9   Chip-Select Option Register configurations.

DSACK1 lines are to be used. Table 16-10 shows the choices. The appropriate value for each external device should be written to its Option Register by the initialization routine.

EXAMPLE 16-4

Assume the RAM of Example 16-3 has a 500-ns access time.

(a) How many wait states should be inserted for DSACK?

(b) Where would they be inserted?

SOLUTION

(a) Because each cycle takes 59.59 ns with a 16.78-MHz clock, the number of wait states required is 500 ns/59.59 ns or 8.39. Thus nine wait states should be inserted.

(b) The bit configuration for nine wait states should be inserted into the DSACK field for Chip-Select Option Register 2. Table 16-4 shows that this register is at $FFA56.

16-7.5 ▼ CSBOOT

The CSBOOT pin on the **68HC16Z1** (the top right-hand signal on Fig. 16-1) allows the system to boot up after reset by using the program in an external memory. If activated by holding DB0 low during reset, the low signal on CSBOOT will enable the boot memory. The program in the boot memory is used to initialize the system.

There are two registers (CSBARBT and CSORBT) associated with the CSBOOT pin. They contain the address and options for the boot memory. The CSBOOT pin is dedicated to a single function because it must function after a reset with no initialization; The other Chip-Select circuits share functions on their output pins. Because initialization software would probably reside in a peripheral memory device controlled by the Chip-Select circuits, this pin and its CSORBT register provides default reset values to support booting from an external ROM.

Table 16-10 Chip-Select wait state selections.

DSACK	Description
0000	No Wait States
0001	1 Wait State
0010	2 Wait States
0011	3 Wait States
0100	4 Wait States
0101	5 Wait States
0110	6 Wait States
0111	7 Wait States
1000	8 Wait States
1001	9 Wait States
1010	10 Wait States
1011	11 Wait States
1100	12 Wait States
1101	13 Wait States
1110	Fast Termination
1111	External DSACK

16-7.6 ▼ System Configuration and Protection

The system configuration and protection block is another submodule of the SIM. It includes many functions formerly implemented in external hardware. It consists of functions as follows:

- Module Configuration
- Reset Status
- Halt Monitor
- Bus Monitor
- Spurious Interrupt Monitor
- Software Watchdog Timer
- Periodic Interrupt Timer

Figure 16-10 shows a block diagram of the system configuration and protection submodule. Most of these functions have an associated register in the SIM register block. Space precludes discussing each bit of each register. The basic functions are described, but further details can be found in the *68HC16Z1 User's Manual* listed in Section 16-19.

Module Configuration. The SIM module allows the user to control system configuration by writing bits in the SIM Configuration Register (SIMCR) at $FFA00; see Table 16-4). It determines whether the MCU allows an external bus master to access the

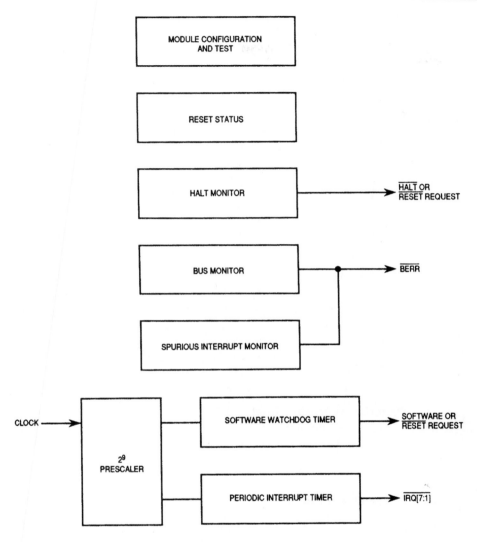

Figure 16-10 System Configuration and Protection subsystem block diagram.

IMB, whether the CLKOUT pin is enabled, and contains an interrupt arbitration field that allows arbitration among simultaneous interrupts of the same priority level. This register also contains the MM bit, which affects the mapping of the IMB modules in the address space. It must always be a 1 for normal operation (see Section 16-6.4).

Reset Status.   There are many possible causes of reset in the **68HC16Z1.** Some examples are external reset, power-up reset, and a watchdog timeout. The Reset Status Register (RSR), an 8-bit, read-only register at $FFA07, shows the cause of the latest reset. This can be useful when testing the MCU.

Halt Monitor. The halt monitor is a circuit in the **68HC16Z1** that responds to an assertion of HALT on the internal bus and places the MCU in the HALT state. If this should occur, a flag in the Reset Status Register (RSR) would indicate that the last reset was caused by the HALT monitor. The HALT monitor can be inhibited by setting the HME bit in the System Protection Control Register (SYPCR). The HALT monitor is disabled after reset.

Bus Monitor. The internal bus monitor checks for a late DSACK, for example, and if bus monitor timeout occurs, it generates a BERR (Bus ERRor) signal. This function uses 2 bits in the SYPCR to select the Bus Monitor timeout period. The period can be set for 8, 16, 32, or 64 system clocks. It monitors the DSACKx response time for all internal bus accesses. An option allows the monitoring of internal to external bus accesses when enabled by the BME bit of SYPCR (See Appendix D of 68HC16Z1 User's Manual).

Spurious Interrupt Monitor. If no interrupt arbitration occurs during an interrupt acknowledge (IACK) cycle, the BERR signal is asserted internally.

Halt Monitor. A bit in the SYPCR enables the halt monitor. This allows halt signals on the internal bus to be recognized.

Software Watchdog. When enabled, the watchdog system monitors the MCU by causing the program to write periodically into the write-only SoftWare Service Register (SWSR) at $FFA27. If this fails to occur in a designated period of time (presumably because it is trapped in a loop or lost), it causes a reset. There are four selectable timeout periods and a prescaler may be used for long timeout periods. The SYPCR also controls the watchdog system and its timing.

Periodic Interrupt Timer. The MCU provides a timer to generate periodic interrupts. The periodic interrupt time period can vary from 122 μs to 15.94 seconds (with a 32.768-kHz crystal used to generate the system clock) (See PITR register at $FFA24).

16-7.7 ▼ System Clock

The clock synthesizer submodule generates the clock signals used by the SIM as well as by the CPU and other modules and external devices. The system clock circuit built into the **68HC16Z1** chip provides timing signals for the modules on the IMB and for an external peripheral bus. A block diagram of the Clock circuit is shown in Fig. 16-11.

The system clock is generated either internally or externally. To use the internal oscillator, a reference crystal can be connected between the EXTAL and XTAL pins. The reference crystal frequency can be any frequency from 25 to 50 kHz. A 32.768-kHz watch crystal is recommended. These crystals are readily available and inexpensive.

The internal clock synthesizer circuit uses a Voltage-Controlled Oscillator (VCO), a divider/counter, and a Phase-Locked Loop (PLL) to effectively multiply the crystal frequency so that it becomes the cycle time of the MCU. The divider bits in the upper byte of the Clock Synthesizer Control Register (SYNCR) at $FFA04 control the frequency. This register also contains several bits that control the way the clock operates.

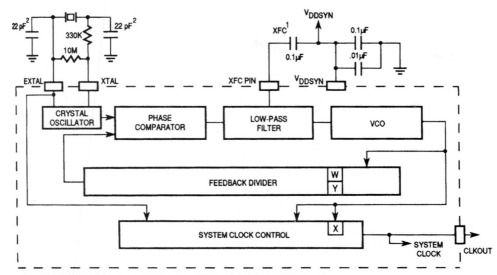

1. MUST BE LOW-LEAKAGE CAPACITOR (INSULATION RESISTANCE 30,000 MΩ OR GREATER).
2. CAPACITANCE BASED ON A TEST CIRCUIT CONSTRUCTED WITH A DAISHINKU DMX-38 32.768 kHz CRYSTAL.

Figure 16-11   System Clock block diagram.

EXAMPLE 16-5

A **68HC16Z1** must operate at a standard frequency of 16.78 MHz. A 32.768-kHz watch crystal is connected between XTAL and EXTAL. What must be the multiplication factor of the PLL?

SOLUTION

The factor is simply 16.78 MHz/32.768 kHz or 512. This is achieved by setting the bits in the upper byte of the control register during initialization, as described in the User's Manual.

Because the **68HC16Z1** is a fully static design, register and memory contents are not affected when the clock rate changes. The chip design supports using software changes to the bits in the SYNCR register, thus changing the clock rate, during operation.

An external oscillator can also be used with the on-chip frequency synthesizer and VCO to generate the system clock, or the system clock frequency can be driven directly into the EXTAL pin (the XTAL pin should be left floating for this case).

16-7.8 ▼ Factory Test Features

One of the submodules of the SIM is called TEST. It provides factory testing of the various MCU modules. It is integrated into the SIM to support factory production testing. There are eight registers and two external pins associated with this function. Register names and addresses are listed in the manuals to show the user that these addresses are occupied and are for Motorola use. The SIM and its features are fully described in the *68331 User's Manual* listed in Section 16-19.

16-8 ▼ ANALOG-TO-DIGITAL CONVERTER MODULE

The AD port shown in Fig. 16-1 can be used as a general-purpose input port or can bring in eight channels of analog signals to be converted to digital using the A/D Converter in the **68HC16Z1.** The ADC module is another of the standardized submodules included in the Modular MCU family and is therefore compatible with the IMB. It is similar in function to those used in the **68HC11** family and is a unipolar, successive-approximation converter with eight modes of operation. It has selectable 8- or 10-bit resolution. Accuracy is ±1 count (1 LSB) in 8-bit mode and ±4 counts (2 LSB) in 10-bit mode. Monotonicity is guaranteed in both modes. With a 16-MHz clock, the ADC can perform an 8-bit single conversion (four-clock sample) in 8 μs, or a 10-bit single conversion in 9 μs.

ADC functions can be grouped into three basic subsystems: an analog front end, a digital control section, and a bus interface. A block diagram of the converter is shown in Fig. 16-12.

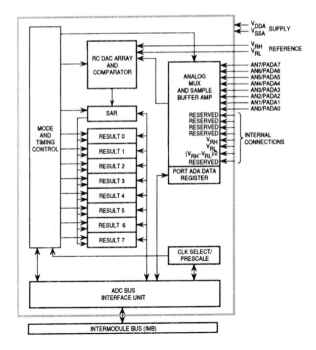

Figure 16-12 ADC block diagram.

16-8.1 ▼ Analog Subsystem

The analog front end consists of a multiplexer, a resistor–capacitor array, and a high-gain comparator. The multiplexer selects one of eight internal or eight external signal sources for conversion. The resistor–capacitor (RC) array performs two functions: it acts as a sample/hold circuit, and it provides the Digital-to-Analog comparison output necessary for successive-approximation conversion. The comparator indicates whether each successive output of the RC array is higher or lower than the sampled input.

16-8.2 ▼ Digital Control Subsystem

The digital control section includes conversion sequence control logic, channel and reference select logic, a successive-approximation register, eight result registers, a port data register, and control/status registers. It controls the multiplexer and the output of the RC array during the sample and conversion periods, stores the results of comparison in the successive-approximation register, then transfers the result to a result register. The ADC module requires many registers to control the conversion and store the results. The address map is shown in Table 16-11.

Table 16-11 ADC module address map.

Address	15 8	7 0
$YFF700	MODULE CONFIGURATION (ADCMCR)	
$YFF702	FACTORY TEST (ADTEST)	
$YFF704	(RESERVED)	
$YFF706	PORT ADA DATA (PORTADA)	
$YFF708	(RESERVED)	
$YFF70A	ADC CONTROL 0 (ADCTL0)	
$YFF70C	ADC CONTROL 1 (ADCTL1)	
$YFF70E	ADC STATUS (ADSTAT)	
$YFF710	RIGHT-JUSTIFIED UNSIGNED RESULT 0 (RJURR0)	
$YFF712	RIGHT-JUSTIFIED UNSIGNED RESULT 1 (RJURR1)	
$YFF714	RIGHT-JUSTIFIED UNSIGNED RESULT 2 (RJURR2)	
$YFF716	RIGHT-JUSTIFIED UNSIGNED RESULT 3 (RJURR3)	
$YFF718	RIGHT-JUSTIFIED UNSIGNED RESULT 4 (RJURR4)	
$YFF71A	RIGHT-JUSTIFIED UNSIGNED RESULT 5 (RJURR5)	
$YFF71C	RIGHT-JUSTIFIED UNSIGNED RESULT 6 (RJURR6)	
$YFF71E	RIGHT-JUSTIFIED UNSIGNED RESULT 7 (RJURR7)	
$YFF720	LEFT-JUSTIFIED SIGNED RESULT 0 (LJSRR0)	
$YFF722	LEFT-JUSTIFIED SIGNED RESULT 1 (LJSRR1)	
$YFF724	LEFT-JUSTIFIED SIGNED RESULT 2 (LJSRR2)	
$YFF726	LEFT-JUSTIFIED SIGNED RESULT 3 (LJSRR3)	
$YFF728	LEFT-JUSTIFIED SIGNED RESULT 4 (LJSRR4)	
$YFF72A	LEFT-JUSTIFIED SIGNED RESULT 5 (LJSRR5)	
$YFF72C	LEFT-JUSTIFIED SIGNED RESULT 6 (LJSRR6)	
$YFF72E	LEFT-JUSTIFIED SIGNED RESULT 7 (LJSRR7)	
$YFF730	LEFT-JUSTIFIED UNSIGNED RESULT 0 (LJURR0)	
$YFF732	LEFT-JUSTIFIED UNSIGNED RESULT 1 (LJURR1)	
$YFF734	LEFT-JUSTIFIED UNSIGNED RESULT 2 (LJURR2)	
$YFF736	LEFT-JUSTIFIED UNSIGNED RESULT 3 (LJURR3)	
$YFF738	LEFT-JUSTIFIED UNSIGNED RESULT 4 (LJURR4)	
$YFF73A	LEFT-JUSTIFIED UNSIGNED RESULT 5 (LJURR5)	
$YFF73C	LEFT-JUSTIFIED UNSIGNED RESULT 6 (LJURR6)	
$YFF73E	LEFT-JUSTIFIED UNSIGNED RESULT 7 (LJURR7)	

16-8.3 ▼ Bus Interface Subsystem

The bus interface contains logic necessary to interface the ADC to the IMB. The ADC is designed to act as a slave device on the bus. The interface must respond with appropriate bus cycle termination signals and supply appropriate interface timing to the other submodules. The ADC function is fully described in the ADC Reference Manual ADCRM/AD listed in Section 16-19.

16-9 ▼ GENERAL-PURPOSE TIMER

The General-Purpose Timer (GPT) is another submodule of the Modular MCU family and is a simple, yet flexible eight-channel timer for use in systems where a moderate degree of external visibility and control is required. The GPT consists of two nearly independent submodules: the Compare/Capture Unit and the Pulse-Width modulator. (Input Capture was explained in Section 10-10.4, and Output Compare in Section 10-10.5.) The pins of port GP on Fig. 16-1 are dual purpose. If not selected for Input Capture or Output Compare timer functions, these pins can be used to form an 8-bit parallel port for general-purpose I/O. When used for I/O, the MSB of register DDRGP at $FF906 is used to select the signal direction (input or output). The LSB is the data register for either direction.

The two Pulse-Width Modulator (PWM) outputs can also be used as general-purpose outputs. They are explained further in Section 16-9.2.

PCLK is an external clock input that is dedicated to the GPT. It can be used in place of one of the prescalar outputs as the clock source for the Capture/Compare Unit or the Pulse-Width Modulator unit. The PAI pin is the input to the pulse accumulator. PAI and PCLK inputs can be used as general-purpose inputs when these functions are not required.

16-9.1 ▼ Compare/Capture Unit

The block diagram for the Compare/Capture unit of the GPT is shown in Fig. 16-13. The Compare/Capture Unit features three Input Capture channels, four Output Compare channels, and one Input Capture/Output Compare channel (function selected via control register). These channels share a 16-bit free-running counter (TCNT) which derives its clock from seven stages of a nine-stage prescaler or from the external clock input PCLK. This section, which is similar to the timer found on the **68HC11F1,** also contains one Pulse Accumulator channel. The Pulse Accumulator logic includes its own 8-bit counter and can operate in either *event counting mode* or *gated time accumulation mode.*

16-9.2 ▼ Pulse-Width Modulation

A block diagram of the Pulse Width Modulator (PWM) submodule is shown in Fig. 16-14. The *PWM* submodule of the GPT has two output pins. The outputs are periodic waveforms controlled by a single frequency whose duty cycles may be selected independently and modified by user software. Each PWM can be independently programmed to run in fast or slow mode. The clocking rate for the PWM logic ranges from 512 Hz to 32.8 kHz in the fast mode (with a 16.78-MHz system clock) depending on the 3 PPR bits of the PWM Control Register C at $FF925. The rate is 128 times

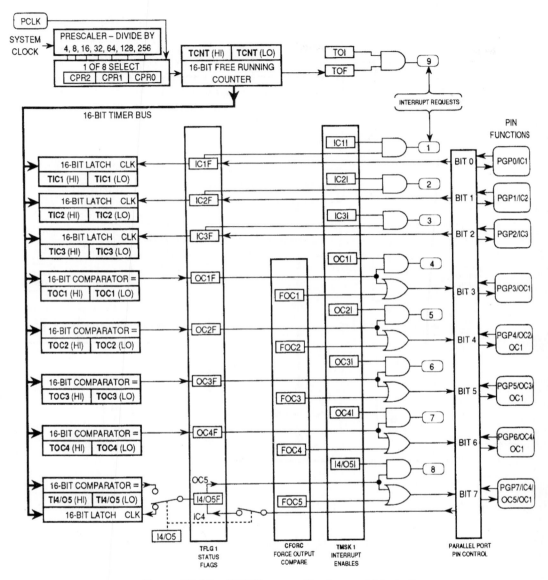

Figure 16-13   GPT Compare/Capture unit block diagram.

slower in the slow mode, ranging from 4 to 256 Hz. The PWM unit has its own 16-bit free-running counter, which is clocked by an output of the nine-stage prescaler (the same prescaler used by the Compare/Capture Unit) or by the clock input pin, PCLK. Each of these integrated modules has a block of control registers, and those for the GPT are shown in Table 16-12. The GPT is fully described in the *General-Purpose Timer Reference Manual* listed in Section 16-19.

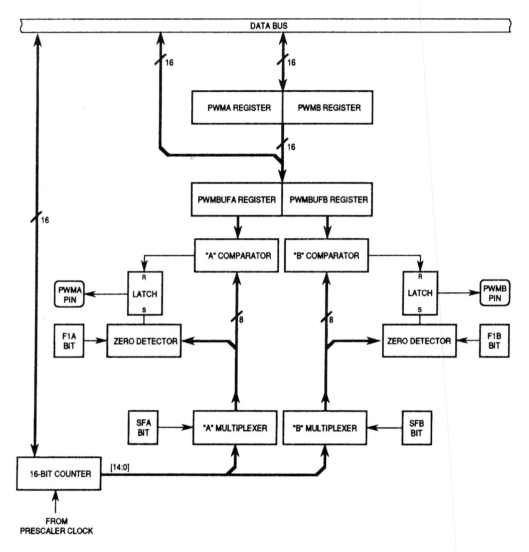

Figure 16-14 GPT PWM unit block diagram.

16-10 ▼ QUEUED SERIAL MODULE

The Queued Serial Module (QSM) is a modular implementation of the serial communications features that exist in most of the MCUs described previously. It contains two serial interfaces, the Serial Communication Interface (SCI) and the Queued Serial Peripheral Interface (QSPI). The SCI controls standard asynchronous serial communication, much like a **6850** ACIA (see Section 7-12). The QSPI functions like the SPI in the **68HC11.** It is used for high-speed serial data transmission between the MCU and peripherals and is

Table 16-12 GPT Address Map

Address	15 8	7 0
$YFF900	GPT MODULE CONFIGURATION (GPTMCR)	
$YFF902	(RESERVED FOR TEST)	
$YFF904	INTERRUPT CONFIGURATION (ICR)	
$YFFE06	PGP DATA DIRECTION (DDRGP)	PGP DATA (PORTGP)
$YFF908	OC1 ACTION MASK (OC1M)	OC1 ACTION DATA (OC1D)
$YFF90A	TIMER COUNTER (TCNT)	
$YFF90C	PA CONTROL (PACTL)	PA COUNTER (PACNT)
$YFF90E	INPUT CAPTURE 1 (TIC1)	
$YFF910	INPUT CAPTURE 2 (TIC2)	
$YFF912	INPUT CAPTURE 3 (TIC3)	
$YFF914	OUTPUT COMPARE 1 (TOC1)	
$YFF916	OUTPUT COMPARE 2 (TOC2)	
$YFF918	OUTPUT COMPARE 3 (TOC3)	
$YFF91A	OUTPUT COMPARE 4 (TOC4)	
$YFF91C	INPUT CAPTURE 4/OUTPUT COMPARE 5 (TI4/O5)	
$YFF91E	TIMER CONTROL 1 (TCTL1)	TIMER CONTROL 2 (TCTL2)
$YFF920	TIMER MASK 1 (TMSK1)	TIMER MASK 2 (TMSK2)
$YFF922	TIMER FLAG 1 (TFLG1)	TIMER FLAG 2 (TFLG2)
$YFF924	FORCE COMPARE (CFORC)	PWM CONTROL C (PWMC)
$YFF926	PWM CONTROL A (PWMA)	PWM CONTROL B (PWMB)
$YFF928	PWM COUNT (PWMCNT)	
$YFF92A	PWMA BUFFER (PWMBUFA)	PWMB BUFFER (PWMBUFB)
$YFF92C	GPT PRESCALER (PRESCL)	
$YFF92E $YFF93F	RESERVED	

capable of operating as a bus master or slave. This implementation differs from the SPI in previous MCUs because it has a self-contained *RAM queue* as part of the QSPI, which allows up to 16 serial transfers of 8 through 16 bits each or transmission of a 256-bit data stream without CPU intervention. The SCI and QSPI submodules operate independently.

The QSPI provides easy peripheral or interprocessor communication via a full-duplex, synchronous, three-line bus: data in, data out, and a serial clock. Four program-mable peripheral select pins provide addressability for up to 16 peripheral devices. A special wraparound mode supports continuous sampling of a serial peripheral. This mode can be used to sample A/D converters continuously and update the conversion values stored in the RAM.

The SCI provides a standard nonreturn-to-zero (NRZ) mark/space format for use with terminals or PCs. It will operate in either full- or half-duplex mode. There are sepa-rate transmitter and receiver enable bits and dual data buffers. A modulus-type baud rate generator provides rates from 64 to 524K baud (with a 16.78-MHz system clock). A word length of either 8 or 9 bits is software selectable. Optional parity generation and detection provide either even- or odd-parity checking capability. Advanced error detection circuitry

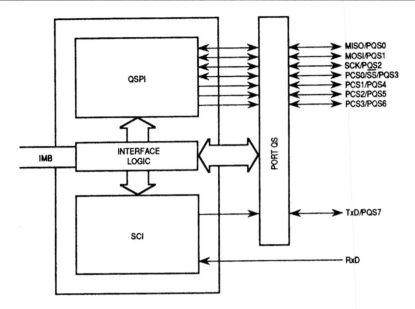

Figure 16-15 QSM block diagram.

catches glitches of up to $\frac{1}{16}$ of a bit time in duration. Wakeup functions allow the CPU to run uninterrupted until meaningful data is available. The block diagram of the QSM is shown in Fig. 16-15. It clearly shows the division of the QSM into its two submodules.

16-10.1 ▼ QSM Address Map

The QSM address map is located in the **68HC16Z1** memory map as shown in Fig. 16-3. The QSM block of addresses is comprised of the global registers, the QSPI and SCI control and status registers, and the addresses for the QSPI transmit and receive RAMs as shown in Table 16-13. The QSM memory map may be divided into two segments: supervisor-only data space and assignable data space. The supervisor-only data space segment contains the QSM global registers. QSM registers are divided into four categories: QSM global registers, QSM pin control registers, QSPI submodule registers, and SCI submodule registers. The global registers control the overall operation of the QSM. The QSM configuration register (QSMCR) contains parameters for interfacing to the CPU16 and the intermodule bus. The QSM test register (QTEST) is used during factory test of the QSM. The QSM interrupt-level register (QILR) determines the priority of interrupts requested by the QSM and the vector used when an interrupt is acknowledged. The QSM interrupt vector register (QIVR) contains the interrupt vector for both QSM submodules. QILR and QIVR are 8-bit registers located at the same word address.

The OSM uses nine pins. Eight of the pins can be used for serial communication or for parallel I/O. Clearing a bit in the port QS pin assignment register (PQSPAR) assigns the corresponding pin to general-purpose I/O; setting a bit assigns the pin to the QSPI. PQSPAR does not affect operation of the SCI. The port QS data direction register

(DDRQS) determines whether pins are inputs or outputs. Clearing a bit makes the corresponding pin an input; setting a bit makes the pin an output. DDRQS affects both QSPI function and I/O function. DDRQS1 determines the direction of the TxD pin only when the SCI transmitter is disabled. When the SCI transmitter is enabled, the TxD pin is an output. The port QS data register (PORTQS) latches I/O data. Writes to PORTQS drives pins defined as outputs. PORTQS reads return data present on the pins. To avoid driving undefined data, first write a byte to PORTQS, then configure DDRQS. PQSPAR and DDRQS are 8-bit registers located at the same word address. The QSPI and SCI registers are defined in separate sections below. Writes to unimplemented register bits have no meaning or effect, and reads from unimplemented bits always return a logic zero value.

16-10.2 ▼ Global Registers

These registers define parameters needed by the QSM to integrate with the MCU. Access to these registers is permitted only when the CPU is operating in the Supervisor Mode. The other registers are in assignable data space and can either be restricted to supervisor only or be unrestricted for user accesses. This is determined by the supervisor bit (SUPV) in the QSM module configuration register (QMCR). The QSM global registers contain

Table 16-13 QSM Address Map.

Address	15　　　　　　　　　　　　　　　8	7　　　　　　　　　　　　　　　0
$YFFC00	QSM MODULE CONFIGURATION (QSMCR)	
$YFFC02	QSM TEST (QTEST)	
$YFFC04	QSM INTERRUPT LEVEL (QUILR)	QSM INTERRUPT VECTOR (QIVR)
$YFFC06	RESERVED	
$YFFC08	SCI CONTROL 0 (SCCR0)	
$YFFC0A	SCI CONTROL 1 (SCCR1)	
$YFFC0C	SCI STATUS (SCSR)	
$YFFC0E	SCI DATA (SCDR)	
$YFFC10	RESERVED	
$YFFC12	RESERVED	
$YFFC14	RESERVED	PQS DATA (PORTQS)
$YFFC16	PQS PIN ASSIGNMENT (PQSPAR)	PQS DATA DIRECTION (DDRQS)
$YFFC18	SPI CONTROL 0 (SPCR0)	
$YFFC1A	SPI CONTROL 1 (SPCR1)	
$YFFC1C	SPI CONTROL 2 (SPCR2)	
$YFFC1E	SPI CONTROL 3 (SPCR3)	SPI STATUS (SPSR)
$YFFC20– $YFFCFF	RESERVED	
$YFFD00– $YFFD1F	RECEIVE RAM (RR[0:F])	
$YFFD20– $YFFD3F	TRANSMIT RAM (TR[0:F])	
$YFFD40– $YFFD4F	COMMAND RAM (CR[0:F])	

system parameters used by both the QSPI and the SCI submodules. Unfortunately, we do not have room to list the settings for each bit of these registers, so we suggest that the Technical Summary or User's Manual listed in Section 16-19 be referenced for details.

16-10.3 ▼ General-Purpose I/O

When selected as general-purpose I/O (as determined by a bit in the SPCR0 and SCCR1 control registers), the QSM Data Direction Register (QDDR) designates each pin (except RxD as input or output. When selected for the QSM functions, the pin functions are as shown in Table 16-14. The table shows that the QSPI operates in either master or slave mode. Master mode is used when the MCU originates data transfers. Slave mode is used when an external device initiates serial transfers to the MCU via the QSPI. Switching between the modes is controlled by MSTR in SPCR0. Prior to entering either mode, appropriate QSM and QSPI registers must be properly initialized.

16-10.4 ▼ QSPI Submodule

The QSPI submodule communicates with external devices via a synchronous serial bus. The QSPI is fully compatible with the Serial Peripheral Interface (SPI) systems found on other Motorola products. The block diagram of the QSPI is shown in Fig. 16-16.

Table 16-14   QMS Pin Functions.

	Pin	Mode	DDRQS Bit	Pin Function
QSPI Pins	MISO	Master	0	Serial Data Input to QSPI
			1	General-Purpose Digital Output
		Slave	0	General-Purpose Digital Input
			1	Serial Data Output from QSPI
	MOSI	Master	0	General-Purpose Digital Input
			1	Serial Data Output from QSPI
		Slave	0	Serial Data Input to QSPI
			1	General-Purpose Digital Output
	SCK	Master	0	General-Purpose Digital Input
			1	Clock Output from QSPI
		Slave	0	Clock Input to QSPI
			1	General-Purpose Digital Output
	PCS0/$\overline{\text{SS}}$	Master	0	Mode Fault Input
			1	Chip-Select Output
		Slave	0	QSPI Slave Select Input
			1	General-Purpose Digital Output
	PCS[3:1]	Master	0	General-Purpose Digital Input
			1	Chip-Select Output
		Slave	0	General-Purpose Digital Input
			1	General-Purpose Digital Output
SCI Pins	TXD	Transmit	X	Serial Data Output from SCI
	RXD	Receive	NA	Serial Data Input to SCI

X = DDRQS bit ignored, data is output when TE = 1

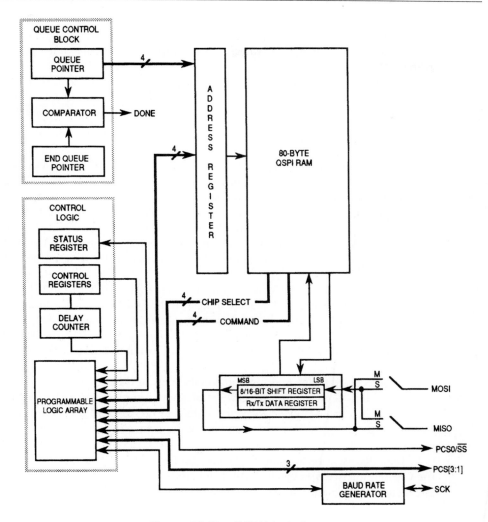

Figure 16-16 QSPI block diagram.

16-10.5 ▼ QSPI Registers

The programmers model for the QSPI submodule consists of the QSM global and pin control registers, four QSPI control registers, one status register, and the 80-byte QSPI RAM. The register addresses are shown in Table 16-13. These registers and the RAM can be read and written by the CPU. The four control registers must be initialized before the QSPI is enabled, to ensure defined operation. SPCR1 should be written last because it contains QSPI enable bit SPE. Asserting this bit starts the QSPI. The QSPI control registers are reset to a defined state and may then be changed by the CPU.

Writing a different value into any control register except SPCR2 while the QSPI is enabled will disrupt operation. SPCR2 is buffered to prevent disruption of the current serial transfer. After completion of the current serial transfer, the new SPCR2 values become effective.

Writing the same value into any control register except SPCR2 while the QSPI is enabled has no effect on QSPI operation. Rewriting the New Queue Pointer value (NEWQP) field in SPCR2 causes execution to restart at the designated location.

16-10.6 ▼ QSPI RAM

The QSPI contains an 80-byte block of dual-access static RAM that is used by both the QSPI and the CPU. This RAM queue allows up to 16 serial transfers of 8 to 16 bits each or transmission of a 256-bit data stream without CPU intervention. The RAM is divided into three segments: receive data (REC.RAM), transmit data (TRAN.RAM), and command control (COMD.RAM). Receive data is information received from a serial device external to the MCU. Transmit data is information stored by the CPU for transmission to an external peripheral. Command control data is used to perform the transfer.

Organization of the RAM is illustrated in Fig. 16-17. Once the CPU has set up the queue of QSPI commands and enabled the QSPI, the QSPI can operate independently of the CPU. The QSPI executes all of the commands in its command RAM queue, sets a flag indicating that it is finished, and then either interrupts the CPU or waits for CPU intervention. It is possible to execute a queue of commands repeatedly without CPU intervention.

Data received by the QSPI is stored in the REC.RAM segment. The CPU reads this segment to retrieve data from the QSPI. Data stored in receive RAM is right-justified. Unused bits in a receive queue entry are set to zero by the QSPI upon completion of the individual queue entry. The CPU can access the data using byte, word, or long-word addressing.

Data that is to be transmitted by the QSPI is stored in the TRAN.RAM segment. The CPU normally writes one word of data into this segment for each queue command to be executed. Information to be transmitted must be written to transmit data RAM in a

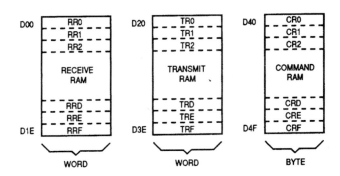

Figure 16-17 QSPI RAM.

right-justified format. The QSPI cannot modify information in the transmit data RAM. The QSPI copies the information to its data serializer for transmission. Information remains in transmit RAM until overwritten.

The command RAM is used by the QSPI when in master mode. The CPU writes 1 byte of control information to the COMD.RAM segment for each QSPI command to be executed. The QSPI cannot modify information in command RAM.

COMD.RAM consists of 16 bytes. Each byte is divided into two fields. The peripheral Chip-Select field enables peripherals for transfer. The command control field provides transfer options. A maximum of 16 commands can be in the queue. Queue execution by the QSPI proceeds from the address in NEWQP through the address in ENDQP (both of these fields are in SPCR2).

Peripheral Chip-Select bits are used to select an external device for serial data transfer. More than one peripheral chip-select may be activated at a time, and more than one peripheral chip may be connected to each PCS pin, provided that proper fanout is observed.

The Slave Select bit (SS) initiates slave mode serial transfer. If SS is taken low when the QSPI is in master mode, a mode fault will be generated.

16-10.7 ▼ Operating Modes

The QSPI operates in either master or slave mode (see Section 10-14.1). Master mode is used when the MCU originates data transfers. Slave mode is used when an external device initiates serial transfers to the MCU via the QSPI. Switching between the modes is controlled by the MSTR bit in SPCR0. Prior to entering either mode, appropriate QSM and QSPI registers must be properly initialized. In master mode, the QSPI executes a queue of commands defined by control bits in each COMD.RAM queue entry. Chip-Select pins are activated, and data is transmitted from TRAN.RAM and received into REC.RAM. In slave mode, operation occurs when the SS (Slave Select) pin is taken low by an external bus master. Operation is similar to master mode, but no peripheral chip selects are generated and the number of bits transferred is controlled in a different manner.

When the QSPI is selected, it automatically executes the next queue transfer to exchange data correctly with the external device. Although the QSPI inherently supports multimaster operation, no special arbitration mechanism is provided. A mode fault flag (MODF) indicates a request for SPI master arbitration—system software must provide arbitration. Note that unlike previous SPI systems, MSTR is not cleared by a mode fault being set nor are the QSPI pin output drivers disabled. The QSPI and associated output drivers must be disabled by clearing SPE in SPCR1.

16-10.8 ▼ SCI Submodule

The SCI submodule is used to communicate with external devices via an asynchronous serial bus. The SCI is fully compatible with the SCI systems found on other Motorola MCUs, such as the **68HC11** and **68HC05** families.

The standard SCI features are listed below, followed by a list of additional features offered.

Standard SCI Two-Wire System Features

- Standard NonReturn-to-Zero (NRZ) Mark-Space format
- Advanced error detection mechanism (detects noise duration up to $\frac{1}{16}$ of a bit time)
- Full-Duplex Operation
- Software selectable word length (8- or 9-bit words)
- Separate Transmitter and Receiver Enable bits
- May be Interrupt Driven
- Four separate Interrupt Enable bits

Standard SCI Receiver Features

- Receiver Wake-up function (idle or address mark bit)
- Idle-Line detection
- Framing Error detection
- Noise detection
- Overrun detection
- Receive Data Register Full Flag

Standard SCI Transmitter Features

- Transmit Data Register Empty flag
- Transmit Complete flag
- Send Break command

QSM-Enhanced SCI Two-Wire System Feature

- 13-bit programmable Baud-Rate modulus counter
- Even/Odd-Parity Generation and Detection

QSM-Enhanced SCI Receiver Features

- Two Idle-Line Detect modes
- Receiver Active Flag

16-10.9 ▼ Newer Features of the SCI

The more advanced features of the SCI are explained below.

13-Bit programmable baud rate modulus counter. A baud rate modulus counter has been added to provide the user with more flexibility in choosing the crystal frequency for the system clock. The modulus counter allows the SCI baud rate generator to produce standard transmission frequencies for a wide range of system clocks. The user is no longer constrained to select crystal frequencies based on the desired serial baud rate. This counter provides baud rates from 64 baud to 524 Kbaud with a 16.78-MHz system clock.

Even/Odd-parity generation and detection.   The user of a **68HC16** MCU has the choice either of 7 or 8 data bits plus 1 parity bit, or of 8 or 9 data bits with no parity bit. Even or odd parity is available. The transmitter automatically generates the parity bit for a transmitted byte. The receiver detects when a parity error has occurred on a received byte and sets a parity error flag.

Two idle-line detect modes.   Standard Motorola SCI systems detect an idle line when 10 or 11 consecutive bit times are all 1s. Used with the receiver wakeup mode, the receiver can be awakened prematurely if the message preceding the start of the idle line contained 1s in advance of its stop bit. The new (second) idle-line detect mode starts counting idle time only after a valid stop bit is received, which ensures correct idle-line detection.

Receiver Active Flag (RAF).   RAF indicates the status of the receiver. It is set when a possible start bit is detected and is cleared when an idle line is detected. RAF is also cleared if the start bit is determined to be line noise. This flag can be used to prevent collisions in systems with multiple masters.

16-10.10 ▼ SCI Pins

There are two unidirectional pins associated with the SCI. The SCI controls the transmit data (TxD) pin when enabled, whereas the receive data (RxD) pin remains a dedicated input pin to the SCI. TxD is available as a general-purpose I/O pin when the SCI transmitter is disabled. When used for I/O, TxD may be configured either as input or output as determined by QSM register QDDR.

16-10.11 ▼ SCI Registers

The SCI programming model includes QSM global and pin control registers, and four SCI registers as shown previously in Table 16-13. There are two SCI control registers, one status register, and one data register. All registers can be read or written at any time by the CPU. Changing the value of SCI control bits during a transfer operation may disrupt operation. Before changing register values, the transmitter should be allowed to complete the current transfer, Then the receiver and transmitter should be disabled. Status flags in register SCSR may be cleared at any time. The SCI registers are described below.

SCI Control Register 0 (SCCR0).   This register contains a 13-bit parameter with the mnemonic SCBR. Its value determines the baud rate which must be set before the SCI is enabled. The CPU can read and write this register at any time. The baud rate is calculated as follows:

$$\text{SCI Baud-Rate} = \frac{\text{System Clock}}{32 \times \text{SCBR}}$$

where SCBR is in the range $\{1, 2, 3, \ldots, 8191\}_{10}$.

Writing a value of zero to SBBR disables the baud rate generator. Table 16-15 shows the Baud-Rates obtained with different values of the 13-bit SCBR.

Table 16-15 SCI Baud Rates.

Nominal Baud Rate	Actual Baud Rate	Percent Error	Value of SCBR
500,000.00	524,288.00	4.86	1
38,400.00	37,449.14	−2.48	14
32,768.00	32,768.00	0.00	16
19,200.00	19,418.07	1.14	27
9,600.00	9,532.51	−0.70	55
4,800.00	4,809.98	0.21	109
2,400.00	2,404.99	0.21	218
1,200.00	1,199.74	−0.02	437
600.00	599.87	−0.02	874
300.00	299.94	−0.02	1,748
110.00	110.01	0.01	4,766
64.00	64.00	0.01	8,191

NOTE: These rates are based on a 16.78-MHz system clock.

EXAMPLE 16-6

What should be written into SCBR to interface the SCI to a 14,400 BPS Modem? Assume that the system clock is 16.78 MHz.

SOLUTION

The equation can be transposed so that

$$SCBR = \frac{\text{System Clock}}{32 \times \text{Baud Rate}}$$

$$= \frac{16.78 \text{ MHz}}{32 \times 14{,}400}$$

$$= 36.41.$$

The user should write in "36".

SCI Control Register 1 (SCCR1). This register contains the SCI configuration parameters. The CPU can read and write this register at any time. The SCI can modify the receiver wakeup bit (RWU) in some circumstances. Changing the value of SCCR1 bits during a character transfer can disrupt operation.

SCI Status Register (SCSR). SCSR contains flags that show SCI operating conditions. These flags are cleared either by SCI hardware or by a CPU read/write sequence. The sequence consists of reading SCSR and then reading or writing SCDR. In general, interrupts enabled by these control bits are cleared by reading SCSR, then by reading or writing SCDR.

SCI Data Register (SCDR). SCDR contains two data registers at the same address. RDR is a read-only register that contains data received by the SCI serial interface. The data comes into the receive serial shifter and is transferred to RDR. TDR is a write-only register that contains data to be transmitted. The data is first written to TDR, then transferred to the transmit serial shifter, where additional format bits are added before transmission. This has been a partial description of the QSM. The QSM is fully described in the *Queued Serial Module Reference Manual* listed in Section 16-19.

16-11 ▼ STANDBY SRAM MODULE

The acronym SRAM normally means *static* RAM. This module not only contains a 1K-byte static array that is fast enough to respond in two bus cycles with a system clock of 16.78 MHz, but it has a battary backup (standby) mode. That is why it is called the *STANDBY* RAM or SRAM. It is especially useful for system stacks and variable storage. The SRAM can be mapped to any 1K-byte boundary in the address map but must not overlap the module control registers: overlap makes the registers inaccessible. Data can be read or written in bytes, words, or long words. The SRAM is powered by V_{DD} in normal operation. During power-down, SRAM contents are maintained by power from the V_{STBY} input. Power switching between sources is automatic.

16-11.1 ▼ SRAM Register Block

There are four SRAM control registers: the RAM module configuration register (RAMMCR), the RAM test register (RAMTST), and the RAM array base address registers (RAMBAH and RAMBAL). The SRAM responds to both program and data space accesses. This allows code to be executed from RAM and permits use of Program Counter Relative (PCR) addressing mode for operand fetches from the array.

The SRAM is positioned to any 1K boundary in the data space by the Base Address Registers in the SRAM CTRL block (see Fig. 16-3). Reset disables the RAM array.

The registers RAMBAH (RAM Base Address High) and RAMBAL (RAM Base Address Low) are used to specify an SRAM base address in the system memory map. RAMBAL contains the 16 LSBs of the base address and RAMBAH contains the higher bits.

16-11.2 ▼ RAM Module Configuration Register

The RAM Module Configuration Register (RAMMCR) controls the operation of the RAM. This 16-bit register at $FFB00 contains only 3 usable bits:

1. STOP (Stop Control)

$$0 = \text{RAM array operates normally}$$
$$1 = \text{RAM array enters low-power stop mode}$$

The reset state is 1, leaving the array configured for LPSTOP operation (see Section 16-6.7). In stop mode, the array retains its contents but cannot be read or written by the CPU. Because the CPU16 operates in supervisor mode, this bit may be read or written at any time.

2. RLCK (RAM base address LoCK)

> 0 = SRAM base address registers are writable from IMB
> 1 = SRAM base address registers cannot be changed (locked)

RLCK defaults to zero on reset: it is one-time writable to 1.

3. RASP (RAM Array SPace field). When = x0, this field allows the SRAM to be used for both programs and data, or if = x1, only for programs.

EXAMPLE 16-7

The RSRAM base address is to be $AB400. What must be written into RAMBAH and RAMBAL to specify this address?

SOLUTION

RAMBAL must contain the LSBs, which are $B400. RAMBAH will contain the higher bits and read $000A. These registers can be written only while the SRAM is in low-power mode. The STOP and RCLK bits of the RAMMCR register are equal to 1 and 0, respectively, following reset. Thus, the address registers RAMBAH and RAMBAL are locked, preventing accidental remapping of the array.

16-11.3 ▼ SRAM Operation

There are five operating modes for the SRAM, as follows.

1. Normal mode. When powered by V_{DD}, the RAM module is in normal mode. The array can be accessed as bytes, words, or long words. A byte or aligned word access, where the high-order byte is at an even address, only takes one bus cycle or two system clocks. A long word or misaligned word access requires two bus cycles.

2. Standby mode. This mode is intended to preserve RAM contents when V_{DD} is removed. Standby and low-power modes should not be confused. Standby mode maintains the RAM array when the MCU main power supply is turned off. Low-power mode minimizes MCU power consumption. Relative voltage levels of the MCU V_{DD} and V_{STBY} pins determine whether the SRAM is in standby mode. SRAM circuitry senses when the difference between the two supply voltages is greater than a specified limit, and switches to the higher-voltage power source. If specified levels are maintained, there is no loss of memory when switching occurs. Access to the array is not guaranteed while the SRAM module is powered from V_{STBY}. If standby operation is not desired, connect the V_{stby} pin to the V_{SS} pin.

Setting the STOP bit in RAMMCR switches the SRAM module to low-power mode. In low-power mode, the array retains its contents, but cannot be read or written by the CPU. If V_{DD} falls below VSB while the SRAM is in low-power mode, internal circuitry switches to V_{STBY}, as in standby mode.

3. Reset mode. This mode allows the CPU to complete the current bus cycle before resetting. When a synchronous reset occurs while a byte or word SRAM access is in progress, the access will be completed. If reset occurs during the first word access of a long-word operation, only the first word access will be completed. If reset occurs during the second word access of a long-word operation, the entire access will be completed. Data being read from or written to the RAM may be corrupted by an asynchronous reset.

4. Test mode. This mode is used for factory testing of the RAM array.

5. Stop mode. Writing the STOP bit of RAMMCR causes the SRAM module to enter stop mode. The RAM array is disabled (which allows external logic to decode SRAM addresses, if necessary), but all data is retained. Stop mode is exited by clearing the STOP bit. Because the CPU16 always operates in supervisor mode, STOP can be read or written at any time. STOP is set during reset. Full details of the Standby RAM (SRAM) Module can be found in the **68HC16Z1** User's Manual MC6816Z1UM/D listed in Section 16-19.

16-12 ▼ 68HC16Z2 MCU

Readers may have noticed that the **68HC16Z1** contains no ROM. Therefore, to be able to start up and run by itself, a complete operable system must include an external non-volatile memory such as EPROM or masked ROM. In late 1992 Motorola introduced the **68HC16Z2** MCU. It is very similiar to the **68HC16Z1** architecturally except for an added Masked ROM (MRM) module. The primary function of the MRM is to serve as nonvolatile memory for the MCU. It can be configured to support system bootstrap during reset. This makes it a complete custom single-chip μC. Its block diagram is shown in Fig. 16-18. Figure 16-19 is a map of the **68HC16Z2** internal subsystems addresses. Although there are 24 intermodule bus (IMB) address lines, the CPU16 uses only 20 of them. The top four lines follow the logic state of ADDR19. The RAM and ROM arrays are positioned by the Base Address Register in the SRAM control block. Reset disables the SRAM array. Unimplemented blocks are mapped externally.

16-12.1 ▼ Masked ROM Module

The Masked ROM Module (MRM) array in the **68HC16Z2** contains 8K bytes. It is arranged in 16-bit words, and like all the other submodules of this family, is accessed through the IMB. Bytes, words, and misaligned words can be accessed. Access time depends on the number of wait states specified at mask programming time, but can be as fast as two system clocks for byte and aligned words. The MRM also responds to back-to-back IMB accesses to provide two bus-cycle long-word accesses.

The array base address must be on an 8K-byte boundary, must not overlap the control registers of other MCU modules, and should not overlap the ROM control register block. If the array is mapped to overlap the control registers of other modules, accesses to those registers are indeterminate; if the array is mapped to overlap the MRM control registers, accesses to the registers are still possible, but accesses to the overlapping 32 bytes of ROM are ignored.

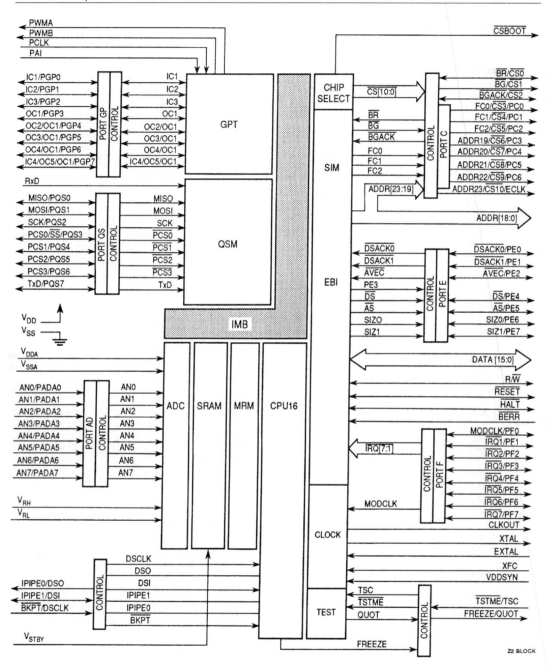

Figure 16-18   68HC16Z2 block diagram.

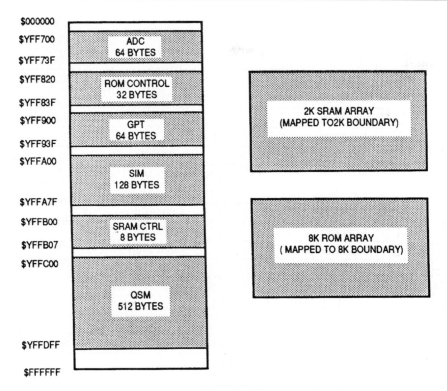

Figure 16-19   68HC16Z2 Address Map.

The MRM array can be used for program code only, or for both program code and data. The MRM can also be programmed to insert wait states to accommodate migration from slower external development memory to the ROM array without retiming.

16-12.2 ▼ Masked ROM Control Registers

The 32-byte control register block shown in Table 16-16 contains the registers that are used to configure the MRM and to control the ROM array function. Configuration information is specified and programmed at the same time as the ROM content. The Masked ROM Module Configuration Register (MRMCR) contains the following bits:

- Stop (STOP)
- Boot ROM control (BOOT)
- Lock registers (LOCK)
- EMULator mode control (EMUL)
- ROM Array SPace field (ASPC)
- Wait States field (WAIT)

The default states of these bits are all user specified when the mask information is provided, but some of them can be changed after reset. Because the **68HC16Z2** operates

Table 16-17 Modular MCU configurations.

Address	15 8	7 0
$YFF820	MRMCR	
$YFF822	NOT IMPLEMENTED	
$YFF824	ROMBAH	
$YFF826	ROMBAL	
$YFF828	SIGHI	
$YFF82A	SIGLO	
$YFF82C	NOT IMPLEMENTED	
$YFF82E	NOT IMPLEMENTED	
$YFF830	ROMBS0	
$YFF832	ROMBS1	
$YFF834	ROMBS2	
$YFF836	ROMBS3	
$YFF838	NOT IMPLEMENTED	
$YFF83A	NOT IMPLEMENTED	
$YFF83C	NOT IMPLEMENTED	
$YFF83E	NOT IMPLEMENTED	

Y = M111, where M is the state of the modmap bit in the module configuration register of the single-chip integration module. In an MC68HC16Y1 system, M must always be set to one.

only in supervisory mode, the ASPC bit determines whether accesses are restricted to program space, or whether accesses are made to both program and data space.

WAIT is a 2-bit field and specifies the number of wait states (from two to five) inserted by the MRM during ROM array accesses. It allows the user to optimize bus speed in a particular application by controlling the number of wait states that are inserted before internal DSACK generation. Each wait state has a duration of one system clock cycle. This allows a user to transport code from a slower emulation or development system memory to the ROM array without retiming the system. The reset state of WAIT is user specified. The following table shows WAIT encoding. A no-wait encoding (00) corresponds to a three-clock-cycle bus. The fast termination encoding (11) corresponds to a two-clock-cycle bus. Microcontroller modules typically respond at this rate, but fast termination can also be used to access fast external memory.

WAIT[1:0]	CYCLES PER TRANSFER
00	3
01	4
10	5
11	2

For details on programming the bits of the many registers, refer to the 68HC16Z2UM/D or to the User's Manual listed in Section 16-19.

16-13 ▼ 68HC16X1 MCU

Still another HC16 family member announced in 1992 is the **68HC16X1** MCU. It is also very similiar to the **68HC16Z1** except that it has a 32K-byte ROM and a 2K-byte Block-Erasable Flash EEPROM module (BEFLASH) with eight independent blocks. The **68HC16X1** block diagram is shown in Fig. 16-20.

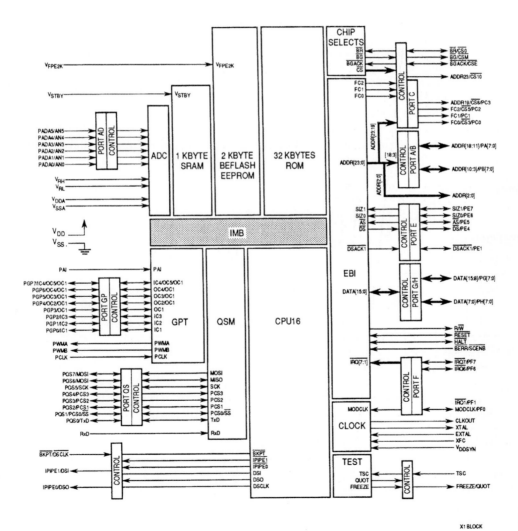

Figure 16-20   68HC16X1 block diagram.

16-14 ▼ 68300 FAMILY

The need for higher-performance MCUs has been growing for some time. One of the first new MCU to fill these requirements was the **68302** Integrated Multiprotocol Processor (IMP). This MCU was introduced in 1991 for use as a controller in the communications industry. It uses a **68000/68008** CPU and includes three high-performance multiprotocol serial communications channel modules. It is a specialized product but became very popular. Because of its complexity we will not attempt to describe it here. Interested parties should refer to the MC68302UM/AD Rev. 2 Manual listed in Section 16-19.

Because these higher-performance MCUs are so complex, further work led to the speeded design processes using the IMB and standardized modules. The introduction of the **68332** was the first of a new **68300** family of more general-purpose MCUs. The original members of the **68300** family include the **68330, 68331, 68332,** and **68340** MCUs. Recently, the **68F333** was added. All of them use the CPU32 (see Section 16-14.1) as the processing unit and are implemented with the same IMB and modular architecture as used in the **68HC16**s. These MCUs also use many of the same submodules, such as the ADC, GPT, QSM, TPU (see Section 16-14.2), and SRAM, as shown in Table 16-17.

The **68F333** includes two FLASH (fast-access) EEPROM memory modules (16K and 48K). It also has an enhanced version of the SIM, which has been modified to work in the single-chip mode as well as with 24-bit address and 8- or 16-bit external data buses.

Table 16-17 Modular MCU configurations.

With CPU 16	ROM	SRAM	EPROM	EEPROM	FLASH	QSM	GPT	TPU	MRM	ADC	MCCI	SIM	DMA	CSIM	TIMER
HC16Z1	0	1K				X	X			X		X			
HC16Z2	0	2K				X	X		8K	X		X			
HC16X1	0	1K			X	X	X		32K	X		X			
HC16Y1	48K	2K				X	X		X	X		X			

With CPU 32	ROM	SRAM	EPROM	EEPROM	FLASH	QSM	GPT	TPU	MRM	ADC	MCCI	SIM	DMA	CSIM	TIMER
68330												X			
68331						X	X		8K			X			
68332	2					X		X	32K			X			
68F333	512 3.5K				16K 48K	X		X			X			X	
68340												X	X		2

16-14.1 ▼ CPU32 PROCESSING MODULE

The CPU32 is the heart of the **68300** family. The CPU32 instruction processing module is based on the **68000** processor but has many features of the **68010** and **68020** μPs. It is binary and source code compatible with the **68000** family. The CPU32 is implemented in HCMOS as is the rest of the **68300** MCU submodules and as a result has the low-power characteristics of CMOS. Object code from the **68000** or **68010** may be executed on the CPU32, and many of the instruction and addressing mode extensions of the **68020** are also supported.

Two new instructions have been added to the **68300** instruction set. They are the Low-Power STOP (LPSTOP) and table lookup and interpolation (TBL) commands. The low-power mode is entered by executing the LPSTOP instruction. Functionally, this is identical to the CPU16's LPSTOP command that was explained in Section 16-6.7. The MCU remains in the stop mode until a user-specified or higher level interrupt, or reset occurs.

To maximize throughput for real-time applications, reference data points are often precalculated and stored in memory for quick access. This storage can require an inordinate amount of memory. The TBL instruction uses linear interpolation to recover intermediate values from a sample of data points and thus conserves memory. When the TBL instruction is executed, The CPU32 looks up two table entries bounding the desired results and performs a linear interpolation between them.

16-14.2 ▼ 68332 MCU

The first 32-bit MCU with the CPU32 and the IMB modular implementation was the **68332.** It has 422,000 transistors. All the additions to the **68300** family since then use the same basic design.

The **68332** MCUs major features include:

- Modular architecture using the InterModule Bus
- A CPU32 instruction processor module featuring:
  - Low-Power mode (500-μW standby power)
  - HCMOS technology
- A QSM serial communications module with two submodules
  - An enhanced SCI fully compatible with **68HC11**
  - A QSPI synchronous interface with queue RAM
- 2K-byte standby RAM
- A System Integration Module (SIM) that has:
  - 12 Programmable Chip-Select logic pins
  - 16.67-MHz synthesized clock-frequency software
  - System failure protection, including a Computer Operating-Properly (COP) Timer and a Periodic Interrupt Timer
- A TPU intelligent 16-bit timer that has:
  - 16 Independent, programmable channels and pins
  - Channels that perform Input Capture, Output Compare, Pulse-Width Modulation (PWM), and so on

- Two timer count registers
- Selectable channel priority levels
- Up to 32 I/O pins

The **68332,** has a modular architecture and IMB similar to the **68HC16Z1.** One major difference in addition to the CPU is that it has a new Time Processor Unit (TPU) instead of the GPT. The TPU is an intelligent peripheral submodule that offers high-resolution timing and multiple time function capability (flexibility) and replaces the servicing of interrupts by the host CPU.

16-15 ▼ TIME PROCESSING UNIT

The Time Processing Unit (TPU) is a new timing module first introduced in the **68332.** It has many advanced features, including higher resolution. Because the TPU also has a dedicated execution unit, it drastically reduces the need for CPU intervention. In addition, it has a trilevel prioritized scheduler, data storage RAM, dual time bases, and microcode ROM.

The TPU controls 16 independent channels. Each channel can be synchronized to either of two 16-bit free-running counters with a prescaler. One counter is based on the system clock and provides resolution to 500 ns. The second counter, based on an external reference, provides resolution to 250 ns. Channels may also be linked together, allowing the user to reference operations on one channel to the occurrence of a specified action on another channel to provide intertask control. Each channel has an I/O pin and is capable of performing any time function. These are shown in Fig. 16-21. The timing algorithms available in the microcoded ROM include the following:

- Discrete Input/Output
- Period Measurement
- Position Synchronized Pulse Generator
- Stepper Motor Control
- Output Match
- Period/Pulse-Width Accumulator

16-15.1 ▼ TPU Emulation Capability

The TPU cannot resolve all timer problems using the predefined time functions listed above. Therefore, development of user-defined time functions is allowed in an emulation mode. Using the RAM module of the MCU as a writable control store provides TPU emulation. In TPU emulation mode, an auxiliary bus connection is made between the RAM module and the TPU module, and access to the RAM module via the intermodule bus is disabled. A 9-bit address bus, a 32-bit data bus, and control lines transfer information between the TPU and RAM modules. To ensure exact emulation, the access timing of the RAM module remains consistent with the TPU ROM control store.

The TPU is a very complex module and Motorola has written a complete manual called the *Time Processor Unit Reference Manual* (see Section 16-19).

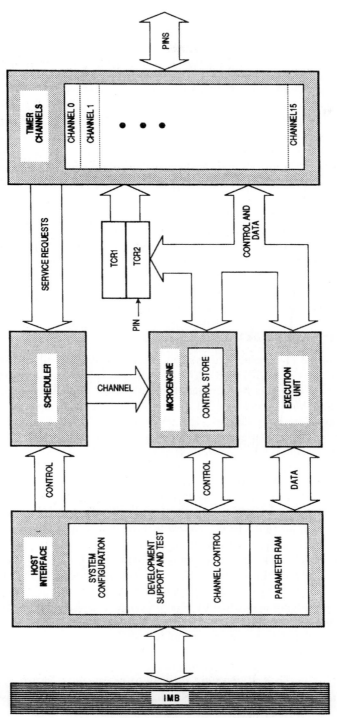

Figure 16-21 TPU simplified block diagram.

16-16 ▼ 16/32-BIT MCU SYSTEM DEVELOPMENT

Motorola provides both low-cost and high-performance development tools to support the 16- and 32-bit MCUs. A **68HC16Z1EVB** is available to support the HC16 family MCUs, and the **68332EVS** evaluation system provides a simple emulation system for the **68332.** The Motorola Modular Development System (MMDS16/32) provides a high-performance emulation environment for all of the **HC16** and **68300** family MCUs. Free assemblers and C compilers are available on the MCU Bulletin Board System (512-891-FREE) and can be downloaded for product evaluation. A number of software tools for MS-DOS computers are available from Motorola to support high-level language development and debugging for both families. Many development support tools from major third-party vendors are also available and are listed in Section 16-19 and particularly in the *MCU Toolbox* manual.

The use of the **68000** family architecture and its external bus (based on the **68020**) for the CPU32-based MCUs permits the use of many existing or slightly modified development tools. The Background Debug Mode (BDM) feature in the MCUs of both families significantly reduces the external logic necessary to provide system testing. This new feature can be incorporated in a user's system at minimum cost simply by providing an interface connector for BDM communication with the MCU and software on the host. These Motorola Development products are described in the following sections.

16-16.1 ▼ 68HC16Z1EVB

To aid in the development of systems using the HC16 family of MCUs, Motorola has provided the 68HC16Z1EVB EValuation Board. Like its predecessors, this product is a single-board computer built around the chip that it is designed to support, in this case the **68HC16Z1** MCU. Locations U1 through U4 on the EVB are sockets for various types and sizes of memory devices. The EVB circuitry includes jumpers, which allows the memory ICs to be configured as either byte or word addressable. This lets the user evaluate HC16 systems with 8- or 16-bit RAMs or EPROMs. Up to 512K devices can be used. The EVB also has seven connectors for Logic Analyzer use.

This CPU16-based EVB uses the *Background Debug Mode* (BDM), that is explained in Section 16-6.8. The only hardware requirement is to provide a communications path from the **68HC16Z1** to a standard terminal or PC acting as a terminal. The EVB connections to the HOST are made through a parallel Centronics printer port of an IBM-PC, or clone, using a standard 25-conductor printer cable.

An RS232 connector is also provided on the EVB but is only used when testing the SCI circuits of the chip. It is not used in the debugging process for the MCU and its software.

Once the EVB is set up and connected, the debugging screens are implemented by an interface program supplied by Motorola that is loaded into the Host computer that is used. That computer must run MS-DOS, PC-DOS, or Dr-DOS. The program provided is called ICD16 and the startup command is C:\ICD16.

The main screen display for the 68HC16Z1EVB is shown in Fig. 16-22. It will be noted that because MS-DOS compatible software is supplied by P & E Microsystems to Motorola, for use in an IBM-PC (or clone), the 68HC16Z1EVB16's screen display is similar to Fig. 11-14 for the P & E Simulator program described in Section 11-7. The dis-

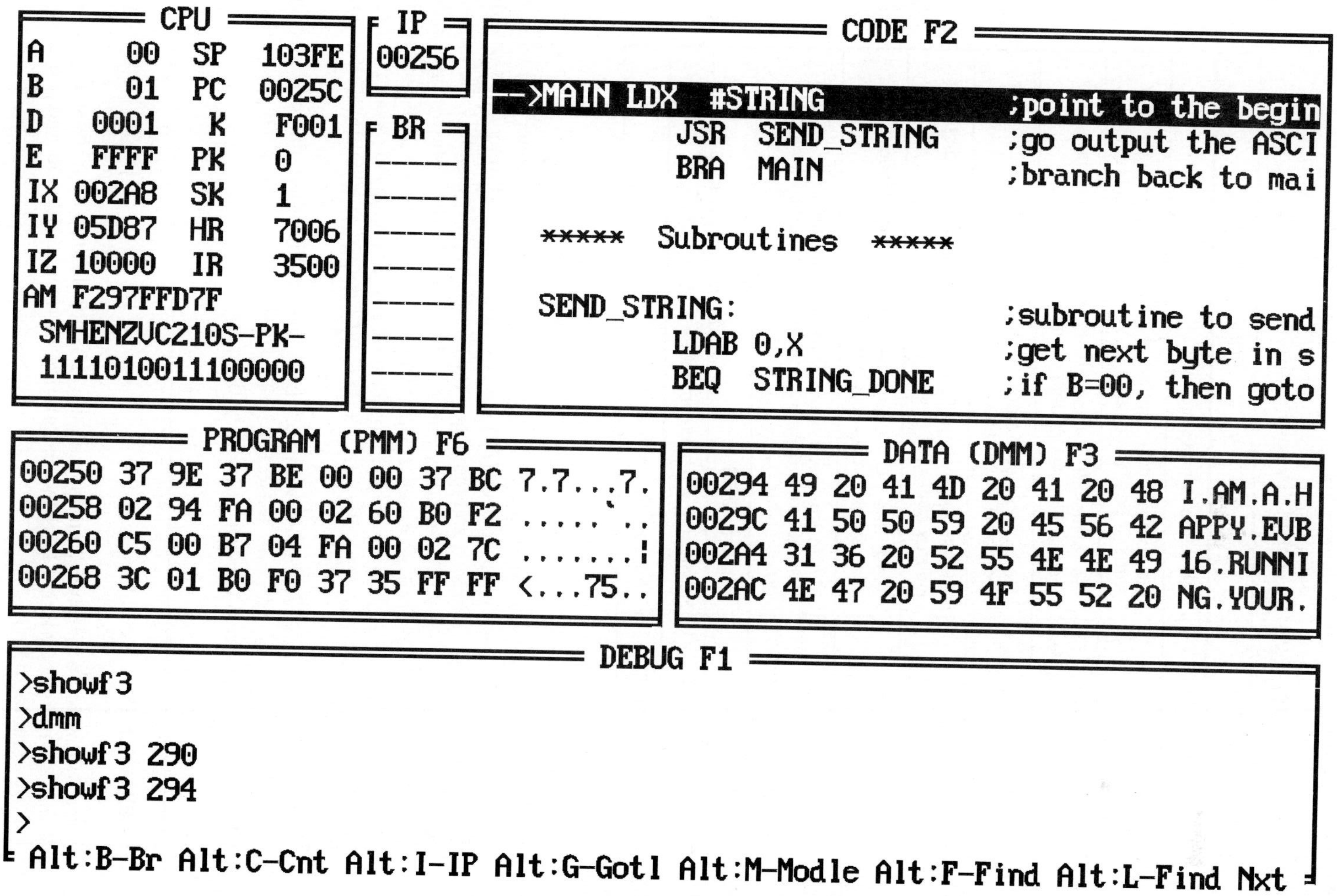

```
=== CPU ===                    = IP =
 A   00  SP  103FE             00256
 B   01  PC  0025C
 D  0001  K   F001             = BR =
 E  FFFF  PK    0
 IX 002A8 SK    1
 IY 05D87 HR 7006
 IZ 10000 IR 3500
 AM F297FFD7F
 SMHENZUC210S-PK-
 1111010011000000
```

=== CODE F2 ===
```
>MAIN LDX  #STRING        ;point to the begin
      JSR  SEND_STRING    ;go output the ASCI
      BRA  MAIN           ;branch back to mai

***** Subroutines *****

SEND_STRING:              ;subroutine to send
      LDAB 0,X            ;get next byte in s
      BEQ  STRING_DONE    ;if B=00, then goto
```

=== DATA (DMM) F3 ===
```
00294 49 20 41 4D 20 41 20 48 I.AM.A.H
0029C 41 50 50 59 20 45 56 42 APPY.EVB
002A4 31 36 20 52 55 4E 4E 49 16.RUNNI
002AC 4E 47 20 59 4F 55 52 20 NG.YOUR.
```

=== PROGRAM (PMM) F6 ===
```
00250 37 9E 37 BE 00 00 37 BC 7.7...7.
00258 02 94 FA 00 02 60 B0 F2 .....`..
00260 C5 00 B7 04 FA 00 02 7C ......|
00268 3C 01 B0 F0 37 35 FF FF <...75..
```

=== DEBUG F1 ===
```
>showf3
>dmm
>showf3 290
>showf3 294
>
```

Alt:B-Br Alt:C-Cnt Alt:I-IP Alt:G-Gotl Alt:M-Modle Alt:F-Find Alt:L-Find Nxt

Figure 16-22 EVB16 Main Screen.

Table 16-18   EVB16 Function Key commands.

F KEY	FUNCTION
F1	Go to the debug window
F2	Go to the code window. In this window, you may scroll or see future code.
F3	Go to the F3 memory window. In this window, you may scroll through data memory.
F4	Do a single-step trace. (This key has the same role as the ST command.)
F5	Shrink or enlarge the code window (if it displays source code).
F6	Go to the F6 memory window. In this window, you may scroll through code memory.
F7	Go to the code window as a trace window. In this format of the code window, you may scroll through the trace buffer.
F8	Shell to DOS.
F9	Repeat the last command.
F10	Activate the help window.

play consists of seven windows: the CPU window, the instruction pointer (IP) window, the breakpoint (BR) window, the code (F2) window, the program (F6) memory window, the data (F3) memory window, and the debug (F1) window. As implied by their names, these windows are almost all selected by Function Keys. Table 16-18 shows the function of each key. The F10 key activates a Help window that describes most everything needed to operate the system, so we will not try to list every command. Also, the user is referred to the *M68HC16Z1EVB/D1 User's Manual* listed in Section 16-19, for complete details.

Motorola also supplies a disk with each EVB, called QuickStart, that contains eight examples of programs for the **68HC16Z1.** To illustrate how the EVB is used, the EXERC_3 example from the disk will now be described.

EXAMPLE 16-8

Provide a program that will use the SCI port to display a message on a terminal. Describe how the program is developed, loaded into the EVB, and tested.

SOLUTION

Figure 16-23 shows the Source file for the EXERC_3 program supplied by Motorola. A program such as this can be written and assembled in several ways. One way is to use a Word Processor (in the ASCII mode) to write a source file and then to assemble it with the Motorola MASM Assembler program. This is a "Toolware" product for MS-DOS and is described in the M68HCASM/D1 manual (see Section 16-19). Alternatively, the assembler on the Motorola BBS in Austin, Texas (see Section 6-6.4) could be downloaded and used. Finally, the IASM16 Integrated Editor/Assembler written by the same company that wrote the EVB16 software (P & E Microsystems Inc., of Woburn, Massachusetts) can be installed on the PC and used both to write and assemble the user's program. The latter has the added advantage that it automatically produces a MAP file that gets downloaded with the S-record file and inserts symbols in the display when running EVB16.

The source file for this EXERC_3 program shown in Fig. 16-23 calls for six "Include" files. These files are on the disk and are needed to initialize all the registers and memory data locations. When the listing file is examined, after assembly, it will be seen that the "Include" files generate 183 EQU statements, 6 Double-Word (DW) RESET Vectors, and 252 other Vector statements. The full listing is therefore too long to show here, but students can acquire valuable information about programming the many registers in the MCU by studying the listing. The MAIN section and three subroutines from that file are shown in the assembled Program Listing of Fig. 16-24 so that the program can be understood. The numbers in brackets following each address is the number of cycles used by each instruction. Lines prior to 597 (not shown) explain the programs initialization including how the K register is used. The rest of the listing should be familiar to students of **68HC11** programs.

The MAIN routine is a very small loop and the real work is done by the subroutines. After the power is applied to the EVB and the EVB16 program is loaded and started, the S-record file and the MAP file can both be downloaded by entering the LOADALL EXERC_3 command. Then if "IP 200" is entered on the command line, the EXERC_3 program is then ready to be executed. To see how it works, the F4 key can be used to step through each instruction while observing the registers or memory locations. F10 is used to get help and to display the commands.

Using these exercises in this EVB is an excellent way to study the **68HC16Z1**. For example, the user can step through the initialization instructions and observe how the K register is used. Also, looking through the "Include" files helps the student realize which registers need to be initialized and what typical values are needed.

16-16.2 ▼ The MMDS16/32 Development System

In 1993, Motorola introduced the Motorola Modular Development System (MMDS16/32). This is a unit similar in function to the MMDS05 described in Section 12-8 but different mechanically and in software operation. It is intended for 16- and 32-

Figure 16-23 Source file for Example 16-8.

```
*       Title : EXERCISE 3
*       Description : This program uses the SCI port to display
*                     a shameless message at a dummy terminal.  It includes
*                     a subroutine to print a single character to the SCI
*                     and a subroutine that uses the single character
*                     subroutine to print an entire string.
*
*******************************************************************************
$INCLUDE   'EQUATES.ASM'          ;table of EQUates for common register addresses
$INCLUDE   'ORG00000.ASM'         ;initialize reset vector
$INCLUDE   'ORG00008.ASM'         ;initialize interrupt vectors

           ORG  $0200             ;start program after exception vector table

*****   Initialize   *****

INIT:

$INCLUDE   'INITSYS.ASM'          ;initially set EK=F, XK=0, YK=0, ZK=0
                                  ;set sys clock at 16.78 MHz, disable COP
$INCLUDE   'INITRAM.ASM'          ;turn on internal SRAM at $10000

$INCLUDE   'INITSCI.ASM'          ;set the SCI baud rate to 9600 baud
                                  ;set stack (SK=1, SP=03FE)
                                  ;enable the SCI receiver and transmitter

           LDAB #$00
           TBXK                   ;set XK to bank 0 for STRING access
           LDAB #$01
           TBZK                   ;set ZK to bank 1 for delay counter access
           LDZ  #$0000            ;clear IZ for later use with delay counter

*****   Main Program   *****

MAIN LDX   #STRING                ;point to the beginning of ASCII string
     JSR   SEND_STRING            ;go output the ASCII string
     BRA   MAIN                   ;branch back to main
```

```
SEND_STRING:                      ;subroutine to send out the entire ASCII string
        LDAB    0,X               ;get next byte in string as pointed to by IX
        BEQ     STRING_DONE       ;if B=00, then goto delay between messages
        JSR     SEND_CH           ;go send out the byte
        AIX     #$01              ;increment IX to point to the next byte
        BRA     SEND_STRING       ;loop back and do next byte in string

STRING_DONE:                      ;subroutine to implement delay between messages
        LDE     #$FFFF            ;load accumulator E with the delay time
        STE     0,Z               ;set up the counter
LOOP:   DECW    0,Z               ;decrement the counter
        BNE     LOOP              ;count down to zero
        RTS                       ;finish delay loop go back to main

SEND_CH:                          ;subroutine to send out one byte to SCI
        LDAA    SCSR              ;read SCI status reg to check/clear TDRE bit
        ANDA    #$01              ;check only the TDRE flag bit
        BEQ     SEND_CH           ;if TDR is not empty, go back to check it again
        LDAA    #$00              ;clear A to send a full word to SCDR ($FFC0E)
        STD     SCDR              ;transmit one ASCII character to the screen

TC_LOOP:
        LDAB    SCSR+1            ;test the TC bit (transfer complete)
        ANDB    #$80              ;continue to wait until TC is set
        BEQ     TC_LOOP

        RTS                       ;finish sending out byte

STRING  DB      'I AM A HAPPY EVB16 RUNNING YOUR CODE!!!',0A,0D,00

****** Interrupts/Exceptions ******

BDM: BGND                         ;exception vectors point here
                                  ;and put the user in background debug mode

***** Reserve data and stack space *****

        ORG     $10000            ;start of 1K internal SRAM for data & stack

COUNTER DS      2                 ;space for delay counter
```

Figure 16-24 Partial Program Listing for Example 16-8.

```
                              597   ******  Main Program  ******
                              598
00256 [04] 37BC0294           599   MAIN LDX #STRING       ;point to the beginning of ASCII string
0025A [10] FA000260           600        JSR  SEND_STRING  ;go output the ASCII string
0025E [06] B0F2               601        BRA  MAIN          ;branch back to main
                              602
                              603   ******  Subroutines  ******
                              604
                              605   SEND_STRING:            ;subroutine to send out the entire ASCII string
00260 [06] C500               606        LDAB 0,X           ;get next byte in string as pointed to by IX
00262 [02] B704               607        BEQ  STRING_DONE   ; B=00, then goto delay between messages
00264 [10] FA00027C           608        JSR  SEND_CH       ;go send out the byte
00268 [02] 3C01               609        AIX  #$01          ;increment IX to point to the next byte
0026A [06] B0F0               610        BRA  SEND_STRING   ;loop back and do next byte in string
                              611
                              612   STRING_DONE:            ;subroutine to implement delay between messages
0026C [04] 3735FFFF           613        LDE  #$FFFF        ;load accumulator E with the delay time
00270 [06] 376A0000           614        STE  0,Z           ;set up the counter
00274 [08] 27210000           615   LOOP: DECW 0,Z          ;decrement the counter
00278 [02] B6F6               616        BNE  LOOP          ;count down to zero
0027A [12] 27F7               617        RTS               ;finish delay loop go back to main
                              618
                              621
                              622   SEND_CH:                ;subroutine to send out one byte to SCI
0027C [06] 1775FC0C           623        LDAA SCSR          ;read SCI status reg to check/clear TDRE bit
00280 [02] 7601               624        ANDA #$01          ;check only the TDRE flag bit
00282 [02] B7F4               625        BEQ  SEND_CH       ;if TDR is not empty, go back to check it again
00284 [02] 7500               626        LDAA #$00          ;clear A to send a full word to SCDR ($FFC0E)
00286 [06] 37FAFC0E           627        STD  SCDR          ;transmit one ASCII character to the screen
                              628   TC_LOOP:
```

```
0028A [06] 17F5FC0D   629              LDAB  SCSR+1       ;test the TC bit (transfer complete)
0028E [02] F680       630              ANDB  #$80         ;continue to wait until TC is set
00290 [02] B7F4       631              BEQ   TC_LOOP
00292 [12] 27F7       633              RTS                ;finish sending out byte
                      634
00294      4920414D   635   STRING     DB    'I AM A HAPPY EVB16 RUNNING YOUR CODE!!',0A,0D,00
           20412048
           41505059
           20455642
           31362052
           554E4E49
           4E472059
           4F555220
           434F4445
           2121210A
           0D00
                      636
                      637   *****  Interrupts/Exception  *****
                      638
002BE [02] 37A6       639   BDM: BGND       ;exception vectors point here
                      640   and put the user in background debug mode
                      641
                      642   *****  Reserve data and stack space  *****
                      643
10000                 644              ORG   $10000   ;start of 1K internal SRAM for data & stack
                      645
10000                 646   COUNTER DS  2    ;space for delay counter
```

bit MCU development. As its name implies, this is a modular emulator, bus state analyzer, and control station for debugging the hardware and software during development of an MCU systems. The MMDS16/32 system hardware consists of an enclosure that contains a single circuit board and power supply. The emulation (target) processor is located on a probe which is a separate assembly that can be plugged into the target system and is connected to the MMDS16/32 by a cable. The probe assembly consists of three small boards that are plugged together to provide the selected MCU and desired packaging arrangement so as to be compatible with the user's system. Thus it is easily possible to change the system configuration by using the appropriate modules. The MMDS16/32 configuration is shown in Figure 16-25. The MMDS16/32 development system includes:

- Built-in emulation memory with:
  - 1 Mbyte of fast emulation RAM memory
  - 4 K bytes of dual port emulation memory
- Real-time bus analysis including:
  - 32K-bytes by 96-bit analyzer buffer memory
  - Instruction disassembly
  - State-machine-driven triggering
- Active probe consisting of three boards: an MCU Personality Board (MPB), a Probe Control Module (PCM), and a Package Personality Board (PPB)
- Four hardware breakpoints
- Complete MCU emulation, including reset and analog/digital functions
- Sixteen logic clips for individual signal monitoring
- Built-in self-test
- Real-time in-circuit emulation

The software is shipped on standard IBM-PC-compatible disks, and unlike the MMDS05, makes use of Microsoft Windows (Version 3.1 or later).

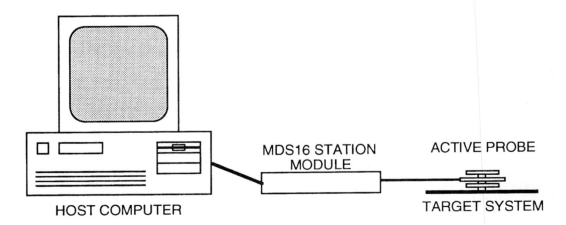

Figure 16-25   MMDS16 Development System.

We will not attempt to describe the operation of this system in the detail used for the MMDS05 because the functions are so similar. The main differences are in the screen presentations, which in this case resembles other typical windows displays. The initial MMDS16/32 screen is shown in Fig. 16-26. This display actually shows three overlaid windows, the Command Log, the Bus Analyzer window, and if those are closed, the main window with the Tool Bar across its top. The Memory Window can be displayed instead of or in addition to the Command Log window. The menus across the top can be accessed either by typed commands or with a mouse as in a typical Windows display.

16-16.3 ▼ 32-Bit 68332EVS

The 68332EVS provides a low-cost solution for initial **68332** MCU evaluation. The common evaluation module (EVM) monitor/debugger functions, such as memory and register modification and display, single stepping and tracing, and breakpoints are supported. A one-line assembler/disassembler provides quick code modification capability. Breakpoints are provided on the access of any address. The EVS is shown in Fig. 16-27. The M68332EVS is composed of separate boards. These boards all plug together to form a total system but can be separated for different modes of use. The M68332BCC may be mounted directly in the user's target application. Different modes of operation are possible, as shown in Fig. 16-28.

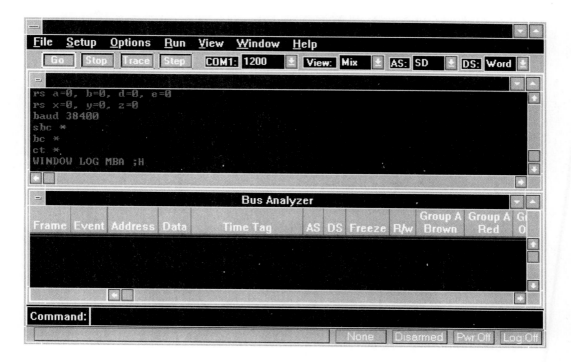

Figure 16-26 Main Screen (Preliminary).

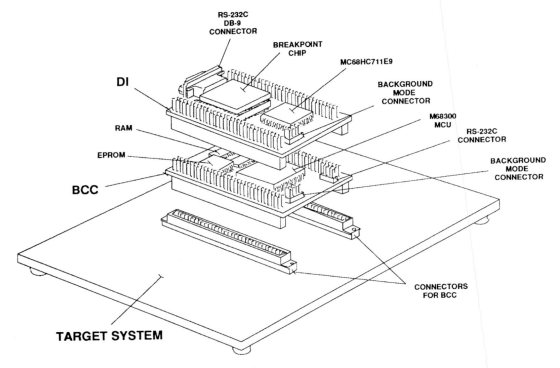

Figure 16-27   68332EVS Evaluation System.

16-17 ▼ SUMMARY

In this chapter we have described the 16- and 32-bit Modular MCU Families. The on-chip InterModule Bus (IMB) and System Integration Module (SIM) architecture were explained and the CPU16 and CPU32 instruction processor modules were fully described. The features of a number of **HC16** and **68300** family MCUs were listed, including several new submodules, such as the TPU, QSM, and SRAM.

16-18 ▼ GLOSSARY

Address space partitioning A technique using the Function Code lines to select different sections of a memory block.

Background Debug Mode (BDM) A feature of the CPU16 and CPU32 processor modules whereby Microcode has been included to provide debugging routines on-chip.

Bank Switching A technique to select blocks of memory, so that more than 64K can be addressed with only 16 address lines.

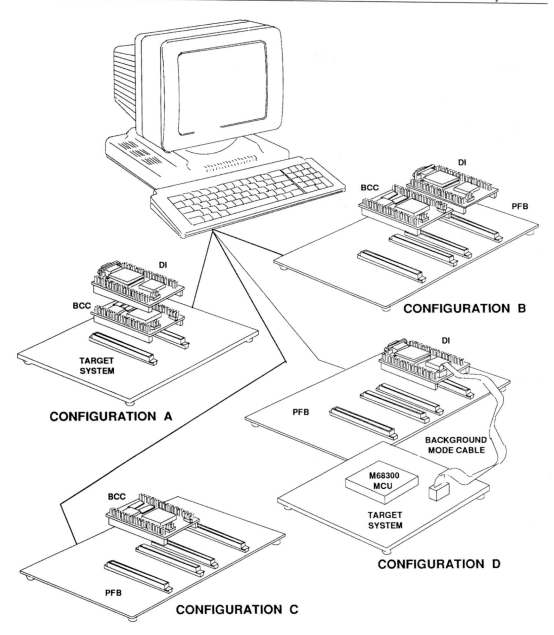

Figure 16-28 EVS Configurations.

BFLASH memory A version of FLASH nonvolatile memory that is Block erasable.

Digital Signal Processor (DSP) A Special high-speed processor similiar to a Microprocessor in construction but designed primarily for digitally encoding analog speech, telecommunications switching, and control applications.

FLASH memory An advanced version of EEPROM that has access times similar to those of typical RAM or ROM.

High-Level Language (HLL) A way of writing source programs that can be "compiled" with a special program into machine language. It is considered to be 25% easier or faster to program than Assembly language.

Wait State A delay of one clock cycle.

16-19 ▼ REFERENCES

Motorola **Manuals, Application Notes, and Development Aids.**

Modular Microcontroller Family:

CPU Central Processor Unit-Reference Manual CPU16RM/AD Rev 1, 1991.
CPU Central Processor Unit-Reference Manual, CPU32RM/AD Rev. 1, 1990.
Analog-To-Digital Converter Reference Manual, ADCRM/AD, 1992.
General Purpose Timer Reference Manual, GPTRM/AD, 1991.
Queued Serial Module Reference Manual, QSMRM/AD, 1991.
Time Processor Unit-Reference Manual TPURM/AD, 1990.
Multichannel Communications Interface Reference Manual, MCCIRM/AD 1992.

MC6HC16 Family:

MC68HC16Z1 User's Manual MC68HC16Z1UM/AD, 1992.
MC68HC16Z2 User's Manual MC68HC16Z2UM/AD, 1992.
MC68HC16Y1 User's Manual MC68HC16Y1UM/AD, 1992.

MC68300 Family:

MC68302 Integrated Multiprotocol Processor User's Manual MC68302UM/AD-Rev. 2, 1991.
MC68330 User's Manual MC68330UM/AD, 1991.
MC68331 User's Manual MC68331UM/AD, 1992.
MC68332 User's Manual MC68332UM/AD, 1990.
MC68340 User's Manual MC68340UM/AD, 1992.

Application Notes:

Using the 68332 Periodic Interrupt Timer, AN437, 1990.
Configuring the M68300 Family Time Processing Unit (TPU) AN1200, 1991.

Development Aids:

The MCU Toolbox Development Tools for Motorola Microcontrollers, September 1991.

ToolWare M68HC16 Macro Assembler User's Manual for MS-DOS-M68HCASM/D1, October 1991.

ToolWare Linker User's Manual for MS-DOS-M68HLINK2/D3, October, 1991.

16-20 ▼ PROBLEMS

16-1. An MCU system requires a 22-bit address bus but does not need the bus arbitration signals. How can this system be set up to provide the maximum number of chip select lines?

16-2. A **68HC16Z1** is reset with pins DB1, DB2, and DB4 held low. What are the functions of the port C pins in this configuration?

16-3. The chip select base address register for CS6 contains $1234B. For what range of addresses will CS6 go low?

16-4. A **68HC16Z1** system has two PIAs at $08000 and $08008. Each PIA requires four memory locations. Show the decoding to access either of these PIAs and what you would write in the chip select base address register. Assume that these are the only peripherals in the 2K-byte memory block from $8000 to $87FF.

16-5. In Problem 16-4 the first PIA can generate DSACK, but the other PIA cannot. Show the connections between the PIAs and the DSACK lines.

16-6. An 8K-byte ROM is to be used as a boot ROM. What must be done so that the system invokes this memory at reset? Place the memory at location $100000.

After attempting to solve these problems, try to answer the self-evaluation questions in Section 16-2. If any of them still seem difficult, review the appropriate sections of the chapter to find the answers.

POSITIVE AND NEGATIVE POWERS OF 2

TABLE A.1 Powers of 2[1]

2^n	n	2^{-n}
1	0	1.0
2	1	0.5
4	2	0.25
8	3	0.125
16	4	0.062 5
32	5	0.031 25
64	6	0.015 625
128	7	0.007 812 5
256	8	0.003 906 25
512	9	0.001 953 125
1 024	10	0.000 976 562 5
2 048	11	0.000 488 281 25
4 096	12	0.000 244 140 625
8 192	13	0.000 122 070 312 5
16 384	14	0.000 061 035 156 25
32 768	15	0.000 030 517 578 125
65 536	16	0.000 015 258 789 062 5
131 072	17	0.000 007 629 394 531 25
262 144	18	0.000 003 814 697 265 625
524 288	19	0.000 001 907 348 632 812 5
1 048 576	20	0.000 000 953 674 316 406 25
2 097 152	21	0.000 000 476 837 153 203 125
4 194 304	22	0.000 000 238 418 579 101 562 5
8 388 608	23	0.000 000 119 209 289 550 781 25
16 777 216	24	0.000 000 059 604 644 775 390 625
33 554 432	25	0.000 000 029 802 322 387 695 312 5
67 108 864	26	0.000 000 014 901 161 191 817 656 25
134 217 728	27	0.000 000 007 450 580 596 923 828 125
268 435 456	28	0.000 000 003 725 290 298 461 914 062 5
536 870 912	29	0.000 000 001 862 645 149 230 957 031 25
1 073 741 824	30	0.000 000 000 931 322 574 615 478 515 625
2 147 483 648	31	0.000 000 000 465 661 287 307 739 257 812 5
4 294 967 296	32	0.000 000 000 232 830 643 653 869 628 906 25
8 589 934 592	33	0.000 000 000 116 415 321 826 934 814 453 125
17 179 869 184	34	0.000 000 000 058 207 660 913 467 407 226 562 5
34 359 738 368	35	0.000 000 000 029 103 830 456 733 703 613 281 25
68 719 476 736	36	0.000 000 000 014 551 915 228 366 851 806 640 625
137 438 953 472	37	0.000 000 000 007 275 957 614 183 425 903 320 312 5
274 877 906 944	38	0.000 000 000 003 637 978 807 091 712 951 660 156 25
549 755 813 888	39	0.000 000 000 001 818 989 403 545 856 475 830 078 125
1 099 511 627 776	40	0.000 000 000 000 909 494 701 772 928 237 915 039 062 5
2 199 023 255 552	41	0.000 000 000 000 454 747 350 886 464 118 957 519 531 25
4 398 046 511 104	42	0.000 000 000 000 227 373 675 443 232 059 478 759 765 625
8 796 093 022 208	43	0.000 000 000 000 113 686 837 721 616 029 739 379 882 812 5
17 592 186 044 416	44	0.000 000 000 000 056 843 418 860 808 014 869 689 941 406 25
35 184 372 038 832	45	0.000 000 000 000 028 421 709 430 404 007 434 844 970 703 125
70 368 744 177 664	46	0.000 000 000 000 014 210 854 715 202 003 717 422 485 351 562 5
140 737 488 355 328	47	0.000 000 000 000 007 105 427 357 601 001 858 711 242 675 781 25
281 474 976 710 656	48	0.000 000 000 000 003 552 713 678 800 500 929 355 621 337 890 625
562 949 953 421 312	49	0.000 000 000 000 001 776 356 839 400 250 464 677 810 668 945 312 5
1 125 899 906 843 624	50	0.000 000 000 000 000 888 178 419 700 125 232 338 905 334 472 656 25
2 251 799 813 685 248	51	0.000 000 000 000 000 444 089 209 850 062 616 169 452 667 236 328 125
4 503 599 627 370 496	52	0.000 000 000 000 000 222 044 604 925 031 308 084 726 333 618 164 062 5
9 007 199 254 740 992	53	0.000 000 000 000 000 111 022 302 462 515 654 042 363 166 809 082 031 25
18 014 398 509 481 984	54	0.000 000 000 000 000 055 511 151 231 257 827 021 181 583 404 541 015 625
36 028 797 018 963 968	55	0.000 000 000 000 000 027 755 575 615 628 913 510 590 791 702 270 507 812 5
72 057 594 037 927 936	56	0.000 000 000 000 000 013 877 787 807 814 456 755 295 395 851 135 253 906 25
144 115 188 075 855 872	57	0.000 000 000 000 000 006 938 893 903 907 228 377 647 697 925 567 626 953 125
288 230 376 151 711 744	58	0.000 000 000 000 000 003 469 446 951 953 614 188 823 848 962 783 813 476 562 5
576 460 752 303 423 488	59	0.000 000 000 000 000 001 734 723 475 976 807 094 411 924 481 391 906 738 281 25
1 152 921 504 606 846 976	60	0.000 000 000 000 000 000 867 361 737 988 403 547 205 962 240 695 953 369 140 625
2 305 843 009 213 693 952	61	0.000 000 000 000 000 000 433 680 868 994 201 773 602 981 120 347 976 684 570 312 5
4 611 686 018 427 387 904	62	0.000 000 000 000 000 000 216 840 434 497 100 886 801 490 560 173 988 342 285 156 25
9 223 372 036 854 775 808	63	0.000 000 000 000 000 000 108 420 217 248 550 443 400 745 280 086 994 171 142 578 125
18 446 744 073 709 551 616	64	0.000 000 000 000 000 000 054 210 108 624 275 221 700 372 640 043 497 085 571 289 062 5
36 893 488 147 419 103 232	65	0.000 000 000 000 000 000 027 105 054 312 137 610 850 186 320 021 748 542 785 644 531 25
73 786 976 294 838 206 464	66	0.000 000 000 000 000 000 013 552 527 156 068 805 425 093 160 010 874 271 392 822 265 625
147 573 952 589 676 412 928	67	0.000 000 000 000 000 000 006 776 263 578 034 402 712 546 580 005 437 135 696 411 132 812 5
295 147 905 179 352 825 856	68	0.000 000 000 000 000 000 003 388 131 789 017 201 356 273 290 002 718 567 848 205 566 406 25
590 295 810 358 705 651 712	69	0.000 000 000 000 000 000 001 694 065 894 508 600 678 136 645 001 359 283 924 102 783 203 125
1 180 591 620 717 411 303 424	70	0.000 000 000 000 000 000 000 847 032 947 254 300 339 068 322 500 679 641 962 051 391 601 562 5
2 361 183 241 434 822 606 848	71	0.000 000 000 000 000 000 000 423 516 473 627 150 169 534 161 250 339 820 981 025 695 800 781 25
4 722 366 482 869 645 213 696	72	0.000 000 000 000 000 000 000 211 758 236 813 575 084 767 080 625 169 910 490 512 847 900 390 625

[1] George K. Kostopoulos. *Digital Engineering.* Copyright John Wiley & Sons, Inc., 1975. Reprinted by permission of John Wiley & Sons, Inc.

THE 6800
INSTRUCTION SET

TABLE B.1 Accumulator and Memory Instructions

		IMMED			DIRECT			INDEX			EXTND			IMPLIED			BOOLEAN/ARITHMETIC OPERATION (All register labels refer to contents)	COND. CODE REG.					
OPERATIONS	MNEMONIC	OP	~	#	OP	~	#	OP	~	#	OP	~	#	OP	~	#		5 H	4 I	3 N	2 Z	1 V	0 C
Add	ADDA	8B	2	2	9B	3	2	AB	5	2	BB	4	3				A + M → A	↕	•	↕	↕	↕	↕
	ADDB	CB	2	2	DB	3	2	EB	5	2	FB	4	3				B + M → B	↕	•	↕	↕	↕	↕
Add Acmltrs	ABA													1B	2	1	A + B → A	↕	•	↕	↕	↕	↕
Add with Carry	ADCA	89	2	2	99	3	2	A9	5	2	B9	4	3				A + M + C → A	↕	•	↕	↕	↕	↕
	ADCB	C9	2	2	D9	3	2	E9	5	2	F9	4	3				B + M + C → B	↕	•	↕	↕	↕	↕
And	ANDA	84	2	2	94	3	2	A4	5	2	B4	4	3				A · M → A	•	•	↕	↕	R	•
	ANDB	C4	2	2	D4	3	2	E4	5	2	F4	4	3				B · M → B	•	•	↕	↕	R	•
Bit Test	BITA	85	2	2	95	3	2	A5	5	2	B5	4	3				A · M	•	•	↕	↕	R	•
	BITB	C5	2	2	D5	3	2	E5	5	2	F5	4	3				B · M	•	•	↕	↕	R	•
Clear	CLR							6F	7	2	7F	6	3				00 → M	•	•	R	S	R	R
	CLRA													4F	2	1	00 → A	•	•	R	S	R	R
	CLRB													5F	2	1	00 → B	•	•	R	S	R	R
Compare	CMPA	81	2	2	91	3	2	A1	5	2	B1	4	3				A − M	•	•	↕	↕	↕	↕
	CMPB	C1	2	2	D1	3	2	E1	5	2	F1	4	3				B − M	•	•	↕	↕	↕	↕
Compare Acmltrs	CBA													11	2	1	A − B	•	•	↕	↕	↕	↕
Complement, 1's	COM							63	7	2	73	6	3				$\overline{M}$ → M	•	•	↕	↕	R	S
	COMA													43	2	1	$\overline{A}$ → A	•	•	↕	↕	R	S
	COMB													53	2	1	$\overline{B}$ → B	•	•	↕	↕	R	S
Complement, 2's	NEG							60	7	2	70	6	3				00 − M → M	•	•	↕	↕	①	②
(Negate)	NEGA													40	2	1	00 − A → A	•	•	↕	↕	①	②
	NEGB													50	2	1	00 − B → B	•	•	↕	↕	①	②
Decimal Adjust, A	DAA													19	2	1	Converts Binary Add. of BCD Characters into BCD Format	•	•	↕	↕	↕	③
Decrement	DEC							6A	7	2	7A	6	3				M − 1 → M	•	•	↕	↕	④	•
	DECA													4A	2	1	A − 1 → A	•	•	↕	↕	④	•
	DECB													5A	2	1	B − 1 → B	•	•	↕	↕	④	•
Exclusive OR	EORA	88	2	2	98	3	2	A8	5	2	B8	4	3				A ⊕ M → A	•	•	↕	↕	R	•
	EORB	C8	2	2	D8	3	2	E8	5	2	F8	4	3				B ⊕ M → B	•	•	↕	↕	R	•
Increment	INC							6C	7	2	7C	6	3				M + 1 → M	•	•	↕	↕	⑤	•
	INCA													4C	2	1	A + 1 → A	•	•	↕	↕	⑤	•
	INCB													5C	2	1	B + 1 → B	•	•	↕	↕	⑤	•
Load Acmltr	LDAA	86	2	2	96	3	2	A6	5	2	B6	4	3				M → A	•	•	↕	↕	R	•
	LDAB	C6	2	2	D6	3	2	E6	5	2	F6	4	3				M → B	•	•	↕	↕	R	•
Or, Inclusive	ORAA	8A	2	2	9A	3	2	AA	5	2	BA	4	3				A + M → A	•	•	↕	↕	R	•
	ORAB	CA	2	2	DA	3	2	EA	5	2	FA	4	3				B + M → B	•	•	↕	↕	R	•
Push Data	PSHA													36	4	1	A → M_{SP}, SP − 1 → SP	•	•	•	•	•	•
	PSHB													37	4	1	B → M_{SP}, SP − 1 → SP	•	•	•	•	•	•
Pull Data	PULA													32	4	1	SP + 1 → SP, M_{SP} → A	•	•	•	•	•	•
	PULB													33	4	1	SP + 1 → SP, M_{SP} → B	•	•	•	•	•	•
Rotate Left	ROL							69	7	2	79	6	3				M	•	•	↕	↕	⑥	↕
	ROLA													49	2	1	A	•	•	↕	↕	⑥	↕
	ROLB													59	2	1	B	•	•	↕	↕	⑥	↕
Rotate Right	ROR							66	7	2	76	6	3				M	•	•	↕	↕	⑥	↕
	RORA													46	2	1	A	•	•	↕	↕	⑥	↕
	RORB													56	2	1	B	•	•	↕	↕	⑥	↕
Shift Left, Arithmetic	ASL							68	7	2	78	6	3				M	•	•	↕	↕	⑥	↕
	ASLA													48	2	1	A	•	•	↕	↕	⑥	↕
	ASLB													58	2	1	B	•	•	↕	↕	⑥	↕
Shift Right, Arithmetic	ASR							67	7	2	77	6	3				M	•	•	↕	↕	⑥	↕
	ASRA													47	2	1	A	•	•	↕	↕	⑥	↕
	ASRB													57	2	1	B	•	•	↕	↕	⑥	↕
Shift Right, Logic	LSR							64	7	2	74	6	3				M	•	•	R	↕	⑥	↕
	LSRA													44	2	1	A	•	•	R	↕	⑥	↕
	LSRB													54	2	1	B	•	•	R	↕	⑥	↕
Store Acmltr.	STAA				97	4	2	A7	6	2	B7	5	3				A → M	•	•	↕	↕	R	•
	STAB				D7	4	2	E7	6	2	F7	5	3				B → M	•	•	↕	↕	R	•
Subtract	SUBA	80	2	2	90	3	2	A0	5	2	B0	4	3				A − M → A	•	•	↕	↕	↕	↕
	SUBB	C0	2	2	D0	3	2	E0	5	2	F0	4	3				B − M → B	•	•	↕	↕	↕	↕
Subtract Acmltrs.	SBA													10	2	1	A − B → A	•	•	↕	↕	↕	↕
Subtr. with Carry	SBCA	82	2	2	92	3	2	A2	5	2	B2	4	3				A − M − C → A	•	•	↕	↕	↕	↕
	SBCB	C2	2	2	D2	3	2	E2	5	2	F2	4	3				B − M − C → B	•	•	↕	↕	↕	↕
Transfer Acmltrs	TAB													16	2	1	A → B	•	•	↕	↕	R	•
	TBA													17	2	1	B → A	•	•	↕	↕	R	•
Test, Zero or Minus	TST							6D	7	2	7D	6	3				M − 00	•	•	↕	↕	R	R
	TSTA													4D	2	1	A − 00	•	•	↕	↕	R	R
	TSTB													5D	2	1	B − 00	•	•	↕	↕	R	R
																		H	I	N	Z	V	C

LEGEND:

OP   Operation Code (Hexadecimal);
~   Number of MPU Cycles;
#   Number of Program Bytes;
+   Arithmetic Plus;
−   Arithmetic Minus;
·   Boolean AND;
M_{SP} Contents of memory location pointed to be Stack Pointer;
+   Boolean Inclusive OR;
⊕   Boolean Exclusive OR;
M   Complement of M;
→   Transfer Into;
0   Bit = Zero;
00   Byte = Zero;

CONDITION CODE SYMBOLS:

H   Half-carry from bit 3;
I   Interrupt mask;
N   Negative (sign bit)
Z   Zero (byte)
V   Overflow, 2's complement
C   Carry from bit 7
R   Reset Always
S   Set Always
↕   Test and set if true, cleared otherwise
•   Not Affected

CONDITION CODE REGISTER NOTES:
(Bit set if test is true and cleared otherwise)

1   (Bit V)   Test: Result = 10000000?
2   (Bit C)   Test: Result = 00000000?
3   (Bit C)   Test: Decimal value of most significant BCD Character greater than nine? (Not cleared if previously set.)
4   (Bit V)   Test: Operand = 10000000 prior to execution?
5   (Bit V)   Test: Operand = 01111111 prior to execution?
6   (Bit V)   Test: Set equal to result of N ⊕ C after shift has occurred.

Note — Accumulator addressing mode instructions are included in the column for IMPLIED addressing

TABLE B-2 Index Register and Stack Manipulation

POINTER OPERATIONS	MNEMONIC	IMMED OP	~	=	DIRECT OP	~	=	INDEX OP	~	=	EXTND OP	~	=	IMPLIED OP	~	=	BOOLEAN/ARITHMETIC OPERATION	H	I	N	Z	V	C
Compare Index Reg	CPX	8C	3	3	9C	4	2	AC	6	2	BC	5	3				$X_H - M, X_L - (M+1)$	•	•	⑦	:	⑧	•
Decrement Index Reg	DEX													09	4	1	$X - 1 \to X$	•	•	•	:	•	•
Decrement Stack Pntr	DES													34	4	1	$SP - 1 \to SP$	•	•	•	•	•	•
Increment Index Reg	INX													08	4	1	$X + 1 \to X$	•	•	•	:	•	•
Increment Stack Pntr	INS													31	4	1	$SP + 1 \to SP$	•	•	•	•	•	•
Load Index Reg	LDX	CE	3	3	DE	4	2	EE	6	2	FE	5	3				$M \to X_H, (M+1) \to X_L$	•	•	⑨	:	R	•
Load Stack Pntr	LDS	8E	3	3	9E	4	2	AE	6	2	BE	5	3				$M \to SP_H, (M+1) \to SP_L$	•	•	⑨	:	R	•
Store Index Reg	STX				DF	5	2	EF	7	2	FF	6	3				$X_H \to M, X_L \to (M+1)$	•	•	⑨	:	R	•
Store Stack Pntr	STS				9F	5	2	AF	7	2	BF	6	3				$SP_H \to M, SP_L \to (M+1)$	•	•	⑨	:	R	•
Indx Reg → Stack Pntr	TXS													35	4	1	$X - 1 \to SP$	•	•	•	•	•	•
Stack Pntr → Indx Reg	TSX													30	4	1	$SP + 1 \to X$	•	•	•	•	•	•

COND. CODE REG. columns: 5(H) 4(I) 3(N) 2(Z) 1(V) 0(C)

TABLE B-3 Jump and Branch Instructions

OPERATIONS	MNEMONIC	RELATIVE OP	~	=	INDEX OP	~	=	EXTND OP	~	=	IMPLIED OP	~	=	BRANCH TEST	H	I	N	Z	V	C
Branch Always	BRA	20	4	2										None	•	•	•	•	•	•
Branch If Carry Clear	BCC	24	4	2										$C = 0$	•	•	•	•	•	•
Branch If Carry Set	BCS	25	4	2										$C = 1$	•	•	•	•	•	•
Branch If = Zero	BEQ	27	4	2										$Z = 1$	•	•	•	•	•	•
Branch If ≥ Zero	BGE	2C	4	2										$N \oplus V = 0$	•	•	•	•	•	•
Branch If > Zero	BGT	2E	4	2										$Z + (N \oplus V) = 0$	•	•	•	•	•	•
Branch If Higher	BHI	22	4	2										$C + Z = 0$	•	•	•	•	•	•
Branch If ≤ Zero	BLE	2F	4	2										$Z + (N \oplus V) = 1$	•	•	•	•	•	•
Branch If Lower Or Same	BLS	23	4	2										$C + Z = 1$	•	•	•	•	•	•
Branch If < Zero	BLT	2D	4	2										$N \oplus V = 1$	•	•	•	•	•	•
Branch If Minus	BMI	2B	4	2										$N = 1$	•	•	•	•	•	•
Branch If Not Equal Zero	BNE	26	4	2										$Z = 0$	•	•	•	•	•	•
Branch If Overflow Clear	BVC	28	4	2										$V = 0$	•	•	•	•	•	•
Branch If Overflow Set	BVS	29	4	2										$V = 1$	•	•	•	•	•	•
Branch If Plus	BPL	2A	4	2										$N = 0$	•	•	•	•	•	•
Branch To Subroutine	BSR	8D	8	2											•	•	•	•	•	•
Jump	JMP				6E	4	2	7E	3	3				See Special Operations	•	•	•	•	•	•
Jump To Subroutine	JSR				AD	8	2	BD	9	3					•	•	•	•	•	•
No Operation	NOP										01	2	1	Advances Prog. Cntr. Only	•	•	•	•	•	•
Return From Interrupt	RTI										3B	10	1		⑩					
Return From Subroutine	RTS										39	5	1	See Special Operations	•	•	•	•	•	•
Software Interrupt	SWI										3F	12	1		•	•	•	•	•	•
Wait for Interrupt*	WAI										3E	9	1		•	⑪	•	•	•	•

COND. CODE REG. columns: 5(H) 4(I) 3(N) 2(Z) 1(V) 0(C)

*WAI puts Address Bus, R/W, and Data Bus in the three state mode while VMA is held low

TABLE B-4 Condition Code Register Manipulation Instructions

OPERATIONS	MNEMONIC	IMPLIED OP	~	=	BOOLEAN OPERATION	H	I	N	Z	V	C
Clear Carry	CLC	0C	2	1	$0 \to C$	•	•	•	•	•	R
Clear Interrupt Mask	CLI	0E	2	1	$0 \to I$	•	R	•	•	•	•
Clear Overflow	CLV	0A	2	1	$0 \to V$	•	•	•	•	R	•
Set Carry	SEC	0D	2	1	$1 \to C$	•	•	•	•	•	S
Set Interrupt Mask	SEI	0F	2	1	$1 \to I$	•	S	•	•	•	•
Set Overflow	SEV	0B	2	1	$1 \to V$	•	•	•	•	S	•
Acmltr A → CCR	TAP	06	2	1	$A \to CCR$			⑫			
CCR → Acmltr A	TPA	07	2	1	$CCR \to A$	•	•	•	•	•	•

COND. CODE REG. columns: 5(H) 4(I) 3(N) 2(Z) 1(V) 0(C)

CONDITION CODE REGISTER NOTES: (Bit set if test is true and cleared otherwise)

1. (Bit V) Test: Result = 10000000?
2. (Bit C) Test: Result = 00000000?
3. (Bit C) Test: Decimal value of most significant BCD Character greater than nine? (Not cleared if previously set.)
4. (Bit V) Test: Operand = 10000000 prior to execution?
5. (Bit V) Test: Operand = 01111111 prior to execution?
6. (Bit V) Test: Set equal to result of $N \oplus C$ after shift has occurred.
7. (Bit N) Test: Sign bit of most significant (MS) byte = 1?
8. (Bit V) Test: 2's complement overflow from subtraction of MS bytes?
9. (Bit N) Test: Result less than zero? (Bit 15 = 1)
10. (All) Load Condition Code Register from Stack. (See Special Operations)
11. (Bit I) Set when interrupt occurs. If previously set, a Non-Maskable Interrupt is required to exit the wait state.
12. (All) Set according to the contents of Accumulator A.

C

TABLE OF CYCLE–BY– CYCLE OPERATION FOR EACH 6800 INSTRUCTION

Table C-1 provides a detailed description of the information present on the address bus, data bus, valid memory address line (VMA), and the read/write line (R/W) during each cycle for each instruction.

This information is useful in comparing actual with expected results during debug of both software and hardware as the control program is executed. The information is categorized in groups according to addressing mode and number of cycles per instruction. (In general, instructions with the same addressing mode and number of cycles execute in the same manner; exceptions are indicated in the table.)

TABLE C-1 Operation Summary

Address Mode and Instructions	Cycles	Cycle #	VMA Line	Address Bus	R/W Line	Data Bus
IMMEDIATE						
ADC EOR ADD LDA AND ORA BIT SBC CMP SUB	2	1 2	1 1	Op Code Address Op Code Address + 1	1 1	Op Code Operand Data
CPX LDS LDX	3	1 2 3	1 1 1	Op Code Address Op Code Address + 1 Op Code Address + 2	1 1 1	Op Code Operand Data (High Order Byte) Operand Data (Low Order Byte)
DIRECT						
ADC EOR ADD LDA AND ORA BIT SBC CMP SUB	3	1 2 3	1 1 1	Op Code Address Op Code Address + 1 Address of Operand	1 1 1	Op Code Address of Operand Operand Data
CPX LDS LDX	4	1 2 3 4	1 1 1 1	Op Code Address Op Code Address + 1 Address of Operand Operand Address + 1	1 1 1 1	Op Code Address of Operand Operand Data (High Order Byte) Operand Data (Low Order Byte)
STA	4	1 2 3 4	1 1 0 1	Op Code Address Op Code Address + 1 Destination Address Destination Address	1 1 1 0	Op Code Destination Address Irrelevant Data (Note 1) Data from Accumulator
STS STX	5	1 2 3 4 5	1 1 0 1 1	Op Code Address Op Code Address + 1 Address of Operand Address of Operand Address of Operand + 1	1 1 1 0 0	Op Code Address of Operand Irrelevant Data (Note 1) Register Data (High Order Byte) Register Data (Low Order Byte)
INDEXED						
JMP	4	1 2 3 4	1 1 0 0	Op Code Address Op Code Address + 1 Index Register Index Register Plus Offset (w/o Carry)	1 1 1 1	Op Code Offset Irrelevant Data (Note 1) Irrelevant Data (Note 1)
ADC EOR ADD LDA AND ORA BIT SBC CMP SUB	5	1 2 3 4 5	1 1 0 0 1	Op Code Address Op Code Address + 1 Index Register Index Register Plus Offset (w/o Carry) Index Register Plus Offset	1 1 1 1 1	Op Code Offset Irrelevant Data (Note 1) Irrelevant Data (Note 1) Operand Data
CPX LDS LDX	6	1 2 3 4 5 6	1 1 0 0 1 1	Op Code Address Op Code Address + 1 Index Register Index Register Plus Offset (w/o Carry) Index Register Plus Offset Index Register Plus Offset + 1	1 1 1 1 1 1	Op Code Offset Irrelevant Data (Note 1) Irrelevant Data (Note 1) Operand Data (High Order Byte) Operand Data (Low Order Byte)

TABLE C-1 Continued

Address Mode and Instructions	Cycles	Cycle #	VMA Line	Address Bus	R/W Line	Data Bus
INDEXED (Continued)						
STA	6	1	1	Op Code Address	1	Op Code
		2	1	Op Code Address + 1	1	Offset
		3	0	Index Register	1	Irrelevant Data (Note 1)
		4	0	Index Register Plus Offset (w/o Carry)	1	Irrelevant Data (Note 1)
		5	0	Index Register Plus Offset	1	Irrelevant Data (Note 1)
		6	1	Index Register Plus Offset	0	Operand Data
ASL LSR ASR NEG CLR ROL COM ROR DEC TST INC	7	1	1	Op Code Address	1	Op Code
		2	1	Op Code Address + 1	1	Offset
		3	0	Index Register	1	Irrelevant Data (Note 1)
		4	0	Index Register Plus Offset (w/o Carry)	1	Irrelevant Data (Note 1)
		5	1	Index Register Plus Offset	1	Current Operand Data
		6	0	Index Register Plus Offset	1	Irrelevant Data (Note 1)
		7	1/0 (Note 3)	Index Register Plus Offset	0	New Operand Data (Note 3)
STS STX	7	1	1	Op Code Address	1	Op Code
		2	1	Op Code Address + 1	1	Offset
		3	0	Index Register	1	Irrelevant Data (Note 1)
		4	0	Index Register Plus Offset (w/o Carry)	1	Irrelevant Data (Note 1)
		5	0	Index Register Plus Offset	1	Irrelevant Data (Note 1)
		6	1	Index Register Plus Offset	0	Operand Data (High Order Byte)
		7	1	Index Register Plus Offset + 1	0	Operand Data (Low Order Byte)
JSR	8	1	1	Op Code Address	1	Op Code
		2	1	Op Code Address + 1	1	Offset
		3	0	Index Register	1	Irrelevant Data (Note 1)
		4	1	Stack Pointer	0	Return Address (Low Order Byte)
		5	1	Stack Pointer − 1	0	Return Address (High Order Byte)
		6	0	Stack Pointer − 2	1	Irrelevant Data (Note 1)
		7	0	Index Register	1	Irrelevant Data (Note 1)
		8	0	Index Register Plus Offset (w/o Carry)	1	Irrelevant Data (Note 1)
EXTENDED						
JMP	3	1	1	Op Code Address	1	Op Code
		2	1	Op Code Address + 1	1	Jump Address (High Order Byte)
		3	1	Op Code Address + 2	1	Jump Address (Low Order Byte)
ADC EOR ADD LDA AND ORA BIT SBC CMP SUB	4	1	1	Op Code Address	1	Op Code
		2	1	Op Code Address + 1	1	Address of Operand (High Order Byte)
		3	1	Op Code Address + 2	1	Address of Operand (Low Order Byte)
		4	1	Address of Operand	1	Operand Data
CPX LDS LDX	5	1	1	Op Code Address	1	Op Code
		2	1	Op Code Address + 1	1	Address of Operand (High Order Byte)
		3	1	Op Code Address + 2	1	Address of Operand (Low Order Byte)
		4	1	Address of Operand	1	Operand Data (High Order Byte)
		5	1	Address of Operand + 1	1	Operand Data (Low Order Byte)
STA A STA B	5	1	1	Op Code Address	1	Op Code
		2	1	Op Code Address + 1	1	Destination Address (High Order Byte)
		3	1	Op Code Address + 2	1	Destination Address (Low Order Byte)
		4	0	Operand Destination Address	1	Irrelevant Data (Note 1)
		5	1	Operand Destination Address	0	Data from Accumulator
ASL LSR ASR NEG CLR ROL COM ROR DEC TST INC	6	1	1	Op Code Address	1	Op Code
		2	1	Op Code Address + 1	1	Address of Operand (High Order Byte)
		3	1	Op Code Address + 2	1	Address of Operand (Low Order Byte)
		4	1	Address of Operand	1	Current Operand Data
		5	0	Address of Operand	1	Irrelevant Data (Note 1)
		6	1/0 (Note 3)	Address of Operand	0	New Operand Data (Note 3)

TABLE C-1 Continued

Address Mode and Instructions	Cycles	Cycle #	VMA Line	Address Bus	R/W Line	Data Bus
EXTENDED (Continued)						
STS STX	6	1	1	Op Code Address	1	Op Code
		2	1	Op Code Address + 1	1	Address of Operand (High Order Byte)
		3	1	Op Code Address + 2	1	Address of Operand (Low Order Byte)
		4	0	Address of Operand	1	Irrelevant Data (Note 1)
		5	1	Address of Operand	0	Operand Data (High Order Byte)
		6	1	Address of Operand + 1	0	Operand Data (Low Order Byte)
JSR	9	1	1	Op Code Address	1	Op Code
		2	1	Op Code Address + 1	1	Address of Subroutine (High Order Byte)
		3	1	Op Code Address + 2	1	Address of Subroutine (Low Order Byte)
		4	1	Subroutine Starting Address	1	Op Code of Next Instruction
		5	1	Stack Pointer	0	Return Address (Low Order Byte)
		6	1	Stack Pointer − 1	0	Return Address (High Order Byte)
		7	0	Stack Pointer − 2	1	Irrelevant Data (Note 1)
		8	0	Op Code Address + 2	1	Irrelevant Data (Note 1)
		9	1	Op Code Address + 2	1	Address of Subroutine (Low Order Byte)
INHERENT						
ABA DAA SEC ASL DEC SEI ASR INC SEV CBA LSR TAB CLC NEG TAP CLI NOP TBA CLR ROL TPA CLV ROR TST COM SBA	2	1	1	Op Code Address	1	Op Code
		2	1	Op Code Address + 1	1	Op Code of Next Instruction
DES DEX INS INX	4	1	1	Op Code Address	1	Op Code
		2	1	Op Code Address + 1	1	Op Code of Next Instruction
		3	0	Previous Register Contents	1	Irrelevant Data (Note 1)
		4	0	New Register Contents	1	Irrelevant Data (Note 1)
PSH	4	1	1	Op Code Address	1	Op Code
		2	1	Op Code Address + 1	1	Op Code of Next Instruction
		3	1	Stack Pointer	0	Accumulator Data
		4	0	Stack Pointer − 1	1	Accumulator Data
PUL	4	1	1	Op Code Address	1	Op Code
		2	1	Op Code Address + 1	1	Op Code of Next Instruction
		3	0	Stack Pointer	1	Irrelevant Data (Note 1)
		4	1	Stack Pointer + 1	1	Operand Data from Stack
TSX	4	1	1	Op Code Address	1	Op Code
		2	1	Op Code Address + 1	1	Op Code of Next Instruction
		3	0	Stack Pointer	1	Irrelevant Data (Note 1)
		4	0	New Index Register	1	Irrelevant Data (Note 1)
TXS	4	1	1	Op Code Address	1	Op Code
		2	1	Op Code Address + 1	1	Op Code of Next Instruction
		3	0	Index Register	1	Irrelevant Data
		4	0	New Stack Pointer	1	Irrelevant Data
RTS	5	1	1	Op Code Address	1	Op Code
		2	1	Op Code Address + 1	1	Irrelevant Data (Note 2)
		3	0	Stack Pointer	1	Irrelevant Data (Note 1)
		4	1	Stack Pointer + 1	1	Address of Next Instruction (High Order Byte)
		5	1	Stack Pointer + 2	1	Address of Next Instruction (Low Order Byte)

TABLE C-1 Continued

Address Mode and Instructions	Cycles	Cycle #	VMA Line	Address Bus	R/W Line	Data Bus
INHERENT (Continued)						
WAI		1	1	Op Code Address	1	Op Code
		2	1	Op Code Address + 1	1	Op Code of Next Instruction
		3	1	Stack Pointer	0	Return Address (Low Order Byte)
		4	1	Stack Pointer − 1	0	Return Address (High Order Byte)
	9	5	1	Stack Pointer − 2	0	Index Register (Low Order Byte)
		6	1	Stack Pointer − 3	0	Index Register (High Order Byte)
		7	1	Stack Pointer − 4	0	Contents of Accumulator A
		8	1	Stack Pointer − 5	0	Contents of Accumulator B
		9	1	Stack Pointer − 6 (Note 4)	1	Contents of Cond. Code Register
RTI		1	1	Op Code Address	1	Op Code
		2	1	Op Code Address + 1	1	Irrelevant Data (Note 2)
		3	0	Stack Pointer	1	Irrelevant Data (Note 1)
		4	1	Stack Pointer + 1	1	Contents of Cond. Code Register from Stack
	10	5	1	Stack Pointer + 2	1	Contents of Accumulator B from Stack
		6	1	Stack Pointer + 3	1	Contents of Accumulator A from Stack
		7	1	Stack Pointer + 4	1	Index Register from Stack (High Order Byte)
		8	1	Stack Pointer + 5	1	Index Register from Stack (Low Order Byte)
		9	1	Stack Pointer + 6	1	Next Instruction Address from Stack (High Order Byte)
		10	1	Stack Pointer + 7	1	Next Instruction Address from Stack (Low Order Byte)
SWI		1	1	Op Code Address	1	Op Code
		2	1	Op Code Address + 1	1	Irrelevant Data (Note 1)
		3	1	Stack Pointer	0	Return Address (Low Order Byte)
		4	1	Stack Pointer − 1	0	Return Address (High Order Byte)
		5	1	Stack Pointer − 2	0	Index Register (Low Order Byte)
		6	1	Stack Pointer − 3	0	Index Register (High Order Byte)
	12	7	1	Stack Pointer − 4	0	Contents of Accumulator A
		8	1	Stack Pointer − 5	0	Contents of Accumulator B
		9	1	Stack Pointer − 6	0	Contents of Cond. Code Register
		10	0	Stack Pointer − 7	1	Irrelevant Data (Note 1)
		11	1	Vector Address FFFA (Hex)	1	Address of Subroutine (High Order Byte)
		12	1	Vector Address FFFB (Hex)	1	Address of Subroutine (Low Order Byte)
RELATIVE						
BCC BHI BNE BCS BLE BPL BEQ BLS BRA BGE BLT BVC BGT BMI BVS	4	1	1	Op Code Address	1	Op Code
		2	1	Op Code Address + 1	1	Branch Offset
		3	0	Op Code Address + 2	1	Irrelevant Data (Note 1)
		4	0	Branch Address	1	Irrelevant Data (Note 1)
BSR		1	1	Op Code Address	1	Op Code
		2	1	Op Code Address + 1	1	Branch Offset
		3	0	Return Address of Main Program	1	Irrelevant Data (Note 1)
	8	4	1	Stack Pointer	0	Return Address (Low Order Byte)
		5	1	Stack Pointer − 1	0	Return Address (High Order Byte)
		6	0	Stack Pointer − 2	1	Irrelevant Data (Note 1)
		7	0	Return Address of Main Program	1	Irrelevant Data (Note 1)
		8	0	Subroutine Address	1	Irrelevant Data (Note 1)

Note 1. If device which is addressed during this cycle uses VMA, then the Data Bus will go to the high impedance three-state condition. Depending on bus capacitance, data from the previous cycle may be retained on the Data Bus.
Note 2. Data is ignored by the MPU.
Note 3. For TST, VMA = 0 and Operand data does not change.
Note 4. While the MPU is waiting for the interrupt, Bus Available will go high indicating the following states of the control lines: VMA is low; Address Bus, R/W, and Data Bus are all in the high impedance state.

APPENDIX

D

ASCII CONVERSION CHART

The conversion chart listed below is helpful in converting from a two-digit (2-byte) hexadecimal number to an ASCII character or from an ASCII character to a two-digit hexadecimal number. The example provided below shows the method of using this conversion chart.

Example

		Bits						
		MSB ←					→ LSB	
ASCII	Hex #	6	5	4	3	2	1	0
T	54	1	0	1	0	1	0	0
?	3F	0	1	1	1	1	1	1
+	2B	0	1	0	1	0	1	1

Bits 0 to 3 Second Hex Digit (LSB)	Bits 4 to 6 First Hex Digit (MSB)							
	0	0	1	2	3	4	5	6	7
0	NUL	DLE	SP	0	@	P		p
1	SOH	DC1	!	1	A	Q	a	q
2	STX	DC2	"	2	B	R	b	r
3	ETX	DC3	#	3	C	S	c	s
4	EOT	DC4	$	4	D	T	d	t
5	ENQ	NAK	%	5	E	U	e	u
6	ACK	SYN	&	6	F	V	f	v
7	BEL	ETB	'	7	G	W	g	w
8	BS	CAN	(	8	H	X	h	x
9	HT	EM	)	9	I	Y	i	y
A	LF	SUB	*	:	J	Z	j	z
B	VT	ESC	+	;	K	[	k	{
C	FF	FS	,	<	L	/	l	/
D	CR	GS	-	=	M	]	m	}
E	SO	RS	.	>	N	∧	n	≈
F	SI	US	/	?	O	—	o	DEL

APPENDIX E

MC68HC11A8 INSTRUCTIONS, ADDRESSING MODES, AND EXECUTION TIMES

Source Form(s)	Operation	Boolean Expression	Addressing Mode for Operand	Machine Coding (Hexadecimal) Opcode	Machine Coding (Hexadecimal) Operand(s)	Bytes	Cycle	Cycle by Cycle*	S	X	H	I	N	Z	V	C
ABA	Add Accumulators	A + B → A	INH	1B		1	2	2-1	-	-	↕	-	↕	↕	↕	↕
ABX	Add B to X	IX + 00:B → IX	INH	3A		1	3	2-2	-	-	-	-	-	-	-	-
ABY	Add B to Y	IY + 00:B → IY	INH	18 3A		2	4	2-4	-	-	-	-	-	-	-	-
ADCA (opr)	Add with Carry to A	A + M + C → A	A IMM	89	ii	2	2	3-1	-	-	↕	-	↕	↕	↕	↕
			A DIR	99	dd	2	3	4-1								
			A EXT	B9	hh ll	3	4	5-2								
			A IND,X	A9	ff	2	4	6-2								
			A IND,Y	18 A9	ff	3	5	7-2								
ADCB (opr)	Add with Carry to B	B + M + C → B	B IMM	C9	ii	2	2	3-1	-	-	↕	-	↕	↕	↕	↕
			B DIR	D9	dd	2	3	4-1								
			B EXT	F9	hh ll	3	4	5-2								
			B IND,X	E9	ff	2	4	6-2								
			B IND,Y	18 E9	ff	3	5	7-2								
ADDA (opr)	Add Memory to A	A + M → A	A IMM	8B	ii	2	2	3-1	-	-	↕	-	↕	↕	↕	↕
			A DIR	9B	dd	2	3	4-1								
			A EXT	BB	hh ll	3	4	5-2								
			A IND,X	AB	ff	2	4	6-2								
			A IND,Y	18 AB	ff	3	5	7-2								
ADDB (opr)	Add Memory to B	B + M → B	B IMM	CB	ii	2	2	3-1	-	-	↕	-	↕	↕	↕	↕
			B DIR	DB	dd	2	3	4-1								
			B EXT	FB	hh ll	3	4	5-2								
			B IND,X	EB	ff	2	4	6-2								
			B IND,Y	18 EB	ff	3	5	7-2								
ADDD (opr)	Add 16-Bit to D	D + M:M + 1 → D	IMM	C3	jj kk	3	4	3-3	-	-	-	-	↕	↕	↕	↕
			DIR	D3	dd	2	5	4-7								
			EXT	F3	hh ll	3	6	5-10								
			IND,X	E3	ff	2	6	6-10								
			IND,Y	18 E3	ff	3	7	7-8								
ANDA (opr)	AND A with Memory	A•M → A	A IMM	84	ii	2	2	3-1	-	-	-	-	↕	↕	0	-
			A DIR	94	dd	2	3	4-1								
			A EXT	B4	hh ll	3	4	5-2								
			A IND,X	A4	ff	2	4	6-2								
			A IND,Y	18 A4	ff	3	5	7-2								

Source Form(s)	Operation	Boolean Expression	Addressing Mode for Operand	Opcode	Operand(s)	Bytes	Cycle	Cycle by Cycle*	S	X	H	I	N	Z	V	C
ANDB (opr)	AND B with Memory	B•M → B	B IMM	C4	ii	2	2	3-1	-	-	-	-	⇕	⇕	0	-
			B DIR	D4	dd	2	3	4-1								
			B EXT	F4	hh ll	3	4	5-2								
			B IND,X	E4	ff	2	4	6-2								
			B IND,Y	18 E4	ff	3	5	7-2								
ASL (opr)	Arithmetic Shift Left		EXT	78	hh ll	3	6	5-8	-	-	-	-	⇕	⇕	⇕	⇕
			IND,X	68	ff	2	6	6-3								
			IND,Y	18 68	ff	3	7	7-3								
ASLA			A INH	48		1	2	2-1								
ASLB			B INH	58		1	2	2-1								
ASLD	Arithmetic Shift Left Double		INH	05		1	3	2-2	-	-	-	-	⇕	⇕	⇕	⇕
ASR (opr)	Arithmetic Shift Right		EXT	77	hh ll	3	6	5-8	-	-	-	-	⇕	⇕	⇕	⇕
			IND,X	67	ff	2	6	6-3								
			IND,Y	18 67	ff	3	7	7-3								
ASRA			A INH	47		1	2	2-1								
ASRB			B INH	57		1	2	2-1								
BCC (rel)	Branch if Carry Clear	? C = 0	REL	24	rr	2	3	8-1	-	-	-	-	-	-	-	-
BCLR (opr) (msk)	Clear Bit(s)	M•(mm̄) → M	DIR	15	dd mm	3	6	4-10	-	-	-	-	⇕	⇕	0	-
			IND,X	1D	ff mm	3	7	6-13								
			IND,Y	18 1D	ff mm	4	8	7-10								
BCS (rel)	Branch if Carry Set	? C = 1	REL	25	rr	2	3	8-1	-	-	-	-	-	-	-	-
BEQ (rel)	Branch if = Zero	? Z = 1	REL	27	rr	2	3	8-1	-	-	-	-	-	-	-	-
BGE (rel)	Branch if ≥ Zero	? N ⊕ V = 0	REL	2C	rr	2	3	8-1	-	-	-	-	-	-	-	-
BGT (rel)	Branch if > Zero	? Z + (N ⊕ V) = 0	REL	2E	rr	2	3	8-1	-	-	-	-	-	-	-	-
BHI (rel)	Branch if Higher	? C + Z = 0	REL	22	rr	2	3	8-1	-	-	-	-	-	-	-	-
BHS (rel)	Branch if Higher or Same	? C = 0	REL	24	rr	2	3	8-1	-	-	-	-	-	-	-	-
BITA (opr)	Bit(s) Test A with Memory	A•M	A IMM	85	ii	2	2	3-1	-	-	-	-	⇕	⇕	0	-
			A DIR	95	dd	2	3	4-1								
			A EXT	B5	hh ll	3	4	5-2								
			A IND,X	A5	ff	2	4	6-2								
			A IND,Y	18 A5	ff	3	5	7-2								
BITB (opr)	Bit(s) Test B with Memory	B•M	B IMM	C5	ii	2	2	3-1	-	-	-	-	⇕	⇕	0	-
			B DIR	D5	dd	2	3	4-1								
			B EXT	F5	hh ll	3	4	5-2								
			B IND,X	E5	ff	2	4	6-2								
			B IND,Y	18 E5	ff	3	5	7-2								
BLE (rel)	Branch if ≤ Zero	? Z + (N ⊕ V) = 1	REL	2F	rr	2	3	8-1	-	-	-	-	-	-	-	-
BLO (rel)	Branch if Lower	? C = 1	REL	25	rr	2	3	8-1	-	-	-	-	-	-	-	-
BLS (rel)	Branch if Lower or Same	? C + Z = 1	REL	23	rr	2	3	8-1	-	-	-	-	-	-	-	-
BLT (rel)	Branch If < Zero	? N ⊕ V = 1	REL	2D	rr	2	3	8-1	-	-	-	-	-	-	-	-
BMI (rel)	Branch if Minus	? N = 1	REL	2B	rr	2	3	8-1	-	-	-	-	-	-	-	-
BNE (rel)	Branch if Not = Zero	? Z = 0	REL	26	rr	2	3	8-1	-	-	-	-	-	-	-	-
BPL (rel)	Branch if Plus	? N = 0	REL	2A	rr	2	3	8-1	-	-	-	-	-	-	-	-
BRA (rel)	Branch Always	? 1 = 1	REL	20	rr	2	3	8-1	-	-	-	-	-	-	-	-
BRCLR(opr) (msk) (rel)	Branch if Bit(s) Clear	? M• mm = 0	DIR	13	dd mm rr	4	6	4-11	-	-	-	-	-	-	-	-
			IND,X	1F	ff mm rr	4	7	6-14								
			IND,Y	18 1F	ff mm rr	5	8	7-11								
BRN (rel)	Branch Never	? 1 = 0	REL	21	rr	2	3	8-1	-	-	-	-	-	-	-	-
BRSET(opr) (msk) (rel)	Branch if Bit(s) Set	? (M̄)•mm = 0	DIR	12	dd mm rr	4	6	4-11	-	-	-	-	-	-	-	-
			IND,X	1E	ff mm rr	4	7	6-14								
			IND,Y	18 1E	ff mm rr	5	8	7-11								
BSET(opr) (msk)	Set Bit(s)	M + mm → M	DIR	14	dd mm	3	6	4-10	-	-	-	-	⇕	⇕	0	-
			IND,X	1C	ff mm	3	7	6-13								
			IND,Y	18 1C	ff mm	4	8	7-10								
BSR (rel)	Branch to Subroutine	See Special Ops	REL	8D	rr	2	6	8-2	-	-	-	-	-	-	-	-
BVC (rel)	Branch if Overflow Clear	? V = 0	REL	28	rr	2	3	8-1	-	-	-	-	-	-	-	-

Source Form(s)	Operation	Boolean Expression	Addressing Mode for Operand	Opcode	Operand(s)	Bytes	Cycle	Cycle by Cycle*	S	X	H	I	N	Z	V	C
BVS (rel)	Branch if Overflow Set	?V = 1	REL	29	rr	2	3	8-1	-	-	-	-	-	-	-	-
CBA	Compare A to B	A-B	INH	11		1	2	2-1	-	-	-	-	↕	↕	↕	↕
CLC	Clear Carry Bit	0 → C	INH	0C		1	2	2-1	-	-	-	-	-	-	-	0
CLI	Clear Interrupt Mask	0 → I	INH	0E		1	2	2-1	-	-	-	0	-	-	-	-
CLR (opr)	Clear Memory Byte	0 → M	EXT	7F	hh ll	3	6	5-8	-	-	-	-	0	1	0	0
			IND,X	6F	ff	2	6	6-3								
			IND,Y	18 6F	ff	3	7	7-3								
CLRA	Clear Accumulator A	0 → A	A INH	4F		1	2	2-1	-	-	-	-	0	1	0	0
CLRB	Clear Accumulator B	0 → B	B INH	5F		1	2	2-1	-	-	-	-	0	1	0	0
CLV	Clear Overflow Flag	0 → V	INH	0A		1	2	2-1	-	-	-	-	-	-	0	-
CMPA (opr)	Compare A to Memory	A – M	A IMM	81	ii	2	2	3-1	-	-	-	-	↕	↕	↕	↕
			A DIR	91	dd	2	3	4-1								
			A EXT	B1	hh ll	3	4	5-2								
			A IND,X	A1	ff	2	4	6-2								
			A IND,Y	18 A1	ff	3	5	7-2								
CMPB (opr)	Compare B to Memory	B – M	B IMM	C1	ii	2	2	3-1	-	-	-	-	↕	↕	↕	↕
			B DIR	D1	dd	2	3	4-1								
			B EXT	F1	hh ll	3	4	5-2								
			B IND,X	E1	ff	2	4	6-2								
			B IND,Y	18 E1	ff	3	5	7-2								
COM (opr)	1's Complement Memory Byte	$FF – M → M	EXT	73	hh ll	3	6	5-8	-	-	-	-	↕	↕	0	1
			IND,X	63	ff	2	6	6-3								
			IND,Y	18 63	ff	3	7	7-3								
COMA	1's Complement A	$FF – A → A	A INH	43		1	2	2-1	-	-	-	-	↕	↕	0	1
COMB	1's Complement B	$FF – B → B	B INH	53		1	2	2-1	-	-	-	-	↕	↕	0	1
CPD (opr)	Compare D to Memory 16-Bit	D – M:M + 1	IMM	1A 83	jj kk	4	5	3-5	-	-	-	-	↕	↕	↕	↕
			DIR	1A 93	dd	3	6	4-9								
			EXT	1A B3	hh ll	4	7	5-11								
			IND,X	1A A3	ff	3	7	6-11								
			IND,Y	CD A3	ff	3	7	7-8								
CPX (opr)	Compare X to Memory 16-Bit	IX – M:M + 1	IMM	8C	jj kk	3	4	3-3	-	-	-	-	↕	↕	↕	↕
			DIR	9C	dd	2	5	4-7								
			EXT	BC	hh ll	3	6	5-10								
			IND,X	AC	ff	2	6	6-10								
			IND,Y	CD AC	ff	3	7	7-8								
CPY (opr)	Compare Y to Memory 16-Bit	IY – M:M + 1	IMM	18 8C	jj kk	4	5	3-5	-	-	-	-	↕	↕	↕	↕
			DIR	18 9C	dd	3	6	4-9								
			EXT	18 BC	hh ll	4	7	5-11								
			IND,X	1A AC	ff	3	7	6-11								
			IND,Y	18 AC	ff	3	7	7-8								
DAA	Decimal Adjust A	Adjust Sum to BCD	INH	19		1	2	2-1	-	-	-	-	↕	↕	↕	↕
DEC (opr)	Decrement Memory Byte	M – 1 → M	EXT	7A	hh ll	3	6	5-8	-	-	-	-	↕	↕	↕	-
			IND,X	6A	ff	2	6	6-3								
			IND,Y	18 6A	ff	3	7	7-3								
DECA	Decrement Accumulator A	A – 1 → A	A INH	4A		1	2	2-1	-	-	-	-	↕	↕	↕	-
DECB	Decrement Accumulator B	B – 1 → B	B INH	5A		1	2	2-1	-	-	-	-	↕	↕	↕	-
DES	Decrement Stack Pointer	SP – 1 → SP	INH	34		1	3	2-3	-	-	-	-	-	-	-	-
DEX	Decrement Index Register X	IX – 1 → IX	INH	09		1	3	2-2	-	-	-	-	-	↕	-	-
DEY	Decrement Index Register Y	IY – 1 → IY	INH	18 09		2	4	2-4	-	-	-	-	-	↕	-	-
EORA (opr)	Exclusive OR A with Memory	A ⊕ M → A	A IMM	88	ii	2	2	3-1	-	-	-	-	↕	↕	0	-
			A DIR	98	dd	2	3	4-1								
			A EXT	B8	hh ll	3	4	5-2								
			A IND,X	A8	ff	2	4	6-2								
			A IND,Y	18 A8	ff	3	5	7-2								
EORB (opr)	Exclusive OR B with Memory	B ⊕ M → B	B IMM	C8	ii	2	2	3-1	-	-	-	-	↕	↕	0	-
			B DIR	D8	dd	2	3	4-1								
			B EXT	F8	hh ll	3	4	5-2								
			B IND,X	E8	ff	2	4	6-2								
			B IND,Y	18 E8	ff	3	5	7-2								

Source Form(s)	Operation	Boolean Expression	Addressing Mode for Operand	Opcode	Operand(s)	Bytes	Cycle	Cycle by Cycle*	S	X	H	I	N	Z	V	C
FDIV	Fractional Divide 16 by 16	D/IX → IX; r → D	INH	03		1	41	2-17	-	-	-	-	-	↕	↕	↕
IDIV	Integer Divide 16 by 16	D/IX → IX; r → D	INH	02		1	41	2-17	-	-	-	-	-	↕	0	↕
INC (opr)	Increment Memory Byte	M + 1 → M	EXT	7C	hh ll	3	6	5-8	-	-	-	-	↕	↕	↕	-
			IND,X	6C	ff	2	6	6-3								
			IND,Y	18 6C	ff	3	7	7-3								
INCA	Increment Accumulator A	A + 1 → A	A INH	4C		1	2	2-1	-	-	-	-	↕	↕	↕	-
INCB	Increment Accumulator B	B + 1 → B	B INH	5C		1	2	2-1	-	-	-	-	↕	↕	↕	-
INS	Increment Stack Pointer	SP + 1 → SP	INH	31		1	3	2-3	-	-	-	-	-	-	-	-
INX	Increment Index Register X	IX + 1 → IX	INH	08		1	3	2-2	-	-	-	-	-	↕	-	-
INY	Increment Index Register Y	IY + 1 → IY	INH	18 08		2	4	2-4	-	-	-	-	-	↕	-	-
JMP (opr)	Jump	See Special Ops	EXT	7E	hh ll	3	3	5-1								
			IND,X	6E	ff	2	3	6-1								
			IND,Y	18 6E	ff	3	4	7-1								
JSR (Opr)	Jump to Subroutine	See Special Ops	DIR	9D	dd	2	5	4-8	-	-	-	-	-	-	-	-
			EXT	BD	hh ll	3	6	5-12								
			IND,X	AD	ff	2	6	6-12								
			IND,Y	18 AD	ff	3	7	7-9								
LDAA (opr)	Load Accumulator A	M → A	A IMM	86	ii	2	2	3-1	-	-	-	-	↕	↕	0	-
			A DIR	96	dd	2	3	4-1								
			A EXT	B6	hh ll	3	4	5-2								
			A IND,X	A6	ff	2	4	6-2								
			A IND,Y	18 A6	ff	3	5	7-2								
LDAB (opr)	Load Accumulator B	M → B	B IMM	C6	ii	2	2	3-1	-	-	-	-	↕	↕	0	-
			B DIR	D6	dd	2	3	4-1								
			B EXT	F6	hh ll	3	4	5-2								
			B IND,X	E6	ff	2	4	6-2								
			B IND,Y	18 E6	ff	3	5	7-2								
LDD (opr)	Load Double Accumulator D	M → A, M + 1 → B	IMM	CC	jj kk	3	3	3-2	-	-	-	-	↕	↕	0	-
			DIR	DC	dd	2	4	4-3								
			EXT	FC	hh ll	3	5	5-4								
			IND,X	EC	ff	2	5	6-6								
			IND,Y	18 EC	ff	3	6	7-6								
LDS (opr)	Load Stack Pointer	M:M + 1 → SP	IMM	8E	jj kk	3	3	3-2	-	-	-	-	↕	↕	0	-
			DIR	9E	dd	2	4	4-3								
			EXT	BE	hh ll	3	5	5-4								
			IND,X	AE	ff	2	5	6-6								
			IND,Y	18 AE	ff	3	6	7-6								
LDX (opr)	Load Index Register X	M:M + 1 → IX	IMM	CE	jj kk	3	3	3-2	-	-	-	-	↕	↕	0	-
			DIR	DE	dd	2	4	4-3								
			EXT	FE	hh ll	3	5	5-4								
			IND,X	EE	ff	2	5	6-6								
			IND,Y	CD EE	ff	3	6	7-6								
LDY (opr)	Load Index Register Y	M:M + 1 → IY	IMM	18 CE	jj kk	4	4	3-4	-	-	-	-	↕	↕	0	-
			DIR	18 DE	dd	3	5	4-5								
			EXT	18 FE	hh ll	4	6	5-6								
			IND,X	1A EE	ff	3	6	6-7								
			IND,Y	18 EE	ff	3	6	7-6								
LSL (opr)	Logical Shift Left	[diagram] C←b7...b0←0	EXT	78	hh ll	3	6	5-8	-	-	-	-	↕	↕	↕	↕
			IND,X	68	ff	2	6	6-3								
			IND,Y	18 68	ff	3	7	7-3								
LSLA			A INH	48		1	2	2-1								
LSLB			B INH	58		1	2	2-1								
LSLD	Logical Shift Left Double	[diagram] C←b15...b0←0	INH	05		1	3	2-2	-	-	-	-	↕	↕	↕	↕
LSR (opr)	Logical Shift Right	[diagram] 0→b7...b0→C	EXT	74	hh ll	3	6	5-8	-	-	-	-	0	↕	↕	↕
			IND,X	64	ff	2	6	6-3								
			IND,Y	18 64	ff	3	7	7-3								
LSRA			A INH	44		1	2	2-1								
LSRB			B INH	54		1	2	2-1								

Source Form(s)	Operation	Boolean Expression	Addressing Mode for Operand	Opcode	Operand(s)	Bytes	Cycle	Cycle by Cycle*	S	X	H	I	N	Z	V	C
LSRD	Logical Shift Right Double	0→☐-...-☐→☐ b15 b0 C	INH	04		1	3	2-2	-	-	-	-	0	↕	↕	↕
MUL	Multiply 8 by 8	AxB→D	INH	3D		1	10	2-13	-	-	-	-	-	-	-	↕
NEG (opr)	2's Complement Memory Byte	0-M→M	EXT	70	hh ll	3	6	5-8	-	-	-	-	↕	↕	↕	↕
			IND,X	60	ff	2	6	6-3								
			IND,Y	18 60	ff	3	7	7-3								
NEGA	2's Complement A	0-A→A	A INH	40		1	2	2-1	-	-	-	-	↕	↕	↕	↕
NEGB	2's Complement B	0-B→B	B INH	50		1	2	2-1	-	-	-	-	↕	↕	↕	↕
NOP	No Operation	No Operation	INH	01		1	2	2-1	-	-	-	-	-	-	-	-
ORAA (opr)	OR Accumulator A (Inclusive)	A+M→A	A IMM	8A	ii	2	2	3-1	-	-	-	-	↕	↕	0	-
			A DIR	9A	dd	2	3	4-1								
			A EXT	BA	hh ll	3	4	5-2								
			A IND,X	AA	ff	2	4	6-2								
			A IND,Y	18 AA	ff	3	5	7-2								
ORAB (opr)	OR Accumulator B (Inclusive)	B+M→B	B IMM	CA	ii	2	2	3-1	-	-	-	-	↕	↕	0	-
			B DIR	DA	dd	2	3	4-1								
			B EXT	FA	hh ll	3	4	5-2								
			B IND,X	EA	ff	2	4	6-2								
			B IND,Y	18 EA	ff	3	5	7-2								
PSHA	Push A onto Stack	A→Stk, SP=SP-1	A INH	36		1	3	2-6	-	-	-	-	-	-	-	-
PSHB	Push B onto Stack	B→Stk, SP=SP-1	B INH	37		1	3	2-6	-	-	-	-	-	-	-	-
PSHX	Push X onto Stack (Lo First)	IX→Stk, SP=SP-2	INH	3C		1	4	2-7	-	-	-	-	-	-	-	-
PSHY	Push Y onto Stack (Lo First)	IY→Stk, SP=SP-2	INH	18 3C		2	5	2-8	-	-	-	-	-	-	-	-
PULA	Pull A from Stack	SP=SP+1, A←Stk	A INH	32		1	4	2-9	-	-	-	-	-	-	-	-
PULB	Pull B from Stack	SP=SP+1, B←Stk	B INH	33		1	4	2-9	-	-	-	-	-	-	-	-
PULX	Pull X from Stack (Hi First)	SP=SP+2, IX←Stk	INH	38		1	5	2-10	-	-	-	-	-	-	-	-
PULY	Pull Y from Stack (Hi First)	SP=SP+2, IY←Stk	INH	18 38		2	6	2-11	-	-	-	-	-	-	-	-
ROL (opr)	Rotate Left	C b7 ← b0 C	EXT	79	hh ll	3	6	5-8	-	-	-	-	↕	↕	↕	↕
			IND,X	69	ff	2	6	6-3								
			IND,Y	18 69	ff	3	7	7-3								
ROLA			A INH	49		1	2	2-1								
ROLB			B INH	59		1	2	2-1								
ROR (opr)	Rotate Right	C b7 → b0 C	EXT	76	hh ll	3	6	5-8	-	-	-	-	↕	↕	↕	↕
			IND,X	66	ff	2	6	6-3								
			IND,Y	18 66	ff	3	7	7-3								
RORA			A INH	46		1	2	2-1								
RORB			B INH	56		1	2	2-1								
RTI	Return from Interrupt	See Special Ops	INH	3B		1	12	2-14	↕	↕	↕	↕	↕	↕	↕	↕
RTS	Return from Subroutine	See Special Ops	INH	39		1	5	2-12	-	-	-	-	-	-	-	-
SBA	Subtract B from A	A-B→A	INH	10		1	2	2-1	-	-	-	-	↕	↕	↕	↕
SBCA (opr)	Subtract with Carry from A	A-M-C→A	A IMM	82	ii	2	2	3-1	-	-	-	-	↕	↕	↕	↕
			A DIR	92	dd	2	3	4-1								
			A EXT	B2	hh ll	3	4	5-2								
			A IND,X	A2	ff	2	4	6-2								
			A IND,Y	18 A2	ff	3	5	7-2								
SBCB (opr)	Subtract from Carry from B	B-M-C→B	B IMM	C2	ii	2	2	3-1	-	-	-	-	↕	↕	↕	↕
			B DIR	D2	dd	2	3	4-1								
			B EXT	F2	hh ll	3	4	5-2								
			B IND,X	E2	ff	2	4	6-2								
			B IND,Y	18 E2	ff	3	5	7-2								
SEC	Set Carry	1→C	INH	0D		1	2	2-1	-	-	-	-	-	-	-	1
SEI	Set Interrupt Mask	1→I	INH	0F		1	2	2-1	-	-	-	1	-	-	-	-
SEV	Set Overflow Flag	1→V	INH	0B		1	2	2-1	-	-	-	-	-	-	1	-
STAA (opr)	Store Accumulator A	A→M	A DIR	97	dd	2	3	4-2	-	-	-	-	↕	↕	0	-
			A EXT	B7	hh ll	3	4	5-3								
			A IND,X	A7	ff	2	4	6-5								
			A IND,Y	18 A7	ff	3	5	7-5								

Source Form(s)	Operation	Boolean Expression	Addressing Mode for Operand	Opcode	Operand(s)	Bytes	Cycle	Cycle by Cycle*	S	X	H	I	N	Z	V	C
STAB (opr)	Store Accumulator B	B → M	B DIR	D7	dd	2	3	4-2	-	-	-	-	↕	↕	0	-
			B EXT	F7	hh ll	3	4	5-3								
			B IND,X	E7	ff	2	4	6-5								
			B IND,Y	18 E7	ff	3	5	7-5								
STD (opr)	Store Accumulator D	A → M, B → M + 1	DIR	DD	dd	2	4	4-4	-	-	-	-	↕	↕	0	-
			EXT	FD	hh ll	3	5	5-5								
			IND,X	ED	ff	2	5	6-8								
			IND,Y	18 ED	ff	3	6	7-7								
STOP	Stop Internal Clocks		INH	CF		1	2	2-1	-	-	-	-	-	-	-	-
STS (opr)	Store Stack Pointer	SP → M:M + 1	DIR	9F	dd	2	4	4-4	-	-	-	-	↕	↕	0	-
			EXT	BF	hh ll	3	5	5-5								
			IND,X	AF	ff	2	5	6-8								
			IND,Y	18 AF	ff	3	6	7-7								
STX (opr)	Store Index Register X	IX → M:M + 1	DIR	DF	dd	2	4	4-4	-	-	-	-	↕	↕	0	-
			EXT	FF	hh ll	3	5	5-5								
			IND,X	EF	ff	2	5	6-8								
			IND,Y	CD EF	ff	3	6	7-7								
STY (opr)	Store Index Register Y	IY → M:M + 1	DIR	18 DF	dd	3	5	4-6	-	-	-	-	↕	↕	0	-
			EXT	18 FF	hh ll	4	6	5-7								
			IND,X	1A EF	ff	3	6	6-9								
			IND,Y	18 EF	ff	3	6	7-7								
SUBA (opr)	Subtract Memory from A	A – M → A	A IMM	80	ii	2	2	3-1	-	-	-	-	↕	↕	↕	↕
			A DIR	90	dd	2	3	4-1								
			A EXT	B0	hh ll	3	4	5-2								
			A IND,X	A0	ff	2	4	6-2								
			A IND,Y	18 A0	ff	3	5	7-2								
SUBB (opr)	Subtract Memory from B	B – M → B	B IMM	C0	ii	2	2	3-1	-	-	-	-	↕	↕	↕	↕
			B DIR	D0	dd	2	3	4-1								
			B EXT	F0	hh ll	3	4	5-2								
			B IND,X	E0	ff	2	4	6-2								
			B IND,Y	18 E0	ff	3	5	7-2								
SUBD (opr)	Subtract Memory from D	D – M:M + 1 → D	IMM	83	jj kk	3	4	3-3	-	-	-	-	↕	↕	↕	↕
			DIR	93	dd	2	5	4-7								
			EXT	B3	hh ll	3	6	5-10								
			IND,X	A3	ff	2	6	6-10								
			IND,Y	18 A3	ff	3	7	7-8								
SWI	Software Interrupt	See Special Ops	INH	3F		1	14	2-15	-	-	-	1	-	-	-	-
TAB	Transfer A to B	A → B	INH	16		1	2	2-1	-	-	-	-	↕	↕	0	-
TAP	Transfer A to CC Register	A → CCR	INH	06		1	2	2-1	↕	↓	↕	↕	↕	↕	↕	↕
TBA	Transfer B to A	B → A	INH	17		1	2	2-1	-	-	-	-	↕	↕	0	-
TEST	TEST (Only in Test Modes)	Address Bus Counts	INH	00		1	**	2-20	-	-	-	-	-	-	-	-
TPA	Transfer CC Register to A	CCR → A	INH	07		1	2	2-1	-	-	-	-	-	-	-	-
TST (opr)	Test for Zero or Minus	M – 0	EXT	7D	hh ll	3	6	5-9	-	-	-	-	↕	↕	0	0
			IND,X	6D	ff	2	6	6-4								
			IND,Y	18 6D	ff	3	7	7-4								
TSTA		A – 0	A INH	4D		1	2	2-1	-	-	-	-	↕	↕	0	0
TSTB		B – 0	B INH	5D		1	2	2-1	-	-	-	-	↕	↕	0	0
TSX	Transfer Stack Pointer to X	SP + 1 → IX	INH	30		1	3	2-3	-	-	-	-	-	-	-	-
TSY	Transfer Stack Pointer to Y	SP + 1 → IY	INH	18 30		2	4	2-5	-	-	-	-	-	-	-	-

Source Form(s)	Operation	Boolean Expression	Addressing Mode for Operand	Machine Coding (Hexadecimal)		Bytes	Cycle	Cycle by Cycle	Condition Codes							
				Opcode	Operand(s)				S	X	H	I	N	Z	V	C
TXS	Transfer X to Stack Pointer	IX – 1 → SP	INH	35		1	3	2-2	-	-	-	-	-	-	-	-
TYS	Transfer Y to Stack Pointer	IY – 1 → SP	INH	18 35		2	4	2-4	-	-	-	-	-	-	-	-
WAI	Wait for Interrupt	Stack Regs & WAIT	INH	3E		2	***	2-16	-	-	-	-	-	-	-	-
XGDX	Exchange D with X	IX → D, D → IX	INH	8F		1	3	2-2	-	-	-	-	-	-	-	-
XGDY	Exchange D with Y	IY → D, D → IY	INH	18 8F		2	4	2-4	-	-	-	-	-	-	-	-

*Infinity or Until Reset Occurs

**12 Cycles are used beginning with the opcode fetch. A wait state is entered which remains in effect for an integer number of MPU E-clock cycles (n) until an interrupt is recognized. Finally, two additional cycles are used to fetch the appropriate interrupt vector (14 + n total).

dd = 8-Bit Direct Address ($0000 – $00FF) (High Byte Assumed to be $00)
ff = 8-Bit Positive Offset $00 (0) to $FF (255) (Is Added to Index)
hh = High Order Byte of 16-Bit Extended Address
ii = One Byte of Immediate Data
jj = High Order Byte of 16-Bit Immediate Data
kk = Low Order Byte of 16-Bit Immediate Data
ll = Low Order Byte of 16-Bit Extended Address
mm = 8-Bit Bit Mask (Set Bits to be Affected)
rr = Signed Relative Offset $80 (– 128) to $7F (+ 127)
        (Offset Relative to the Address Following the Machine Code Offset Byte)

APPENDIX

F

THE 6805 INSTRUCTION SET

Mnemonic	Inherent	Immediate	Direct	Extended	Relative	Indexed (No Offset)	Indexed (8 Bits)	Indexed (16 Bits)	Bit Set/ Clear	Bit Test & Branch	H	I	N	Z	C
ADC		x	x	x		x	x	x			Λ	●	Λ	Λ	Λ
ADD		x	x	x		x	x	x			Λ	●	Λ	Λ	Λ
AND		x	x	x		x	x	x			●	●	Λ	Λ	●
ASL	x		x			x	x				●	●	Λ	Λ	Λ
ASR	x		x			x	x				●	●	Λ	Λ	Λ
BCC					x						●	●	●	●	●
BCLR									x		●	●	●	●	●
BCS					x						●	●	●	●	●
BEQ					x						●	●	●	●	●
BHCC					x						●	●	●	●	●
BHCS					x						●	●	●	●	●
BHI					x						●	●	●	●	●
BHS					x						●	●	●	●	●
BIH					x						●	●	●	●	●
BIL					x						●	●	●	●	●
BIT		x	x	x		x	x	x			●	●	Λ	Λ	●
BLO					x						●	●	●	●	●
BLS					x						●	●	●	●	●
BMC					x						●	●	●	●	●
BMI					x						●	●	●	●	●
BMS					x						●	●	●	●	●
BNE					x						●	●	●	●	●
BPL					x						●	●	●	●	●
BRA					x						●	●	●	●	●
BRN					x						●	●	●	●	●
BRCLR										x	●	●	●	●	Λ
BRSET										x	●	●	●	●	Λ
BSET									x		●	●	●	●	●
BSR					x						●	●	●	●	●
CLC	x										●	●	●	●	0
CLI	x										●	0	●	●	●
CLR	x		x			x	x				●	●	0	1	●
CMP		x	x	x		x	x	x			●	●	Λ	Λ	Λ

Mnemonic	Addressing Modes										Condition Codes				
	Inherent	Immediate	Direct	Extended	Relative	Indexed (No Offset)	Indexed (8 Bits)	Indexed (16 Bits)	Bit Set/ Clear	Bit Test & Branch	H	I	N	Z	C
COM	x		x			x	x				●	●	Λ	Λ	1
CPx		x	x	x		x	x	x			●	●	Λ	Λ	Λ
DEC	x		x			x	x				●	●	Λ	Λ	●
EOR		x	x	x		x	x	x			●	●	Λ	Λ	●
INC	x		x			x	x				●	●	Λ	Λ	●
JMP			x	x		x	x	x			●	●	●	●	●
JSR			x	x		x	x	x			●	●	●	●	●
LDA		x	x	x		x	x	x			●	●	Λ	Λ	●
LDX		x	x	x		x	x	x			●	●	Λ	Λ	●
LSL	x		x			x	x				●	●	Λ	Λ	Λ
LSR	x		x			x	x				●	●	0	Λ	Λ
MUL	x										0	●	●	●	0
NEG	x		x			x	x				●	●	Λ	Λ	Λ
NOP	x										●	●	●	●	●
ORA		x	x	x		x	x	x			●	●	Λ	Λ	●
ROL	x		x			x	x				●	●	Λ	Λ	Λ
ROR	x		x			x	x				●	●	Λ	Λ	Λ
RSP	x										●	●	●	●	●
RTI	x										?	?	?	?	?
RTS	x										●	●	●	●	●
SBC		x	x	x		x	x	x			●	●	Λ	Λ	Λ
SEC	x										●	●	●	●	1
SEI	x										●	1	●	●	●
STA			x	x		x	x	x			●	●	Λ	Λ	●
STOP	x										●	0	●	●	●
STX			x	x		x	x	x			●	●	Λ	Λ	●
SUB		x	x	x		x	x	x			●	●	Λ	Λ	Λ
SWI	x										●	1	●	●	●
TAX	x										●	●	●	●	●
TST	x		x			x	x				●	●	Λ	Λ	●
TXA	x										●	●	●	●	●
WAIT	x										●	0	●	●	●

Condition Code Symbols:

H	Half Carry (From Bit 3)	Λ	Test and Set if True Cleared Otherwise
I	Interrupt Mask	●	Not Affected
N	Negate (Sign Bit)	?	Load CC Register From Stack
Z	Zero	0	Cleared
C	Carry/Borrow	1	Set

INDEX

E

F

G

H